E. A. GUGGENHEIM

THERMODYNAMICS

AN ADVANCED TREATMENT FOR CHEMISTS AND PHYSICISTS

MONOGRAPHS ON THEORETICAL
AND APPLIED PHYSICS
II

EDITED BY

H. B. G. CASIMIR
Director of the Philips Laboratories,
Eindhoven

H. BRINKMAN
Professor in the University of
Groningen

and

J. DE BOER
Professor in the University of Amsterdam

1950
NORTH-HOLLAND PUBLISHING COMPANY
AMSTERDAM
INTERSCIENCE PUBLISHERS, INC. NEW YORK

THERMODYNAMICS

AN ADVANCED TREATMENT FOR CHEMISTS
AND PHYSICISTS

BY

E. A. GUGGENHEIM, M.A., Sc.D., F.R.S.
PROFESSOR OF CHEMISTRY AT READING UNIVERSITY

Second Edition

1950
NORTH-HOLLAND PUBLISHING COMPANY
AMSTERDAM
INTERSCIENCE PUBLISHERS, INC. NEW YORK

First edition 1949

Second edition 1950

Sole distributors for U.S.A.:

Interscience Publishers, Inc., New York

PRINTED IN THE NETHERLANDS

PREFACE

In view of the large number of books on thermodynamics it may seem surprising that there should be any need for yet another. A cursory survey of all the existing books will however show that only very few are at all comparable. The total number is considerably reduced if we reject the ones which G. N. Lewis so aptly described as containing "cyclical processes limping about eccentric and not quite completed cycles" and consider only those which present thermodynamics as an exact science. Many of these, including some of the best, are out of date. No book written before 1929 even attempts an account of any of the following matters: the modern definition of heat given by Born in 1921; the quantal theory of the entropy of gases and its experimental verification; Debye's formulae for the activity coefficients of electrolytes; the use of electrochemical potentials of ions; the application of thermodynamics to dielectrics and to paramagnetic substances. The first textbook on thermodynamics to include any of these matters is that of Schottky published in 1929. The number of textbooks on thermodynamics written since then is in single figures and of these fewer than half a dozen are in English. The only two available bearing any appreciable resemblance to this book are Zemansky's "Heat and Thermodynamics" and Macdougall's "Thermodynamics and Chemistry". I have a great admiration for both these books, but they are quite different from each other and from this book. Zemansky's book is supremely good on the fundamentals of thermodynamics and should be equally useful to physicists, chemists and engineers. It includes especially thorough discussions on the meaning of heat, on calorimetry, on thermometry, on steam engines and on refrigerators. On the other hand there are important applications to physical chemistry, such as solutions, interfaces, electrochemistry, the third principle, entropy constants which are dealt with sketchily or not at all. Macdougall's book on the other hand is, as its title indicates, devoted mainly to applications of thermodynamics to chemistry. Less attention has been paid to a logical formulation of the fundamental principles and there is no application to dielectrics or to paramagnetics.

The present book is addressed equally to physicists and to chemists, but not to engineers. It is thus in a sense intermediate between the other two books mentioned. It is written for graduates, but much of it should be useful to undergraduates intending to specialize in physical chemistry or chemical physics.

There are several novel or unusual features in the treatment, notably the following. The third principle of thermodynamics is introduced near the beginning and is then used throughout the book. As the third principle can be properly understood only through statistical mechanics an early chapter is devoted to a digression on this subject. Considerable use is made of a function λ, called the absolute activity, related to the chemical potential μ by $\lambda = \exp(\mu/RT)$ or $\mu = RT \log \lambda$. This function plays an important part in statistical mechanics, more especially in Bose–Einstein and in Fermi–Dirac statistics, but its close relation to μ has not always been appreciated. At the same time λ is often more convenient than μ for formulating equilibrium conditions, especially those of chemical reactions. Physico-chemical systems are classified in chapters according to the number and nature of the components, not according to the number or nature of the phases. Interfaces are treated as thin phases after the manner of van der Waals and Bakker, not as fictitious geometrical surfaces after the manner of Gibbs. There is no separate chapter on interfaces, but they are dealt with according to the number of components. The thermo-dynamics of an interface in a two component system is much more complicated than that of a single component system and conveniently comes at a later stage. The treatment of electrolyte solutions is split into two chapters; in the first of these electric potential need not be mentioned, while the second, entitled electrochemistry, is by contrast devoted to electrochemical cells. The treatment of systems in electric and in magnetic fields, especially the latter, is more detailed than usual.

Choice of notation always leads to difficulties. No notation is perfect, but some are better than others. I have tried to be guided by the principle that the symbols used should be as simple as possible provided they are unambiguous. I will mention two examples. The symbol V_i for the partial molar volume of the species i is better than $\overline{V}_i$ because the bar serves no useful purpose and in fact does harm by suggesting an average. Again if the superscript ^{0} is used to refer to a component in the pure state, then to denote the value at a standard pressure a different superscript, such as †, should be used. It is unfortunate that there is not yet uniformity in the use of symbols for Gibbs' four thermodynamic potentials $\varepsilon, \chi, \psi, \zeta$. I have used those recommended both by the International Union of Chemistry (1947) and by the International Union of Physics (1948), namely U, H, F, G. In my opinion there is no disrespect to Gibbs, nor to anyone else, in finding these symbols more convenient than their alternatives.

Experimental data and detailed calculations have been included here and there for illustrative purposes only. In all such examples care has been taken to use the most reliable modern data available.

Copious references have been given to modern literature, but references have usually not been given for theorems and formulae now become classical unless there seemed to be a special reason for so doing, as for example to emphasize a point of historical interest or to throw light on a controversial matter.

There is an author index of the references to the literature. The omission of a subject index is deliberate as it would have had to be either excessively long or incomplete. There is however a detailed table of contents which should almost always enable an experienced reader to find what he is looking for.

A few of the diagrams have by permission been copied from diagrams in other books or in journals. I am grateful for such permission to the Royal Society, the American Institute of Physics, the Cambridge University Press and Messrs. Taylor and Francis.

I want to thank Dr. G. S. Rushbrooke for reading, checking and correcting the last four chapters of the book. The rest of the book has been checked by Mr. B. Topley, to whom my debt of gratitude cannot be adequately expressed in words. He has been of inestimable help to me in eliminating not only misprints and errors of transcription but also poor English, bad grammar, false reasoning and obscurity. If, as I hope, there remain but few examples of these, the credit is his.

E. A. GUGGENHEIM.

Reading University,
August 1949.

PREFACE TO SECOND EDITION

The text of this edition is essentially the same as that of the first edition, the only significant change being at the end of § 4.06. Several typographical errors in the first edition have been corrected. A subject index compiled by Mr. M. L. McGlashan has been added.

A distinguished American reviewer of the first edition has proposed that this book might have the sub-title "Pride and Prejudice". Each reader must decide for himself on the merit of this proposal.

E. A. GUGGENHEIM.

Reading University,
June 1950.

CONTENTS

CHAPTER I

INTRODUCTION AND FUNDAMENTAL PRINCIPLES . . 1

CHAPTER II

DIGRESSION ON STATISTICAL THERMODYNAMICS . . . 48

CHAPTER III

SOME RELATIONS OF GENERAL VALIDITY 68

CHAPTER IV

SYSTEMS OF A SINGLE COMPONENT 79

CHAPTER V

SYSTEMS OF TWO NON-REACTING COMPONENTS . . 170

CHAPTER VI

SYSTEMS OF SEVERAL NON–REACTING COMPONENTS 230

CHAPTER VII
SYSTEMS OF CHEMICALLY REACTING SPECIES . . . 258

CHAPTER VIII
EXTREMELY DILUTE SOLUTIONS 290

CHAPTER IX

SOLUTIONS OF ELECTROLYTES 296

CHAPTER X

ELECTROCHEMICAL SYSTEMS 330

CHAPTER XI

GRAVITATIONAL FIELD 355

CHAPTER XII

ELECTROSTATIC SYSTEMS 361

CHAPTER XIII

MAGNETIC SYSTEMS 367

CHAPTER XIV

RADIATION 390

LIST OF MOST IMPORTANT SYMBOLS

A	Affinity
A	Area
B	Second virial coefficient
C or C_P	Heat capacity at constant pressure
C_V	Heat capacity at constant volume
$\mathcal{G}$	Number of components
D	Variation due to change of composition at constant temperature and constant pressure
E	Electromotive force
F	Free energy or Helmholtz function
$\mathcal{F}$	Faraday
G	Gibbs function
H	Heat function
I	Moment of inertia
J	Massieu function
K	Equilibrium constant
M	Molar mass
M_1	Molar mass of solvent/Kg
N	Avogadro's number
P	Pressure
$P^\dagger$	Standard pressure, e.g. atmospheric
$\mathcal{P}$	Number of phases
Q	Electric charge
R	Gas constant
S	Entropy
T	Absolute temperature
U	Energy
V	Volume
Y	Planck function
B	Magnetic force vector (induction)
D	Electric derived vector (displacement)
E	Electric force vector
H	Magnetic derived vector (field)
J	Current density
M	Magnetization
P	Electric polarization

a	Van der Waals' or Dieterici's constant
a	Stefan's constant
b	Van der Waals' or Dieterici's constant
c	Concentration
e	Charge of proton
f	Activity coefficient defined with reference to pure liquid
g	Osmotic coefficient
h	Planck's constant
h	Henry's law constant
i	Electric current
k	Boltzmann's constant
m	Molality
m	Mass of molecule
n	Number of moles
n	Number of photons
p	Partial vapour pressure
$p^{\star}$	Fugacity
q	Heat absorbed by system
r	Radius
t	Transport number
w	Work done on system
x	Mole fraction
y	Electric moment of molecule
z	Electrovalency of ion
α	Coefficient of thermal expansion
α	Constant in Debye's limiting law
β	Ionic specific interaction coefficient
β	Bohr's magneton
γ	(without any subscript) Surface tension
γ	(with subscript) Activity coefficient of solute defined with reference to infinitely dilute solution
ε	Energy of individual molecule or photon
ε	Permittivity
Θ	Characteristic temperature
$\varkappa$	Compressibility
$\varkappa$	Susceptibility
λ	Absolute activity
μ	Chemical potential, or ionic electrochemical potential
μ	Permeability
ν	Stoichiometric coefficient
ν	Frequency
o	Orientational weight
Π	Osmotic pressure

ϖ Statistical weight of quantum state
ϱ Density
ϱ Radius of curvature
σ Symmetry number
τ Thickness of interfacial layer
$\varPhi$ Gravitational potential
ψ Electrical potential

Subscripts almost always refer to component species, e.g. p_i is the partial vapour pressure of the component species i. In particular

1 refers to solvent species
s ,,   to solute species
i ,,   especially to ionic species
R ,,   to cation
X ,,   to anion
m denotes mean molar

Subscripts attached to the operator symbol $\triangle$ refer to processes as follows:

e refers to evaporation
f ,,   to fusion
s ,,   to sublimation
$\alpha \rightarrow \beta$,,   to transfer from phase α to phase β

Superscripts almost always refer to phases, e.g. p_i^α is the partial vapour pressure of the species i in the phase α. In particular

α, β refer to bulk phases in general
σ refers to surface phase
G ,,   to gas
I ,,   to ideal solution or infinitely dilute solution
L ,,   to liquid
S ,,   to solid
e ,,   to exterior
i ,,   to interior

The superscript ^{0} is used to denote quantities referring to a pure substance, especially the pure solvent. It is sometimes used to denote the value at a given temperature T^0, especially the absolute zero.

An asterisk is used to distinguish the fugacity $p^\star$ from the partial vapour pressure p.

A dagger is used in the symbol $P^\dagger$ to denote a standard pressure, e.g. atmospheric. Attached to other symbols, e.g. μ, it denotes the value at the standard pressure.

The following operator signs are used:

d	Ordinary differential
$\dfrac{\partial}{\partial}$	Partial differential coefficient
D	Differential at varying composition, but constant temperature constant pressure
$\triangle$	Excess of final over initial value
Σ	Summation
$\displaystyle\int$	Integral
Π	Product
$\Pi\,(\ )$	Product referring to species on right of chemical formula divided by product referring to species on left
[ ]	Average between two temperatures or two pressures, usually one relating to a solution the other to the pure solvent
log	Natural logarithm
$\log_{10}$	Logarithm to base 10

VALUES OF IMPORTANT PHYSICAL CONSTANTS

See Birge, Phys. Soc. Rep. Prog. Phys. 1941 **8** 90

Ice–point	T_{ice}	$=$	$273.16\,^{\circ}K$
Avogadro's number	N	$=$	0.60228×10^{24} molecules/mole
Atmosphere	1 atm.	$=$	1.0132×10^{6} dyne cm.$^{-2}$
		$=$	1.0132×10^{5} joule m.$^{-3}$
Thermochemical calorie	1 cal.	$=$	4.1840 joule
Gas constant	R	$=$	8.3144 joule/deg. mole
	RT_{ice}	$=$	2271.2 joule/mole
Boltzmann's constant	$k = R/N$	$=$	1.3805×10^{-16} erg/deg.
Planck's constant	h	$=$	6.624×10^{-27} erg sec.
Faraday	F	$=$	0.96488×10^{5} coul.
Proton charge	$e = F/N$	$=$	1.6020×10^{-19} coul.
Speed of light	c	$=$	2.9978×10^{8} m./sec.
Bohr's magneton	β	$=$	9.273×10^{-24} amp. m.^{2}
	$N\beta$	$=$	5.585 amp. m.^{2}

Conversion factors of various energy units to characteristic temperatures in centigrade degrees:

$$k^{-1} = 7.244 \times 10^{15} \text{ deg./erg} = 1\,4385 \text{ deg./wave number}$$
$$= 1.1605 \times 10^{4} \text{ deg./electron volt}$$

CHAPTER I

INTRODUCTION AND FUNDAMENTAL PRINCIPLES

§ 1.01   Thermodynamics or Thermophysics

The word *thermodynamics* is a misleading name. This, possibly surprising statement, will now be elaborated.

Consider as a typical example of a mechanical system a heavy weight suspended by a spring of comparatively negligible weight. Such a system has a characteristic frequency determined by the magnitude of the weight, the dimensions and material of the spring. But that is not all. In general the characteristic frequency varies according as the spring is hot or cold. This variation can be related to the energy that has to be supplied to the spring to prevent it from becoming hotter or colder when compressed or extended. The quantitative study of such relations would reasonably be called *thermo-mechanics* or perhaps *thermo-dynamics*.

Again, consider a simple compressible fluid. Its compressibility in general depends on the pressure and on the nature of the fluid. But that is not all. It also generally varies according as the fluid is hot or cold. This variation can be related to the energy that has to be supplied to the fluid to prevent it from becoming hotter or colder when compressed. The quantitative study of such relations would reasonably be called *thermo-hydrodynamics*.

Again, consider a parallel plate condenser immersed in a uniform liquid. The capacity of such a condenser depends on the size and spacing of the plates and on the nature of the liquid, but it also in general varies according as the liquid is hot or cold. This variation can be related to the energy that has to be supplied to the liquid to prevent it from becoming hotter or colder when the condenser is charged or discharged. The quantitative study of such relations would reasonably be called *thermo-electrostatics*. (The word *thermo-electricity* has a different meaning.)

Again, consider a transformer consisting of two co-axial coils of insulated copper wire, the whole completely immersed in a solution of a ferric salt. The mutual inductance of the transformer depends on the geometry of the two coils and on the composition of the ferric salt solution, but it also varies according as the solution is hot or cold. This variation can be related to the energy that has to be supplied to the solution to prevent it from becoming hotter or colder when the primary circuit is made or broken. The quantitative study of such relations would reasonably be called *thermo-electrodynamics* or *thermo-magnetics*.

As a last example consider the chemical system consisting of a gaseous mixture of hydrogen, nitrogen and ammonia in the presence of an efficient catalyst. The equilibrium quantity of ammonia depends on the total

1

quantities, combined or free, of hydrogen and nitrogen and on the pressure, but it also varies according as the mixture is hot or cold. This variation can be related to the energy that has to be supplied to the mixture to prevent it from becoming hotter or colder during the chemical synthesis or decomposition of ammonia. The quantitative study of such relations would reasonably be called *thermo-chemics*. (The word *thermochemistry* is generally used in a much more restricted sense.)

We have now seen what might reasonably be called *thermo-mechanics* (or *thermo-dynamics*), *thermo-hydrodynamics*, *thermo-electrostatics*, *thermo-electrodynamics* (or *thermo-magnetics*) and *thermo-chemics*. These examples are not exhaustive. For example we could reasonably define *thermo-capillarity* and *thermo-acoustics*. The natural and obvious name for the science which embraces all these classes is THERMOPHYSICS. Unfortunately the name THERMODYNAMICS is used instead. Its use is so firmly established, that it would probably be futile to suggest a change of name. It does however seem worth while stressing that this science, whether called THERMOPHYSICS or not, does in fact have a bearing on nearly all branches of physics, as well as chemistry.

§ 1.02   Method of Treatment

Thermodynamics, like classical mechanics and classical electro-magnetism, is an exact mathematical science. Each such science may be based on a small number of premises or laws from which all the remaining laws of the science are deducible by purely logical reasoning. In the case of each of these sciences there is a certain amount of arbitrariness as to which of the laws one chooses as the premises from which the others are to be deduced.

In classical mechanics, for instance, one might begin with Newton's laws of motion or alternatively one might use as the basis of the whole theory the Principle of Least Action. For an elementary exposition of the subject it is customary to choose the former, but to a reader already comparatively familiar with the subject the latter choice might be more satisfying. Whichever basis one chooses for the development of the theory this basis postulates the existence and definiteness of certain measurable quantities. In the one case they may be distance, time, mass and force, in the other generalized co-ordinates, generalized momenta, time and energy. There is a common tendency to regard the conceptions of mass and force as more fundamental than those of generalized momenta and energy, and therefore to regard them as more natural "bricks" with which to build up the complete structure of classical mechanics. But surely this is begging the question. When we first learn the elements of mechanics we always do, in fact, commence by using mass and force as the "bricks". As a consequence of this they are the more familiar "bricks" and so, without pausing to think why they are more familiar, we are apt to regard them as the natural ones. Actually if we analyse the claim of mass to priority over energy and momentum, we find it due to the accidental fact that we live in a very nearly constant gravitational field, as a consequence of which the mass of a body is proportional to its weight and so is readily measured with a common weighing machine. Newton's laws may be the best starting-point in the elementary teaching of classical mechanics, but the complete theory can be built up on other bases which, from a logical point of view, are at least equally solid. They may be less satisfactory practically but more so intellectually.

Similarly the classical theory of electro-magnetism is still usually built up from conceptions such as electric and magnetic poles. Whether or not this choice is desirable for a first introduction to the subject, there are undoubtedly other more solid "bricks" from which to build the structure in an advanced treatment, such as for example the "four-potential" and "four-current" of the special relativity theory.

In the case of thermodynamics the situation is no different. It is customary to regard *temperature*, the measure of *hotness*, as a natural *brick* and *entropy*, the measure of direction of change, as an unnatural one. This attitude is due to a feeling that temperature is more directly measurable. If, however, we analyse the question of how to measure temperature, we find a choice of two answers, neither of which is satisfactory:

1. Measure it anyhow with any kind of "thermometer". We then obtain clumsy *unnatural* scales of temperature.

2. Measure it by means of a particular type of thermometer involving the use of a special kind of substance called a *perfect gas*. We thus obtain a convenient and natural temperature scale known as the absolute scale. But if we ask what is a *perfect gas* and by what criterion are we to recognize one, the only answer obtainable without leaving the province of thermodynamics is that a *perfect gas* is a substance with certain properties, the most important of which is that when used as a thermometer it gives the convenient and natural temperature scale.

Obviously this kind of basis for an exact mathematical science is deplorable. This apparent vicious circle is due to an unconscious attempt to build up the structure without having chosen the right bricks. The usual introduction to entropy is unsatisfactory. For it is made dependent on the absolute temperature, a definition of which, independent of the postulate that certain substances make more perfect thermometers than others, involves conceptions, such as that of a Carnot cycle, which are at least as complex as the conception of entropy itself.

We have deliberately chosen to regard *absolute temperature* and *entropy*, just as we regard pressure and volume, as two quantities both fundamental. We therefore do not attempt to define them in terms of other quantities regarded as simpler, for we do not admit the existence of simpler thermodynamic quantities. Nor do we attempt to define the one in terms of the other as we regard them as equally fundamental. We define them merely by their properties, expressed either in words or by mathematical formulae.

§ 1.03 Thermodynamic State. Phases

The simplest example of a system to which thermodynamics can be applied is a single homogeneous substance. In this simplest case a complete description of its thermodynamic state requires a specification of its content, i.e. quantity of each chemical substance contained, and further a specification of two other quantities such as for example volume and viscosity, or density and pressure. If all the physical properties of the system in which we are interested were independent of whether the system is hot or cold, it would to describe its state be sufficient to specify, apart from the quantity of each chemical substance contained, only one quantity, such as volume. Usually some, if not all, of the properties of interest do depend on whether the body is hot or cold and the specification of one extra independent quantity fixes the degree of hotness or coldness. Thus this simple *thermo-hydrodynamic system* has one more degree of freedom than the corresponding *hydrodynamic system*.

If the system is not homogeneous, in order to describe its thermodynamic state we have to consider it as composed of a number, small or large, of homogeneous parts called *phases* each of which is described by specifying its content and a sufficient number of other properties; the sufficient number for each *thermo-physical phase* is always one more than in the corresponding hypothetical *physical system* with all its properties of interest independent of whether it is hot or cold.

In some cases the complete description of the thermodynamic state of a system may require it to be regarded as composed of an infinite number of infinitesimal phases. If the physical properties vary continuously over macroscopic parts of the system, this procedure offers no difficulty. An example is a long column of gas in a gravitational field. If on the other hand there are infinitely many discontinuities over infinitesimal regions, it may be difficult if not impossible to give a complete description of the thermodynamic state. An example is a gas flowing turbulently through an orifice.

In considering the properties of interfaces, we shall have to include phases which are extremely thin in the direction normal to the interface.

To sum up: the complete description of the thermodynamic state of any system involves a description of the thermodynamic state of each of its homogeneous phases, which may be few or many or infinite in number. The description of the thermodynamic state of each phase requires the specification of one more property than the description of the physical state of an analogous hypothetical phase all of whose properties of interest are independent of whether it be hot or cold.

§ 1.04 Thermodynamic Process

If on comparing the state of a thermodynamic system at two different times it is found that there is a difference in any macroscopic property of the system, then we say that between the two times of observation a *process* has taken place. If, for example, two equal quantities of gas are allowed to intermix, this will constitute a *process* from a thermodynamic point of view provided the two initially separate gases are distinguishable by any macroscopic property, even though their difference is very slight, as, for example, might be the case for two isotopes. If, on the other hand, the two initially separate gases are not distinguishable by any macroscopic property, then from a thermodynamic point of view no *process* takes place, although from a molecular standpoint there is a never-ceasing intermixing.

§ 1.05 Infinitesimal Process

A process taking place to such an extent that there is only an infinitesimal change in any of the macroscopic properties of a system is called an infinitesimal process.

§ 1.06 Insulating Walls. Adiabatic Processes

The boundary or *wall* separating two systems is said to be *insulating* if it has the following property. If any system in complete internal equilibrium is completely surrounded by an *insulating* wall then no change can be produced in the system by external agency except by

(*a*)   movement of the containing wall or part of it

(*b*)   long range forces, e.g. movement of electrically charged bodies.

When a system is surrounded by an insulating boundary the system is said to be *thermally insulated* and any process taking place in the system is called *adiabatic*. The name adiabatic appears to be due to Rankine *.

§ 1.07 Conducting Walls. Thermal Equilibrium

The boundary or *wall* separating two systems is said to be *thermally conducting* if it has the following property. If any two separate systems each in complete internal equilibrium are brought together so as to be in contact through a *thermally conducting wall* then in general the two systems will be found not to be in mutual equilibrium, but will gradually adjust themselves until eventually they do reach mutual equilibrium after which there will of course be no further change. The two systems are then said to have reached a state of *thermal equilibrium*. It was necessary to include the words "in general" in the definition to allow for the exceptional case that the two systems started in thermal equilibrium. Systems separated by a conducting boundary are said to be in *thermal contact*.

§ 1.08 Zeroth Principle. Temperature

We are now ready to formulate one of the important principles of thermodynamics, namely:

If two systems are both in thermal equilibrium with a third system then they are in thermal equilibrium with each other.

This will be referred to as the *zeroth principle* of thermodynamics.

---

* See Maxwell, *Theory of Heat* (1871 ed.) p. 129.

Consider now a reference system in a well-defined state. Then all other systems in thermal equilibrium with it have a property in common, namely the property of being in thermal equilibrium with one another. This property is called *temperature*. In other words systems in *thermal equilibrium* are said to have the *same temperature*. Systems not in thermal equilibrium are said to have different temperatures.

§ 1.09   Thermostats and Thermometers

Consider two systems in thermal contact, one very much smaller than the other, for example a short thin metallic wire immersed in a large quantity of water. If the quantity of water is large enough (or the wire small enough), then in the process of attaining thermal equilibrium the change in the physical state of the water will be entirely negligible compared with that of the wire. This situation is described differently according as we are primarily interested in the small system or in the large one.

If we are primarily interested in the small system, the wire, then we regard the water as a means of controlling the temperature of the wire and we refer to the water as a *temperature bath* or *thermostat*.

If on the other hand we are primarily interested in the large system, the water, we regard the wire as an instrument for recording the temperature of the water and we refer to the wire as a *thermometer*. This recording of temperature can be rendered quantitative by measuring some property of the thermometer, such as its electrical resistance, which varies with temperature.

§ 1.10   Temperature scales

Since there is an infinite choice of kinds of thermometers so there is an infinite choice of empirical scales of temperature. We shall however see later that there is one particular scale of temperature which has outstandingly simple characteristics which can be described in a manner independent of the properties of any particular substance or class of substances. This scale is called the *absolute scale*. We shall later describe methods by which temperatures can be determined on the absolute scale. These methods, if they are to be precise, require elaborate apparatus and are extremely tedious. It is therefore general practice to use such a procedure to determine accurately a few standard temperatures on the absolute scale. Other subsidiary thermometers of high sensitivity and convenient to use are calibrated at these standard temperatures according to the absolute scale. Intermediate temperatures are then measured by the subsidiary thermometers according to specified interpolation formulae between the standard temperatures. These interpolation formulae are so chosen that the temperatures recorded according to them are exactly the same as on the absolute scale at all the standard points and only differ very slightly, if at all, from the absolute scale at intermediate points. The unit of temperature is called a *degree* and is denoted by the symbol °.

§ 1.11 First Principle. Energy

We now formulate the *first principle* of thermodynamics.

The work required to bring a *thermally insulated* system from one completely specified state to a second completely specified state is independent of the source of the work and of the path through which the system passes from the initial to the final state.

It follows that when a system passes *adiabatically* from a state 1 to a state 2 the work w done on the system is given by

$$w = U(2) - U(1), \qquad \text{(adiabatic process)}, \qquad (1.11.1)$$

where $U(1)$, $U(2)$ depend only on the states 1, 2 respectively. In other words the work w done on the system is equal to the increase in the value of a function U of the state of the system. Using the symbol $\triangle$ to denote the increase in the value of a function, we can rewrite (1) as

$$w = \triangle U, \qquad \text{(adiabatic process)}, \qquad (1.11.2)$$

where U is called the *energy* of the system. According to this property U is for a given system completely defined apart from an arbitrary additive constant, which is without physical significance since only changes of energy are measurable. The complete definition of U for each independent system thus requires an arbitrary conventional fixing of the state of zero energy. When this has been fixed, the energy in any other state is uniquely determined.

If the state of a system is defined by its temperature and certain other parameters such as composition and volume, and its temperature is changed while the other parameters are kept unchanged, then the change in the energy of the system may be referred to as a change in its *thermal energy*.

§ 1.12 Heat

The equality (1.11.2) holds only for an adiabatic process. In a process which is not adiabatic the system is said to *absorb a quantity of heat q*, or alternatively to *give off a quantity of heat* $- q$, where

$$q = \triangle U - w. \qquad (1.12.1)$$

This formula, which defines q, can be rewritten as

$$w + q = \triangle U. \qquad (1.12.2)$$

If we regard this as a statement of the *conservation of energy* and compare it with the corresponding statement for an adiabatic process, we observe that the energy of a system can be increased either by work done on it or by absorption of heat.

For an infinitesimal process equation (1) becomes

$$q = dU - w. \qquad (1.12.3)$$

If of two systems in thermal contact the one *absorbs heat* and the other *gives off* this same quantity of *heat*, then we speak of a *flow of heat* from the second to the first. According to the zeroth principle such a *flow of heat* will take place only if the two systems are at different temperatures. We may thus regard *flow of heat* as a transfer of energy resulting from a temperature difference.

The extension of the mechanical principle of conservation of energy to include changes in thermal energy and the flow of heat was a gradual process, the earlier formulations being less rigorous than later ones. The principle is implied in a posthumous publication of Carnot (died 1832) and was placed on a firm experimental basis * by Joule (1840—45). More explicit statements of the principle were formulated by Helmholtz (1847) and by Clausius (1850). The formulation adopted here, which surpasses in rigour and clarity all earlier attempts, is due to Born ** (1921).

§ 1.13 Conversion of Work to Heat

The expression *conversion of work to heat* should be used with caution, since in general w and $-q$ are not numerically equal to each other. If however a system is taken through a complete cycle, then since its initial and final state are identical the initial and final values of U are the same and so

$$\triangle U = 0, \qquad w = -q, \qquad \text{(complete cycle)}. \qquad (1.13.1)$$

We may then say that in the cycle the work w done on the system is converted into the balance of heat $-q$ given off by the system during the cycle, that is to say the excess of the heat given off over the heat absorbed in various parts of the cycle.

Again if a system is kept in a steady state while work is done on it, then, since its state remains unaltered, U does not change and so

$$\triangle U = 0, \qquad w = -q, \qquad \text{(steady state)}. \qquad (1.13.2)$$

Here again we may say that in the steady state the work w done on the system is converted into the heat $-q$ given off by the system.

Except in the two special cases just mentioned, it is in general dangerous, if not meaningless, to speak of the conversion of work into heat or vice-versa. Unfortunately the expression is sometimes used incorrectly. Let us consider two simple practical examples which serve to illustrate the correct and incorrect use of the expression.

Consider as our system an ordinary *electric heater*, that is to say a resistance across which an electric potential difference E can be produced by closing a switch. Suppose that initially the resistance is in thermal equilibrium with its surroundings and the switch is open. When the switch is closed a current i flows through the resistance and the electrical work done on the heater in an element of time dt is

$$w = E\,i\,dt. \qquad (1.13.3)$$

---

* The reader interested in the history will find useful a critical summary with references to the original literature in Partington, *Chemical Thermodynamics* (1924), p. 11.
** Born, *Physik. Zeit.* (1921) **22** 218.

In the first instant this work produces an increase in the thermal energy of the resistance, so that

$$w = dU, \qquad \text{(initially)}. \qquad (1.13.4)$$

But immediately the temperature of the resistance becomes different from that of its surroundings and so there is a flow of heat q from the resistance to its surroundings. Thus in a time dt

$$w = dU - q, \qquad \text{(general)}. \qquad (1.13.5)$$

As the temperature difference between the resistance and its surroundings increases, so $-q/w$ increases towards the value unity. Eventually a steady state is reached, the temperature of the resistance no longer increases and we have

$$w = -q, \qquad dU = 0, \text{ (steady state)}. \qquad (1.13.6)$$

When this steady state has been reached, and not until then, may one correctly speak of the conversion of the work w into the heat $-q$ in the time dt.

Now by way of contrast consider the system consisting of the electric heater together with a fluid surrounding it, the whole being thermally insulated. The work done on the system is still given by (3). But now since the whole system, consisting of resistance and fluid, is thermally insulated q is by definition zero, so that

$$w = dU, \qquad q = 0, \qquad \text{(thermal insulation)}. \qquad (1.13.7)$$

We may now say that the work w is converted into thermal energy; to speak of its conversion to heat would evidently be nonsense.

§ 1.14 Natural, Unnatural and Reversible Processes

All the independent infinitesimal processes that might conceivably take place may be divided into three types: *natural processes, unnatural processes* and *reversible processes*. This classification is due to Planck *.

Natural processes are all such as actually do occur in nature; they proceed in a direction towards equilibrium.

An *unnatural process* is one in a direction away from equilibrium; such a process never occurs in nature.

As a limiting case between natural and unnatural processes we have *reversible processes*, which consist of the passage in either direction through a continuous series of equilibrium states. Reversible processes do not actually occur in nature, but in whichever direction we contemplate a reversible process we can by a small change in the conditions produce a natural process differing as little as we choose from the reversible process contemplated.

We shall illustrate the three types by examples. Consider a system consisting of a liquid together with its vapour at a pressure P. Let the equilibrium vapour pressure of the liquid be p. Consider now the process

---

* Planck, *Ann. Physik* (1887) **30** 563.

of the evaporation of a small quantity of the liquid. If $P < p$, this is a natural process and will in fact take place. If on the other hand $P > p$, the process contemplated is unnatural and cannot take place; in fact the contrary process of condensation will take place. If $P = p$ then the process contemplated and its converse are reversible, for by slightly decreasing or increasing P we can make either occur. The last case may be described in an alternative manner as follows. If $P = p - \delta$, where $\delta > 0$, then the process of evaporation is a natural one. Now suppose δ gradually decreased. In the limit $\delta \to 0$, the process becomes reversible.

§ 1.15 Reversible Process and Reversible Change

We have defined a *reversible process* as a hypothetical passage through equilibrium states. If we have a system interacting with its surroundings either through the performance of work or through the flow of heat, we shall use the term *reversible process* only if there is throughout the process equilibrium between the system and its surroundings. If we wish to refer to the hypothetical passage of the system through a sequence of internal equilibrium states, without necessarily being in equilibrium with its surroundings we shall refer to a *reversible change*. We shall illustrate this distinction by examples.

Consider a system consisting of a liquid and its vapour in mutual equilibrium in a cylinder closed by a piston opposed by a pressure equal to the equilibrium vapour pressure corresponding to the temperature of the system. Suppose now that there is a flow of heat through the walls of the cylinder, with a consequent evaporation of liquid and work done on the piston at constant temperature and pressure. The change in the system is a *reversible change*, but the whole process is a *reversible process* only if the medium surrounding the cylinder is at the same temperature as the liquid and vapour; otherwise the flow of heat through the walls of the cylinder is not reversible and so the process as a whole is not reversible, though the change in the system within the cylinder is reversible.

As a second example consider a flow of heat from one system in complete internal equilibrium to another system in complete internal equilibrium. Provided both systems remain in internal equilibrium then the change which each system undergoes is a *reversible change*, but the whole process of heat flow is not a *reversible process* unless the two systems are at the same temperature.

§ 1.16 Equilibrium and Reversible Changes

If a system is in complete equilibrium, any conceivable infinitesimal change in it must be reversible. For a natural process is an approach towards equilibrium, and as the system is already in equilibrium the change cannot be a natural one. Nor can it be an unnatural one, for in that case the opposite infinitesimal change would be a natural one, and this would contradict the supposition that the system is already in equilibrium.

The only remaining possibility is that, if the system is in complete equilibrium, any conceivable infinitesimal change must be reversible.

§ 1.17 Entropy, Absolute Temperature and Second Principle

There exists a function S of the state of a system called the *entropy* of the system having the following properties.

The entropy of a system is the sum of the entropies of its parts. In this respect entropy is similar to mass, volume and energy. In other words entropy is an *extensive property* in the meaning to be defined in § 1.23.

The entropy of a system can change in two distinct ways, namely by interaction with the surroundings and by changes taking place inside the system. Symbolically we may write this as

$$dS = d_e S + d_i S, \qquad (1.17.1)$$

where dS denotes the increase of entropy of the system, $d_e S$ denotes the part of this increase due to interaction with the surroundings and $d_i S$ denotes the part of this increase due to changes taking place inside the system.

The entropy increase $d_e S$ due to interaction with the surroundings is related to the heat q absorbed by the system from its surroundings by

$$d_e S = \frac{q}{T}, \qquad (1.17.2)$$

where T is a positive quantity depending only on the temperature of the system. We may therefore regard T as a particular scale of temperature and we accordingly call T the *absolute temperature*.

The entropy increase $d_i S$ due to changes taking place inside the system is positive for all natural changes, is zero for all reversible changes and is never negative. In symbols

$$d_i S > 0, \qquad \text{(natural changes)}, \qquad (1.17.3)$$
$$d^i S = 0, \qquad \text{(reversible changes)}. \qquad (1.17.4)$$

Substituting (2) and (3) into (1), we obtain for a system at the absolute temperature T

$$dS > \frac{q}{T}, \qquad \text{(natural changes)}. \qquad (1.17.5)$$

If a system is not at a uniform temperature then we cannot apply (2) or (5) to the whole system, but we can do so to each part of the system which is at a uniform temperature.

Similarly substituting (2) and (4) into (1), we obtain

$$dS = \frac{q}{T}, \qquad \text{(reversible changes)}. \qquad (1.17.6)$$

These relations constitute the *second principle* of thermodynamics. It is to be noted that in this formulation the *absolute temperature* T and the *entropy* S are introduced simultaneously as two fundamental quantities. In a more mathematical formulation T^{-1} appears as an integrating factor leading to the complete differential dS.

The second principle was foreshadowed by the work of Carnot (1824) but was more clearly enunciated by Clausius (1850) and independently by Kelvin (1851). The conception of *entropy* is due to the former (1854) and of *absolute temperature* to the latter.

According to the above relations S is indefinite to the extent of an arbitrary additive constant. This arbitrariness is however without physical significance, since only changes of entropy are observable or measurable. This indefiniteness can be removed by an arbitrary conventional fixing of a state of zero entropy for each independent system.

For a finite change, reversible throughout, equation (6) applies to each of the infinitesimal steps into which the finite change may be divided. Hence using $\triangle$ to denote the increase from the initial to the final value, we have

$$\triangle S = \Sigma \frac{q}{T}, \qquad \text{(reversible change)}, \qquad (1.17.7)$$

where Σ denotes summation over all the steps.

In particular for a reversible cycle which leaves the system in a final state idential with the initial state

$$\triangle S = 0, \qquad \Sigma \frac{q}{T} = 0 \qquad \text{(reversible cycle)}. \qquad (1.17.8)$$

§ 1.18   Kelvin Scale of Temperature

It is obvious that the fundamental relation (1.17.2) used in defining entropy and absolute temperature would remain valid if the signs of S and T were simultaneously reversed. We accordingly fixed the signs unambiguously by deciding that T shall be positive. The same relation (1.17.2) still remains valid if S is replaced by cS and T by $c^{-1}T$ where c is any positive number. Thus to complete the definitions of S and T we have to fix their scales, in other words to fix the unit of temperature called the *degree*. This is simply accomplished by assigning an arbitrary value to T at some specified temperature.

We accordingly define the temperature of equilibrium between liquid water and ice at a pressure of one atmosphere as 273.16 degrees. The absolute scale of temperature with the size of the degree thus fixed is called the Kelvin scale, denoted by the letter K. Thus the normal (i.e. at one atmosphere) freezing-point of water is 273.16 °K.

§ 1.19   Centigrade Degree

We shall describe later in § 4.13 how it is possible to measure the ratio of any two absolute temperatures, in particular the ratio of any absolute temperature to that of the normal freezing-point (N.F.P.) of water. Having then assigned the value 273.16 °K to the N.F.P. of water, it thus becomes possible to determine unambiguously any other temperature on the Kelvin scale. If then the boiling-point of water at one atmosphere or the normal boiling-point (N.B.P.) of water is so determined, it will be found to be 373.16 °K. Thus the N.B.P. of water exceeds the N.F.P. of water by just 100 degrees. This is of course no accident, but was the determining factor in the arbitrary choice of the size of the degree. Owing to this property of the chosen scale the degree is called a *centigrade degree*.

In defining the degree we have followed Giauque * (1939) who stresses the fact that only one standard temperature is required to fix the size of the degree. The procedure adopted in the past of fixing the size of the degree by means of two temperatures (the N.F.P. and N.B.P. of water) is, as pointed out by Giauque, less direct, less reasonable and less convenient. There is reason for hoping that Giauque's method of defining the degree may soon be adopted universally, especially since it has recently (1948) been recommended by the International Union of Physics **.

§ 1.20　Celsius Scale of Temperature

For many practical purposes it is considered convenient to use a temperature scale such that the temperatures most usually met in the laboratory and in ordinary life shall be represented by numbers between 0 and 100. For this purpose the scale most used in scientific work is the *Celsius scale* (sometimes loosely called the *centigrade scale*) and denoted by the letter C. The temperature on the Celsius scale is defined as the excess of the temperature on the Kelvin scale over that of the N.F.P. of water also on the Kelvin scale. Thus the relation between the two scales is

$$x \,°K = (x - 273.16) \,°C. \tag{1.20.1}$$
$$y \,°C = (y + 273.16) \,°K. \tag{1.20.2}$$
$$\text{N.F.P. of water} = 273.16 \,°K = 0 \,°C. \tag{1.20.3}$$
$$\text{N.B.P. of water} = 373.16 \,°K = 100 \,°C. \tag{1.20.4}$$

In both the *Kelvin scale* and the *Celsius scale* the unit is the *centigrade degree*. There are other scales based on other kinds of degrees, but these are little used in scientific work and need not be mentioned further.

§ 1.21　Heat Flow and Temperature

According to the zeroth principle of thermodynamics the condition for thermal equilibrium between two parts of a system is equality of temperature. We can now verify that this condition is consistent with the general condition of equilibrium, namely that any infinitesimal change should be reversible. We consider a thermally insulated system consisting of two parts α and β at uniform temperatures T^α and T^β respectively. The entropy S of the whole system is equal to the sum of S^α the entropy of α and S^β the entropy of β; that is to say

$$S = S^\alpha + S^\beta. \tag{1.21.1}$$

---

* Giauque, *Nature* (1939) **143** 623.
** *International Union of Physics*, Document SG 48—6.

Consider now the flow of an infinitesimal positive quantity q of heat from α to β. Then according to (1. 17. 2)

$$d_e S^\alpha = -\frac{q}{T^\alpha},\qquad\qquad\text{(1. 21. 2)}$$

$$d_e S^\beta = \frac{q}{T^\beta}.\qquad\qquad\text{(1. 21. 3)}$$

The increase in the entropy of the whole system due to this flow of heat is therefore

$$d_e S^\alpha + d_e S^\beta = -\frac{q}{T^\alpha} + \frac{q}{T^\beta}$$
$$= q\left(\frac{1}{T^\beta} - \frac{1}{T^\alpha}\right).\qquad\text{(1. 21. 4)}$$

The condition that the flow of positive heat q from α to β should be a natural process is that the consequent change of entropy of the whole system should be an increase, that is to say that the expression (4) should be positive. Thus heat will flow naturally from α to β provided

$$T^\alpha > T^\beta.\qquad\qquad\text{(1. 21. 5)}$$

We have thus reached the conclusion that according to our definition of the absolute temperature T, heat flows naturally from a higher to a lower absolute temperature.

If each of the phases α and β is in internal equilibrium then there are no changes of entropy other than that due to the flow of heat from α to β. If on the other hand, either phase, or both, is not in internal equilibrium there may be other entropy changes $d_i S^\alpha$, $d_i S^\beta$ superposed on that due to the flow of heat. These can only be positive, so that the increase in entropy of the whole system will then be greater than the expression (4). The above argument is not affected by such other natural processes proceeding as well as the flow of heat. This is an advantage of the particular formulation of the second principle which we have chosen *.

In the particular case that $T^\alpha = T^\beta$, the expression (4) vanishes; there is no entropy increase associated with the flow of heat. The two parts of the system are in thermal equilibrium and so the flow of heat contemplated is reversible.

§ 1. 22 Phases

The simplest and most important kind of thermodynamic system may be considered as consisting of a finite number of homogeneous parts. As already mentioned in § 1. 03 each such homogeneous part is called a phase. Strictly, we should also include a finite number of non-homogeneous parts

---

* Compare Prigogine, *Etude Thermodynamique des Phénomènes Irréversibles* (1947) p. 14.

forming the boundaries between various pairs of homogeneous phases. However, for many purposes these non-homogeneous parts are of such small extent compared with the homogeneous parts that they may be ignored. We shall for the sake of simplicity so ignore them for the time being. At a later stage beginning at § 1.51 we shall show how we may take account of them in an exact manner.

§ 1.23 Extensive Properties

The mass of a system is clearly equal to the sum of the masses of its constituent phases. Any property, such as mass, whose value for the whole system is equal to the sum of its values for the separate phases is called an *extensive property* or a *capacity factor*.

Important examples of *extensive properties* are the energy U, the entropy S and the volume V. The energy U of a system is related to the energies U^α of the separate phases α by

$$U = \Sigma_\alpha U^\alpha. \tag{1.23.1}$$

Similarly, for the entropy, we have

$$S = \Sigma_\alpha S^\alpha, \tag{1.23.2}$$

and for the volume

$$V = \Sigma_\alpha V^\alpha. \tag{1.23.3}$$

When we are considering a system of one phase only we may obviously omit the superscript α and shall usually do so.

§ 1.24 Intensive Properties

The density of a phase is clearly constant throughout the phase, because the phase is by definition homogeneous. Further, the density of a phase of a given kind and state is independent of the quantity of the phase. Any property of a phase with these characteristics is called an *intensive property* or an *intensity factor*.

The temperature T^α and the pressure P^α of a phase α are important examples of intensive properties.

§ 1.25 Pressure of Phase

The fundamental property of the pressure is familiar from hydrostatics. It may be described by the statement that for any infinitesimal change dV^α of the volume of the phase α the work w^α done on the phase is given by

$$w^\alpha = - P^\alpha \, dV^\alpha. \tag{1.25.1}$$

where P^α is the pressure of the phase α.

§ 1.26 Chemical Content of Phase

The chemical content of a phase α is defined by the number n_i^α of units of quantity of each of a finite number of *independently variable chemical species* in the phase. The unit of quantity may be the gram, the pound or any other unit of mass. It need not necessarily be the same mass for different chemical species. In fact, it is most usual to take as units of quantity the *gram-molecule* or *mole*, that is a mass proportional to that given by the accepted chemical formula of the particular species. A thermodynamic definition of the mole will be given in § 4.14. In anticipation of this we may use the mole as the unit of quantity for each chemical species.

§ 1.27 Chemically Inert Species

We must emphasise that in the previous section we specified that the chemical species by which the chemical content of the phase is described must be *independently variable*. In the absence of any chemical reactions there is no difficulty, but if some of the species can react chemically the recipe required for selecting a set of *independently variable* species is not so simple. In order to postpone this complication we shall exclude the possibility of chemical reactions until we come to § 1.48 where we revert to the subject.

§ 1.28 Closed and Open Phases

It will be convenient to refer to a phase of fixed content as *closed* and to one whose content can be varied by passage of substances to or from other phases as *open*. In a similar sense any part of a system may be referred to as *closed* or *open*.

§ 1.29 Degrees of Freedom of a Closed Phase

Provided a closed phase is at rest and chemical reactions are excluded, the phase is always in internal equilibrium and so any infinitesimal change is reversible. An infinitesimal change can be irreversible (natural) only if more than one phase or a chemical reaction is involved. Hence for a closed phase at rest, excluding chemical reactions, we have for any infinitesimal change

$$q = TdS. \qquad \text{(closed phase)}, \qquad (1.29.1)$$

$$w = -PdV, \qquad \text{(closed phase)}, \qquad (1.29.2)$$

while the first principle of thermodynamics gives for any infinitesimal process

$$dU = q + w. \qquad (1.29.3)$$

Substituting from (1) and (2) into (3) we obtain

$$dU = TdS - PdV, \qquad \text{(closed phase)}. \qquad (1.29.4)$$

As already mentioned in § 1.03 a closed single phase has *two degrees of freedom*; that is to say two quantities must be fixed to complete the specification of its state. There is of course a wide possible choice of such pairs of independent variables. If one chooses the entropy S and the volume V as the two independent variables then equation (4) shows how the energy U depends on them. Such a choice of independent variables is not necessarily the most convenient. For example it might be preferable to choose the energy U and the volume V as the independent variables; the dependence on them of the entropy S is then obtained by simple transformation of (4) as

$$dS = \frac{1}{T}\, dU + \frac{P}{T}\, dV \qquad \text{(closed phase).} \qquad (1.29.5)$$

Other choices of independent variables will be discussed later.

§ 1.30 Chemical Potentials

We can generalize formula (1.29.4) to an open phase or phase of variable content by writing formally

$$dU = TdS - PdV + \Sigma_i\, \mu_i\, dn_i, \qquad (1.30.1)$$

where Σ_i denotes summation over all the chemical species in the phase and μ_i is defined by

$$\mu_i = \left(\frac{\partial U}{\partial n_i}\right)_{S,V,n_j}, \qquad (1.30.2)$$

n_j denoting all quantities like n_i except n_i itself.

The quantities μ_i were first introduced in this manner by Gibbs (1875), who called μ_i the *potential* * of the species i. It is more usual to call μ_i the *chemical potential* of i; sometimes μ_i is called the *partial potential* of i. All three names are unobjectionable.

The reader may well find the definition (2) of μ_i puzzling because a variation in the content of a phase keeping its entropy constant is an abstract idea not corresponding to any simple physical process. It must indeed be admitted that at this stage it is by no means clear to what extent equation (2) is a sufficient definition of μ_i. It should however be clear that there is nothing contradictory or inconsistent about equations (1) and (2). At the worst the definition of the μ_i's may be incomplete. We shall return to this point later in § 1.36 and § 1.47, meanwhile using (1) as a basis for development until we can obtain a simpler physical meaning of the chemical potentials μ_i.

The chemical potentials μ_i are intensive properties; that is to say that, like density, they have the same value in any phase as in a larger or smaller phase having the same temperature, pressure and relative composition. This may not be obvious at this stage but will become so later. Meanwhile this will be assumed.

§ 1.31 Other Thermodynamic Potentials

Formula (1.30.1) expresses the dependence of the energy U on the set of independent variables S, V, n_i. This set of independent variables is not

---

* Gibbs, *Collected Works* vol. 1 p. 65.

by any means the most convenient. It is usually preferable to use T as an independent variable instead of S, and often preferable to use P as an independent variable instead of V. In order to change over to such alternative sets of variables, it is expedient to introduce certain new thermodynamic functions defined for each phase as follows:

$$F = U - TS, \tag{1.31.1}$$
$$H = U + PV, \tag{1.31.2}$$
$$G = U - TS + PV. \tag{1.31.3}$$

If now we differentiate each of these and substitute for dU from (1.30.1) we obtain

$$dF = -SdT - PdV + \Sigma_i \mu_i \, dn_i, \tag{1.31.4}$$
$$dH = \quad TdS + VdP + \Sigma_i \mu_i \, dn_i, \tag{1.31.5}$$
$$dG = -SdT + VdP + \Sigma_i \mu_i \, dn_i. \tag{1.31.6}$$

Since F, H, G like S, V, U are evidently extensive properties the F, H, G in a system of several phases are related to the $F^\alpha, H^\alpha, G^\alpha$ of the individual phases α by

$$F = \Sigma_\alpha F^\alpha, \tag{1.31.7}$$
$$H = \Sigma_\alpha H^\alpha, \tag{1.31.8}$$
$$G = \Sigma_\alpha G^\alpha. \tag{1.31.9}$$

It is clear that the dependence of F on the independent variables T, V, n_i is given simply and explicitly by (4). Similarly according to (5) and (6) H and G are simply expressed in terms of the independent variables S, P, n_i and T, P, n_i respectively. In view of these characteristics U is called a *thermodynamic potential* for the variables S, V, n_i, and F is a *thermodynamic potential* for the variables T, V, n_i; similarly H is a *thermodynamic potential* for the variables S, P, n_i and G for the variables T, P, n_i.

The *thermodynamic potentials* U, F, H, G are sufficient for all requirements. They are not however the only possible ones. For example by simple transformation of (1.30.1) we have

$$dS = \frac{1}{T} dU + \frac{P}{T} dV - \frac{1}{T} \Sigma_i \mu_i \, dn_i. \tag{1.31.10}$$

showing that S is a thermodynamic potential for the variables U, V, n_i. Again let us define two new quantities J and Y by

$$J = S - \frac{U}{T} = -\frac{F}{T}, \tag{1.31.11}$$

$$Y = S - \frac{U}{T} - \frac{PV}{T} = -\frac{G}{T}. \tag{1.31.12}$$

Now differentiate (11) and (12) and substitute for dS from (10). We obtain

$$dJ = \frac{U}{T^2} dT + \frac{P}{T} dV - \frac{1}{T} \Sigma_i \mu_i \, dn_i, \tag{1.31.13}$$

$$dY = \frac{H}{T^2} dT - \frac{V}{T} dP - \frac{1}{T} \Sigma_i \mu_i \, dn_i, \tag{1.31.14}$$

from which we see that J, like F, is a *thermodynamic potential* for the variables T, V, n_i and Y, like G, is one for the variables T, P, n_i.

The functions J, Y have in recent times been largely superseded by F, G. In some applications the former have advantages over the latter, as will be seen later. In particular we shall see in Chapter II that J, Y are more simply related to what is called statistical probability. We shall use sometimes F, G and on other occasions J, Y.

In a system of several phases α evidently

$$J = \Sigma_\alpha J^\alpha \qquad (1.31.15)$$
$$Y = \Sigma_\alpha Y^\alpha. \qquad (1.31.16)$$

§ 1.32   Names and Symbols for Thermodynamic Potentials

Whereas the definition of the several thermodynamic functions is unambiguous and straightforward, there is unfortunately almost unbelievable absence of uniformity as to their names. We shall record briefly some of the alternative terminologies.

U, which we call *energy*, is sometimes called *total energy* and sometimes *internal energy*, the name used by Clausius.

H was called by Gibbs (1875) the *heat function for constant pressure*. It has the alternative names *heat function, total heat, heat content* and *enthalpy*. Of these we choose *heat function* because this name best emphasizes that H, in contrast to q the heat absorbed, is a function of the state of the system.

The function F was called by Gibbs (1875) the *force function for constant temperature* [*] and by Helmholtz (1882) the *free energy* [**]. It has also been called the *work function* and the *Helmholtz free energy*. We shall use the alternative names *free energy* and *Helmholtz function*.

The function G is also due to Gibbs (1875). It is sometimes called the *total thermodynamic potential* and sometimes merely the *thermodynamic potential*. Unfortunately G has sometimes been called *free energy*, thus causing confusion between F and G. To avoid such confusion we have in the past called G the *Gibbs free energy*. We now propose to use the simpler name *Gibbs function* with the alternative name *useful energy*.

The functions J and Y were introduced by Massieu [***] (1869) and the latter was widely used by Planck. We accordingly propose to call J the *Massieu function* and Y the *Planck function*. It is interesting to note that these were the earliest thermodynamic potentials, six years earlier than those introduced by Gibbs, namely F, G and H.

There has also been wide disparity between the notations of various authors. The table below gives a comparison of the choice of some of the best known authors.

---

[*]   Gibbs, *Collected Works*, vol. 1 p. 89.
[**]   Helmholtz, *Sitzungsber. Akad. Wiss. Berlin* (1882) **1** 22.
[***]   Massieu, *Comptes rendus* (1869) **69** 858.

Preferred Names	Entropy	Energy	Heat Function	Free Energy or Helmholtz Function	Gibbs Function or Useful Energy	Massieu Function	Planck Function
Present Notation	S	U	H	F	G	J	Y
Massieu (1869)		U	U'			ψ	ψ'
Gibbs (1876)	η	ε	χ	ψ	3		
Helmholtz (1882)	S	U		F			
Duhem (1886)	S	U		F	ϕ		
Lorentz (1921, 1927)	η	ε		Ψ	3		
Planck (1932 edition)	S	U		F		Ψ	Φ
Lewis and Randall (1923)	S	E	H	A	F		
Partington (1924)	S	U	H	F	Z		
Schottky (1929)	S	U	H	F	G		
Guggenheim (1933)	S	E	H	F	G		
Fowler (1936)	S	E	H	F	G		
Brönsted (1936)	S	E	H	F	G		
De Donder and Van Rysselberghe (1936)	S	E	H	F	G		
Fowler and Guggenheim (1939)	S	E	H	F	G		
McDougall (1939)	S	E	H	A	F		
MacInnes (1939)	S	U	H	F	Z		
Slater (1939)	S	U	H	A	G		
Mayer and Mayer (1940)	S	E	H	A	F		
Zemansky (1943)	S	U	H	A	G		
Prigogine and Defay (1944)	S	E	H	F	G		
De Boer (1946)	S	U	$W.$	F	G		

Our notation has been chosen so as to agree with, or at least not to contradict, as many authors as possible especially those still alive, of whatever nationality *. In the use of S, U and F it conforms to the notation of Helmholtz (1882). It is unfortunate that pupils of the famous school in California founded by G. N. Lewis use F to denote the *Gibbs function*, whereas other American authors, as well as Belgian, British, Danish, Dutch, French, and German authors all use F to denote the *Helmholtz function*. It is to be hoped that eventually international agreement will be reached.

---

* This notation has the support of the International Union of Physics (1948) and of the International Union of Pure and Applied Chemistry (1947).

§ 1.33 Fundamental Equations

Let us recollect four important relations from § 1.30 and § 1.31, namely

$$dU = TdS - PdV + \Sigma_i \, \mu_i \, dn_i, \qquad (1.33.1)$$

$$dF = -SdT - PdV + \Sigma_i \, \mu_i \, dn_i, \qquad (1.33.2)$$

$$dH = TdS + VdP + \Sigma_i \, \mu_i \, dn_i, \qquad (1.33.3)$$

$$dG = -SdT + VdP + \Sigma_i \, \mu_i \, dn_i. \qquad (1.33.4)$$

Each of these relates a *thermodynamic potential* to its appropriate independent variables. Following Gibbs we call these *fundamental equations*. The relationship between the four *thermodynamic potentials* U, H, F, G and the various pairs of independent variables chosen from the set S, T, V, P can be expressed schematically by

$$
\begin{matrix}
S & U & V \\
H & & F \\
P & G & T
\end{matrix}
\qquad (1.33.5)
$$

By means of a *fundamental equation* all the thermodynamic functions can be expressed in terms of the chosen thermodynamic potential and its derivatives with respect to the corresponding independent variables.

For example choosing $G \, (T, P, n_i)$ we obtain directly from (4)

$$S = -\frac{\partial G}{\partial T}, \qquad (1.33.6)$$

$$H = G - T\frac{\partial G}{\partial T}, \qquad (1.33.7)$$

$$V = \frac{\partial G}{\partial P}, \qquad (1.33.8)$$

$$F = G - P\frac{\partial G}{\partial P}, \qquad (1.33.9)$$

$$U = G - T\frac{\partial G}{\partial T} - P\frac{\partial G}{\partial P}, \qquad (1.33.10)$$

$$\mu_i = \frac{\partial G}{\partial n_i}. \qquad (1.33.11)$$

Similarly we could express all the thermodynamic functions in terms of U and its differential coefficients with respect to S, V, n_i, but not in terms of its differential coefficients with respect to T, V, n_i. This accounts for the muddle produced by certain so-called elementary treatments wherein U, T, V, n_i are introduced as fundamental quantities without mentioning entropy until a late stage.

The set of fundamental equations (1) to (4) used by Gibbs has symmetry expressed by the scheme (5). It is the best known and most

used set. It is however not always the most useful set. In some respects
the set

$$dS = \frac{1}{T} dU + \frac{P}{T} dV - \frac{1}{T} \Sigma_i \mu_i dn_i, \qquad (1.33.12)$$

$$dJ = \frac{U}{T^2} dT + \frac{P}{T} dV - \frac{1}{T} \Sigma_i \mu_i dn_i, \qquad (1.33.13)$$

$$dY = \frac{H}{T^2} dT - \frac{V}{T} dP - \frac{1}{T} \Sigma_i \mu_i dn_i \qquad (1.33.14)$$

is more convenient. We recall that J is the *Massieu function* and Y the
Planck function, defined respectively by

$$J = S - \frac{U}{T} = -\frac{F}{T}, \qquad (1.33.15)$$

$$Y = S - \frac{U}{T} - \frac{PV}{T} = -\frac{G}{T}. \qquad (1.33.16)$$

In particular we shall in Chapter II find the fundamental equations
(12) to (14) most convenient in relating *classical thermodynamics* to
statistical thermodynamics. For this purpose a fourth thermodynamic
potential is not needed.

§ 1.34 Dimensions and Units

It is clear from the relations of § 1.31 that U, H, F, G all have the
same dimensions as energy and can be measured in joules or any other
unit of energy. The products TS, PV and $\mu_i'n_i$ also have the same
dimensions as energy. Hence S has the same dimensions as energy/tempera-
ture and can be measured for example in joule/degree centigrade. μ_i has
the same dimensions as energy/mole and can be measured for example in
joule/mole.

Thermodynamic data are in fact often expressed in terms of a different
energy unit the *calorie* equal to 4.1840 (absolute) joules and referred
to again in § 4.06.

This is perhaps the appropriate place to mention that we do and shall
consistently use symbols to denote *physical quantities*, not their measure
in terms of particular units. This is sometimes called Stroud's system of
notation [*]. For example we may write

$$P = 1.2 \text{ atm.}$$
$$= 91.2 \text{ cm. Hg.}$$
$$= 0.912 \text{ m. Hg.}$$
$$= 1.216 \times 10^6 \text{ dyne/cm.}^2$$
$$= 0.1216 \text{ joule/cm.}^3,$$

but under no circumstances shall we equate P to 1.2 or any other number.

---

[*] See Lodge, *Nature* (1888) 38 281,
    Henderson, *Math. Gazette* (1924) 12 99,
    Guggenheim, *Phil. Mag.* (1942) 33 479,
    Jeffries and Jeffries, *Methods of Mathematical Physics* (1946) p. 3.

§ 1.35 Integrated Relation

Any of the relations (1.33.1), (1.33.2), (1.33.3) or (1.33.4) can be integrated by the following artifice. Each of these relations holds for any variations of the independent variables. Let us now choose to keep T, P constant and make each n_i change by an increment proportional to itself. We accordingly put

$$dT = 0, \qquad dP = 0, \qquad dn_i = n_i \, d\xi. \qquad (1.35.1)$$

Physically this means that we increase the quantity of the phase in the proportion $(1 + d\xi) : 1$ without altering its temperature, pressure or relative composition. Evidently then all other intensive properties, in particular the μ_i's remain unaltered while all other extensive properties, in particular S, V, U, H, F, G also increase in the proportion $(1 + d\xi) : 1$. We have therefore

$$d\mu_i = 0, \qquad dS = S \, d\xi, \qquad dV = V \, d\xi. \qquad (1.35.2)$$

Substituting from (1) and (2) into (1.33.1) we obtain

$$U \, d\xi = TS \, d\xi - PV \, d\xi + \Sigma_i \, \mu_i \, n_i \, d\xi. \qquad (1.35.3)$$

Now integrating from $\xi = 0$ to $\xi = 1$, or dividing by $d\xi$, we obtain

$$U = TS - PV + \Sigma_i \, \mu_i \, n_i. \qquad (1.35.4)$$

Alternatively we might substitute from (1) and (2) into (1.33.4), obtaining

$$G \, d\xi = \Sigma_i \, \mu_i \, n_i \, d\xi. \qquad (1.35.5)$$

Integrating from $\xi = 0$ to $\xi = 1$, or dividing by $d\xi$, we obtain

$$G = \Sigma_i \, \mu_i \, n_i, \qquad (1.35.6)$$

which is equivalent to (4).

If instead we substituted into (1.33.2) or (1.33.3), we should again obtain the same result equivalent to (6).

We could also obtain the same result more directly by observing that U is homogeneous and of first degree in the extensive properties S, V, n_i. Consequently by Euler's theorem

$$U = \frac{\partial U}{\partial S} S + \frac{\partial U}{\partial V} V + \Sigma_i \frac{\partial U}{\partial n_i} n_i$$

$$= TS - PV + \Sigma_i \, \mu_i \, n_i, \qquad (1.35.7)$$

the same as (4) and equivalent to (6).

§ 1.36 Single Component Phase

In a phase containing only one chemical species formula (1.35.6) reduces to

$$G = \mu n \qquad (1.36.1)$$

or

$$\mu = G/n = G_m, \qquad (1.36.2)$$

where G_m denotes the value of the Gibbs function per mole.

Suppose now that for a chemical species in its pure state, we conventionally assign an arbitrary value to U_m the energy per mole at some chosen value of the temperature, pressure and state of aggregation (e.g. crystal or liquid or gas). Suppose also we do the like for S_m the entropy per mole. Then subject to these arbitrary conventions, which are physically insignificant, U_m and S_m are completely defined at any other temperature and pressure and state of aggregation. Moreover T, P and V_m, the volume per mole, are unambiguously defined. Hence G_m is completely determined by

$$G_m = U_m - TS_m + PV_m. \qquad (1.36.3)$$

It follows according to (2), that having once chosen arbitrary zeros of U_m and S_m for a pure chemical substance μ is unambiguously defined.

This disposes of the question raised in § 1.30 so far as pure chemical substances are concerned. The preciseness of definition of μ_i in a phase of several components will be examined in § 1.47

If now we apply the relation (1.33.4) to one mole of a single component, using (2) we obtain

$$d\mu = dG_m = -S_m dT + V_m dP. \qquad (1.36.4)$$

There is no term in dn, since n has the constant value unity. From (4) it follows immediately that

$$\frac{\partial \mu}{\partial T} = -S_m, \qquad (1.36.5)$$

$$\frac{\partial \mu}{\partial P} = V_m. \qquad (1.36.6)$$

By using the identity

$$\mu = G_m = H_m - TS_m, \qquad (1.36.7)$$

we can transform (5) to

$$\mu - T\frac{\partial \mu}{\partial T} = H_m, \qquad (1.36.8)$$

or

$$\frac{\partial (\mu/T)}{\partial T} = -\frac{H_m}{T^2}. \qquad (1.36.9)$$

§ 1.37   Mole Fractions

We are often interested only in the intensive properties of a phase and not at all in the amount of the phase. It is then convenient to describe the phase entirely by intensive variables. One such set of variables is T, P, x_i where x_i denotes the *mole fraction* defined by

$$x_i = \frac{n_i}{\Sigma_k n_k}, \qquad (1.37.1)$$

where Σ_k denotes summation over all the species.

By definition the mole fractions satisfy the identity.

$$\Sigma_i x_i = 1. \tag{1.37.2}$$

If the number of independent species or *components* it G, then of the $G + 2$ quantities T, P, x_i used to describe the state of the phase, apart from its amount, only $G + 1$ are independent owing to (2). We therefore say that a single phase of G components has $G + 1$ *degrees of freedom*.

§ 1.38 Gibbs–Duhem Relation

We may, if we choose, describe the state of a single phase, apart from its size, by the set of intensive quantities T, P, μ_i. The number of these is $G + 2$. We have however seen that the number of degrees of freedom of a single phase is only $G + 1$. It follows that T, P μ_i cannot be independently variable, but there must be some relation between them corresponding to the identity (1.37.2) between mole fractions. We shall now derive such a relation.

We differentiate (1.35.6) and obtain

$$dG = \Sigma_i \mu_i \, dn_i + \Sigma_i n_i \, d\mu_i. \tag{1.38.1}$$

From (1) we subtract (1.33.4) and obtain

$$SdT - VdP + \Sigma_i n_i \, d\mu_i = 0. \tag{1.38.2}$$

Dividing (2) by $\Sigma_i n_i$ and denoting the average entropy and volume per mole by S_m and V_m respectively, we find

$$S_m dT - V_m dP + \Sigma_i x_i \, d\mu_i = 0. \tag{1.38.3}$$

This is the sought relation between T, P and the μ_i's. Either (2) or (3) is known as the Gibbs–Duhem relation[*]. It is particularly useful in its application to changes at constant temperature and pressure, when it may be written

$$\Sigma_i x_i D\mu_i = 0, \qquad (T, P \text{ constant}), \tag{1.38.4}$$

where we have used D to denote variations due to changes of composition at constant temperature and pressure. We shall frequently use this notation. In particular we shall return to formula (4) in § 6.06.

§ 1.39 Multiphase Systems

In the previous ten sections most of the formulae have been written explicitly for a single phase. Corresponding formulae for a system con-

---

[*] Gibbs, *Collected Works*, vol. 1 p. 88;

Duhem, *Le Potentiel Thermodynamique et ses Applications* (1886) p. 33. (The author has been unable to find any derivation of this relation by Duhem in any scientific journal. The derivation in the above mentioned text-book is the basis of that given here.)

sisting of several phases are obtained by summation over all the phases. In particular from the fundamental equations in § 1. 33 we obtain

$$dU = \quad \Sigma_\alpha T^\alpha \, dS^\alpha - \Sigma_\alpha P^\alpha \, dV^\alpha + \Sigma_\alpha \Sigma_i \mu_i^\alpha \, dn_i^\alpha, \quad (1.39.1)$$

$$dF = - \Sigma_\alpha S^\alpha \, dT^\alpha - \Sigma_\alpha P^\alpha \, dV^\alpha + \Sigma_\alpha \Sigma_i \mu_i^\alpha \, dn_i^\alpha, \quad (1.39.2)$$

$$dH = \quad \Sigma_\alpha T^\alpha \, dS^\alpha + \Sigma_\alpha V^\alpha \, dP^\alpha + \Sigma_\alpha \Sigma_i \mu_i^\alpha \, dn_i^\alpha, \quad (1.39.3)$$

$$dG = - \Sigma_\alpha S^\alpha \, dT^\alpha + \Sigma_\alpha V^\alpha \, dP^\alpha + \Sigma_\alpha \Sigma_i \mu_i^\alpha \, dn_i^\alpha, \quad (1.39.4)$$

where Σ_i denotes summation over the components and Σ_α denotes summation over the phases.

We are still postulating the absence of chemical reactions. This restriction will be removed in § 1. 48.

§ 1. 40 Adiabatic Changes in Closed System

We recall that for any infinitesimal change in a closed system

$$dU = w + q. \qquad (1.40.1)$$

If the change is *adiabatic*, then by definition

$$q = 0, \qquad dU = w, \qquad \text{(adiabatic)}. \qquad (1.40.2)$$

All conceivable infinitesimal adiabatic changes can moreover, according to the definitions in § 1. 15 and § 1. 17, be classified as follows.

$$dU = w, \qquad dS > 0, \qquad \text{(natural adiabatic)}; \qquad (1.40.3)$$
$$dU = w, \qquad dS = 0, \qquad \text{(reversible adiabatic)}; \qquad (1.40.4)$$
$$dU = w, \qquad dS < 0, \qquad \text{(unnatural adiabatic)}. \qquad (1.40.5)$$

Suppose now that the whole system is enclosed by fixed rigid walls, so that $w = 0$. We then have the classification

$$dU = 0, \quad dV = 0, \quad dS > 0, \quad \text{(natural adiabatic)}; \qquad (1.40.6)$$
$$dU = 0, \quad dV = 0, \quad dS = 0, \quad \text{(reversible adiabatic)}; \qquad (1.40.7)$$
$$dU = 0, \quad dV = 0, \quad dS < 0, \quad \text{(unnatural adiabatic)}. \qquad (1.40.8)$$

Suppose now, instead, that each phase α is partly bounded by a piston acting against a constant pressure P^α, so that

$$w = - \Sigma_\alpha P^\alpha \, dV^\alpha = - \Sigma_\alpha d(P^\alpha V^\alpha) = - d\Sigma_\alpha P^\alpha V^\alpha. \quad (1.40.9)$$

Then we have

$$dU = - d \Sigma_\alpha P^\alpha V^\alpha, \qquad (1.40.10)$$

$$dH = d(U + \Sigma_\alpha P^\alpha V^\alpha) = 0. \qquad (1.40.11)$$

Consequently in this case we have the classification

$$dH = 0, \quad dP^\alpha = 0, \quad dS > 0, \quad \text{(natural adiabatic)}; \qquad (1.40.12)$$
$$dH = 0, \quad dP^\alpha = 0, \quad dS = 0, \quad \text{(reversible adiabatic)}; \qquad (1.40.13)$$
$$dH = 0, \quad dP^\alpha = 0, \quad dS < 0, \quad \text{(unnatural adiabatic)}. \qquad (1.40.14)$$

§ 1. 41 Isothermal Changes in Closed System

Instead of a thermally insulated system, let us now consider a system whose temperature T is kept uniform and constant. This may be achieved by keeping the system in a temperature bath at the temperature T. Then according to the fundamental properties of entropy expounded in § 1. 17 and in particular formulae (1. 17. 5) and (1. 17. 6) we have the classification of possible infinitesimal changes

$$dT = 0, \qquad d(TS) > q, \qquad \text{(natural isothermal);} \qquad (1.41.1)$$
$$dT = 0, \qquad d(TS) = q, \qquad \text{(reversible isothermal);} \qquad (1.41.2)$$
$$dT = 0, \qquad d(TS) < q, \qquad \text{(unnatural isothermal).} \qquad (1.41.3)$$

We also have according to the first principle of thermodynamics, in particular formula (1. 12. 3),

$$q = dU - w = dF + d(TS) - w, \qquad (1.41.4)$$

using the definition (1. 31. 1) of F. Substituting from (4) into (1), (2) and (3) in turn we obtain

$$dT = 0, \qquad w > dF, \qquad \text{(natural isothermal);} \qquad (1.41.5)$$
$$dT = 0, \qquad w = dF, \qquad \text{(reversible isothermal);} \qquad (1.41.6)$$
$$dT = 0, \qquad w < dF, \qquad \text{(unnatural isothermal).} \qquad (1.41.7)$$

In particular if the system is enclosed by fixed rigid walls, so that $w = 0$, the classification becomes

$$dT = 0, \quad dV = 0, \quad dF < 0, \qquad \text{(natural isothermal);} \qquad (1.41.8)$$
$$dT = 0, \quad dV = 0, \quad dF = 0, \qquad \text{(reversible isothermal);} \qquad (1.41.9)$$
$$dT = 0, \quad dV = 0, \quad dF > 0, \qquad \text{(unnatural isothermal).} \quad (1.41.10)$$

If on the other hand each phase α is partly bounded by a piston acting against a constant pressure P^α, then

$$w = - \Sigma_\alpha P^\alpha \, dV^\alpha = - \Sigma_\alpha d(P^\alpha V^\alpha) = - d \Sigma_\alpha P^\alpha V^\alpha$$
$$= d(F - G) = dF - dG \qquad (1.41.11)$$

from the definitions (1. 31. 1) and (1. 31. 3) of F and G respectively. Substituting from (11) into (5), (6) and (7) in turn, we obtain

$$dT = 0, \quad dP^\alpha = 0, \quad dG < 0, \qquad \text{(natural isothermal);} \qquad (1.41.12)$$
$$dT = 0, \quad dP^\alpha = 0, \quad dG = 0, \qquad \text{(reversible isothermal);} \qquad (1.41.13)$$
$$dT = 0, \quad dP^\alpha = 0, \quad dG > 0, \qquad \text{(unnatural isothermal).} \qquad (1.41.14)$$

§ 1.42 Equilibrium Conditions. General Form

We saw in § 1. 16 that if a system is in complete equilibrium then any conceivable change in it must be reversible. This enables us to put the conditions for equilibrium into various forms each of general validity.

If we first consider an infinitesimal change at constant volume, the system being thermally insulated, we have according to (1.40.7) the equilibrium conditions

$$dS = 0, \qquad dV = 0, \qquad dU = 0. \qquad (1.42.1)$$

If instead we consider an infinitesimal change keeping each phase α at constant pressure P^{α} the whole system being thermally insulated, we have according to (1.40.13) the equilibrium conditions

$$dS = 0, \qquad dP^{\alpha} = 0, \qquad dH = 0. \qquad (1.42.2)$$

Thirdly let us consider an infinitesimal change at constant volume and constant uniform temperature (isothermal change). We now have according to (1.41.9) the equilibrium conditions

$$dT = 0, \qquad dV = 0, \qquad dF = 0. \qquad (1.42.3)$$

Lastly by considering an infinitesimal change keeping each phase α at a constant pressure P^{α} and a constant uniform temperature T, we have according to (1.41.13) the equilibrium conditions

$$dT = 0, \qquad dP^{\alpha} = 0, \qquad dG = 0. \qquad (1.42.4)$$

Any one of the four sets of equilibrium conditions (1), (2), (3), (4) is sufficient by itself. They are all equivalent and each has an equal claim to be regarded as fundamental. It is therefore curious that many text-books omit the second set (2). This omission disguises the symmetry between the several thermodynamic functions to which attention was drawn in § 1.33.

§ 1.43   Conditions of Stability

In order to make clear what is meant by stability and instability in thermodynamic systems, we shall first discuss the significance of these expressions in a purely mechanical system. In Fig. 1.1 are shown in

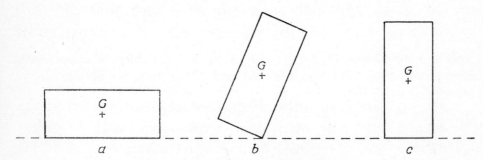

Fig. **1.1**.   Stable and unstable equilibrium.

section three different equilibrium positions of a box on a stand. In positions *a* and *c* the centre of gravity G is lower than in any infinitely near position (consistent with the box resting on the stand); the gravitational potential energy is a minimum and the equilibrium is stable. If the position of the box be very slightly disturbed, it will of itself return to its former position. In position b, on the other hand, the centre of gravity G is higher than in any infinitely near position (consistent with the box resting on the stand), the gravitational potential energy is a maximum and the equilibrium is unstable. If the position of the box be very slightly disturbed, it will of itself move right away from its original position, and finally settle in some state of stable equilibrium such as a or c. As maxima and minima of the potential energy must alternate, so must positions of stable and of unstable equilibrium. Only stable equilibria are realizable in practice as the realization of an unstable equilibrium requires the complete absence of any possible disturbing factors.

Whereas positions a and c are both stable, one may describe a as *more stable than* c. Or one may say that a is *absolutely stable*, while c is *unstable compared to* a. By this is meant that in position c the potential energy is less than in any position differing only infinitesimally from c, but is greater than the potential energy in position a.

Similarly, the equilibrium of a thermodynamic system may be *absolutely stable*. On the other hand it may be stable compared with all states differing only infinitesimally from the given state, but unstable compared with some other state differing finitely from the given state; such states are called *metastable*. Truly *unstable* states analogous to b are not realizable in thermodynamics, just as they are not in mechanics.

The fact that all thermodynamic equilibria are stable or metastable, but never unstable, is equivalent to the fact that every natural process proceeds towards an equilibrium state, never away from it. Bearing this in mind and referring to the inequalities (1. 40. 6), (1. 40. 12), (1. 41. 8) and (1. 41. 12), we obtain the following alternative conditions for equilibrium:

for given U and V that S is a *maximum* $\qquad$ (1. 43. 1)

for given H and P 's that S is a *maximum* $\qquad$ (1. 43. 2)

for given T and V that F is a *minimum* or that J is a *maximum* $\quad$ (1. 43. 3)

for given T and P 's that G is a *minimum* or that Y is a *maximum* $\quad$ (1. 43. 4)

Since $(\partial U/\partial S)_V = T > 0$. we may replace the first two conditions above by two others so as to obtain the more symmetrical set of equivalent conditions:

for given S and V that U is a *minimum* $\qquad$ (1. 43. 5)

for given S and P 's that H is a *minimum* $\qquad$ (1. 43. 6)

for given T and V that F is a *minimum* $\qquad$ (1. 43. 7)

for given T and P 's that G is a *minimum* $\qquad$ (1. 43. 8)

Since T is a more convenient independent variable than S, the last two conditions are more useful, but nowise more fundamental, than the previous two.

Each of the above is the condition for stable equilibrium or metastable equilibrium according as the minimum (or maximum) is absolute or only relative to immediately neighbouring states.

§ 1.44   Hydrostatic Equilibrium

Consider a system of several phases in equilibrium at the temperature T. Suppose the phase α to increase in volume by an amount dV^α and the phase β to decrease by the same amount, the temperature and volume of the whole system and the composition of each phase remaining unchanged. Then, according to (1.42.3), the condition for equilibrium is

$$dF = dF^\alpha + dF^\beta = 0, \tag{1.44.1}$$

or using (1.39.2)

$$-P^\alpha dV^\alpha + P^\beta dV^\alpha = 0, \tag{1.44.2}$$

and so

$$P^\alpha = P^\beta. \tag{1.44.3}$$

That is to say that any two phases in hydrostatic equilibrium must be at the same pressure.

If we now consider two phases at the same temperature T and different pressures P^α and P^β, there will then not be hydrostatic equilibrium. There will be a tendency for the system to approach hydrostatic equilibrium by a change in which the volume of one phase, say α, increases by dV^α and that of the other phase β decreases by the same amount. Such a change is by definition a natural one. If we keep the temperatures of both phases constant, we therefore have, according to (1.41.8)

$$dF^\alpha + dF^\beta < 0, \tag{1.44.4}$$

or using (1.39.2)

$$-P^\alpha dV^\alpha + P^\beta dV^\alpha < 0. \tag{1.44.5}$$

If we suppose dV^α to be positive, it follows that

$$P^\alpha > P^\beta. \tag{1.44.6}$$

That is to say, that the phase α with the greater pressure P^α will increase in volume at the expense of the phase β with the smaller pressure.

§ 1.45   Equilibrium Distribution between Phases

Consider a system of several phases, all at the same temperature T, but not necessarily at the same pressure. Suppose a small quantity dn_i^α of the species i to pass from the phase β to the phase α, the temperature of the whole system being kept constant. Then according to (1.39.2)

$$dF = -\Sigma_\gamma P^\gamma dV^\gamma + \mu_i^\alpha dn_i^\alpha - \mu_i^\beta dn_i^\alpha, \tag{1.45.1}$$

omitting the terms which obviously vanish. Since the total work w done on the whole system is $-\Sigma_\gamma P^\gamma dV^\gamma$, it follows from (1.41.5) that the process considered will be a natural one if

$$dF < -\Sigma_\gamma P^\gamma dV^\gamma, \quad \text{(natural process)}. \tag{1.45.2}$$

Comparing (1) with (2) we obtain

$$(\mu_i^\alpha - \mu_i^\beta)\, dn_i^\alpha < 0, \qquad \text{(natural process)}. \qquad (1.45.3)$$

Thus dn_i^α in a natural process has the same sign as $\mu_i^\beta - \mu_i^\alpha$. In other words each chemical species i tends to move from a phase where its potential μ_i is higher to another phase in which its potential is lower. Hence the name *potential* or *chemical potential* for μ_i.

If, instead of natural processes, we consider reversible processes we have equalities instead of inequalities; in particular instead of (3) we have

$$(\mu_i^\alpha - \mu_i^\beta)\, dn_i^\alpha = 0, \qquad \text{(reversible process)}. \qquad (1.45.4)$$

or

$$\mu_i^\alpha = \mu_i^\beta, \qquad \text{(equilibrium)}. \qquad (1.45.5)$$

We have obtained the important result that the condition for the phases to be in equilibrium with respect to any species is that the chemical potential of that species should have the same value in the two phases.

§ 1.46 Membrane Equilibrium

It is important to notice that, provided a system is at a uniform temperature, the condition for equilibrium between two phases of each chemical species is independent of that for other species and of that for hydrostatic equilibrium. If then two phases α and β are separated by a fixed wall permeable to some components i but not to other components j, the condition for the two phases to be in equilibrium as regards i is still

$$\mu_i^\alpha = \mu_i^\beta, \qquad (1.46.1)$$

but in this case in general

$$P^\alpha \neq P^\beta, \qquad \mu_j^\alpha \neq \mu_j^\beta. \qquad (1.46.2)$$

Such a partial equilibrium is called a *membrane equilibrium*.

§ 1.47 Definiteness of Chemical Potentials

In § 1.30 we provisionally used Gibbs' definition of μ_i and pointed out the uncertainty at that stage whether that definition was sufficient. Later in § 1.36 we showed that for a phase consisting of a single chemical substance μ is in fact completely defined by $\mu = G_m$, apart from trivial additive constants in U_m and S_m. At last we are in a position to confirm that μ_i is likewise well defined in all phases.

We have merely to imagine the phase α in question separated from a phase β consisting of the pure substance i by a membrane permeable only to i. By adjustment of the pressure in the phase β it is in principle possible to achieve equilibrium with respect to i across the membrane. We then have

$$\mu_i^\alpha = \mu_i^\beta \qquad (1.47.1)$$

and, since μ_i^β is adequately defined, we may regard (1) as a possible and sufficient definition of μ_i^α.

Incidentally the property of the μ_i's expressed by (1.46.1) or by (1) confirms that μ_i is, as hitherto assumed, an intensive property.

§ 1.48 Chemical Reactions. Frozen Equilibrium

Hitherto we have explicitly excluded chemically reacting species from the systems considered. We shall now explain how this restriction can be removed.

Owing to the slowness of attainment of some chemical equilibria, it can happen that the change towards chemical equilibrium is negligible during a time sufficient for other kinds of equilibria to be observed and measured. In other cases the attainment of chemical equilibrium if not sufficiently slow for this to be the case can be made so by the addition to the system of a small quantity of a substance called an *anticatalyst* or merely by rigid exclusion of all traces of some other substance called a *catalyst*. Even in cases where the attainment of chemical equilibrium cannot be adequately slowed down in practice it is possible and legitimate to consider the hypothetical case wherein this has been achieved.

We are thus led to consider a system not in chemical equilibrium in which however the chemical reactions leading towards its attainment have been virtually suppressed. The system is then in a special kind of metastable equilibrium sometimes called *frozen equilibrium*. The several chemical species present are then virtually independent and so we can suppose a chemical potential μ assigned to each such species.

If we now suppose the addition of a suitable catalyst so as to *thaw* the *frozen equilibrium* then generally changes of composition will take place as a result of chemical reactions; such changes are of course natural processes. In the special case that the state of frozen equilibrium corresponds to complete chemical equilibrium, then on thawing no chemical change will take place. If we imagine a virtual chemical change to take place, such a change will then be a typical reversible change. If we write down the condition for this, we therefore obtain a relation between the μ's which is a condition of chemical equilibrium.

The final result may be described as follows. Instead of choosing a set of independent chemical species or *components*, we use the set of all the chemical species present whether independent or not and then obtain restrictive relations on their behaviour. The actual form of these restrictive relations will be obtained in the next section.

§ 1.49 Chemical Equilibrium

We consider a system of any number of phases maintained at a constant temperature T and constant pressure P. Then according to (1.39.4)

$$dG = \Sigma_\alpha \, \Sigma_i \, \mu_i^\alpha \, dn_i^\alpha, \qquad (T, P \text{ constant}), \qquad (1.49.1)$$

where now, in contrast to previous practice, the species i are no longer all incapable of interacting chemically. According to (1. 41. 12) the condition for a natural process is

$$dG < 0, \qquad (T, P \text{ constant}), \qquad \text{(natural process)}. \qquad (1.49.2)$$

Combining (1) and (2) we obtain as the condition for a natural process

$$\Sigma_\alpha \Sigma_i \mu_i^\alpha \, dn_i^\alpha < 0, \qquad \text{(natural process)}. \qquad (1.49.3)$$

Any chemical reaction at a given temperature and pressure can be described by a formula. As typical examples we quote

$$CaCO_3(s) \rightarrow CaO(s) + CO_2(g);$$
$$2NH_3(g) \rightarrow N_2(g) + 3H_2(g);$$
$$\alpha\text{-glucose (aq.)} \rightarrow \beta\text{-glucose (aq.)};$$

where (s) denotes a solid phase, (g) the gaseous phase and (aq.) denotes an aqueous solution.

We can represent the most general chemical reaction symbolically by

$$\Sigma \nu_A A \rightarrow \Sigma \nu_B B. \qquad (1.49.4)$$

meaning that ν_A moles of A and the like react together to give ν_B moles of B and the like. The unit of quantity the *mole* is defined in such a way that the *stoichiometric numbers* ν can all be small integers. The symbols A and B are supposed to specify not only the kind of chemical species i but also in what phase it is present; in other words the label A corresponds to the pair of labels i and α.

Now imagine the chemical process (4) to take place to the extent

$$\Sigma \, d\xi \, \nu_A \, A \rightarrow \Sigma \, d\xi \, \nu_B B, \qquad (1.49.5)$$

where $d\xi$ denotes a small number. Then the dn_i^α corresponding to A is just $d\xi \, \nu_A$. The inequality (3) thus becomes

$$\Sigma \, d\xi \, \nu_B \, \mu_B < \Sigma \, d\xi \, \nu_A \, \mu_A, \qquad \text{(natural process)}, \qquad (1.49.6)$$

or if we assume $d\xi > 0$

$$\Sigma \, \nu_B \, \mu_B < \Sigma \, \nu_A \, \mu_A, \qquad \text{(natural process)}. \qquad (1.49.7)$$

Thus the chemical reaction will in fact take place from left to right if the inequality (7) holds and conversely.

If we replace the inequalities by equalities we obtain as the condition for the chemical change in either direction to be a reversible process

$$\Sigma \nu_A \mu_A = \Sigma \nu_B \mu_B, \qquad \text{(reversible process)}. \qquad (1.49.8)$$

In other words the condition for equilibrium with respect to the chemical process (5) is

$$\Sigma \nu_A \mu_A = \Sigma \nu_B \mu_B, \qquad \text{(equilibrium)}. \qquad (1.49.9)$$

It is to be observed that the condition for equilibrium is obtained from the formula for the reaction by replacing the symbol for each species by that of the corresponding potential and replacing the sign $\rightarrow$ by $=$.

3

§ 1.50   Affinity and Degree of Advancement

Let us consider a system consisting of any number of phases and chemical species all at the same temperature T. We need not however restrict ourselves to the usual case that all phases are at the same pressure, but may include membrane equilibria of the kind described in § 1.46. Let us now consider the most general type of isothermal chemical or physico-chemical change which can conceivably take place in the system, denoting it symbolically as in the previous section by

$$\Sigma \nu_A A \rightarrow \Sigma \nu_B B. \tag{1.50.1}$$

Two particularly simple examples of such changes are:

(1)   the passage of one mole of the substance i from phase α to phase β, provided of course that, if these two phases are separated by a membrane, this membrane is permeable to the species i;

(2)   a homogeneous chemical reaction taking place in a single phase.

Any conceivable process can be regarded as a superposition of processes of types (1) and (2).

Let us now introduce a dimensionless quantity ξ, called the *degree of advancement* of the process, such that a change of ξ to $\xi + d\xi$ means that $\nu_A \, d\xi$ moles of A and the like react to form $\nu_B \, d\xi$ moles of B and the like. If now we suppose ξ to change to $\xi + d\xi$, we have according to (1.39.2)

$$dT = 0, \qquad dF = - \Sigma_\alpha P^\alpha \, dV^\alpha + (\Sigma \nu_B \mu_B - \Sigma \nu_A \mu_A) \, d\xi. \tag{1.50.2}$$

while the work done on the system is

$$w = - \Sigma_\alpha P^\alpha \, dV^\alpha. \tag{1.50.3}$$

But we know from (1.41.5), (1.41.6) and (1.41.7) that the process considered is natural, reversible or unnatural according as w is greater than, equal to, or less than dF. Hence from (2) and (3) we obtain the conditions

$$(\Sigma \nu_B \mu_B - \Sigma \nu_A \mu_A) \, d\xi < 0, \qquad \text{(natural)}; \tag{1.50.4}$$

$$(\Sigma \nu_B \mu_B - \Sigma \nu_A \mu_A) \, d\xi = 0, \qquad \text{(reversible)}; \tag{1.50.5}$$

$$(\Sigma \nu_B \mu_B - \Sigma \nu_A \mu_A) \, d\xi > 0, \qquad \text{(unnatural)}. \tag{1.50.6}$$

We now define a thermodynamic quantity A (not to be confused with the species A) by

$$A = \Sigma \nu_A \mu_A - \Sigma \nu_B \mu_B \tag{1.50.7}$$

and call A the *affinity* of the change (1). We can then rewrite (4), (5) and (6) as

$$A d\xi > 0, \qquad \text{(natural)}; \tag{1.50.8}$$

$$A d\xi = 0, \qquad \text{(reversible)}; \tag{1.50.9}$$

$$A d\xi < 0, \qquad \text{(unnatural)}. \tag{1.50.10}$$

We can express this result simply, as follows. Any chemical or physico-chemical change will take place in the direction in which the *affinity* is positive. In the particular case that the *affinity* is zero, no change can take place in either direction and the system is in equilibrium with respect to the process considered.

The relation between the *affinity* A and the free energy F may be written symbolically

$$dT = 0, \qquad dV = 0, \qquad dF = -A d\xi, \qquad (1.50.11)$$

or alternatively

$$A = -\left(\frac{\partial F}{\partial \xi}\right)_{T,V}, \qquad (1.50.12)$$

provided it is understood that in varying F, not only are T and the V^{α}'s kept constant, but no process takes place other than the one to which ξ refers. The affinity is likewise closely related to the other thermodynamic potentials U, H and G. In fact

$$A = -\left(\frac{\partial U}{\partial \xi}\right)_{S,V} = -\left(\frac{\partial H}{\partial \xi}\right)_{S,P} = -\left(\frac{\partial F}{\partial \xi}\right)_{T,V} = -\left(\frac{\partial G}{\partial \xi}\right)_{T,P}$$

$$= \Sigma \nu_A \mu_A - \Sigma \nu_B \mu_B. \qquad (1.50.13)$$

These definitions of *affinity* A and *degree of advancement* are essentially those introduced by De Donder [*] in 1922. This notation has not yet attained as wide a usage as it deserves. It is related to the better known notation due to G. N. Lewis as follows. In writing a chemical or physico-chemical process of the most general type as

$$\Sigma \nu_A A \rightarrow \Sigma \nu_A B, \qquad (1.50.14)$$

let us now agree that this shall imply:

(1) constancy of T as previously;
(2) constancy of each P;
(3) increase of ξ by unity.

Let us further use the operator symbol $\triangle$ to denote the increase of any function of a state when the change considered takes place. Subject to this interpretation of (14), we then have

$$A = -\triangle G = \Sigma \nu_A \mu_A - \Sigma \nu_B \mu_B. \qquad (1.50.15)$$

Thus at constant uniform temperature T and constant pressures P^{α} on the various phases, the *affinity* A any change is equal to the decrease in the Gibbs function G and such a change will be a natural one if this *affinity* is positive.

§ 1.51 Surface Phases

We have hitherto assumed that every system consists of one or more completely homogeneous phases bounded by sharply defined geometrical

---

[*] See De Donder and Van Rysselberghe, *Affinity* (1936).

surfaces. This is an over-simplification, for the interface between any two phases will rather be a thin layer across which the physical properties vary continuously from those of the interior of one phase to those of the interior of the other. We must now consider the thermodynamic properties of these surface layers between two phases. We shall begin by considering a plane interface and shall in § 1. 56 extend our considerations to curved interfaces.

The following treatment * is essentially that of van der Waals junior and Bakker. It is less abstract than the alternative treatment of Gibbs.

Fig. 1. 2 represents two homogeneous bulk phases, α and β, between which lies the surface layer σ. The boundary between σ and α is the

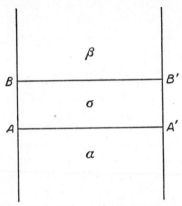

Fig. **1. 2**.   Plane interface between two phases.

plane AA', that between σ and β the parallel plane BB'. All properties of σ are uniform in directions parallel to AA', but not in the direction normal to AA'. At and near AA' the properties are identical with those of the phase α; at and near BB' they are identical with those of the phase β. Subject to these conditions there is freedom of choice in placing the planes AA' and BB'. It will be possible and therefore natural, though not essential, so to place the planes AA' and BB' that the uniform distance between them is submicroscopic and usually less than 10^{-6} cm., if not less than 10^{-7} cm.

§ 1. 52 Interfacial Tension of Plane Interface

Since the surface layer σ is a material system with a well defined volume and material content, its thermodynamic properties require no special definition. We may speak of its temperature, free energy, composition and so on just as for a homogeneous bulk phase. The only functions that

---

*   Van der Waals and Bakker, *Handb. Experimentalphysik* vol. 6 (1928).

See also Verschaffelt, *Acad. Roy. Belgique, Bull. classe sciences,* (1936) **22** No. 4 pp. 373, 390, 402.

Guggenheim, *Trans. Faraday Soc.* (1940) **36**·398.

call for special comment are the pressure and the interfacial tension. In any homogeneous bulk phase the force across any unit area is equal in all directions and is called the pressure. But in σ the force across unit area is not the same in all directions. If, however, we choose any plane of unit area parallel to AA' and BB', then the force across it has the same value for all positions of the plane whether it lie in α, β or σ; this value of the force across unit area is called the pressure P. Suppose, on the other hand, we choose a plane perpendicular to AA' and extending above AA' and below BB'; let this plane have the form of a rectangle of height h (parallel to AB) and of thickness l (perpendicular to the plane of the paper). Then the force across this plane will be equal to $Ph-\gamma l$, where P is the above-defined pressure and γ is called the *interfacial tension*. If the height of this plane is chosen to extend exactly from AA' to BB', then the force across it will be equal to $P\tau l-\gamma l$, if the height AB is denoted by τ. Let the surface layer have an area A, a perimeter s and a volume V^σ so that

$$V^\sigma = \tau A. \qquad (1.52.1)$$

Suppose the area to be increased to $A + dA$, the perimeter to $s + ds$, the thickness to $\tau + d\tau$ and the volume to $V^\sigma + dV^\sigma$, the material content remaining unaltered. Then the work done on σ consists of $-PAd\tau$ by the forces across AA' and BB' and $-(P\tau s-\gamma s)dA/s$ by the forces parallel to the planes AA' and BB'. The total work done on σ is therefore

$$\begin{aligned}
&-PAd\tau-(P\tau s-\gamma s)dA/s \\
&= -P(Ad\tau + \tau dA) + \gamma dA \\
&= -PdV^\sigma + \gamma dA. \qquad (1.52.2)
\end{aligned}$$

This expression takes the place of $-PdV^\alpha$ for a homogeneous bulk phase.

§ 1.53. Free Energy of Surface Layer

For the most general variation of the free energy F^α of a homogeneous bulk phase we have the fundamental equation (1.33.2)

$$dF^\alpha = -S^\alpha dT - PdV^\alpha + \Sigma_i \mu_i dn_i^\alpha. \qquad (1.53.1)$$

For a surface phase σ the dependence of the free energy F^σ on the temperature and the composition will be exactly parallel to that for a bulk phase; this follows directly from the definitions of entropy and chemical potentials. But for the dependence of F^σ on size and shape we must replace $-PdV^\alpha$ by the expression (1.52.2). We thus obtain the formula

$$dF^\sigma = -S^\sigma dT - PdV^\sigma + \gamma dA + \Sigma_i \mu_i dn_i^\sigma. \qquad (1.53.2)$$

There is no need to add superscripts to T, P, μ_i, because these must have values uniform throughout α, β and σ in order that there may be thermal, hydrostatic and physico-chemical equilibrium.

§ 1.54   Integrated Relation. Gibbs Function of Surface Phase

Formula (1.53.2) can be integrated by an artifice analogous to that used in § 1.35 for integrating the fundamental equations of a bulk phase. We proceed as follows.

In formula (1.53.2) we now set

$$dT = 0, \quad dV^\sigma = -V^\sigma d\xi, \quad dA = -A d\xi, \quad dn_i^\sigma = -n_i^\sigma d\xi, \quad (1.54.1)$$

and obtain

$$dF^\sigma = -d\xi(-PV^\sigma + \gamma A + \Sigma_i \mu_i n_i^\sigma). \quad (1.54.2)$$

This substitution corresponds physically to decreasing the extent of the surface layer σ by simply cutting off a portion at its edge, so that what remains is exactly like the original system except that it is reduced in extent in the ratio $(1 - d\xi) : 1$. It is therefore obvious that F^σ will also be reduced in the same ratio. It is equally obvious that P, γ, μ_i remain unaltered. In mathematical terminology: at constant temperature and thickness F^σ is homogeneous of first degree in V^σ, A and n_i^σ and of zero degree in P, γ, μ_i. Thus the conditions (1) imply the simultaneous conditions

$$dF^\sigma = -F^\sigma d\zeta, \quad dP = 0, \quad d\gamma = 0, \quad d\mu_i = 0. \quad (1.54.3)$$

Substituting the value of dF^σ into (2) we obtain

$$-F^\sigma d\xi = -(-PV^\sigma + \gamma A + \Sigma_i \mu_i n_i) d\xi, \quad (1.54.4)$$

and equating coefficients of $d\xi$, or alternatively integrating from $\xi = 1$ to $\xi = 0$,

$$F^\sigma = -PV^\sigma + \gamma A + \Sigma_i \mu_i n_i^\sigma, \quad (1.54.5)$$

or

$$F^\sigma + PV^\sigma - \gamma A = \Sigma_i \mu_i n_i^\sigma. \quad (1.54.6)$$

Alternatively formula (6) can be derived mathematically from (1.53.2) by using Euler's theorem. Formula (6) is the analogue of

$$F^\alpha + PV^\alpha = \Sigma_i \mu_i n_i^\alpha. \quad (1.54.7)$$

for a homogeneous bulk phase.

In analogy with the definition of the Gibbs function G^α of a bulk phase α

$$G^\alpha = F^\alpha + PV^\alpha. \quad (1.54.8)$$

we now define the Gibbs function G^σ of the surface phase σ by

$$G^\sigma = F^\sigma + PV^\sigma - \gamma A. \quad (1.54.9)$$

We deduce from (1.53.2) and (9)

$$dG^\sigma = -S^\sigma dT + V^\sigma dP - A d\gamma + \Sigma_i \mu_i dn_i^\sigma, \quad (1.54.10)$$

$$G^\sigma = \Sigma_i \mu_i n_i^\sigma. \quad (1.54.11)$$

These two formulae are the analogues of the formulae

$$dG^{\alpha} = -S^{\alpha} dT + V^{\alpha} dP + \Sigma_i \mu_i dn_i^{\alpha}. \qquad (1.54.12)$$

$$G^{\alpha} = \Sigma_i \mu_i n_i^{\alpha} \qquad (1.54.13)$$

for a homogeneous bulk phase.

§ 1.55. Analogue of Gibbs–Duhem Relation

If we differentiate (1.54.6) we obtain

$$dF^{\sigma} + PdV^{\sigma} + V^{\sigma} dP - \gamma dA - A d\gamma = \Sigma_i \mu_i dn_i^{\sigma} + \Sigma_i n_i^{\sigma} d\mu_i. \qquad (1.55.1)$$

If we now subtract (1) from (1.53.2) we obtain

$$S^{\sigma} dT - V^{\sigma} dP + A d\gamma + \Sigma_i n_i^{\sigma} d\mu_i = 0, \qquad (1.55.2)$$

which is the analogue for a surface phase of the Gibbs–Duhem relation (1.38.2) for a bulk phase.

If we divide (2) throughout by A we obtain the more convenient form

$$S_u^{\sigma} dT - \tau dP + d\gamma + \Sigma_i \Gamma_i d\mu_i = 0 \qquad (1.55.3)$$

where S_u^{σ} is the entropy per unit area and Γ_i the number of moles of the component i in unit area of the surface phase σ, defined respectively by

$$S_u^{\sigma} = S^{\sigma}/A, \qquad (1.55.4)$$

$$\Gamma_i = n_i^{\sigma}/A. \qquad (1.55.5)$$

We recall that τ is the thickness of the surface layer, that is to say the length AB in Fig. 1.2.

§1.56 Interfacial Tension of Curved Interface

We must now consider under what conditions the formulae already derived for plane interfaces may be applied to curved interfaces. We shall see that the formulae strictly derived for plane interfaces may be applied to curved interfaces with an accuracy sufficient for experimental purposes provided that the thickness of the inhomogeneous surface layer is small compared with its radii of curvature *.

For the sake of simplicity let us first consider a system consisting of two homogeneous bulk phases α and β connected by a surface layer σ having the form of a circular cylindrical shell. Fig. 1.3 shows a cross-section of the phases α and β separated by the surface layer σ, bounded by the circular cylinders AA' and BB' with common axis O. There is complete homogeneity in the direction normal to the diagram. The properties of the surface layer σ are supposed identical at all points the same distance from the axis through O. Throughout the phase α and extending up to AA' there is a uniform pressure P^{α}; throughout the phase β, and extending down to BB', there is a uniform pressure P^{β}.

---

* Compare Guggenheim, *Trans. Faraday Soc.* (1940) **36** 408.

Between AA' and BB' the pressure P_r parallel to the radii of the cylinders AA' and BB' varies continuously, but not necessarily monotonically, from the value P^α to the value P^β.

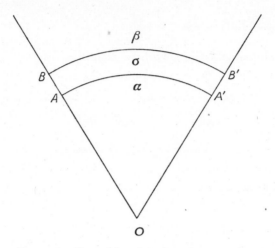

Fig. 1.3. Curved interface between two phases.

In the previous discussion of plane surfaces it was pointed out that the geometrical planes AA' and BB' may be placed an arbitrary distance apart, provided that the inhomogeneous layer is contained between them. For the present discussion of curved surfaces it is on the contrary essential that the circular cylindrical surfaces AA' and BB' should be placed as near together as is consistent with the condition that the inhomogeneous layer be contained between them. According to this condition we may usually expect the distance AB to be about 10^{-7} or at most 10^{-6} cm. We shall denote by r distances measured radially from O, and in particular by r_α and r_β, the distances OA and OB respectively.

Whereas the force per unit area across any element of surface inside either homogeneous phase is independent of the orientation of the element (Pascal's Law), this is not the case in the inhomogeneous layer σ. It is convenient to denote the force per unit area in the direction parallel to the surface AA' and BB' by $P_r - Q$. Both P_r and Q are functions of r. Q is zero at $r = r_\alpha$ and at $r = r_\beta$, but at least somewhere between Q is greater than zero. It is conceivable that Q might be negative somewhere between $r = r_\alpha$ and $r = r_\beta$, but its average value in this range is unquestionably positive.

According to elementary statics the mechanical equilibrium of the matter enclosed by $AA'B'B$ requires that for all values of r

$$d(P_r r) = (P_r - Q)dr, \tag{1.56.1}$$

or

$$dP_r = -Qdr/r. \tag{1.56.2}$$

If we integrate (2) from r_β to r_α, we obtain

$$P^\alpha - P^\beta = \int_{r_\alpha}^{r_\beta} \frac{Q}{r}\, dr. \qquad (1.56.3)$$

We now define quantities $\bar{r}$, γ, γ' by

$$2\bar{r} = r_\alpha + r_\beta, \qquad (1.56.4)$$

$$\gamma = \int_{r_\alpha}^{r_\beta} Q\, dr. \qquad (1.56.5)$$

$$\gamma' = \bar{r} \int_{r_\alpha}^{r_\beta} \frac{Q}{r}\, dr. \qquad (1.56.6)$$

According to (6) we can rewrite (3) in the form

$$P^\alpha - P^\beta = \gamma'/\bar{r}. \qquad (1.56.7)$$

If now the thickness of the interfacial layer is small compared with its curvature, that is to say

$$r_\beta - r_\alpha \ll \bar{r}, \qquad (1.56.8)$$

so that we may ignore any distinction between r_α, r_β, $\bar{r}$, then we may also ignore the distinction between γ and γ', and instead of (7) we may write

$$P^\alpha - P^\beta = \gamma/\bar{r}. \qquad (1.56.9)$$

For the sake of simplicity we have confined ourselves to an interface in the form of a circular cylinder. For a spherical interface, we should have found by similar reasoning instead of (9),

$$P^\alpha - P^\beta = 2\gamma/\bar{r}. \qquad (1.56.10)$$

For an interface of arbitrary shape the geometry is somewhat more complicated and the general formula obtained is

$$P^\alpha - P^\beta = \gamma \left(\frac{1}{\varrho_1} + \frac{1}{\varrho_2} \right), \qquad (1.56.11)$$

where ϱ_1, ϱ_2 are the principal radii of curvature of the interface.

Formula (11), like (9) and (10), implies ignoring the difference between lengths such as r_α, r_β. When the inequality (8) is not satisfied, the very definition of interfacial tension becomes ill-defined and probably useless.

Formula (11) is the basis, as we shall see, for the experimental determination of γ. The quantities measured are ϱ_1, ϱ_2 and $P^\alpha - P^\beta$; then γ is calculated by means of (11). It follows that the very measurement of interfacial tension implies that the thickness of the interfacial layer be small compared with its radii of curvature.

§ 1.57 Discussion of Pressure Terms

Although the pressure difference $P^\alpha - P^\beta$ is fundamental in the measurement of γ and so, one may say, in the definition of γ, we shall show that this pressure difference in certain other respects is insignificant for the properties of the interface. Let us again use τ to denote the thickness of the surface layer, so that

$$\tau = r_\beta - r_\alpha. \qquad (1.57.1)$$

Our fundamental assumption for γ to be precisely defined may then be written

$$\frac{1}{\tau} \gg \frac{1}{\varrho_1} + \frac{1}{\varrho_2}. \qquad (1.57.2)$$

Comparing (1.56.11) with (2) we see that

$$(P^\alpha - P^\beta)\,\tau \ll \gamma, \qquad (1.57.3)$$

Now according to formula (1.52.2) the total work done on a plane surface layer when its volume and area are altered is

$$-P\,dV^\tau + \gamma\,dA. \qquad (1.57.4)$$

We cannot immediately apply this formula to a curved interface owing to the ambiguity in the meaning of P. Owing however to the inequality (3) we may expect and can in fact verify that in practice

$$|(P^\alpha - P^\beta)\,dV| \ll |\gamma\,dA|. \qquad (1.57.5)$$

Consequently formula (4) is sufficiently accurate if P denotes either P^α or P^β or any intermediate pressure.

To recapitulate, for an interface whose thickness is small compared with its curvature, and it is only for such interfaces that the interfacial tension is defined, we may apply unchanged the fundamental formulae obtained for plane interfaces in §§ 1.51 — 1.55.

§ 1.58.   Pressure within a Bubble

Let us now consider a bubble having the form of a thin spherical film of liquid of internal and external radii r_i and r_e. If P^i denotes the pressure nearer to the centre than the film, P^e the pressure further from the centre than the film, and P' the pressure in the liquid film itself, we have, according to (1.56.10)

$$P^i - P' = \frac{2}{r_i}\,\gamma, \qquad (1.58.1)$$

$$P' - P^e = \frac{2}{r_e}\,\gamma, \qquad (1.58.2)$$

so that

$$P^i - P^e = \left(\frac{2}{r_i} + \frac{2}{r_e}\right)\gamma, \qquad (1.58.3)$$

or, neglecting the difference between r_i and r_e

$$P^i - P^e = \frac{4}{r}\,\gamma. \qquad (1.58.4)$$

§ 1.59   Determination of Interfacial Tension

The commonest method of determining the value of the interfacial tension γ depends on formula (1.56.11). This method is shown diagrammatically in Fig. 1.4. Two fluid phases α and β are represented, the one shaded

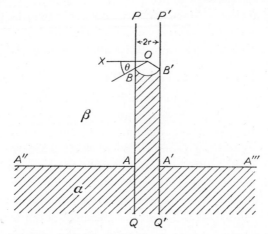

Fig. **1.4**. Capillary rise due to interfacial tension.

the other not shaded. They are separated partly by the plane surfaces AA'' and $A'A'''$, and partly by the curved surface BB' in the capillary tube $PP'Q'Q$ of internal radius r. We may, with sufficient accuracy, regard the surface BB' as a segment of a sphere. Let the centre of this sphere be O and let θ be the angle between OB and the horizontal OX, or alternatively the angle between the tangential plane to BB' at B and the wall of the vertical capillary tube. Then the radius of curvature of the surface BB' is $r/\cos\theta$.

Let P^0 denote the pressure at the plane surfaces AA'' and $A'A'''$. It will also be the pressure inside the capillary tube at the height AA' Let the pressures at the height BB' be denoted by P^α in the phase α and by P^β in the phase β. Then

$$P^\alpha = P^0 - \varrho^\alpha gh, \qquad (1.59.1)$$
$$P^\beta = P^0 - \varrho^\beta gh, \qquad (1.59.2)$$

where ϱ^α, ϱ^β denote the densities of the phases α and β, g is the acceleration due to gravity, and h is the height AB. But, according to (1.56.11)

$$P^\beta - P^\alpha = 2\frac{\cos\theta}{r}\gamma. \qquad (1.59.3)$$

Comparing (1), (2) and (3), we obtain

$$2\frac{\cos\theta}{r}\gamma = (\varrho^\alpha - \varrho^\beta)gh. \qquad (1.59.4)$$

Thus, from measurement of ϱ^α, ϱ^β, r, θ and h, one can calculate γ. In the special case that α is a liquid and β the vapour phase in equilibrium with it, it will usually be allowable to neglect ϱ^β compared with ϱ^α so that (4) simplifies to

$$2\frac{\cos\theta}{r}\gamma = \varrho^\alpha gh. \qquad (1.59.5)$$

In the case that the surface BB' is concave towards the bottom, its radius of curvature will have the opposite sign, and so h will also have the opposite sign. That is to say, BB' will lie below AA'.

§ 1.60   Independence of Interfacial Tension of Curvature

Let us now turn to the question whether the interfacial tension depends on the curvatures. We shall see that when the question is precisely defined it answers itself. In asking the question it is not sufficient to state that we vary the curvatures; we require also to state what we keep constant. For the question to be useful it should apply to the actual conditions of the experimental measurement of interfacial tension. For definiteness let us consider the capillary rise method described in the preceding section. The values of the temperature T and the chemical potentials μ are uniform throughout the system, and so, whatever be the size and shape of the capillary, these variables have the same values at the curved surface where the surface tension is measured, as in the bulk phases. Hence to be useful the question should be worded: how does γ depend on ϱ_1, ϱ_2 for given values of T and the μ's? According to equation (1.55.3) the variation of γ under these restrictions is given by

$$d\gamma = \tau dP \qquad (1.60.1)$$

In its present application the ambiguity in the exact meaning of P does not matter, since we have already verified that $(P^\alpha - P^\beta)\tau$ is negligible. If now we consider a curved interface, say in a capillary, in equilibrium with a plane interface and we integrate (1) from the pressure at the plane surface to the pressure at the curved interface (either side of it) we again find that the integral of the right side is always negligible. Consequently γ has effectively the same value for the curved surface as for the plane surface with which it is in equilibrium. This is a statement of a principle usually assumed whenever an interfacial tension is measured. It is experimentally verified by the fact that within the experimental accuracy the same value is found for the interfacial tension when capillaries of different size are used, but this verification can be realized only for capillaries with diameters considerably greater than the lower bound 10^{-5} cm., allowed by the theory.

§ 1.61   Gibbs Treatment of Curved Interfaces

The problem of curved interfaces was treated by Gibbs in a manner which appears to be quite different and more rigid. The essence of Gibbs' treatment is that he replaced the term

$$\gamma dA \qquad (1.61.1)$$

for a plane interface by terms of the form

$$\gamma \, dA + C_1 \, d\left(\frac{1}{\varrho_1}\right) + C_2 \, d\left(\frac{1}{\varrho_2}\right), \qquad (1.61.2)$$

and assumed implicitly that, provided the radii of curvature are not too small, one may assign to C_1 and C_2 the values appropriate to a plane surface. It is then obvious from symmetry that $C_1 = C_2$, and so (2) can be written in the simpler form

$$\gamma \, dA + C \, d\left(\frac{1}{\varrho_1} + \frac{1}{\varrho_2}\right), \qquad (1.61.3)$$

where C is independent of ϱ_1, ϱ_2. So far so good. Gibbs then set out to prove that his geometrical surface could be so placed that C vanishes. The reasoning adduced is far from simple, and Gibbs' meaning is not even always clear. It seems that Gibbs was himself aware of the difficulty of being precise in this particular piece of reasoning. He discussed the variation of a plane interface by bending it and used the sentence * "also at and about the surface let the state of the matter *so far as possible be the same* as at and about the plane surface in the initial state of the system". The words written in italics are in their vagueness unlike Gibbs' usual style. The whole treatment of Gibbs, like the treatment in this book, postulates complete equilibrium throughout the entire system. It is therefore impossible to conceive of a variation of an interface apart from a variation in at least one of the bulk phases. It is clear that Gibbs realized this difficulty and tried to overcome it by flexible wording.

Gibbs then claimed to show that the position required for his geometrical surface to make C vanish would be either inside the nonhomogeneous layer or at most at a distance from it comparable to the thickness of the layer. He here used the words "on account of the thinness of the non-homogeneous film", and it seems clear that this *thinness* is an essential assumption common to Gibbs' treatment and that outlined above. If then the assumption $\tau \ll \varrho$ is essential, it seems preferable to introduce it at the outset and so considerably simplify the whole argument.

§ 1.62   Basis of Thermodynamic Principles

The *zeroth principle* in § 1.08, the *first principle* in § 1.11 and the *second principle* in § 1.17 have all been quoted as fundamentally independent assumptions. From this point of view their justification is the empirical fact that all conclusions from these assumptions are without exception in agreement with the experimentally observed behaviour in nature.

The form in which these principles have been enunciated is essentially that used by Born ** There are other alternative forms some more, others

---

* Gibbs, *Collected Works* vol. 1 p. 226.
** Born, *Physik. Zeit.* (1921) **22** 218.

less abstract, but all of an entirely empirical nature; that is to say that their justification is agreement between their implications on the one hand and experiment on the other.

It is, however, possible to obtain a deeper insight into the fundamental principles from a statistical point of view. It is in fact possible to derive these principles from our knowledge of the structure of matter including the elements of quantum theory together with a single statistical assumption of a very general form. It is a matter of taste whether to choose as a basis several empirical principles which make reference neither to atomic theory nor to quantum theory, or to choose a single principle superposed on atomic theory and quantum theory. The former choice, the one adopted in this book, is the method of *classical thermodynamics*; the latter choice corresponds to the more modern science which we call *statistical thermodynamics*.

There are however other relations of a general nature which follow naturally and directly from the statistical thermodynamic formulation, but which cannot be derived from the zeroth, first and second principles of classical thermodynamics. The relations to which we refer are of several types concerning respectively

- (a) entropy changes in highly disperse systems (i.e. gases);
- (b) entropy changes in very cold systems (i.e. when $T \to 0$);
- (c) entropy changes associated with mixing of very similar substances (e.g. isotopes).

The three types are of comparable importance. They resemble one another in relating to entropy changes. Their formulation in terms of classical thermodynamics is either complicated or inaccurate or else involves reference to conceptions inherently foreign to classical thermodynamics. As already mentioned they all follow naturally and directly from the statistical thermodynamic formulation.

We shall therefore devote the following chapter to a digression on *statistical thermodynamics*, describing in very general terms the methods of this science just sufficiently to give the reader an idea of the source of the relations in question without attempting to derive them in detail. The reader interested in the complete derivations must refer to a standard text-book on *statistical thermodynamics*.

§ 1. 63 Third Principle

It is customary to refer to the three types of general relations mentioned in the preceding section in three quite different ways. The relations of type (a) are referred to as the determination of *entropy constants*, those of type (b) as the *third law* of thermodynamics and those of type (c) merely as the formulae for *entropy of mixing*. This biased discrimination between types of relations of comparable importance and generality is difficult to defend. We accordingly reject this unbalanced terminology and instead choose as our *third principle* the following statement:

By the standard methods of *statistical thermodynamics* it is possible to derive for certain entropy changes general formulae which cannot be derived from the *zeroth, first* or *second principles of classical thermodynamics*. In particular one can obtain formulae for entropy changes in highly disperse systems (i.e. gases), for those in very cold systems (i.e. when $T \to 0$) and for those associated with the mixing of very similar substances (e.g. isotopes).

CHAPTER II

DIGRESSION ON STATISTICAL THERMODYNAMICS

§ 2.01 Micro- and Macro-descriptions of a System

According to quantum theory the state of a system is completely described by its eigenfunction. To each state there corresponds one eigenfunction and to each eigenfunction one state. The expression *degenerate state of weight* Ω is an abbreviation for a group of states between which we do not care to distinguish. Such a description of the system we shall call a *microdescription*.

It is often though not always, possible to regard the system as consisting of a large number of almost independent *units* (molecules, atoms, ions, electrons) and to express each eigenfunction of the system as a linear combination of products of the eigenfunctions of all the units. According to the *symmetry restrictions*, if any, imposed on the eigenfunctions of the system, one then obtains three alternative sets of statistical formulae referred to by the names of Fermi–Dirac, Bose–Einstein and Boltzmann, respectively. These three alternatives, however, arise only when one expresses the eigenfunctions of the system in terms of those of the constituent units. As long as we refer only to the eigenfunctions of the whole system, we shall not need to consider these three alternatives separately. Nor shall we do so until we reach § 2.10.

When we describe the equilibrium properties of a system by thermodynamic methods, we are not interested in such a precise description as the *microdescription*, but are content with a more crude large scale description, which we shall call a *macrodescription*. For example a possible *macrodescription* of the system would be a precise statement of the energy, the volume, the exact chemical composition (and in special cases other quantities all measurable on a large scale) of each homogeneous part or phase. For brevity we shall confine our discussion initially to systems whose macrodescription requires a precise statement of only four quantities. The extension of the argument to more complicated systems should be obvious. Initially we shall take the first of these quantities to be the energy, the second to be the volume, the third to be the empirical composition; the nature of the fourth quantity is best indicated by some specific examples.

Example 1. Let us consider a definite quantity of hydrogen (free from deuterium) of given energy and given volume. Then we can complete the description by a statement of what fraction of it is *para*, the remaining fraction being *ortho*.

Example 2. If instead of hydrogen, we have lactic acid we can complete the description by a statement of what fraction is *dextro*, the remaining fraction being *laevo*.

Example 3.   If the system consists of a given quantity of iodine of given energy and volume we can complete the description by a statement of what fraction is in the *diatomic* form I_2, the remainder being in the *monatomic* form I.

Example 4.   If the system consists of a given quantity of tin of given energy and volume, we can complete the description by stating what fraction is *white*, the remainder being *grey*.

Example 5.   If the system consists of a given quantity of carbon dioxide, we may complete the description by stating what fraction is *liquid*, the remainder being *vapour*.

In examples 1—3 it is tacitly assumed either that the system is homogeneous or, if it consists of two phases, that we are not interested in the relative amounts, these being determined by the other conditions. Another example that might be suggested is a system of a given quantity of hydrogen of given energy and volume for which we were interested both in the ratio of *para* to *ortho* and in the ratio of *liquid* to *vapour*. Such a system, however, requires five quantities, instead of four, to complete its macrodescription and so lies outside the class which we shall discuss, although the extension of the treatment to such a system in fact offers no difficulty.

Having made clear by these examples the nature of the fourth independent variable describing the assembly we shall denote this variable by ξ. It corresponds closely to the quantity ξ which we introduced in § 1. 50 and which, following De Donder, we call the *degree of advancement* of a physico-chemical change. It is not a necessary property of ξ that one should be able completely to control its value, provided that its value can in principle be measured by *macroexperiments*.

§ 2. 02   System of Given Energy, Volume and Composition

Let us now consider in more detail a system of prescribed energy U, prescribed volume V and containing a prescribed number N of atoms or molecules of a given kind. Let the number of independent eigenfunctions of the system consistent with the prescribed values of U, V, N and corresponding to a particular value of the parameter ξ be denoted by $\Omega(\xi)$. As long as we are not interested in distinguishing between the states of equal ξ, we may group them together into a degenerate state of weight $\Omega(\xi)$.

Then the *fundamental assumption of statistical thermodynamics* is the following:

The average properties of the system for prescribed values of U, V, N can be derived statistically by averaging over all degenerate states of given ξ, assigning to each a weight $\Omega(\xi)$.

In other words it is assumed that for given U, V, N the *probability* of a particular value of ξ is

$$\frac{\Omega(\xi)}{\Sigma_\xi \Omega(\xi)}. \qquad (2.02.1)$$

It is customary to refer to the numerator $\Omega(\xi)$ in (1) as the *thermodynamic probability* of the particular value of ξ. It must be emphasised that a *thermodynamic probability* thus defined is not a *probability* in the usual sense of the word. Whereas an ordinary *probability* such as (1) is a number less than or equal to unity, the *thermodynamic probability* is generally a large number.

For reasons which will appear later $\Omega(\xi)$ had better be called the *thermodynamic probability of ξ for given U, V, N* than merely the thermodynamic probability of ξ. Another name for $\Omega(\xi)$ is the *partition function for given U, V, N, ξ*. The reason for this name will also become clearer as we proceed.

We now define a quantity $S(U, V, N, \xi)$ by the relation

$$S(U, V, N, \xi) = k \log \Omega(\xi), \qquad (2.02.2)$$

where k is an arbitrary constant whose value will be settled later. It can then be shown as we shall see later that in a macroscopic system S has all the properties of the entropy of the system in the macrostate defined by U, V, N, ξ. Formula (2) is a precise formulation of the well-known relation due to Boltzmann to whom the name *thermodynamic probability* is due.

We shall see that Boltzmann's relation (2) between the *entropy* and the *thermodynamic probability* or *partition function* for given U, V, N, ξ is merely one of a number of relations of a similar type between a *thermodynamic potential* for a particular set of variables on the one hand and the *thermodynamic probability* or *partition function* for the same set of variables on the other.

§ 2.03   Characteristic of Macroscopic System

According to the *fundamental assumption* of statistical thermodynamics in a system of given U, V, N the average value ξ_{Av} of ξ is determined by

$$\xi_{Av} = \frac{\Sigma_\xi \xi \Omega(\xi)}{\Sigma_\xi \Omega(\xi)}, \qquad (2.03.1)$$

and the average value of ξ^2 by

$$(\xi^2)_{Av} = \frac{\Sigma_\xi \xi^2 \Omega(\xi)}{\Sigma_\xi \Omega(\xi)}. \qquad (2.03.2)$$

Thus in general $(\xi_{Av})^2$ is not the same as $(\xi^2)_{Av}$.

In other words there are fluctuations measured by

$$[(\xi - \xi_{Av})^2]_{Av} = (\xi^2)_{Av} - (\xi_{Av})^2$$

$$= \frac{\Sigma_\xi \Omega(\xi) \Sigma_\xi \xi^2 \Omega(\xi) - \Sigma_\xi \xi \Omega(\xi) \Sigma_\xi \xi \Omega(\xi)}{\Sigma_\xi \Omega(\xi) \Sigma_\xi \Omega(\xi)}. \qquad (2.03.3)$$

It can be shown generally that the larger the system the less important is this fluctuation and that for any macroscopic system the fluctuation is entirely trivial compared with $(\xi_{Av})^2$ itself. Without attempting a proof we shall consider a little more closely how this comes about.

There is some value ξ_m of ξ for which $\Omega(\xi)$ has a maximum Generally speaking the larger the system the sharper is this maximum and for any macroscopic system it is very sharp indeed. On each side of this maximum term $\Omega(\xi_m)$ there will be many terms almost as great as $\Omega(\xi_m)$. Then there will be a still greater number of terms appreciably smaller but not negligible; but an overwhelming majority of the terms will be entirely negligible, and this majority includes all those terms in which ξ differs appreciably from ξ_m.

As a result of such considerations it can be shown that whereas the average properties are strictly determined by attributing to each ξ the weight $\Omega(\xi)$, in any macroscopic system we may with trivial inaccuracy ignore all values of ξ other than the value ξ_m at which $\Omega(\xi)$ is maximum.

Thus for any macroscopic system we have with trivial inaccuracy

$$\xi_{Av} = \xi_m, \qquad\qquad (2.03.4)$$

$$(\xi^2)_{Av} = \xi_m^2, \qquad\qquad (2.03.5)$$

and so on.

It is instructive to relate this important characteristic of a macroscopic system to the quantity $S(U, V, N, \xi)$ defined by (2.02.2), namely

$$S(U, V, N, \xi) = k \log \Omega(\xi). \qquad\qquad (2.03.6)$$

Let us now define another quantity $S(U, V, N)$ by

$$S(U, V, N) = k \log \Sigma_\xi \Omega(\xi). \qquad\qquad (2.03.7)$$

Then by definition

$$S(U, V, N) > S(U, V, N, \xi), \qquad \text{(all values of } \xi\text{)}. \quad (2.03.8)$$

Let us now consider the ratio

$$\frac{\log \Sigma_\xi \Omega(\xi) - \log \Omega(\xi_m)}{\log \Omega(\xi_m)}. \qquad\qquad (2.03.9)$$

It can be shown that roughly speaking $\Omega(\xi_m)$ is of the order $N!$ and $\Sigma_\xi\Omega(\xi)/\Omega(\xi_m)$ is of the order N^α where α is comparable to unity. Hence the numerator in (9) is of the order $\alpha \log N$ and the denominator of the order $N \log N$. Thus the expression (9) is of the order α/N or near enough N^{-1}, which is entirely negligible in any macroscopic system. Hence, although the inequality (8) is strictly true by definition for all values of ξ, in any macroscopic system when ξ has the special value ξ_m we may with trivial inaccuracy replace the inequality (8) by the equality

$$S(U, V, N) = S(U, V, N, \xi_m). \qquad\qquad (2.03.10)$$

We shall see in § 2.05 that the functions denoted by S have in fact the properties of entropy. Anticipating this identification let us call $S(U, V, N, \xi)$ the *entropy for fixed* ξ and $S(U, V, N)$ the *entropy for equilibrium* ξ.

Consider now a system of given U, V, N with ξ *frozen*. Now suppose that by introduction of a catalyst ξ is *thawed*, so that it takes its equilibrium value. By definition the entropy changes from $S(U, V, N, \xi)$ to $S(U, V, N)$ and also by definition this is always an increase. Only in the special case that the initial value of ξ was ξ_m, the entropy increase from $S(U, V, N, \xi_m)$ to $S(U, V, N)$ for any macroscopic system is trivial. In other words although $S(U, V, N)$ the entropy for *equilibrium* ξ is by definition greater than the entropy for ξ *fixed at its equilibrium value* ξ_m, the difference is in a macroscopic system negligible and trivial.

We shall see later that a macroscopic system has other characteristics similar and parallel to that just formulated. These characteristics can be summed up in the single sentence that in a *macroscopic* system *fluctuations* of measurable properties are *negligible*.

§ 2.04 System of Given Temperature, Volume and Composition

We shall now consider a system whose volume V and composition N are still prescribed, but instead of prescribing the energy we shall suppose the system to be immersed in a large temperature bath with which it can exchange energy so that the energy of the system can now take various values U_0, U_1, and so on. Let us now enumerate the eigenfunctions of the system for the prescribed values of V and N and for some definite value of ξ; let there be Ω_r such eigenfunctions corresponding to an energy $U_r (V, N, \xi)$.

From the *fundamental assumption of statistical thermodynamics*, as stated in § 2.01, without any further assumptions it can be shown that the average properties of the system in the temperature bath for the prescribed values of V and N can be derived statistically by averaging over all degenerate states attaching to each state r of specified ξ and U_r a weight

$$\Omega_r e^{-\beta U_r}, \tag{2.04.1}$$

where β is determined entirely by the temperature bath and so may be regarded as a temperature scale.

The fact that the parameter β is found to appear without any new assumptions is the statistical thermodynamic basis of the *zeroth principle of classical thermodynamics*. The *statistical thermodynamic* equivalent of the *first principle of classical thermodynamics* is merely the principle of *conservation of energy* applied on the microscopic scale, that is to say applied to molecules, atoms, electrons, etc. Thus this principle is from the point of view of statistical thermodynamics not a new law but merely one item in general atomic quantum theory.

To relate the *second principle of classical thermodynamics* to *statistical thermodynamics* we make certain algebraic transformations. We begin by defining a function $J(\beta, V, N, \xi)$ by

$$J(\beta, V, N, \xi) = k \log \Sigma_r \, \Omega_r(\xi) \, e^{-\beta U_r}, \qquad (2.04.2)$$

where the summation is over all states of given ξ and k is an arbitrary constant.

In the system with temperature specified by β there will be fluctuations of U, but the experimentally measurable U will be U_{Av} the average value of U. Let us now consider the value of U_{Av} for specified β, V, N and ξ. Using the weighting factors (1) we have

$$U_{Av}(\beta, V, N, \xi) = \frac{\Sigma_r \, U_r \, \Omega_r(\xi) \, e^{-\beta U_r}}{\Sigma_r \, \Omega_r(\xi) \, e^{-\beta U_r}}$$

$$= -\frac{\partial}{\partial \beta} \log \Sigma_r \, \Omega_r(\xi) \, e^{-\beta U_r} = -\frac{1}{k} \frac{\partial}{\partial \beta} J(\beta, V, N, \xi), \quad (2.04.3)$$

using (2).

Again associated with the fluctuations in U there will be fluctuations in the pressure $-(\partial U/\partial V)$, but the experimentally measured pressure P will be $(\partial U/\partial V)_{Av}$, where the subscript Av denotes averaging with the weight factor (1). We accordingly have for given β, V N and ξ

$$P = -\left(\frac{\partial U}{\partial V}\right)_{Av} = \frac{-\Sigma_r \dfrac{\partial U_r}{\partial V} \, \Omega_r(\xi) \, e^{-\beta U_r}}{\Sigma_r \, \Omega_r(\xi) \, e^{-\beta U_r}}$$

$$= \frac{1}{\beta} \frac{\partial}{\partial V} \log \Sigma_r \, \Omega_r(\xi) \, e^{-\beta U_r} = \frac{1}{k\beta} \frac{\partial}{\partial V} J(\beta, V, N, \xi), \quad (2.04.4)$$

using (2).

Let us now make the further algebraic substitution

$$k\beta = T^{-1} \qquad \qquad (2.04.5)$$

and use T as an independent variable instead of β. We now have in place of (3) and (4)

$$U_{Av}(T, V, N, \xi) = -\frac{\partial}{\partial (T^{-1})} J(T, V, N, \xi)$$

$$= T^2 \frac{\partial}{\partial T} J(T, V, N, \xi). \qquad (2.04.6)$$

$$P = T \frac{\partial}{\partial V} J(T, V, N, \xi). \qquad (2.04.7)$$

Combining (6) with (7) we have

$$dJ = \frac{U_{Av}}{T^2} \, dT + \frac{P}{T} \, dV, \qquad \text{(given } N, \xi\text{).} \qquad (2.04.8)$$

Comparing (8) with (1.31.13) we see that the dependence of J defined by (2) on T defined by (5) and on P is precisely the same as the dependence of the *Massieu Function* on the absolute temperature and on the pressure. It can in fact be shown that T defined by (5) has all the properties of absolute temperature and J defined by (2) has all the properties of the *Massieu Function*. This constitutes a brief summary of how the *second principle of classical thermodynamics* follows as a natural deduction from *statistical thermodynamics*.

For the benefit of the reader not familiar with the *Massieu function* J, we recall that it is related to the *free energy* or *Helmholtz function* F by

$$J = -F/T, \qquad (2.04.9)$$

and that either J or F is a thermodynamic potential for the independent variables T, V, N.

We can now substitute from (5) into (1) and so have as a weighting factor for each state r

$$\Omega_r e^{-U_r/kT}, \qquad (2.04.10)$$

and this factor is called *Boltzmann's factor*. From (10) it is clear that kT has the dimensions of energy. k is a universal constant called *Boltzmann's constant*. If we use the *Kelvin scale* of temperature with the *centigrade degree* then

$$k = 1.380_5 \times 10^{-16} \text{ erg/deg.} \qquad (2.04.11)$$

From (10) we see that the average properties of the system for prescribed values of T, V, N and unspecified ξ can be obtained by averaging over all ξ attaching to each ξ a weight $Q(T, \xi)$ defined by

$$Q(T, \xi) = \Sigma_r \, \Omega_r(\xi) \, e^{-U_r/kT}. \qquad (2.04.12)$$

The function $Q(T, \xi)$ is usually called the *partition function*, but a more precise name is the *partition function for given* T, V, N, ξ. An alternative name is the *thermodynamic probability for given* T, V, N, ξ.

Substituting from (5) and (12) into (2) we obtain

$$J(T, V, N, \xi) = k \log Q(T, \xi). \qquad (2.04.13)$$

We observe that this relation between the *thermodynamic potential* J and the *statistical probability* $Q(T, \xi)$ for given T, V, N, ξ is completely analogous to *Boltzmann's relation* (2.02.2) between the thermodynamic potential S and the thermodynamic probability $\Omega(\xi)$ for given U, V, N, ξ.

§ 2.05   Further Characteristics of Macroscopic Systems

Let us consider the individual terms of $Q(T, \xi)$ defined by (2.04.12). Let us denote the maximum term by

$$\Omega_m e^{-U_m/kT}, \qquad (2.05.1)$$

noting that this Ω_m is not the same as the $\Omega(\xi_m)$ of § 2.03. Generally speaking the larger the system the sharper this maximum and for any macroscopic system it is so sharp that all terms in $Q(T, \xi)$ in which U_r differs appreciably from U_m are entirely trivial. Moreover, although the actual number of terms $Q(T, \xi)$ comparable with (1) may be great, the ratio

$$\frac{\log Q(T, \xi) - \log \Omega_m \, e^{-U_m/kT}}{\log \Omega_m \, e^{-U_m/kT}} \qquad (2.05.2)$$

is roughly of the order α/N where α is far nearer to unity than to N. Hence in any macroscopic system the ratio (2) is effectively zero and we may therefore replace the definition (2.04.2) of J by

$$J = k \, \log \, \Omega_m \, e^{-U_m/kT}. \qquad (2.05.3)$$

It follows that with an inaccuracy again trivial for a macroscopic system

$$U_{Av} = T^2 \frac{\partial J}{\partial T} = U_m. \qquad (2.05.4)$$

From the classical definition (1.31.11) or (1.33.15) of the *Massieu function J*, we have

$$S = J + \frac{U}{T}. \qquad (2.05.5)$$

We accordingly in *statistical thermodynamics* define a function $S(T, V, N, \xi)$ by

$$S(T, V, N, \xi) = J(T, V, N, \xi) + \frac{U_{Av}}{T}. \qquad (2.05.6)$$

Using (3), (4) and (5) we obtain from (6)

$$S(T, V, N, \xi) = k \, \log \, \Omega_m(\xi). \qquad (2.05.7)$$

Now comparing (7) with (2.02.2) we obtain the striking result

$$S(T, V, N, \xi) = S(U_{Av}, V, N, \xi). \qquad (2.05.8)$$

Thus although the definition of entropy at a specified temperature by means of (2.04.13) together with (6) is entirely different from the definition of entropy at a specified energy by means of (2.02.2), yet for a macroscopic system the difference between the two is quite trivial.

This characteristic property of a macroscopic system may be described in the following instructive but less exact way. If we define S by

$$S = k \, \log \, \Omega(\xi) \qquad (2.05.9)$$

then in a system of specified energy Ω must denote the number of states having *precisely* this energy, whereas in a system of specified temperature Ω denotes the number of states of energy *nearly* equal to the average energy. The question immediately arises how nearly. The answer is that for a *macroscopic system* it just does not make any difference.

§ 2.06   System of Given Temperature, Pressure and Composition

We now consider a system of prescribed composition surrounded by a temperature bath and enclosed by a piston subjected to a prescribed pressure P. We construct the double sum

$$W(T, P, N, \xi) = \Sigma_r \, \Sigma_s \, \Omega_{rs}(\xi) \, e^{-U_r/kT} e^{-PV_s/kT}, \qquad (2.06.1)$$

where the summation extends over all energies U_r and all volumes V_s consistent with the prescribed value of ξ. It can then be shown without any new assumptions that we can correctly derive the average (equilibrium) properties of the system for the prescribed values of T, P, N by averaging over all values of ξ attaching to each a weight $W(T, P, N, \xi)$.

We call $W(T, P, N, \xi)$ the *thermodynamic probability for given T, P, N, ξ* or the *partition function for given T, P, N, ξ*. It is related to the *Planck function Y*, which is a thermodynamic potential for the independent variables T, P, N, ξ, by

$$Y(T, P, N, \xi) = k \log W(T, P, N, \xi), \qquad (2.06.2)$$

analogous to (2.02.2) and (2.04.13).

For the benefit of the reader unfamiliar with the *Planck function Y* we recall its relation to the *Gibbs function G*, namely

$$Y = -G/T. \qquad (2.06.3)$$

Provided the system is macroscopic we may again with only trivial inaccuracy replace W by its maximum term, say

$$\Omega_m(\xi) \, e^{-U_m/kT} \, e^{-PV_m/kT}, \qquad (2.06.4)$$

so that we may replace (2) by

$$Y(T, N, N, \xi) = k \, \log \, \Omega_m(\xi) - \frac{U_m}{T} - \frac{PV_m}{T}. \qquad (2.06.5)$$

From (1) and (5) we immediately verify that

$$(U + PV)_{Av} = T^2 \frac{\partial Y}{\partial T} = U_m + PV_m \qquad (2.06.6)$$

$$V_{Av} = -T \frac{\partial Y}{\partial P} = V_m \qquad (2.06.7)$$

as we should expect according to (1.31.14). Furthermore comparing (5) with (1.33.16) we obtain

$$S(T, P, N, \xi) = k \log \Omega_m(\xi), \qquad (2.06.8)$$

verifying that for a macroscopic system the entropy at given T, P is indistinguishable from the entropy at given $U = U_m$ and $V = V_m$.

§ 2.07   System at Given Temperature, Pressure and Partial Potential

To conclude we choose as independent variables the temperature T, pressure P and partial potential μ. An illustrative example is a gas in contact with a crystal of the same substance; the crystal is not considered as part of the system. Such a system is called *open*.

We now construct the triple sum

$$W(T, P, \mu, \xi) = \Sigma_r \Sigma_s \Sigma_t \, \Omega_{rst}(\xi) \, e^{-U_r/kT} \, e^{-PV_s/kT} \, e^{\mu N_t/kT}, \quad (2.07.1)$$

where $\Omega_{rst}(\xi)$ denotes the number of states of energy U_r, volume V_s and content N_t corresponding to the given value of ξ and the triple summation extends over all sets of values of U_r, V_s, N_t corresponding to the given value of ξ. It can then be shown without any new assumptions that all the average properties of the system for the prescribed values of T, P, μ are correctly obtained by averaging over all values of ξ attaching to each a weight $W(T, P, \mu, \xi)$, this expression being the *partition function* or *thermodynamic probability* of ξ for the given values of T, P, μ.

For a macroscopic system W can in the usual way be replaced by its maximum term say

$$\Omega_m(\xi) \, e^{-U_m/kT} \, e^{-PV_m/kT} \, e^{\mu N_m/kT}. \quad (2.07.2)$$

If we now define a quantity $O(T, P, \mu, \xi)$ by

$$O(T, P, \mu, \xi) = k \log W(T, P, \mu, \xi). \quad (2.07.3)$$

we may for a macroscopic system replace (3) by

$$O(T, P, \mu, \xi) = k \log \Omega_m(\xi) - \frac{U_m}{T} - \frac{PV_m}{T} + \frac{\mu N_m}{T}. \quad (2.07.4)$$

Moreover for a macroscopic system we have as usual

$$S = k \log \Omega_m(\xi), \quad (2.07.5)$$

$$U_{Av} = U_m, \quad (2.07.6)$$

$$V_{Av} = V_m, \quad (2.07.7)$$

$$N_{Av} = N_m. \quad (2.07.8)$$

Comparing (5) to (8) with (4) we find dropping subscripts that

$$O(T, P, \mu, \xi) = \frac{TS - U - PV + \mu N}{T} = 0 \quad (2.07.9)$$

according to (1.35.4).

From the analogy between (3), (2.02.2), (2.04.13) and (2.06.2) we expect $O(T, P, \mu, \xi)$ to be a *thermodynamic potential* for the variables $T, P,$ and μ. According to (9) this thermodynamic potential is identically zero. We now recall the Gibbs–Duhem relation (1.38.2)

$$SdT - VdP + \Sigma_i n_i d\mu_i = 0. \quad (2.07.10)$$

In a system of one component the sum $\Sigma_i n_i d\mu_i$ reduces to $n d\mu$ and if we denote by μ the partial potential per molecule, instead of per mole as in Chapter I, (10) becomes

$$0 = SdT - VdP + Nd\mu, \quad (2.07.11)$$

showing that the thermodynamic potential for the independent variables T, P, μ is indeed zero.

§ 2.08   Recapitulation

We can now summarize the content of the several preceding sections [*]. For each selected set of three independent variables, other than ξ, a different kind of weighting factor w has to be attached to the microstates. The sum Σw for all microstates consistent with the prescribed values of the three chosen independent variables other than ξ and corresponding to a definite value of ξ is called the *partition function* or the *thermodynamic probability* for the prescribed values of ξ and the other three independent variables. Furthermore in each case $k \log \Sigma w$ is a *thermodynamic potential* for the chosen set of three independent variables other than ξ. These relationships are shown in Table 2.1.

TABLE 2.1

Independent Variables	Weighting Factor for each Independent Microstate	*Thermodynamic Potential* equal to $k \log \Sigma w$
U, V, N, ξ	1	S
T, V, N, ξ	$e^{-U/kT}$	$J = -F/T$
T, P, N, ξ	$e^{-U/kT} e^{-PV/kT}$	$Y = -G/T$
T, P, μ, ξ	$e^{-U/kT} e^{-PV/kT} e^{\mu N/kT}$	0

We emphasize again that each of the listed *thermodynamic potentials* S, J, Y and zero is related to the corresponding *thermodynamic probability* according to

thermodynamic potential $= k \log$ (*thermodynamic probability*).

The earliest and best known example of this form is Boltzmann's relation for $S(U, V, N, \xi)$, but the others and particularly that for $J(T, V, N, \xi)$ are in fact more useful.

Once again we mention that we have introduced J and Y largely because of their close analogy to S; for the benefit of the reader more familiar with F and G we again recall that

$$J = -F/T \tag{2.08.1}$$

$$Y = -G/T \tag{2.08.2}$$

It is a fundamental characteristic of a macroscopic system that any partition function may with trivial inaccuracy be replaced by its maximum term. It follows that the equilibrium value of ξ is that value which maximizes

---

[*]   Compare Guggenheim, *J. Chem. Phys.* (1939) **7** 103,
    Forh. 5te Nordiske Kemikermóde Kóbenhavn 1939 p. 205.

the thermodynamic potential belonging to the chosen set of independent variables. The alternative equilibrium conditions

$$\text{for given } U \text{ and } V \text{ that } S \text{ is a } maximum, \qquad (2.08.3)$$
$$\text{for given } T \text{ and } V \text{ that } J \text{ is a } maximum, \qquad (2.08.4)$$
$$\text{for given } T \text{ and } P \text{ that } Y \text{ is a } maximum, \qquad (2.08.5)$$

thus obtained are precisely equivalent to (1.43.1), (1.43.3) and (1.43.4) respectively.

§ 2.09 Extension to Several Components. Absolute Activities

We have hitherto restricted our exposition to systems of a single component purely for the sake of brevity. The extension to systems of several components is straightforward.

In particular for a system at given values of the independent variables T, P and the μ_i's, the weighting factor for each independent microstate will be

$$e^{-U/kT} e^{-PV/kT} \Pi (\lambda_i)^{N_i}, \qquad (2.09.1)$$

where for brevity we have introduced quantities λ_i defined by

$$\lambda_i = e^{\mu_i/kT}$$

or

$$\mu_i = k T \log \lambda_i. \qquad (2.09.2)$$

These quantities λ_i may be used instead of the μ_i's and are often more convenient. λ_i is called the *absolute activity* of the species i.

In later chapters we shall meet these formulae with a slightly different appearance in that Boltzmann's constant k will be replaced by another constant denoted by R. The explanation is simply that in this chapter μ denotes the partial potential *per molecule,* whereas in all other chapters it denotes the partial potential *per mole.* The two constants k and R are accordingly related by

$$R = N k, \qquad (2.09.3)$$

where N, called *Avogadro's number,* denotes the number of molecules in one mole.

§ 2.10 Antisymmetric and Symmetric Eigenfunctions

In § 2.01 we mentioned that it is often, though not always, possible to regard the units (molecules, atoms, ions, electrons) composing the system as almost independent. In this case each eigenfunction of the system can be expressed as a linear combination of products of the eigenfunctions of all the units. We begin by considering the case that all the units are of the same kind. We denote the eigenfunctions of the units by φ and the eigenfunctions of the whole system by ψ. We have now to distinguish two cases.

If each unit is a fundamental particle (proton, neutron or electron) or is composed of an odd number of fundamental particles, then each eigenfunction ψ of the system is constructed by forming a determinant of the eigenfunctions of the individual units. For the sake of simplicity and brevity we consider a system consisting of only three units, numbered 1, 2, 3. The symbol $\varphi_\alpha(1)$ then denotes the eigenfunction of the unit 1 when in the state α. The eigenfunction $\psi_{\alpha\beta\gamma}$ is then constructed as follows:

$$\psi_{\alpha\beta\gamma} \equiv \begin{vmatrix} \varphi_\alpha(1), & \varphi_\beta(1), & \varphi_\gamma(1) \\ \varphi_\alpha(2), & \varphi_\beta(2), & \varphi_\gamma(2) \\ \varphi_\alpha(3), & \varphi_\beta(3), & \varphi_\gamma(3) \end{vmatrix}. \qquad (2.\,10.\,1)$$

We notice that if we interchange the states of any two units, ψ changes sign. We accordingly describe the eigenfunctions ψ as *antisymmetric* with respect to every pair of units. It follows at once that if any two of the states α, β, γ are identical then $\psi_{\alpha\beta\gamma}$ vanishes. Thus there is one independent ψ for each combination of three φ_α, φ_β, φ_γ provided α, β, γ are all different but none if any two of α, β, γ are the same.

If on the other hand each unit is a photon or is composed of an even number of fundamental particles (protons, neutrons, electrons), then each eigenfunction of the system is constructed from the eigenfunctions of the units by forming linear combinations similar to determinants, but in which all the terms are added. Thus in the case of only three units 1, 2, 3 the eigenfunction $\psi_{\alpha\beta\gamma}$ is defined by

$$\psi_{\alpha\beta\gamma} \equiv \left\| \begin{matrix} \varphi_\alpha(1), & \varphi_\beta(1), & \varphi_\gamma(1) \\ \varphi_\alpha(2), & \varphi_\beta(2), & \varphi_\gamma(2) \\ \varphi_\alpha(3), & \varphi_\beta(3), & \varphi_\gamma(3) \end{matrix} \right\|, \qquad (2.\,10.\,2)$$

which differs from (1) in that all the six terms are added. We notice that if we interchange the states of any two units, ψ remains unchanged. We accordingly describe the eigenfunction ψ as *symmetric* in all the units. It is clear that there is one independent ψ for every combination of three eigenfunctions φ_α, φ_β, φ_γ whether or not any two or more of α, β, γ are the same.

§ 2.11   Fermi–Dirac and Bose–Einstein Statistics

Let us now consider a system containing N indistinguishable units and enquire how many eigenfunctions ψ of the system can be constructed out of g eigenfunctions φ of the units. There are two distinct problems with different answers according as ψ is to be antisymmetric or symmetric in the units.

In the case where ψ is to be antisymmetric, to obtain any such ψ at all g must be at least as great as N and the number of such eigenfunctions ψ is then

$$\frac{g!}{N!(g-N)!}, \qquad \text{antisymmetric, } (g \geqslant N). \qquad (2.11.1)$$

In the other case where ψ is to be symmetric, the number of such eigenfunctions ψ is

$$\frac{(g+N-1)!}{(g-1)!\,N!}, \qquad \text{symmetric,} \qquad (2.11.2)$$

which, when $g \gg 1$, is not significantly different from the simpler expression

$$\frac{(g+N)!}{g!\,N!}, \qquad \text{symmetric, } (g \gg 1). \qquad (2.11.3)$$

It is of interest to note that when $g \gg N$, both (1) and (3) are nearly the same as

$$\frac{g^N}{N!}, \qquad \text{antisymmetric or symmetric, } (g \gg N). \qquad (2.11.4)$$

If now we translate the laws governing the average properties of the whole system outlined in §§ 2.01—2.09 into forms relating to the average distributions of the component units, we shall as a result of the difference between (1) and (2) find different results according as the eigenfunctions ψ are to be antisymmetric or symmetric in the units. These distribution laws take the simplest form if we choose as independent variables the temperature T, the volume V and the absolute activity λ. We shall now state these laws without any derivation.

Let ε_α denote the energy of a unit in the non-degenerate state α having the eigenfunction φ_α. Then if the unit is a fundamental particle (proton, neutron or electron) or is composed of an odd number of fundamental particles, the eigenfunction ψ must be antisymmetrical in the units and the average number N_α of units in the state α is found to be given by

$$\frac{N_\alpha}{1-N_\alpha} = \lambda e^{-\varepsilon_\alpha/kT}. \qquad (2.11.5)$$

where λ denotes the absolute activity of the unit, T the absolute temperature and k Boltzmann's constant. This distribution law is called that of *Fermi–Dirac Statistics*.

If on the other hand the unit is a photon or is composed of an even number of fundamental particles, the eigenfunction ψ must be symmetrical in the units and the average number N_α of units in the state α is found to be given by

$$\frac{N_\alpha}{1+N_\alpha} = \lambda e^{-\varepsilon_\alpha/kT}. \qquad (2.11.6)$$

This distribution law is called that of *Bose–Einstein Statistics*.

It is to be noted that in both the cases of *Fermi–Dirac Statistics* and *Bose–Einstein Statistics* the average number N_α of units in each state is related simply and explicity to the temperature T and the absolute activity λ, which we recall is related to the potential μ by (2.09.2).

§ 2.12   Boltzmann Statistics

Let the subscript 0 denote the state of lowest energy ε_0 and let us consider the case that

$$\lambda e^{-\varepsilon_0/kT} \ll 1, \tag{2.12.1}$$

so that *a fortiori*

$$\lambda e^{-\varepsilon_\alpha/kT} \ll 1, \qquad (\text{all } \alpha). \tag{2.12.2}$$

It then follows from either (2.11.5) or (2.11.6) that

$$N_\alpha \ll 1. \tag{2.12.3}$$

We may then without loss of accuracy replace either (2.11.5) or (2.11.6) by

$$N_\alpha = \lambda e^{-\varepsilon_\alpha/kT}. \tag{2.12.4}$$

This distribution law is called that of *Boltzmann Statistics*.

We now state without any proof that in almost all the systems met in practice the condition (1) is satisfied. There are only two important exceptions. The first is the system of conducting electrons in a metal; these obey the Fermi–Dirac distribution law and will not be discussed in this book. The other is the system of photons forming radiation; these obey the Bose–Einstein distribution law and will be discussed in Chapter XIV. Boltzmann Statistics are sufficient for all the other systems to be met in this book and from here onwards we shall confine our attention to these.

§ 2.13   Partition Functions of Units and Thermodynamic Functions

For any system obeying Boltzmann Statistics, we have according to (2.12.4)

$$N_\alpha = \lambda e^{-\varepsilon_\alpha/kT}. \tag{2.13.1}$$

If we apply (1) to every state α and add, we obtain

$$N = \lambda \, \Sigma_\alpha \, e^{-\varepsilon_\alpha/kT}, \tag{2.13.2}$$

so that

$$u = kT \log \lambda = kT \log \frac{N}{\Sigma_\alpha \, e^{-\varepsilon_\alpha/kT}}. \tag{2.13.3}$$

The sum $\Sigma_\alpha e^{-\varepsilon_\alpha/kT}$ is called the *partition function* of the *units*. Its structure is similar to that of the *partition function* for the independent variables T, V, N of the *whole system*. Formula (3) is the basis for the evaluation of the thermodynamic functions in terms of the energies of all the states of the component units.

Formula (3) is equivalent to the formula of the *Massieu function J* and the *free energy F*

$$J = -\frac{F}{T} = k \log \left\{ \frac{(\Sigma_\alpha e^{-\varepsilon_\alpha / kT})^N}{N!} \right\}. \qquad (2.13.4)$$

If we compare (4) with (2.04.13) we see that the two are equivalent when we bear in mind that the factor $N!$ in the denominator in (4) is required to avoid counting as distinct states those obtainable from one another by a mere permutation of indistinguishable units.

The more general formula for a system containing more than one kind of units (molecules) is

$$J = -\frac{F}{T} = k \Sigma_i \log \left\{ \frac{(\Sigma_\alpha e^{-\varepsilon_\alpha / kT})^{N_i}}{N_i!} \right\}. \qquad (2.13.5)$$

§ 2.14 Separable Degrees of Freedom

It is often the case that there is no appreciable interaction between two or more degrees of freedom of a unit. Such degrees of freedom are said to be *separable*. Each eigenfunction φ may then be expressed as a product of the eigenfunctions for the several separable degrees of freedom, and the energy ε_α as the sum of the energies of each separable degree of freedom. It then follows immediately that the partition function of the unit can be expressed as the product of partition functions for its several separable degrees of freedom.

In particular the translational degrees of freedom of molecules are usually separable from the internal degrees of freedom. Among the internal degrees of freedom we here include rotational degrees of freedom as well as atomic vibrations, electronic and nuclear degrees of freedom. We may accordingly write for the partition function of a molecule

$$e^{-\varepsilon_\alpha / kT} = e^{-\varepsilon_{tr} / kT} e^{-\varepsilon_{int} / kT}, \qquad (2.14.1)$$

where ε_{tr} denotes the energy of the translational degrees of freedom and ε_{int} the energy of the internal degrees of freedom. Substituting (1) into (2.13.5) we obtain for the Massieu function J and the free energy F

$$J = -\frac{F}{T} = k \Sigma_i \log \left\{ \frac{(\Sigma e^{-\varepsilon_{tr} / kT} \Sigma e^{-\varepsilon_{int} / kT})^{N_i}}{N_i!} \right\}. \qquad (2.14.2)$$

Alternatively we may write

$$J = J_{tr} + J_{int}, \qquad (2.14.3)$$

$$F = F_{tr} + F_{int}, \qquad (2.14.4)$$

$$J_{tr} = -\frac{F_{tr}}{T} = k \Sigma_i \log \left\{ \frac{(\Sigma e^{-\varepsilon_{tr} / kT})^{N_i}}{N_i!} \right\}. \qquad (2.14.5)$$

$$J_{int} = -\frac{F_{int}}{T} = k \Sigma_i N_i \log (\Sigma e^{-\varepsilon_{int} / kT}), \qquad (2.14.6)$$

where the subscript *tr* refers throughout to contributions from the translational degrees of freedom and the subscript *int* to contributions from the internal degrees of freedom.

§ 2.15   Classical and Unexcited Degrees of Freedom

It may happen that there are many energy levels less than kT. When this is the case, the sum which defines the partition function may without loss of accuracy be replaced by an integral, whose evaluation is often elementary. Such a degree of freedom is called a *classical degree of freedom*. Whether a particular degree of freedom is classical depends on the temperature. Under ordinary conditions the translational and rotational degrees of freedom of the molecules in a gas are classical.

In the opposite case it may happen that the separation between the states of lowest energy level and those of the next energy level is several times greater than kT. The partition function then reduces effectively to the terms corresponding to the lowest energy level, that is to

$$\varpi_0\, e^{-\varepsilon_0/kT}, \tag{2.15.1}$$

where ε_0 denotes the lowest energy level and ϖ_0 denotes the number of states having this energy. Such degrees of freedom are called *unexcited degrees of freedom*. The contribution of each such unexcited degree of freedom to the free energy F is clearly

$$\varepsilon_0 - kT\, \log\, \varpi_0, \tag{2.15.2}$$

and the corresponding contribution to the entropy

$$k\, \log\, \varpi_0. \tag{2.15.3}$$

which we notice is independent of the temperature. Whether a particular degree of freedom is unexcited depends by definition on the temperature. At all the temperatures with which we are concerned all degrees of freedom internal to the atomic nucleus are unexcited. The electronic degrees of freedom of most molecules may also be regarded as unexcited at most of the temperatures which concern us; there are however a few exceptions, notably the molecule NO.

§ 2.16   Translational Degrees of Freedom

The translational degrees of freedom of a dilute gas may be regarded as classical. When the partition function for the translational degrees of freedom of a molecule is replaced by an integral and the integration is performed, one obtains

$$\left(\frac{2\pi m k T}{h^2}\right)^{\frac{3}{2}} V, \tag{2.16.1}$$

where m denotes the mass of a molecule and V the volume in which it is enclosed; h denotes Planck's constant and k as usual Boltzmann's constant. Thus for a dilute gaseous mixture according to (2.14.5) we have

$$J_{tr} = -\frac{F_{tr}}{T} = k\, \Sigma_i\, \log\left\{\frac{(2\pi m_i k T)^{\frac{3}{2}N_i}\, V^{N_i}}{h^{3N_i}\, N_i!}\right\}. \tag{2.16.2}$$

Let us now consider the translational degrees of freedom in a crystal. We may regard each molecule as vibrating about an equilibrium position in the crystal lattice. Let us denote by q the partition function for a molecule attached to a given lattice position and for the moment let us imagine all the N molecules to be individually distinguishable but sufficiently alike so that any one can be interchanged with any other without destroying the crystal structure. Then the molecules can be permuted over the lattice positions in $N!$ ways, so that the partition function for the translational motion of the molecules of the whole crystal would be $N! q^N$. Actually the molecules are of course not individually distinguishable and we must consider only states whose eigenfunction is symmetric in molecules containing an even number of fundamental particles and anti-symmetric in molecules containing an odd number of fundamental particles. In the simplest case when all the molecules in the crystal are of the same kind the number of states is thus reduced by a factor $N!$, which cancels the other $N!$, so that the partition function for the whole crystal becomes q^N. We thus have for a crystal of a pure substance

$$J_{tr} = -\frac{F_{tr}}{T} = k \log q^N. \qquad (2.16.3)$$

Each molecule has at a given lattice position only one state of lowest translational energy and so at low temperatures q tends to unity. We therefore have for a crystal of a pure substance

$$J_{tr} = -\frac{F_{tr}}{T} \rightarrow 0. \qquad (T \rightarrow 0). \qquad (2.16.4)$$

For a mixed crystal containing several distinguishable kinds of molecules, e.g. isotopes, the eigenfunctions have to be symmetric, or anti-symmetric, only with respect to identical molecules. Hence we have to divide only by the product of all the $N_i!$ instead of by $N!$. We therefore have instead of (3)

$$J_{tr} = -\frac{F_{tr}}{T} = k \log N! + k \Sigma_i \log \frac{q_i^{N_i}}{N_i!}. \qquad (2.16.5)$$

where $N = \Sigma_i N_i$. It has been implicitly assumed that interchanging two molecules of different kinds in the crystal does not affect the partition function q_i of either of them. This assumption is justified provided the molecules are sufficiently similar, e.g. isotopic. Since at low temperatures each q_i tends to unity it follows that

$$J_{tr} = -\frac{F_{tr}}{T} \rightarrow k \log N! - k \Sigma_i \log N_i!. \qquad (T \rightarrow 0). \qquad (2.16.6)$$

§ 2.17 Third Principle of Thermodynamics

After this brief and admittedly incomplete sketch of statistical thermodynamics we recall the formulation of the *third principle of thermodynamics* which we adopted in § 1.63, namely:

By the standard methods of statistical thermodynamics it is possible to derive for certain entropy changes general formulae which cannot be derived from the zeroth, first or second principles of thermodynamics. In particular one can obtain formulae for entropy changes in highly disperse systems (i.e. gases), those in very cold systems (i.e. when $T \to 0$) and those associated with the mixing of very similar substances (e.g. isotopes).

We shall now briefly state these deductions from statistical thermodynamics without giving detailed derivations.

In the first place we consider the translational term in the thermodynamic functions of a highly disperse system, i.e. a gas, containing N_i molecules of type i having a mass m_i. The contributions to the Massieu function J and to the free energy F are given by

$$J_{tr} = - \frac{F_{tr}}{T} = k \, \Sigma_i \, \log \frac{(2 \pi m_i k T)^{\frac{3}{2} N_i} \, V^{N_i}}{h^{3 N_i} \, N_i !} \,, \qquad (2.17.1)$$

The corresponding contribution S_{tr} to the entropy S is

$$S_{tr} = k \, \Sigma_i \, \log \frac{(2 \pi m_i k T)^{\frac{3}{2} N_i} \, V^{N_i}}{h^{3 N_i} \, N_i !} + k \, \Sigma_i \, \tfrac{3}{2} \, N_i \,, \qquad (2.17.2)$$

In particular in a gaseous single substance

$$S_{tr} = k \, \log \frac{(2 \pi m k T)^{\frac{3}{2} N} \, V^N}{h^{3 N} \, N !} + \tfrac{3}{2} N k. \qquad (2.17.3)$$

Using Stirling's formula for large N

$$\log N! = N \log N - N, \qquad (2.17.4)$$

we can rewrite (3) as

$$\frac{S_{tr}}{Nk} = \log \frac{(2 \pi m k T)^{\frac{3}{2}} \, V}{h^3 \, N} + \tfrac{5}{2}. \qquad (2.17.5)$$

Anticipating the formula for the pressure P of a perfect gas

$$P = \frac{N}{V} kT, \qquad (2.17.6)$$

we can replace (5) by

$$\frac{S_{tr}}{Nk} = \log \frac{(2 \pi m)^{\frac{3}{2}} \, (kT)^{\frac{5}{2}}}{h^3 \, P} + \tfrac{5}{2}. \qquad (2.17.7)$$

We shall use the equivalent of formula (2.17.7) in § 4.56.

Our second example is the translational term in the entropy of a crystal of a pure substance. As the temperature tends towards zero, this contribution tends to zero. We shall return to this law in § 4.60.

Finally we consider the entropy of mixtures of very similar substances, such as isotopes. If several very similar substances, such as isotopes, all at the same temperature and same number of molecules per unit volume are mixed, keeping the temperature and number of molecules per unit volume unchanged, the entropy is increased by $\triangle S$ given by

$$\frac{\triangle S}{k} = \log N! - \Sigma_i \log N_i!, \qquad (2.17.8)$$

where N_i denotes the number of molecules of the species i and $N = \Sigma_i N_i$ denotes the total number of molecules of all species. Using Stirling's formula (4), we can rewrite (8) as

$$\frac{\triangle S}{k} = \Sigma_i N_i \log \frac{N}{N_i}. \qquad (2.17.9)$$

This applies to solids, and incidentally liquids, as well as to gases, provided the various species are sufficiently similar, e.g. isotopic. We shall make use of this in § 4.57.

When we meet these formulae again in Chapter IV, the number of molecules N_i will be replaced by the number of moles n_i and correspondingly Boltzmann's constant k will be replaced by the gas constant R. In particular $N_i k$ becomes $n_i R$.

CHAPTER III

SOME RELATIONS OF GENERAL VALIDITY

§ 3.01 Identities between Partial Differential Coefficients

We begin this chapter by summarizing certain important properties of partial differential coefficients, which will constantly be required.

Let x, y and z denote three quantities any one of which is completely determined by the other two, so that we may regard any one as a function of the other two. Symbolically

$$z = z(x, y), \tag{3.01.1}$$

$$x = x(y, z), \tag{3.01.2}$$

$$y = y(z, x). \tag{3.01.3}$$

The partial differential coefficients are defined by relations such as

$$\left(\frac{\partial z}{\partial x}\right)_y = \mathop{Lt}_{\delta x \to 0} \frac{z(x + \delta x, y) - z(x, y)}{\delta x}. \tag{3.01.4}$$

From this definition it follows immediately that

$$\left(\frac{\partial z}{\partial x}\right)_y \left(\frac{\partial x}{\partial z}\right)_y = 1, \tag{3.01.5}$$

and there are of course two other similar relations obtained by permuting x, y, z.

Subject to certain conditions concerning the smoothness of the function $z(x, y)$ which will always be fulfilled in the physical applications, the order of successive differentiations of $z(x, y)$ is immaterial. In particular

$$\left\{\frac{\partial}{\partial x}\left(\frac{\partial z}{\partial y}\right)_x\right\}_y = \left\{\frac{\partial}{\partial y}\left(\frac{\partial z}{\partial x}\right)_y\right\}_x. \tag{3.01.6}$$

or more briefly

$$\frac{\partial}{\partial x}\frac{\partial z}{\partial y} = \frac{\partial}{\partial y}\frac{\partial z}{\partial x}. \tag{3.01.7}$$

We shall make much use of this relation and for the sake of brevity shall refer to it as the *cross-differentiation identity*.

When we differentiate (1), (2) and (3), using the definitions of partial differential coefficients, we obtain

$$dz = \left(\frac{\partial z}{\partial x}\right)_y dx + \left(\frac{\partial z}{\partial y}\right)_x dy, \tag{3.01.8}$$

$$dx = \left(\frac{\partial x}{\partial y}\right)_z dy + \left(\frac{\partial x}{\partial z}\right)_y dz, \tag{3.01.9}$$

$$dy = \left(\frac{\partial y}{\partial z}\right)_x dz + \left(\frac{\partial y}{\partial x}\right)_z dx. \tag{3.01.10}$$

Substituting (9) into (8) we obtain

$$dz = \left(\frac{\partial z}{\partial x}\right)_y \left(\frac{\partial x}{\partial z}\right)_y dz + \left\{\left(\frac{\partial z}{\partial x}\right)_y \left(\frac{\partial x}{\partial y}\right)_z + \left(\frac{\partial z}{\partial y}\right)_x\right\} dy \qquad (3.01.11)$$

and using (5)

$$dz = dz + \left\{\left(\frac{\partial z}{\partial x}\right)_y \left(\frac{\partial x}{\partial y}\right)_z + \left(\frac{\partial z}{\partial y}\right)_x\right\} dy. \qquad (3.01.12)$$

or since dy is arbitrary

$$\left(\frac{\partial z}{\partial x}\right)_y \left(\frac{\partial x}{\partial y}\right)_z + \left(\frac{\partial z}{\partial y}\right)_x = 0. \qquad (3.01.13)$$

We can rewrite (13) in the alternative form

$$\left(\frac{\partial x}{\partial y}\right)_z = -\left(\frac{\partial z}{\partial y}\right)_x \bigg/ \left(\frac{\partial z}{\partial x}\right)_y, \qquad (3.01.14)$$

or, by using relations of the form (5), in the symmetrical form

$$\left(\frac{\partial x}{\partial y}\right)_z \left(\frac{\partial y}{\partial z}\right)_x \left(\frac{\partial z}{\partial x}\right)_y = -1. \qquad (3.01.15)$$

All the above differential relations between x, y, z remain valid even when there are further variables provided all the remaining variables are held constant. For example an extension of (15) is

$$\left(\frac{\partial x}{\partial y}\right)_{z,u,v} \left(\frac{\partial y}{\partial z}\right)_{x,u,v} \left(\frac{\partial z}{\partial x}\right)_{y,u,v} = -1. \qquad (3.01.16)$$

Among the useful applications of (7) there will be cases where one of the independent variables is the degree of advancement defined in § 1.50. Thus

$$\frac{\partial}{\partial x}\frac{\partial z}{\partial \xi} = \frac{\partial}{\partial \xi}\frac{\partial z}{\partial x}. \qquad (3.01.17)$$

The equivalent relation in alternative notation is

$$\frac{\partial}{\partial x}\triangle z = \triangle \frac{\partial z}{\partial x}. \qquad (3.01.18)$$

where the operator symbol $\triangle$, as usual, denotes the increase of any quantity when the particular change being considered takes place. As just one of many concrete examples of (18) we may mention

$$\left(\frac{\partial \triangle H}{\partial P}\right)_T = \triangle \left(\frac{\partial H}{\partial P}\right)_T. \qquad (3.01.19)$$

There is a further relation, which we shall require, between the four quantities w, x, y, z such that any two completely determine the other two.

If we regard w firstly as a function of x, y and secondly as a function of x, z we have

$$dw = \left(\frac{\partial w}{\partial x}\right)_y dx + \left(\frac{\partial w}{\partial y}\right)_x dy. \qquad (3.01.20)$$

$$dw = \left(\frac{\partial w}{\partial x}\right)_z dx + \left(\frac{\partial w}{\partial z}\right)_x dz. \qquad (3.01.21)$$

Substituting from (8) into (21) we obtain

$$dw = \left\{\left(\frac{\partial w}{dx}\right)_z + \left(\frac{\partial w}{\partial z}\right)_x \left(\frac{\partial z}{\partial x}\right)_y\right\} dx + \left(\frac{\partial w}{\partial z}\right)_x \left(\frac{\partial z}{\partial y}\right)_x dy. \qquad (3.01.22)$$

Comparing (22) with (20) and equating coefficients of the independent variations dx, dy we obtain

$$\left(\frac{\partial w}{\partial x}\right)_y = \left(\frac{\partial w}{\partial x}\right)_z + \left(\frac{\partial w}{\partial z}\right)_x \left(\frac{\partial z}{\partial x}\right)_y, \qquad (3.01.23)$$

$$\left(\frac{\partial w}{\partial y}\right)_x = \left(\frac{\partial w}{\partial z}\right)_x \left(\frac{\partial z}{\partial y}\right)_x. \qquad (3.01.24)$$

The relation (24) is rather obvious; for, since x is held constant throughout, we may ignore x and think of w, y, z as three quantities any one of which determines the other two. Then evidently

$$\frac{dw}{dy} = \frac{dw}{dz}\frac{dz}{dy}. \qquad (3.01.25)$$

and (24) merely states that this remains true when w, y, z also depend on x provided x is kept constant. The relation (23) is more important and will be required.

§ 3.02 Choice of Independent Variables

For practical purposes the most convenient independent variables to describe any single phase are, usually, temperature and pressure. We shall therefore require to express most thermodynamic properties as functions of T, P and shall be interested in their partial derivatives with respect to T and P. In the case of gases, as opposed to liquids and solids, it is sometimes convenient to choose as independent variables T, V instead of T, P. We shall accordingly also require to express thermodynamic properties as functions of T, V and shall be interested in their partial derivatives with respect to T and V.

§ 3.03 Coefficient of Thermal Expansion and Isothermal Compressibility

If we regard the volume of a phase of fixed composition as a function of temperature and pressure, we have

$$dV = \left(\frac{\partial V}{\partial T}\right)_P dT + \left(\frac{\partial V}{\partial P}\right)_T dP. \qquad (3.03.1)$$

We define α the *coefficient of* (cubic) *thermal expansion*, by

$$\alpha = \frac{1}{V}\left(\frac{\partial V}{\partial T}\right)_P, \qquad (3.03.2)$$

and $\varkappa$ the (isothermal) *compressibility* by

$$\varkappa = -\frac{1}{V}\left(\frac{\partial V}{\partial P}\right)_T. \qquad (3.03.3)$$

Substituting (2) and (3) into (1) we obtain

$$dV = \alpha V dT - \varkappa V dP, \qquad (3.03.4)$$

or

$$d \log V = \alpha dT - \varkappa dP. \qquad (3.03.5)$$

Alternatively if we choose to regard P as a function of T, V, we have

$$dP = \frac{\alpha}{\varkappa} dT - \frac{1}{\varkappa V} dV. \qquad (3.03.6)$$

By applying the cross-differentiation identity (3.01.7) to (5), we obtain

$$\left(\frac{\partial \alpha}{\partial P}\right)_T = -\left(\frac{\partial \varkappa}{\partial T}\right)_P. \qquad (3.03.7)$$

§ 3.04 Maxwell's Relations

For a closed system in the absence of chemical reactions and in particular for a single phase of fixed content, formulae (1.31.4) and (1.31.6) reduce to

$$dF = -SdT - PdV, \qquad (3.04.1)$$
$$dG = -SdT + VdP. \qquad (3.04.2)$$

Making use of the cross differentiation identity (3.01.7), we have

$$\left(\frac{\partial S}{\partial V}\right)_T = \left(\frac{\partial P}{\partial T}\right)_V = \frac{\alpha}{\varkappa} \qquad (3.04.3)$$

$$\left(\frac{\partial S}{\partial P}\right)_T = -\left(\frac{\partial V}{\partial T}\right)_P = -\alpha V. \qquad (3.04.4)$$

These two relations, due to Maxwell[*], are of great importance as they express the dependence of entropy on volume or pressure in terms of the more readily measurable quantities α and $\varkappa$.

§ 3.05 Dependence of Thermodynamic Functions on Pressure

If, as will usually be our choice, we take as independent variables, other than the composition of each phase, the temperature T and the pressure P the relevant thermodynamic potential is the Gibbs function G and according to (1.33.8) we have

$$\left(\frac{\partial G}{\partial P}\right)_T = V. \qquad (3.05.1)$$

---

[*] Maxwell, *Theory of Heat* (1871 ed.) p. 167.

We also have Maxwell's relation (3. 04. 4)

$$\left(\frac{\partial S}{\partial P}\right)_T = -\,aV. \tag{3.05.2}$$

Since the heat function H is related to G and S by

$$H = G + TS, \tag{3.05.3}$$

we have using (1) and (2)

$$\left(\frac{\partial H}{\partial P}\right)_T = \left(\frac{\partial G}{\partial P}\right)_T + T\left(\frac{\partial S}{\partial P}\right)_T = V\,(1-aT). \tag{3.05.4}$$

When we use the independent variables T, P the functions F, U are much less important than G, H. If nevertheless we should require their dependence on the pressure, it is readily derived as follows. By definition

$$F = G - PV \tag{3.05.5}$$

and so by differentiation with respect to P at constant T

$$\left(\frac{\partial F}{\partial P}\right)_T = \left(\frac{\partial G}{\partial P}\right)_T - V - P\left(\frac{\partial V}{\partial P}\right)_T = -\,P\left(\frac{\partial V}{\partial P}\right)_T. \tag{3.05.6}$$

using (1). Substituting (3. 03. 3) into (6) we obtain

$$\left(\frac{\partial F}{\partial P}\right)_T = \varkappa PV. \tag{3.05.7}$$

Finally since by definition

$$H - U = G - F \tag{3.05.8}$$

we obtain from (1), (4) and (7)

$$\left(\frac{\partial U}{\partial P}\right)_T = V\,(\varkappa P - a\,T). \tag{3.05.9}$$

§ 3. 06   Gibbs–Helmholtz Relation

If, as will usually be our choice, we take as independent variables, other than the composition of each phase, the temperature and the pressure we have for the temperature dependence of the relevant thermodynamic potential G according to (1. 33. 6)

$$\left(\frac{\partial G}{\partial T}\right)_P = -\,S. \tag{3.06.1}$$

If we compare this with the definition of G, namely

$$G = H - TS, \tag{3.06.2}$$

and eliminate S, we obtain

$$H = G - T\left(\frac{\partial G}{\partial T}\right)_P \tag{3.06.3}$$

If we apply this relation to the final state II and to the initial state I in any isothermal process and take the difference, we obtain

$$\Delta H = \Delta G - T \left(\frac{\partial \Delta G}{\partial T} \right)_{P^I, P^{II}},$$ (3.06.4)

where P^I, P^{II} denote the initial and final pressures respectively. Formula (4) is known as the *Gibbs–Helmholtz relation*. This name is also sometimes given to formula (3).

By simple transformation we can rewrite these formulae as

$$\left\{ \frac{\partial (G/T)}{\partial T} \right\}_P = - \frac{H}{T^2},$$ (3.06.5)

$$\left\{ \frac{\partial (\Delta G/T)}{\partial T} \right\}_{P^I, P^{II}} = - \frac{\Delta H}{T^2},$$ (3.06.6)

or alternatively as

$$\left\{ \frac{\partial (G/T)}{\partial (1/T)} \right\}_P = H,$$ (3.06.7)

$$\left\{ \frac{\partial (\Delta G/T)}{\partial (1/T)} \right\}_{P^I, P^{II}} = \Delta H.$$ (3.06.8)

If instead of the Gibbs Function G, we use the Planck function Y defined by

$$Y = - G/T,$$ (3.06.9)

we have

$$\left\{ \frac{\partial Y}{\partial (1/T)} \right\}_P = - H,$$ (3.06.10)

$$\left\{ \frac{\partial (\Delta Y)}{\partial (1/T)} \right\}_{P^I, P^{II}} = - \Delta H.$$ (3.06.11)

§ 3.07 Dependence of Thermodynamic Functions on T, V

As already stated, it is usually convenient to take T, P as independent variables. Only in the case of gases is it sometimes convenient to use instead the independent variables T, V. The dependence of the various thermodynamic functions on these variables is readily obtained and we give the chief results for a phase of fixed composition in the order in which they are conveniently derived without however giving details of the derivations.

$$dF = - S dT - P dV,$$ (3.07.1)

$$dP = \frac{a}{\varkappa} dT - \frac{1}{\varkappa V} dV,$$ (3.07.2)

$$dS = \left(\frac{\partial S}{\partial T} \right)_V dT + \frac{a}{\varkappa} dV,$$ (3.07.3)

$$dU = T \left(\frac{\partial S}{\partial T} \right)_V dT + \left(\frac{aT}{\varkappa} - P \right) dV,$$ (3.07.4)

$$d\left(\frac{F}{T}\right) = -\frac{U}{T^2}\,dT - \frac{P}{T}\,dV.$$

(3.07.5)

$$dJ = \frac{U}{T^2}\,dT + \frac{P}{T}\,dV.$$

(3.07.6)

By applying (5) or (6) to the final state II and the initial state I of an isothermal process and taking the difference we obtain the analogues of the Gibbs–Helmholtz relation

$$\left\{\frac{\partial\,(\Delta F/T)}{\partial T}\right\}_{V^I,V^{II}} = -\frac{\Delta U}{T^2}.$$

(3.07.7)

$$\left\{\frac{\partial\,(\Delta J)}{\partial T}\right\}_{V^I,V^{II}} = \frac{\Delta U}{T^2}.$$

(3.07.8)

These may also be written in the forms

$$\left\{\frac{\partial\,(\Delta F/T)}{\partial\,(1/T)}\right\}_{V^I,V^{II}} = \Delta U,$$

(3.07.9)

$$\left\{\frac{\partial\,(\Delta J)}{\partial\,(1/T)}\right\}_{V^I,V^{II}} = -\Delta U.$$

(3..07.10)

§ 3.08   Use of Jacobians

Many thermodynamic identities, including those obtained in the preceding sections, can be obtained rapidly and elegantly by the use of Jacobians. The procedures are due to Norman Shaw *, who has shown how to apply them to obtain a tremendous number of identities, some important, others merely amusing. We shall here give a brief sketch of the method, which we shall illustrate by a few simple examples. We would however emphasize that all the simple and most important relations are deduced in this book without using Jacobians, so that the reader not interested in their use may omit this section which does not affect the rest of the book.

We recall that Jacobians are defined by

$$\frac{\partial\,(x,\,y)}{\partial\,(a,\,\beta)} \equiv -\frac{\partial\,(y,\,x)}{\partial\,(a,\,\beta)} \equiv \left(\frac{\partial x}{\partial a}\right)_\beta \left(\frac{\partial y}{\partial\beta}\right)_\alpha - \left(\frac{\partial x}{\partial\beta}\right)_\alpha \left(\frac{\partial y}{\partial a}\right)_\beta,$$

(3.08.1)

and that they obey the multiplicative law

$$\frac{\partial\,(x,\,y)}{\partial\,(u,\,v)}\,\frac{\partial\,(u,\,v)}{\partial\,(a,\,\beta)} = \frac{\partial\,(x,\,y)}{\partial\,(a,\,\beta)},$$

(3.08.2)

which can be derived by simple geometrical or algebraical considerations on transformation of coordinates.

As particular cases of (1) we have

$$\left(\frac{\partial x}{\partial a}\right)_\beta = \frac{\partial\,(x,\,\beta)}{\partial\,(a,\,\beta)} = -\frac{\partial\,(\beta,\,x)}{\partial\,(a,\,\beta)}.$$

(3.08.3)

$$\left(\frac{\partial y}{\partial\beta}\right)_\alpha = \frac{\partial\,(a,\,y)}{\partial\,(a,\,\beta)} = -\frac{\partial\,(y,\,a)}{\partial\,(a,\,\beta)}.$$

(3.08.4)

---

* Norman Shaw, *Phil. Trans. Roy. Soc.* A (1935) **234** 299.

Using (3) and (4) we derive from (2)

$$\left(\frac{\partial x}{\partial z}\right)_y = \frac{\partial (x, y)}{\partial (z, y)} = \frac{\partial (x, y)}{\partial (a, \beta)} \bigg/ \frac{\partial (z, y)}{\partial (a, \beta)}. \tag{3.08.5}$$

We now replace a, β by the pair of quantities which we regard as the usually most convenient independent variables, namely the temperature T and the pressure P. We further introduce the following new notation

$$J(x, y) \equiv \frac{\partial (x, y)}{\partial (T, P)} \equiv \left(\frac{\partial x}{\partial T}\right)_P \left(\frac{\partial y}{\partial P}\right)_T - \left(\frac{\partial x}{\partial P}\right)_T \left(\frac{\partial y}{\partial T}\right)_P. \tag{3.08.6}$$

In particular we have

$$\left(\frac{\partial x}{\partial T}\right)_P = J(x, P) = -J(P, x), \tag{3.08.7}$$

$$\left(\frac{\partial x}{\partial P}\right)_T = -J(x, T) = J(T, x). \tag{3.08.8}$$

Using our new notation we have instead of (5)

$$\left(\frac{\partial x}{\partial z}\right)_y = \frac{J(x, y)}{J(z, y)}. \tag{3.08.9}$$

The relations (6) and (9) together enable us to express any quantity of the type $(\partial x/\partial z)_y$ in terms of the partial differential coefficients of x, y, z with respect to T, P.

We shall illustrate by two examples, the first a useful one, the second more far-fetched. We have

$$\left(\frac{\partial T}{\partial P}\right)_H = \frac{J(T, H)}{J(P, H)} = -\left(\frac{\partial H}{\partial P}\right)_T \bigg/ \left(\frac{\partial H}{\partial T}\right)_P. \tag{3.08.10}$$

a relation which we shall meet again in § 4.17, where it is derived more simply by using (3.01.14).

We now take a more complicated, but less useful, example

$$\left(\frac{\partial H}{\partial G}\right)_F = \frac{J(H, F)}{J(G, F)} = \frac{\left(\frac{\partial H}{\partial T}\right)_P \left(\frac{\partial F}{\partial P}\right)_T - \left(\frac{\partial H}{\partial P}\right)_T \left(\frac{\partial F}{\partial T}\right)_P}{\left(\frac{\partial G}{\partial T}\right)_P \left(\frac{\partial F}{\partial P}\right)_T - \left(\frac{\partial G}{\partial P}\right)_T \left(\frac{\partial F}{\partial T}\right)_P}, \tag{3.08.11}$$

in which all the derivatives on the right can be expressed in terms of readily measurably quantities. Thus the derivatives of G occurring on the right of (11) have the simple values

$$\left(\frac{\partial G}{\partial T}\right)_P = -S. \tag{3.08.12}$$

$$\left(\frac{\partial G}{\partial P}\right)_T = V. \tag{3.08.13}$$

The values of the derivatives of H are given by

$$\left(\frac{\partial H}{\partial T}\right)_P = \left(\frac{\partial [G+TS]}{\partial T}\right)_P = T\left(\frac{\partial S}{\partial T}\right)_P. \qquad (3.08.14)$$

$$\left(\frac{\partial H}{\partial P}\right)_T = \left(\frac{\partial [G+TS]}{\partial P}\right)_T = \left(\frac{\partial G}{\partial P}\right)_T + T\left(\frac{\partial S}{\partial P}\right)_T = V(1-aT). \qquad (3.08.15)$$

Similarly the values of the derivatives of F are given by

$$\left(\frac{\partial F}{\partial T}\right)_P = \left(\frac{\partial [G-PV]}{\partial T}\right)_P = \left(\frac{\partial G}{\partial T}\right)_P - P\left(\frac{\partial V}{\partial T}\right)_P = -(S+aVP). \qquad (3.08.16)$$

$$\left(\frac{\partial F}{\partial P}\right)_T = \left(\frac{\partial [G-PV]}{\partial P}\right)_T = -P\left(\frac{\partial V}{\partial P}\right)_T = \varkappa PV. \qquad (3.08.17)$$

Now substituting (12) to (17) into (11) we obtain

$$\left(\frac{\partial H}{\partial G}\right)_F = \frac{C\varkappa PV + V(1-aT)(S+aVP)}{-S\varkappa PV + V(S+aVP)}$$

$$= \frac{C\varkappa P + (1-aT)(S+aVP)}{-S\varkappa P + (S+aVP)}, \qquad (3.08.18)$$

where we have used the symbol C to denote $(\partial H/\partial T)_P$.

These illustrative examples by no means exhaust the uses to which Jacobians can be put. The reader who is interested is referred to the original papers by Norman Shaw.

§ 3.09   Reversible Cycles

Suppose a system is taken through a complete cycle of states. Then as its final state is identical with its initial state, its entropy must obviously be the same at the end as at the beginning. Thus

$$\triangle S = 0, \qquad \text{(any cycle)}. \qquad (3.09.1)$$

If at all stages the system is in equilibrium, so that no irreversible (natural) change takes place, then

$$\triangle S = \Sigma_i \frac{q_i}{T_i}, \qquad \text{(reversible changes)}, \qquad (3.09.2)$$

where q_i denotes the heat absorbed at the temperature T_i and the summation extends over all the temperatures through which the system passes. Substituting (2) into (1) we obtain

$$\Sigma_i \frac{q_i}{T_i} = 0, \qquad \text{(reversible cycle)}. \qquad (3.09.3)$$

Evidently, since T_i is always positive, some of the q_i's must be positive and some negative. It is convenient to modify our notation so as to distinguish between the positive and negative q_i's. We accordingly replace (3) by

$$\Sigma_r \frac{q_r}{T_r} = \Sigma_s \frac{Q_s}{T_s}, \qquad \text{(reversible cycle)}, \qquad (3.09.4)$$

where each q_r is a positive quantity of heat taken in at the temperature T_r and each Q_s is a positive quantity of heat given out at the temperature T_s.

According to the first principle of thermodynamics the work $-w$ done by the system during the cycle is given by

$$-w = \Sigma_i\, q_i = \Sigma_r\, q_r - \Sigma_s\, Q_s. \qquad (3.09.5)$$

The ratio η defined by

$$\eta = \frac{-w}{\Sigma_r\, q_r} = \frac{\Sigma_r\, q_r - \Sigma_s\, Q_s}{\Sigma_r\, q_r} = 1 - \frac{\Sigma_s\, Q_s}{\Sigma_r\, q_r}, \qquad (3.09.6)$$

is called by engineers the *thermodynamic efficiency* of the cycle.

Let us suppose that there is a maximum temperature T_{max} and a minimum temperature T_{min}, between which temperatures the cycle is confined. The following question arises. Subject to this restriction on the temperatures, what is the maximum possible value of η? The answer is obviously obtained by making

$$T_r = T_{max}, \qquad \text{(all } r\text{)}; \qquad (3.09.7)$$

$$T_s = T_{min}, \qquad \text{(all } s\text{)}. \qquad (3.09.8)$$

This means that positive absorption of heat occurs only at the highest temperature T_{max} and positive loss of heat occurs only at the lowest temperature T_{min}. No heat is exchanged with the surroundings at any temperature intermediate between T_{max} and T_{min}. In other words the passages from T_{max} to T_{min} and the reverse are adiabatic. Thus the cycle consists entirely of isothermal absorption of heat at T_{max}, isothermal emission of heat at T_{min}, and adiabatic changes from T_{max} to T_{min} and from T_{min} to T_{max}. Such a cycle was first considered by Carnot and is called *Carnot's cycle*.

For Carnot's cycle we have by substituting from (7) and (8) into (4)

$$\frac{\Sigma_r\, q_r}{T_{max}} = \frac{\Sigma_s\, Q_s}{T_{min}}, \qquad \text{(Carnot's cycle)}. \qquad (3.09.9)$$

Now substituting from (9) into (6) we obtain

$$\eta = 1 - \frac{T_{min}}{T_{max}}, \qquad \text{(Carnot's cycle)}. \qquad (3.09.10)$$

There is sometimes confusion between Carnot's cycle and reversible cycles. It will be observed that Carnot's cycle is a very special case of a reversible cycle.

A completely isothermal cycle is a special case of Carnot's cycle. For such a cycle

$$T_{max} = T_{min} = T \qquad \text{(isothermal cycle)} \qquad (3.09.11)$$
$$\Sigma_r q_r = \Sigma_s Q_s \qquad \text{(isothermal cycle)} \qquad (3.09.12)$$
$$w = 0 \qquad \text{(isothermal cycle)} \qquad (3.09.13)$$
$$\eta = 0 \qquad \text{(isothermal cycle)} \qquad (3.09.14)$$

Formula (13) is known as *Moutier's theorem.*

We shall have no occasion to make any further reference to cycles. They are important in engineering thermodynamics for the treatment of engines and refrigerators, but these fall outside the subject matter of this book.

CHAPTER IV

SYSTEMS OF A SINGLE COMPONENT

§ 4.01   Thermal Condition of Internal Stability

Consider a homogeneous pure single substance, that is to say a single phase of one component. Let its entropy be S, its volume V and its energy U. Imagine one half the mass of this phase to change so as have an entropy $\frac{1}{2}(S + \delta S)$ and volume $\frac{1}{2}V$ while the other half changes so as to have an entropy $\frac{1}{2}(S - \delta S)$ and volume $\frac{1}{2}V$. According to Taylor's expansion the energy of the first half becomes

$$\frac{1}{2}\left\{ U + \frac{\partial U}{\partial S}\, \delta S + \frac{1}{2}\frac{\partial^2 U}{\partial S^2}\,(\delta S)^2 \right\}. \tag{4.01.1}$$

neglecting small quantities of third and higher orders; all partial differentiations in (1) are at constant V. The energy of the second half becomes similarly

$$\frac{1}{2}\left\{ U - \frac{\partial U}{\partial S}\, \delta S + \frac{1}{2}\frac{\partial^2 U}{\partial S^2}\,(\delta S)^2 \right\}. \tag{4.01.2}$$

Hence by addition the energy of the whole system has increased by the second order small quantity

$$\frac{1}{2}\left(\frac{\partial^2 U}{\partial S^2} \right)_V (\delta S)^2. \tag{4.01.3}$$

while the total entropy and volume remain unchanged. Now a condition for a system to be in *stable* equilibrium is that, for given values of the entropy and the volume, the energy should be a *minimum*. If then the original state of the system was *stable*, the change considered must lead to an *increase* of energy and the expression (3) must be positive. Hence we obtain as a necessary condition for stable equilibrium

$$\left(\frac{\partial^2 U}{\partial S^2} \right)_V > 0. \tag{4.01.4}$$

Since according to (1.29.4) or (1.30.1)

$$\left(\frac{\partial U}{\partial S} \right)_V = T, \tag{4.01.5}$$

we can replace (4) by

$$\left(\frac{\partial S}{\partial T} \right)_V > 0. \tag{4.01.6}$$

The physical meaning of (6) is that when at constant volume heat is supplied to a stable phase its temperature is raised.

§ 4.02   Hydrostatic Condition of Internal Stability

Consider again a single phase of one component. Let its temperature[b] be T, its volume V and its free energy F. Imagine half the mass to change so as to have a volume $\frac{1}{2}(V + \delta V)$, and the other half to change so as to have a volume $\frac{1}{2}(V - \delta V)$, the temperature remaining uniform and unchanged. Then by an argument precisely analogous to that of the previous section we find that the free energy of the whole system has increased by the second order small quantity

$$\frac{1}{2}\left(\frac{\partial^2 F}{\partial V^2}\right)_T (\delta V)^2, \tag{4.02.1}$$

while the temperature and total volume are unchanged. Now a condition for a system to be in *stable* equilibrium is that for given values of temperature and volume, the free energy should be a *minimum*. If then the original state of the system was *stable*, the change considered must lead to an *increase* of free energy and the expression (1) must be positive. Hence we obtain as a necessary condition for stable equilibrium

$$\left(\frac{\partial^2 F}{\partial V^2}\right)_T > 0. \tag{4.02.2}$$

Since according to (1.31.4)

$$\left(\frac{\partial F}{\partial V}\right)_T = -P, \tag{4.02.3}$$

we can replace (2) by

$$\left(\frac{\partial V}{\partial P}\right)_T < 0, \tag{4.02.4}$$

or using (3.03.3), since V is always positive,

$$\varkappa > 0. \tag{4.02.5}$$

This means that when the pressure of a stable phase is increased, the volume must decrease. Whilst this condition is necessary, we shall see in § 4.49 that it is not sufficient for stability.

§ 4.03   Other Conditions of Internal Stability

By reasoning similar to that of the two previous sections, we can obtain other conditions necessary for internal equilibrium of a single phase of one component. In particular we could obtain the conditions

$$\left(\frac{\partial S}{\partial T}\right)_P > 0, \tag{4.03.1}$$

and

$$\left(\frac{\partial V}{\partial P}\right)_S < 0. \tag{4.03.2}$$

Such other conditions are however not independent but can be derived from the previous ones. In fact we shall in § 4.09 find that

$$\left(\frac{\partial S}{\partial T}\right)_P \geqslant \left(\frac{\partial S}{\partial T}\right)_V, \tag{4.03.3}$$

so that (1) follows from (4.01.6). We shall also find in § 4.26 that

$$\left(\frac{\partial V}{\partial P}\right)_S \bigg/ \left(\frac{\partial V}{\partial P}\right)_T = \left(\frac{\partial S}{\partial T}\right)_V \bigg/ \left(\frac{\partial S}{\partial T}\right)_P, \tag{4.03.4}$$

so that (2) follows from (4.02.4) with (4.01.6) and (1).

§ 4.04   Dependence of Entropy on Temperature

The experimental determination of entropy and absolute temperature are inter-linked. We have not yet described how either can be directly or conveniently measured. In § 4.13 we shall describe an especially convenient way of measuring absolute temperature. Anticipating this result, that is to say assuming we have a thermometer which measures absolute temperature, we shall now describe how we can determine the dependence of entropy on temperature at constant pressure.

For a single closed phase, we have according to (1.31.5)

$$dH = TdS + VdP, \tag{4.04.1}$$

or if we keep the pressure constant

$$dH = TdS, \qquad (P \text{ const.}). \tag{4.04.2}$$

If then we supply heat q to a single component system, since the change in the system must be reversible, quite regardless of whether the process of supplying the heat is reversible (see § 1.15), we have

$$q = dH = TdS, \qquad (P \text{ const.}). \tag{4.04.3}$$

Furthermore if we supply the heat by means of an electric element, the heat will be equal to the electrical work done on the element. To be precise, if the potential difference across the element is E and the current flowing is i, then in a time t the heat given up by the element to the system is $E\,i\,t$. Since E, i and t are all measurable we can calculate q. We see then that, apart from experimental difficulties, there is no difficulty in principle in measuring increases of H. As already mentioned we are postulating, in anticipation of § 4.13, the availability of a thermometer which measures T. We thus obtain a direct experimental relationship between T and H, or rather changes in H which itself contains an arbitrary additive constant.

As an illustration we show in Fig. 4.1 the experimental data * for one mole of H_2O at a constant pressure of one atmosphere. The first curve on the left applies to ice from 0 °K to 273.16 °K, at which temperature the

---

* Giauque and Stout, *J. Am. Chem. Soc.* (1936) 58 1144.

ice melts; the value of the heat function then rises at constant temperature by an amount equal to the molar heat of fusion. As this change would run off the paper the scale of the curve for the liquid has been shifted down-

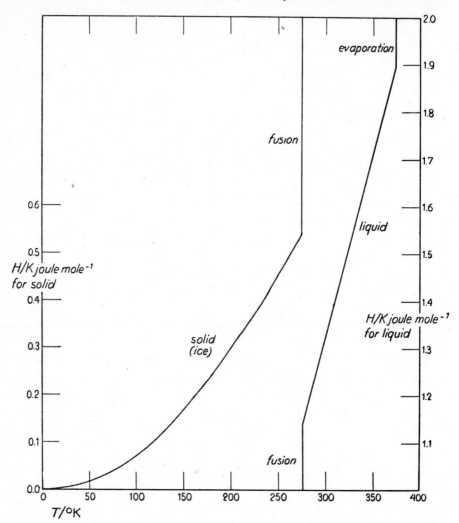

Fig. 4. 1.   Heat function of H_2O at one atmosphere.

wards by 1 kilojoule. This curve on the right of the figure runs from $273.16 \,^{\circ}K$ to $373.16 \,^{\circ}K$ at which temperature the water boils; the value of the heat function again rises at constant temperature and runs off the paper.

In Fig. 4. 2 we show the data in a somewhat different form, $(\partial H/\partial T)_P$ being now plotted against $\log T$. The three separate curves apply to ice, liquid water and steam respectively. From (2) we have

$$S = \int dS = \int \frac{dH}{T} = \int \left(\frac{\partial H}{\partial T}\right)_P \frac{dT}{T} = \int \left(\frac{\partial H}{\partial T}\right)_P d\log T. \qquad (4.04.4)$$

We see then that apart from an arbitrary constant the entropy of ice at a temperature T is equal to the area under the part of the curve to the left of T. In particular the entropy of ice at the fusion-point exceeds that

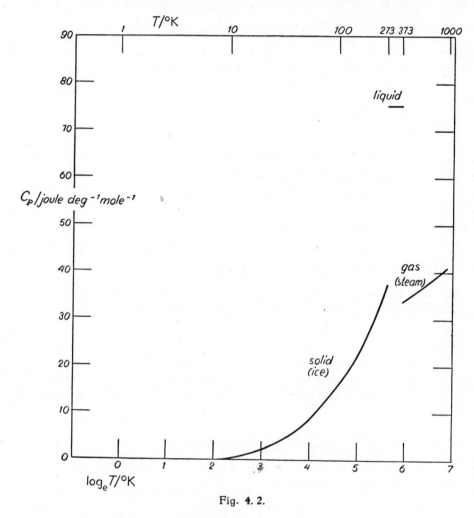

Fig. 4. 2.

at $0\,°K$ by an amount corresponding to the whole area under the ice curve. This amounts to 38.09 joule/mole deg.

When the ice changes to liquid water there is an increase of entropy called the *entropy of fusion* equal to the heat of fusion divided by the temperature. Thus

$$\triangle S = \frac{\triangle H}{T} = \frac{6007 \text{ joule/mole}}{273.16 \text{ deg.}} = 21.99 \text{ joule/mole deg.}$$

Suppose we wish to know by how much the entropy of steam at $1000\,°K$ and 1 atmosphere exceeds the entropy of ice at $0\,°K$. We have to add the following contributions.

(a)   Ice at $0\,°K \rightarrow$ ice at $273.16\,°K$

$\triangle S = 38.09$ joule/mole deg..   (area under ice curve)

(b)   Ice at $273.16\,°K \rightarrow$ liquid water at $273.16\,°K$

$$\triangle S = \frac{\triangle H}{T} = \frac{6007 \text{ joule/mole}}{273.16 \text{ deg.}} = 21.99 \text{ joule/mole deg.}$$

(c)   Water at $273.16\,°K \rightarrow$ water at $373.16\,°K$

$\triangle S = 23.52$ joule/mole deg.,   (area under water curve)

(d)   Water at $373.16\,°K \rightarrow$ steam at $373.16\,°K$

$$\triangle S = \frac{\triangle H}{T} = \frac{40656 \text{ joule/mole}}{373.16 \text{ deg.}} = 108.95 \text{ joule/mole deg.}$$

(e)   Steam at $373.16\,°K \rightarrow$ steam at $1000\,°K$

$\triangle S = 35.8$ joule/mole deg.,   (area under steam curve)

By addition we obtain for the change

Ice at $0\,°K \rightarrow$ steam at $1000\,°K$ (both at 1 atm.)

$\triangle S = 228.4$ joule/mole deg.

In the case of some substances there may be several solid phases with transition temperatures at which the entropy increase $\triangle S$ is equal to the increase $\triangle H$ divided by T, but such transitions cause no further complication.

We see then that the determination of changes in the entropy of any single substance through any range of temperature at constant pressure becomes straightforward provided the heat input and absolute temperature can be measured.

§ 4. 05   Heat Capacity at Constant Pressure

In the previous section we saw that the determination of entropy requires us to use the relation

$$T \left(\frac{\partial S}{\partial T} \right)_P = \left(\frac{\partial H}{\partial T} \right)_P . \qquad (4.05.1)$$

This quantity is called the *heat capacity at constant pressure* of the system. If referred to one mole of substance this is called the *molar heat capacity at constant pressure* and will be denoted by C, or by C_P when it is desired to emphasize the contrast with another quantity C_V defined in § 4. 08. Thus using the subscript m to denote *molar* quantities

$$C = C_P = T \left(\frac{\partial S_m}{\partial T} \right)_P = \left(\frac{\partial H_m}{\partial T} \right)_P . \qquad (4.05.2)$$

The real importance of C is that it forms the connecting link between S and H. One measures directly H as a function of T and then determines

S by the relation (1). Importance was in the past attached to C for a completely different, accidental and inadequate reason, namely that for many substances at the most usual temperatures C happens to be approximately independent of the temperature. For example we notice from Fig. 4.2 that C is nearly constant for liquid water, only roughly constant for steam, but not at all constant for ice.

§ 4.06 So-called Mechanical Equivalent of Heat

Before the classical experiments of Joule, the relationship between work, heat and energy was not understood. These experiments established that within the experimental error the work or energy input required to raise the temperature of a given mass of water through a given temperature range is independent of the particular mechanism used. The formulation of the first principle of thermodynamics is largely based on these experiments and later repetitions and improvements of them. Since Joule's experiments were performed before the formulation of the first principle, the terminology of Joule was necessarily different from the terminology based on familiarity with the principles of thermodynamics. Joule described some of his experiments as the "determination of the mechanical equivalent of heat". Once the principles of thermodynamics are understood, this phrase becomes meaningless. What Joule in fact did was

(a)   to establish an experimental basis for the formulation of the first principle of thermodynamics;

(b)   to measure the *heat capacity of water.*

Before the first principle of thermodynamics was formulated or understood the unit of heat was the quantity of heat required to raise the temperature of one gram of water by one degree centigrade and this unit was called the *calorie.* Work was however measured in joules. It is found that the heat capacity of liquid water is about 4.18 joule/gram degree but in fact varies appreciably with the temperature. Nowadays almost all accurate thermal experiments involve measurements of volts, amperes and seconds leading to energy values in joules. Moreover the International Union of Physics has recently (1948) recommended * that all accurate calorimetric data should be expressed in joules. It is difficult to understand why the use of the calorie as a unit persists, except as a habit. The most careful experimental workers have in fact abandoned the old definition of the calorie and have replaced it by the more satisfactory definition

$$1 \text{ calorie} = 4.1840 \text{ absolute joules.}$$

The calorie thus defined is called the *thermochemical calorie.*

As already mentioned the heat capacity of water is approximately, but by no means exactly, independent of the temperature. Its value

---

*   *International Union of Physics, Document* SG 48—6.

is very near 1 cal./gram deg. at 290 °K. The experimental values at a few other temperatures are, according to Osborne, Stimson and Ginnings (1939), as follows:

$$
\begin{array}{llllll}
\text{At} & 0.°\,\text{C} & 4.2176 \text{ abs. joule/gram deg.} \\
& 15°\,\text{C} & 4.1857 & \text{,,} & \text{,,} & \text{,,} & \text{,,} \\
& 17°\,\text{C} & 4.1839 & \text{,,} & \text{,,} & \text{,,} & \text{,,} \\
& 18°\,\text{C} & 4.1831 & \text{,,} & \text{,,} & \text{,,} & \text{,,} \\
& 25°\,\text{C} & 4.1795 & \text{,,} & \text{,,} & \text{,,} & \text{,,}
\end{array}
$$

§ 4. 07 Dependence of Entropy on Pressure

In § 4.04 we saw how the variation of entropy with the temperature at a constant pressure is determined experimentally. In order to determine the entropy as a function of temperature and pressure, this procedure has to be supplemented by a determination of the dependence of entropy on pressure at constant temperature. This dependence is given according to Maxwell's relation (3.04.4) by

$$\left(\frac{\partial S}{\partial P}\right)_T = -aV, \tag{4.07.1}$$

which integrated becomes

$$S(T, P^{II}) - S(T, P^{I}) = -\int_{P^{I}}^{P^{II}} a\,V\,dP. \tag{4.07.2}$$

If we differentiate (1) with respect to T, keeping P constant, and multiply by T we obtain

$$\left(\frac{\partial C}{\partial P}\right)_T = -T\left\{\frac{\partial(aV)}{\partial T}\right\}_P = -a^2 T V - T\left(\frac{\partial a}{\partial T}\right)_P V. \tag{4.07.3}$$

The second term on the right will usually be small compared with the first for solids and liquids; for gases on the contrary the two terms are nearly equal and opposite.

§ 4. 08 Heat Capacity at Constant Volume

In §§ 4.04 — 4.07 we have collected the most important formulae required to determine the entropy in terms of temperature and pressure. There is an analogous set of relations for the alternative choice of temperature and volume as independent variables. Except for gases these relations are considerably less used than those relating to the independent variables T, P. We shall refer to them quite briefly, without giving detailed derivations; these are in all cases quite analogous to those in the T, P system.

For the dependence of entropy on temperature at constant volume, we have

$$\left(\frac{\partial S}{\partial T}\right)_V = \frac{1}{T}\left(\frac{\partial U}{\partial T}\right)_V, \tag{4.08.1}$$

which integrated becomes

$$S(T_2, V) - S(T_1, V) = \int_{T_1}^{T_2}\left(\frac{\partial U}{\partial T}\right)_V \frac{dT}{T}. \tag{4.08.2}$$

Correspondingly for the dependence of entropy on volume at constant temperature, we have according to Maxwell's relation (3.04.3)

$$\left(\frac{\partial S}{\partial V}\right)_T = \frac{\alpha}{\varkappa},$$ (4.08.3)

which integrated becomes

$$S(T, V^{II}) - S(T, V^{I}) = \int_{V^{I}}^{V^{II}} \frac{\alpha}{\varkappa} \, dV.$$ (4.08.4)

The quantity $(\partial U/\partial T)_V$ in formula (1) is called the *heat capacity at constant volume* of the system. The corresponding quantity referred to one mole is called the *molar heat capacity at constant volume* and is denoted by C_V. Thus

$$C_V = T\left(\frac{\partial S_m}{\partial T}\right)_V = \left(\frac{\partial U_m}{\partial T}\right)_V.$$ (4.08.5)

§ 4.09 Relation between Heat Capacities

If in the general relation (3.01.23) we substitute S for w, T for x, P for y and V for z we find

$$\left(\frac{\partial S}{\partial T}\right)_P = \left(\frac{\partial S}{\partial T}\right)_V + \left(\frac{\partial S}{\partial V}\right)_T \left(\frac{\partial V}{\partial T}\right)_P.$$ (4.09.1)

Substituting from (3.03.2) and from Maxwell's relation (3.04.3) into (1), we obtain

$$\left(\frac{\partial S}{\partial T}\right)_P = \left(\frac{\partial S}{\partial T}\right)_V + \frac{\alpha^2 V}{\varkappa}.$$ (4.09.2)

Applying (2) to one mole, multiplying by T and using the definitions (4.05.2) and (4.08.5) of C_P and C_V respectively we find

$$C_P = C_V + \frac{\alpha^2 T V_m}{\varkappa}.$$ (4.09.3)

Since in a stable phase none of the quantities $\alpha^2, T, V_m, \varkappa$ can ever be negative, it follows that C_P can never be less than C_V.

C_V is much more difficult to measure than C_P. If the value of C_V is required, it is usual to measure C_P and then calculate C_V from (3). C_V is altogether less important than C_P. There seems to be a widespread belief that in the comparison of a theoretical model with experimental data the most suitable quantity for the comparison is C_V. This is however a misconception. Any theoretical model susceptible to explicit analytical treatment, such as for example Debye's model of a crystal, discussed in § 4.37, leads to an explicit formula for the free energy and so by differentiation with respect to T to explicit formulae for the energy and the entropy, both of which are directly measurable as a function of temperature. These are clearly the most suitable quantities for comparison between a theoretical model and experimental data. There is no reason or excuse for a further differentiation to obtain a heat capacity except in the case that the agreement between theory and experiment is so good that a more sensitive test is required. This may in fact be the case for gases, but it is certainly not the case for solids or liquids.

§ 4. 10   Condensed Phases and Gases

Solids and liquids, which we shall class together under the name *condensed phases,* are under most conditions sharply distinguished from gases by a striking difference in compressibility. It is true that in the neighbourhood of the critical point, as we shall see in § 4. 48 the distinction between liquid and gas disappears, but at least for liquids or solids at temperatures well below the critical temperature and for gases at pressures well below the critical pressure the contrast is striking.

In a condensed phase at a given temperature the compressibility is small and practically independent of the pressure. That is to say that to a first approximation the volume is independent of the pressure and to a better approximation decreases linearly with the pressure. In a gas on the other hand the compressibility is much greater and far from independent of the pressure. In fact it is at least roughly true that the volume of a gas varies inversely as the pressure, according to *Boyle's Law.* In other words it is PV, not V, which to a first approximation is independent of P.

§ 4. 11   Isothermal Behaviour of a Gas

It is reasonable to expect that the volume of any phase at constant temperature can be expressed as a power series in the pressure. In view of what was said in the previous section, the leading term will in the case of a gas be an inverse first power. We may accordingly write

$$V = \frac{A}{P} + B + C'P + \dots \qquad (4.11.1)$$

In principle the number of terms is indefinite, depending on the accuracy aimed at. Up to quite high pressures, of say a hundred atmospheres, it is usually unnecessary to use terms beyond $C'P$. At pressures up to a few atmospheres even this term is usually negligible, only the terms A/P and B being required. All the coefficients $A, B, C', \dots$ of course depend on the temperature, but not on the pressure.

In the treatment of gases it is sometimes convenient to regard T, V rather than T, P as independent variables. We then express the pressure as a power series in the density or in the reciprocal of the volume. We accordingly write

$$P = \frac{A}{V}\left\{1 + \frac{B}{V} + \frac{C}{V^2} + \dots\right\}. \qquad (4.11.2)$$

The coefficients A and B are common to the two formulae (1) and (2); C and C' are connected by

$$C = B^2 + AC'. \qquad (4.11.3)$$

There are more complicated relations between any higher coefficients which may be included.

B is called the *second virial coefficient*; C is called the *third virial coefficient* and so on.

It is purely a question of convenience or taste whether one uses a formula of type (1) or of type (2). For our immediate purpose, it is more convenient to use (1). Fortunately at ordinary pressures all terms beyond the second are usually negligible and either formula then reduces to

$$V = \frac{A}{P} + B, \qquad \text{(low pressures).} \qquad (4.11.4)$$

From (1) we readily obtain the Gibbs Function G as a function of pressure by substituting into (3.05.1) and integrating. We thus find

$$G(T, P) - G(T, P^\dagger) = A \log \frac{P}{P^\dagger} + B(P - P^\dagger) + \tfrac{1}{2} C'(P^2 - P^{\dagger 2}) \qquad (4.11.5)$$

where $P^\dagger$ is an arbitrarily chosen standard pressure.

We obtain for the heat function H by substituting (5) into (3.06.3)

$$H(T, P) - H(T, P^\dagger) = \left(A - T \frac{dA}{dT}\right) \log \frac{P}{P^\dagger}$$

$$+ \left(B - T \frac{dB}{dT}\right)(P - P^\dagger) + \frac{1}{2}\left(C' - T \frac{dC'}{dT}\right)(P^2 - P^{\dagger 2}). \qquad (4.11.6)$$

§ 4.12 Throttling Experiment

In the previous section we set up an empirical formula for V as a function of P based on experiment. From this we deduced a formula for G and thence a formula for H. We shall now consider the comparison between this formula for H and experiment.

The experiment which supplies the most direct information concerning the dependence of H on the pressure at constant temperature is known as *throttling*. The first experiment of this type was performed by Joule and Lord Kelvin (William Thomson); it is accordingly often called the *Joule–Thomson experiment*. In this experiment a stream of gas in a thermally insulated container is forced through a plug, the pressure being greater on the near side than on the far side and the temperatures of the gas stream approaching and leaving the plug are measured *on an arbitrary scale;* we denote the temperatures on this scale by θ to distinguish them sharply from absolute temperatures T, which we do not yet know how to measure. Consider now the whole system in a steady state such that in each unit of time a certain mass of gas is pushed in at a pressure P_1 and during the same time an equal mass of gas streams away at a pressure P_2. We use the subscript 1 to denote the state of the gas being pushed in and the subscript 2 to denote that of the gas streaming away. Then during the time considered a mass of gas of pressure P_2, volume V_2, temperature θ_2 and energy U_2 is displaced by an equal mass of pressure P_1, volume V_1, temperature θ_1 and energy U_1. During this time the work done on the system is $P_1 V_1 - P_2 V_2$. Since the system is supposed thermally insulated this work must be equal to the increase in energy of the system. Thus

$$U_2 - U_1 = P_1 V_1 - P_2 V_2. \qquad (4.12.1)$$

Hence according to the definition (1.31.2) of H, we have

$$H_2 = H_1. \qquad (4.12.2)$$

or choosing θ, P as independent variables

$$H(\theta_1, P_1) = H(\theta_2, P_2). \qquad (4.12.3)$$

Suppose that the effect of throttling is to cool the gas, so that θ_2 is a lower temperature than θ_1, then there is no difficulty in principle in heating the throttled gas at constant pressure so as to restore its temperature from θ_2 to θ_1. If the heat required for this purpose is measured, we then know the value of

$$H(\theta_1, P_2) - H(\theta_2, P_2), \qquad (4.12.4)$$

which according to (3) is equal to

$$H(\theta_1, P_2) - H(\theta_1, P_1). \qquad (4.12.5)$$

If on the contrary the effect of throttling is to warm the gas, then we must do a subsidiary experiment to determine the heat required to raise the temperature of the gas at the pressure P_2 from θ_1 to θ_2. We thus obtain an experimental value of

$$H(\theta_2, P_2) - H(\theta_1, P_2) \qquad (4.12.6)$$

which according to (3) is equal to

$$H(\theta_1, P_1) - H(\theta_1, P_2). \qquad (4.12.7)$$

In either case we obtain experimental values of $H(\theta_1, P_2) - H(\theta_1, P_1)$ positive in the former case, negative in the latter. It is important to notice that this experiment does not require any knowledge of how the arbitrary θ scale of temperature is related to the absolute scale or to any other scale.

We shall now describe the experimental results obtained. It is found that, whatever the temperature, $H(P_1) - H(P_2)$ is at least approximately proportional to $P_1 - P_2$ and not very sensitive to the absolute magnitude of P_1. It is quite certain that at very low values of P_2, the value of $H(P_1) - H(P_2)$ does not tend towards infinity, which is what one should expect from formula (4.11.6) owing to the term in $\log P$. In short the Joule–Thomson experiment shows that the first term on the right of formula (4.11.6) is in fact missing and the linear term in P is in fact the leading one.

§ 4.13 Measurement of Absolute Temperature

In principle to determine T, one should measure $\triangle H$ and $\triangle G$ for the same isothermal process and by comparing these obtain a differential equation for T. In particular, we can determine the coefficients A, B, C' in the formula for G simply by pressure measurements and one can obtain independent measurements of $(A-T\,dA/dT)$, $(B-T\,dB/dT)$, $(C'-T\,dC'/dT)$ the coefficients in H, from the throttling experiment. By comparison we obtain information concerning T, but admittedly in a rather awkward form.

To our agreeable surprise the information is in a strikingly convenient form in the case of the coefficient A. The Joule–Thomson experiment shows unmistakably that H contains no term tending to infinity as P tends to zero, that is to say no term in log P. Hence from (4. 11. 5) we conclude that

$$A-T\frac{dA}{dT}=0 \qquad (4.13.1)$$

which is equivalent to

$$A \propto T. \qquad (4.13.2)$$

At last we have found a simple, direct and reliable way of determining the ratio of any two absolute temperatures. We use as a thermometer a fixed quantity of gas. We measure several pairs of values of P, V at the same temperature and extrapolate the product PV to $P = 0$, thus obtaining the value of A. We repeat this at another temperature thus obtaining another value of A. Then the ratio of these two values of A is equal to the ratio of the two values of T. Having thus established a way of determining the ratio of any two temperatures, the numerical values are fixed by the convention described in § 1. 18 so that the normal melting point of ice is 273.16 degrees and this is called the Kelvin scale.

§ 4. 14   The Gas Constant and the Mole.   Equation of State of Gas

We have found that the coefficient A is directly proportional to the temperature. Since the volume is an extensive quantity, it is obvious that A is also an extensive quantity proportional to the quantity of gas to which it applies. We accordingly write

$$A = nRT, \qquad (4.14.1)$$

where n denotes the number of moles and R is clearly independent of temperature, pressure and quantity of gas. R is actually also independent of the nature of the gas. In fact from a purely thermodynamic view point, we may regard the *mole* as defined as that quantity of gas for which $A = RT$, where R is a universal constant called the *gas constant* and having the value

$$R = 8.3144 \times 10^7 \text{ erg/mole deg.}$$
$$= 8.3144 \text{ abs. joule/mole deg.}$$
$$= 1.98718 \text{ cal./mole deg.}$$
$$= 0.082054 \text{ litre atm./mole deg.} \qquad (4.14.2)$$

When the mole is defined in this manner, then it can be shown by statistical mechanics or kinetic theory that the number of molecules in a mole is the same for every gas. This number is called *Avogadro s number*. It is defined as the number of atoms of oxygen in 16 grams and is denoted by N. Its value is

$$N = 0.6023 \times 10^{24} \text{ molecules/mole.} \tag{4.14.3}$$

The gas constant R is related to Boltzmann's constant k introduced in Chapter II by

$$R = N k. \tag{4.14.4}$$

We now consider formula (4.11.1) applied to one mole of a gas and we accordingly replace A by RT. We thus obtain

$$V_m = \frac{RT}{P} + B + C'P. \tag{4.14.5}$$

This is called the *equation of state* of a gas. Under ordinary conditions the term in $C'P$ is negligible and for the sake of brevity we shall omit it. If it is required, it should be obvious how to insert it into the formulae. We accordingly replace (5) by

$$V_m = \frac{RT}{P} + B(T). \tag{4.14.6}$$

It is important to remember that B has the dimensions of a volume and depends on the temperature.

§ 4.15   Absolute Activity

In Chapter II we met a quantity called the absolute activity which plays an important part in the statistical thermodynamics of open systems. It is related to the molecular chemical potential μ by $\lambda = e^{\mu/kT}$. We now give a purely thermodynamic definition of the absolute activity, which is somewhat out of place in the present chapter, but we could not give it earlier because it involves the gas constant R. We accordingly define* the *absolute activity* as related to the molar chemical potential μ by

$$\lambda = e^{\mu/RT}, \tag{4.15.1}$$

or

$$\mu = RT \log \lambda. \tag{4.15.2}$$

Whereas it is not necessary to use λ as well as μ, we shall find that the absolute activity λ is often a very convenient function in the study of equilibria of all kinds whether involving one species or several. In § 1.49 we showed that for the most general chemical reaction represented symbolically by

$$\Sigma \nu_A A \rightarrow \Sigma \nu_B B, \tag{4.15.3}$$

---

* See Fowler and Guggenheim, *Statistical Thermodynamics* (1939) p. 66.

the condition for equilibrium is according to (1.49.9)

$$\Sigma \, \nu_A \, \mu_A = \Sigma \, \nu_B \, \mu_B.$$ (4.15.4)

We now see that this condition can equally be expressed in terms of absolute activites in the form

$$\Pi \, (\lambda_A)^{\nu_A} = \Pi \, (\lambda_B)^{\nu_B},$$ (4.15.5)

or

$$\frac{\Pi \, (\lambda_B)^{\nu_B}}{\Pi \, (\lambda_A)^{\nu_A}} = 1,$$ (4.15.6)

where the denominator is the product of the absolute activities of all the reactants in the process (3) and the numerator is the product of the absolute activities of all the products of this process.

In particular the condition for the equilibrium distribution of a species i between the phases α and β may be written

$$\lambda_i^\alpha = \lambda_i^\beta.$$ (4.15.7)

We may note that the fundamental equations (1.33.12), (1.33.13) and (1.33.14) can be written

$$dS = \frac{1}{T} \, dU + \frac{P}{T} \, dV - R \, \Sigma_i \, \log \lambda_i \, dn_i,$$ (4.15.8)

$$dJ = \frac{U}{T^2} \, dT + \frac{P}{T} \, dV - R \, \Sigma_i \, \log \lambda_i \, dn_i,$$ (4.15.9)

$$dY = \frac{H}{T^2} \, dT - \frac{V}{T} \, dP - R \, \Sigma_i \, \log \lambda_i \, dn_i.$$ (4.15.10)

§ 4.16 Thermodynamic Functions of a Gas

In § 4.11 we derived various thermodynamic functions from (4.11.1). Proceeding alternatively from (4.14.6) we obtain

$$\mu = \frac{G}{n} = G_m = \mu \, (P^\dagger) + RT \, \log \frac{P}{P^\dagger} + BP - BP^\dagger,$$ (4.16.1)

where $P^\dagger$ is an arbitrarily chosen standard pressure. We may write (1) in the alternative form

$$\mu = \frac{G}{n} = G_m = \mu^\dagger + RT \, \log \frac{P}{P^\dagger} + BP,$$ (4.16.2)

where $\mu^\dagger$ is a function of the temperature only, $\mu^\dagger$ is not exactly equal to the value of μ when the pressure is $P^\dagger$ but differs from it by $BP^\dagger$, which however can be made small by choosing a small pressure as the standard $P^\dagger$.

From (2) we derive immediately

$$S_m = \frac{S}{n} = -\frac{d\mu^\dagger}{dT} - R \log \frac{P}{P^\dagger} - P \frac{dB}{dT},$$ (4.16.3)

$$H_m = \frac{H}{n} = \mu^\dagger - T \frac{d\mu^\dagger}{dT} + \left(B - T \frac{dB}{dT} \right) P.$$ (4.16.4)

The compressibility $\varkappa$ is given by

$$\varkappa = -\frac{1}{V_m}\left(\frac{\partial V_m}{\partial P}\right)_T = P^{-1}\left(1 + \frac{PB}{RT}\right)^{-1}, \qquad (4.16.5)$$

and the coefficient of thermal expansion α by

$$\alpha V_m = \left(\frac{\partial V_m}{\partial T}\right)_P = \frac{R}{P} + \frac{dB}{dT}. \qquad (4.16.6)$$

The molar heat capacity at constant pressure is given by

$$C = T\left(\frac{\partial S_m}{\partial T}\right)_P = \left(\frac{\partial H_m}{\partial T}\right)_P = -T\frac{d^2\mu^\dagger}{dT^2} - TP\frac{d^2B}{dT^2}. \qquad (4.16.7)$$

or

$$C = C^\dagger - TP\frac{d^2B}{dT^2}. \qquad (4.16.8)$$

where $C^\dagger$ denotes the limiting value of C at zero pressure.

From (2) and (4.15.1) we obtain for the absolute activity

$$\lambda = \lambda^\dagger \frac{P}{P^\dagger} e^{BP/RT}. \qquad (4.16.9)$$

where

$$\lambda^\dagger = e^{\mu^\dagger/RT}, \qquad (4.16.10)$$

is a function of the temperature only.

§ 4.17   Joule–Thomson Coefficient

When we discussed the throttling experiment in § 4.12, we stressed the fact that at that stage we could not yet measure the absolute temperature. Now that we know how to do this by means of a gas thermometer, it is profitable to return to a discussion of throttling. The conditions of the gas before and after throttling are related by

$$H(T_2, P_2) = H(T_1, P_1). \qquad (4.17.1)$$

Provided the pressure drop is not too great, we may usefully replace this by the differential relation

$$dH = \left(\frac{\partial H}{\partial T}\right)_P dT + \left(\frac{\partial H}{\partial P}\right)_T dP = 0. \qquad (4.17.2)$$

The Joule–Thomson coefficient, which measures the ratio of the temperature *fall* to the pressure *drop*, is then

$$\left(\frac{\partial T}{\partial P}\right)_H = -\left(\frac{\partial H}{\partial P}\right)_T\bigg/\left(\frac{\partial H}{\partial T}\right)_P = -\left(\frac{\partial H_m}{\partial P}\right)_T\bigg/\left(\frac{\partial H_m}{\partial T}\right)_P. \qquad (4.17.3)$$

By substitution from (3. 05. 4) and (4. 05. 2), this becomes

$$\left(\frac{\partial T}{\partial P}\right)_H = \frac{-V_m(1-\alpha T)}{C_P}. \qquad (4.17.4)$$

where we have written C_P rather than C to avoid possible confusion with the third virial coefficient.

If we assume the equation of state (4. 14. 6) then α is given by (4. 16. 6). Substituting this value of α into (4) we obtain for the Joule–Thomson coefficient

$$\left(\frac{\partial T}{\partial P}\right)_H = \frac{-B + T\dfrac{dB}{dT}}{C_P} = \frac{T^2}{C_P}\frac{d\,(B/T)}{dT}. \qquad (4.17.5)$$

§ 4.18   Dependence of Second Virial Coefficient on Temperature

The second virial coefficient B is negative at low temperatures, but increases with the temperature and eventually becomes positive.

It is customary to measure B for each gas in a unit of volume equal to that of one mole at $0\,°C$ and a pressure of one atmosphere. This is called

TABLE 4. 1

Second virial coefficient of nitrogen.

T	$10^4 B$/Amagat units	
°K	experiment	calculated
143	−35.6	−27.8
173	−23.1	−19.2
223	−11.8	−10.1
273	− 4.61	− 4.3
323	− 0.11	− 0.2
373	2.74	2.6
423	5.14	4.8
473	6.85	6.6
573	9.21	9.25
673	10.5	11.1

$$B = b - \frac{a}{RT}$$
$$b = 21.5 \times 10^{-4} \text{ Amagat units}$$
$$\frac{a}{bR} = 327°$$

the *Amagat unit* of volume. It varies slightly from one gas to another according to the value of B but is always near to 22. 4 litres.

As a typical example of the way B depends on the temperature, we give in Table 4.1 the experimental values * for nitrogen. This dependence on temperature cannot be represented accurately by any simple formula, but at the higher temperatures it can be represented approximately by a formula of the form

$$B = b - \frac{a}{RT}, \qquad (a, b \text{ constant}). \qquad (4.18.1)$$

The values so calculated for nitrogen, assuming

$$b = 21.5 \times 10^{-4} \text{ Amagat units}, \qquad \frac{a}{bR} = 327 \text{ deg}. \qquad (4.18.2)$$

are given in the last column of the Table.

§ 4.19 Boyle Temperature and Inversion Temperature

At the temperature T_B at which B changes sign, Boyle's Law $PV_m = RT_B$ is accurate and this temperature T_B is accordingly called the *Boyle temperature*. Insofar as formula (4.18.1) is valid, we have

$$T_B = \frac{a}{bR}. \qquad (4.19.1)$$

and so for nitrogen the Boyle temperature is approximately 327° K.

According to the way B depends on the temperature the Joule–Thomson coefficient is positive at the lowest temperatures (cooling by throttling) but is negative at higher temperatures (heating by throttling). The temperature T_i at which the effect changes sign is called the inversion temperature. According to (4.17.5) the inversion temperature is determined by

$$\frac{d(B/T)}{dT} = 0. \qquad (4.19.2)$$

Insofar as formula (4.18.1) is valid, we have

$$T_i = \frac{2a}{bR}. \qquad (4.19.3)$$

and so for nitrogen the inversion temperature is approximately 654° K.

By comparison of (1) and (3) we obtain

$$T_i = 2 T_B. \qquad (4.19.4)$$

but this relation is only approximate since formula (4.18.1) is not accurate.

§ 4.20 Van der Waals' Formula

In 1873 van der Waals suggested the formula

$$\left(P + \frac{a}{V_m^2}\right) (V_m - b) = RT, \qquad (a, b \text{ constant}) \qquad (4.20.1)$$

---

* Holborn and Otto, *Zeit. f. Physik* (1925) **33** 5. These authors' unit of B is the volume occupied by one mole at a pressure of 1 m. Hg. Their value of B have been converted to the Amagat unit, namely the volume occupied by one mole at one atmosphere.

as the equation of state for a gas with a, b constants characteristic of the gas. This equation does give a qualitative description of the behaviour of gases and also of liquids (see § 4. 52), and it has the one merit of simplicity. It is far from accurate and has no sound theoretical basis except for low pressures and high temperatures. But at low pressures formula (1) is, apart from second order small quantities, equivalent to

$$V_m = \frac{RT}{P} + b - \frac{a}{RT}.$$ (4. 20. 2)

According to the definition of the second virial coefficient B, formula (2) is equivalent to

$$B = b - \frac{a}{RT},$$ (4. 20. 3)

which is the same as (4. 18. 1). We have already seen that this is a fair approximation at temperatures near and above the Boyle temperature, but becomes seriously inaccurate at low temperatures.

§ 4. 21 Perfect Gas

For many purposes, especially at low pressures, it is allowable to neglect the second and a fortiori the higher virial coefficients. The thermodynamic formulae of a gas then reduce to particularly simple forms, which are called the *formulae of a perfect gas*. It must be emphasized that there is no such thing as a perfect gas, which is an abstraction to which any real gas approximates more or less depending on the nature of the gas and on the conditions. From a molecular point of view the perfect gas laws correspond to the idealized behaviour of a system of molecules whose mutual interactions are neglected.

The most important formulae of a perfect gas are obtained directly from § 4. 14 and § 4. 16 by omitting all terms containing B.

We thus obtain

$$\mu = \frac{G}{n} = G_m = \mu^\dagger + RT \log \frac{P}{P^\dagger}.$$ (4. 21. 1)

$$S_m = \frac{S}{n} = -\frac{d\mu^\dagger}{dT} - R \log \frac{P}{P^\dagger}.$$ (4. 21. 2)

$$H_m = \frac{H}{n} = \mu^\dagger - T \frac{d\mu^\dagger}{dT}.$$ (4. 21. 3)

$$V_m = \left(\frac{\partial \mu}{\partial P}\right)_T = \frac{RT}{P}.$$ (4. 21. 4)

It will be observed that for a perfect gas the molar heat function H_m is independent of the pressure; this is merely another way of saying that B is ignored.

We have further

$$\varkappa = - \frac{1}{V_m} \left(\frac{\partial V_m}{\partial P} \right)_T = P^{-1}, \qquad (4.21.5)$$

$$a = \frac{1}{V_m} \left(\frac{\partial V_m}{\partial T} \right)_P = T^{-1}, \qquad (4.21.6)$$

$$C = T \left(\frac{\partial S_m}{\partial T} \right)_P = \frac{dH_m}{dT} = - T \frac{d^2 \mu^\dagger}{dT^2}. \qquad (4.21.7)$$

$$\frac{\lambda}{\lambda^\dagger} = \frac{P}{P^\dagger}. \qquad (4.21.8)$$

§ 4.22 Fugacity

Some of the formulae for real gases can be transcribed to forms having a simplicity resembling that of the formulae of perfect gases by the device due to G. N. Lewis * of introducing a fictitious pressure called the *fugacity*. We accordingly define the fugacity p^* by the two properties

$$\frac{p^*}{\lambda} = \text{const.}, \qquad (T \text{ const.}); \qquad (4.22.1)$$

$$\frac{p^*}{P} \to 1 \text{ as } P \to 0, \qquad (\text{all } T). \qquad (4.22.2)$$

According to this definition, at low pressures the fugacity p^* is indistinguishable from the pressure P. At a given temperature as the pressure is increased so p^* deviates from P in such a manner that whereas the formula (4.21.8) becomes progressively less accurate formula (1) remains identically true.

From (4.15.2), (4.16.10) and (1) we obtain

$$\mu = \mu^\dagger + RT \log \frac{p^*}{P^\dagger}. \qquad (4.22.3)$$

From (3) all other thermodynamic functions can be derived, if required, by differentiation. For example

$$S_m = - \frac{d\mu^\dagger}{dT} - R \log \frac{p^*}{P^\dagger} - RT \left(\frac{\partial \log p^*}{\partial T} \right)_P, \qquad (4.22.4)$$

$$V_m = RT \left(\frac{\partial \log p^*}{\partial P} \right)_T. \qquad (4.22.5)$$

The simplification attained by the introduction of the fugacity is one of appearance or elegance, but leads to nothing quantitative unless we express the fugacity in terms of the pressure and we are then back where we started. Thus at ordinary pressures when we may neglect all virial

---

* Lewis, *Proc. Am. Acad. Sci.* (1901) **37** 49; *Zeit. Physik. Chem.*, (1901) **38** 205.

coefficients beyond the second, the absolute activity is given by (4. 16. 9). Comparing this with (1) we see that

$$p^* = Pe^{BP/RT}, \qquad (4.22.6)$$

or

$$\log p^* = \log P + \frac{BP}{RT}. \qquad (4.22.7)$$

When we substitute (7) into (3) and (4) we recover (4. 16. 2) and (4.·16. 3) respectively.

In general we can obtain a formula for p^* by integrating (5) adjusting the integration constant so as to satisfy (2). For example, at pressures where we have to use (4. 14. 5) instead of (4. 14. 6) we obtain

$$\log p^* = \log P + \frac{1}{RT}\,(BP + \tfrac{1}{2}\,C'\,P^2). \qquad (4.22.8)$$

§ 4. 23   T, V Formulae for Gases

In all our discussion of gases we have up to the present chosen the independent variables T, P and we accordingly started from formula (4. 14. 5), namely

$$V_m = \frac{RT}{P} + B + C'\,P. \qquad (4.23.1)$$

If however we prefer to use the independent variables T, V then we should start from the formula

$$P = \frac{RT}{V_m}\left\{1 + \frac{B}{V_m} + \frac{C}{V_m^2}\right\}, \qquad (4.23.2)$$

which is equivalent to (1) apart from small quantities of a higher order involving the fourth virial coefficient. C and C' are related by

$$C = B^2 + RTC'. \qquad (4.23.3)$$

We shall actually neglect the terms containing C, just as we previously neglected terms containing C'. If they are required there is no difficulty in inserting them. We accordingly reduce (2) to

$$P = \frac{RT}{V_m}\left(1 + \frac{B}{V_m}\right) = \frac{nRT}{V}\left(1 + \frac{nB}{V}\right). \qquad (4.23.4)$$

By integrating (4) with respect to V we obtain

$$F = nF_m = n\mu^\dagger - nRT + nRT\,\log\frac{nRT}{P^\dagger V} + \frac{n^2RTB}{V}, \qquad (4.23.5)$$

wherein the integration constant, a function of T, has been written in a form so as to be consistent with (4. 16. 2). For if we differentiate (5) with respect to n we obtain

$$\mu = \left(\frac{\partial F}{\partial n}\right)_{T,V} = \mu^\dagger + RT\,\log\frac{RT}{P^\dagger V_m} + \frac{2RTB}{V_m}, \qquad (4.23.6)$$

which is equivalent to (4. 16. 2) apart from higher order small terms. By differentiation of (5) with respect to T we obtain

$$S_m = \frac{S}{n} = -\frac{d\mu^\dagger}{dT} - R \log \frac{RT}{P^\dagger V_m} - R\frac{B}{V_m} - \frac{RT}{V_m}\frac{dB}{dT}, \qquad (4.\,23.\,7)$$

and

$$U_m = \frac{U}{n} = \mu^\dagger - T\frac{d\mu^\dagger}{dT} - RT - \frac{RT^2}{V_m}\frac{dB}{dT}. \qquad (4.\,23.\,8)$$

By further differentiation of (7) or (8) with respect to T, we obtain

$$C_V = T\left(\frac{\partial S_m}{\partial T}\right)_{V,n} = \left(\frac{\partial U_m}{\partial T}\right)_{V,n}$$

$$= -T\frac{d^2\mu^\dagger}{dT^2} - R - \frac{R}{V_m}\frac{d}{dT}\left(T^2\frac{dB}{dT}\right). \qquad (4.\,23.\,9)$$

§ 4. 24   Relation between C_P and C_V for Gases

Neglecting all small quantities of higher orders than B/V_m, we may replace (4. 23. 9) by

$$C_V = -T\frac{d^2\mu^\dagger}{dT^2} - R - \frac{P}{T}\frac{d}{dT}\left(T^2\frac{dB}{dT}\right). \qquad (4.\,24.\,1)$$

Subtracting this from (4. 16. 7) we obtain

$$C_P - C_V = R + 2P\frac{dB}{dT}. \qquad (4.\,24.\,2)$$

To the same order of accuracy we have from (4. 14. 6) and (4. 16. 5)

$$\varkappa V_m = \frac{RT}{P^2} \qquad (4.\,24.\,3)$$

with no term of order B/V_m, and according to (4. 16. 6)

$$a V_m = \frac{R}{P}\left(1 + \frac{P}{R}\frac{dB}{dT}\right). \qquad (4.\,24.\,4)$$

From (3) and (4) we deduce, still neglecting all terms small compared with B/V_m,

$$\frac{a^2 T V_m}{\varkappa} = R + 2P\frac{dB}{dT}. \qquad (4.\,24.\,5)$$

By comparing (2) with (5) we thus verify at least as high as the terms of order B/V_m the general relation (4. 09. 3), namely

$$C_P - C_V = \frac{a^2 T V_m}{\varkappa}. \qquad (4.\,24.\,6)$$

§ 4. 25 T, V Formulae for Perfect Gases

If in the formulae of the last two sections we omit all terms containing B, we obtain the corresponding simpler formulae for perfect gases. In particular

$$F_m = \frac{F}{n} = \mu^\dagger - RT + RT \log \frac{RT}{P^\dagger V_m}, \qquad (4.25.1)$$

$$\mu = \mu^\dagger + RT \log \frac{RT}{P^\dagger V_m}, \qquad (4.25.2)$$

$$P = \frac{RT}{V_m}, \qquad (4.25.3)$$

$$U_m = \frac{U}{n} = \mu^\dagger - T \frac{d\mu^\dagger}{dT} - RT, \qquad (4.25.4)$$

$$C_V = -T \frac{d^2\mu^\dagger}{dT^2} - R = C_P - R. \qquad (4.25.5)$$

We see from the formulae of § 4.21 and the present section that for a perfect gas at a given temperature each of the following quantities is independent of pressure or volume: PV_m, H_m, U_m, C_P, C_V.

§ 4.26 Adiabatic Compressibility

In § 3.03 the isothermal compressibility $\varkappa$ or $\varkappa_T$ was defined by

$$\varkappa_T = -\frac{1}{V} \left(\frac{\partial V}{\partial P} \right)_T. \qquad (4.26.1)$$

The adiabatic compressibility $\varkappa_S$ is similarly defined by

$$\varkappa_S = -\frac{1}{V} \left(\frac{\partial V}{\partial P} \right)_S. \qquad (4.26.2)$$

If in formula (3.01.14) we write V for x, P for y and S for z we obtain

$$\left(\frac{\partial V}{\partial P} \right)_S = -\left(\frac{\partial S}{\partial P} \right)_V \bigg/ \left(\frac{\partial S}{\partial V} \right)_P, \qquad (4.26.3)$$

whereas if we write V for x, P for y and T for z we obtain

$$\left(\frac{\partial V}{\partial P} \right)_T = -\left(\frac{\partial T}{\partial P} \right)_V \bigg/ \left(\frac{\partial T}{\partial V} \right)_P. \qquad (4.26.4)$$

Dividing (3) by (4) and comparing with (1), (2) we obtain

$$\frac{\varkappa_S}{\varkappa_T} = \frac{\left(\frac{\partial V}{\partial P} \right)_S}{\left(\frac{\partial V}{\partial P} \right)_T} = \frac{\left(\frac{\partial S}{\partial P} \right)_V}{\left(\frac{\partial T}{\partial P} \right)_V} \cdot \frac{\left(\frac{\partial T}{\partial V} \right)_P}{\left(\frac{\partial S}{\partial V} \right)_P} = \frac{\left(\frac{\partial S}{\partial T} \right)_V}{\left(\frac{\partial S}{\partial T} \right)_P}, \qquad (4.26.5)$$

using (3.01.24). According to the definitions (4.05.2) of C_P and (4.08.5) of C_V, (5) becomes

$$\frac{\varkappa_S}{\varkappa_T} = \frac{C_V}{C_P}. \tag{4.26.6}$$

§ 4.27 Adiabatic Equations

For an adiabatic change we have by combining (4.26.2) with (4.26.6)

$$-\frac{1}{V}\frac{dV}{dP} = \frac{C_V}{C_P}\varkappa_T, \qquad (S \text{ constant}). \tag{4.27.1}$$

This differential equation for an adiabatic change can not be integrated unless the right side can be expressed as an explicit function of P, V and not necessarily even then. In the special case of a perfect gas, according to (4.21.5) $\varkappa_T = P^{-1}$ and so (1) becomes

$$\frac{d\log V}{d\log P} = -\frac{C_V}{C_P}, \qquad (S \text{ constant}). \tag{4.27.2}$$

We have seen that for a perfect gas C_P and C_V are constants at constant T but they are usually not constant at constant S (varying T). In the exceptional case of a perfect gas with monatomic molecules, we shall see in § 4.29 that

$$C_V = \tfrac{3}{2} R, \quad C_P = \tfrac{5}{2} R, \quad \text{(monatomic molecules)}, \tag{4.27.3}$$

so that (2) becomes

$$\frac{d\log V}{d\log P} = -\tfrac{3}{5}, \qquad \text{(monatomic molecules)}, \tag{4.27.4}$$

which can be integrated to

$$P V^{5/3} = \text{const.} \qquad \text{(monatomic molecules)}. \tag{4.27.5}$$

Again for a perfect gas of diatomic molecules, we shall see in § 4.30 that over a wide range of temperature

$$C_V = \tfrac{5}{2} R, \quad C_P = \tfrac{7}{2} R, \quad \text{(diatomic molecules)}, \tag{4.27.6}$$

so that (2) becomes

$$\frac{d\log V}{d\log P} = -\tfrac{5}{7}, \qquad \text{(diatomic molecules)}, \tag{4.27.7}$$

which can be integrated to

$$P V^{7/5} = \text{const.} \qquad \text{(diatomic molecules)}. \tag{4.27.8}$$

In other cases (2) cannot be integrated exactly.

§ 4.28 Temperature Dependence of $\mu^\dagger$ and $\lambda^\dagger$

We have in § 4.16 and § 4.23 expressed all the most important thermodynamic functions in terms of $\mu^\dagger$ a function of temperature only, and we have now to consider the form of $\mu^\dagger$.

In the first place $\mu^\dagger$ contains an arbitrary constant term, which we shall denote by H^0, depending only on the arbitrarily chosen zero of energy. Since H^0 is a constant, dH^0/dT is zero and so by (4.16.4) the corresponding term in H_m is just H^0. This explains our choice of the notation H^0. According to (4.23.8) the corresponding term in U_m is $H^0 - RT$. According to (4.16.10) there is a corresponding arbitrary factor $e^{H^0/RT}$ in $\lambda^\dagger$.

Apart from the arbitrary constant in $\mu^\dagger$ and arbitrary factor in $\lambda^\dagger$, these quantities depend on the temperature in a manner determined by the nature of the gaseous molecules and it is convenient to divide these into four classes, namely

> monatomic molecules,
> diatomic molecules,
> polyatomic linear molecules,
> polyatomic non-linear molecules,

which we shall consider in turn.

§ 4.29 Monatomic Molecules

For gases having monatomic molecules $\lambda^\dagger$ has the simple form

$$e^{H^0/RT} \left(\frac{\Theta^\dagger}{T} \right)^{\frac{5}{2}}, \qquad (4.29.1)$$

where $\Theta^\dagger$ is a constant, with the dimensions of temperature, depending on the arbitrarily chosen standard pressure $P^\dagger$ and also on the arbitrarily chosen zero of entropy. We shall return to the more detailed consideration of $\Theta^\dagger$ in § 4.56.

By substituting (1) into the formulae of § 4.16 we derive

$$\mu^\dagger = H^0 - \tfrac{5}{2} RT \log \frac{T}{\Theta^\dagger}, \qquad (4.29.2)$$

$$\mu = G_m = H^0 - \tfrac{5}{2} RT \log \frac{T}{\Theta^\dagger} + RT \log \frac{P}{P^\dagger} + BP, \quad (4.29.3)$$

$$S_m = \tfrac{5}{2} R + \tfrac{5}{2} R \log \frac{T}{\Theta^\dagger} - R \log \frac{P}{P^\dagger} - P \frac{dB}{dT}. \qquad (4.29.4)$$

$$H_m = H^0 + \tfrac{5}{2} RT + \left(B - T \frac{dB}{dT} \right) P, \qquad (4.29.5)$$

$$C = \tfrac{5}{2} R - TP \frac{d^2B}{dT^2}, \qquad (4.29.6)$$

$$\lambda = e^{H^0/RT} \left(\frac{\Theta^\dagger}{T} \right)^{\frac{5}{2}} \frac{p^*}{P^\dagger}. \qquad (4.29.7)$$

Similarly by substitution of (2) into the formulae of § 4.23 we derive

$$F_m = H^0 - RT - \tfrac{5}{2} RT \log \frac{T}{\Theta^\dagger} + RT \log \frac{RT}{P^\dagger V_m} + \frac{RTB}{V_m}, \quad (4.29.8)$$

$$\mu = H^0 - \tfrac{5}{2} RT \log \frac{T}{\Theta^\dagger} + RT \log \frac{RT}{P^\dagger V_m} + \frac{2RTB}{V_m}, \quad (4.29.9)$$

$$S_m = \tfrac{5}{2} R + \tfrac{5}{2} R \log \frac{T}{\Theta^\dagger} - R \log \frac{RT}{P^\dagger V_m} - R \frac{B}{V_m} - \frac{RT}{V_m} \frac{dB}{dT}, \quad (4.29.10)$$

$$U_m = H^0 + \tfrac{3}{2} RT - \frac{RT^2}{V_m} \frac{dB}{dT}, \quad (4.29.11)$$

$$C_V = \tfrac{3}{2} R - \frac{R}{V_m} \frac{d}{dT} \left(T^2 \frac{dB}{dT} \right). \quad (4.29.12)$$

We observe that S_m is independent of H^0.

§ 4.30 Diatomic Molecules

For gases consisting of diatomic molecules $\lambda^\dagger$ has the form

$$\lambda^\dagger = e^{H^0/RT} \left(\frac{\Theta^\dagger}{T} \right)^{\frac{5}{2}} \lambda_r(T) \lambda_v(T), \quad (4.30.1)$$

where, as compared with (4.29.1), the extra factor $\lambda_r(T)$ is due to the two rotational degrees of freedom of the molecule and the extra factor $\lambda_v(T)$ is due to the vibrational degree of freedom of the molecule. We now consider these two factors in turn.

In connection with the rotational degree of freedom we define a characteristic temperature Θ_r by

$$\Theta_r = \frac{h^2}{8\pi^2 Ik} = \frac{39.60 \text{ deg.}}{\cdot 10^{40} I/\text{g.cm.}^2}, \quad (4.30.2)$$

where I is the principle moment of inertia of the molecule, h is Planck's constant and k is Boltzmann's constant. Then, provided $T > 3\Theta_r$, with an accuracy of 1 % or better

$$\lambda_r(T) = \frac{\sigma \Theta_r}{T} \left(1 + \frac{1}{3} \frac{\Theta_r}{T} + \frac{1}{15} \frac{\Theta_r^2}{T^2} \right)^{-1}, \quad (T \gg \Theta_r), \quad (4.30.3)$$

where σ is a symmetry number equal to 2 for symmetrical molecules such as N_2 and 1 for unsymmetrical molecules such as CO.

Values of Θ_r for some typical diatomic molecules are given * in Table 4.2. From this we see that the condition for the validity of formula (3) is fulfilled for all gases, except hydrogen, at all temperatures at which the gases can exist at conveniently measurable pressures. Even for hydrogen

---

*   See Fowler and Guggenheim, *Statistical Thermodynamics* (1939) p. 90.

Compare Slater, *Introduction to Chemical Physics* (1939) p. 136, observing that there Θ_{rot} is equal to twice our Θ_r.

formula (3) is applicable with an accuracy of a few per cent at ordinary temperatures and better at higher temperatures. At lower temperatures, however, formula (3) may not be used for hydrogen. The thermodynamic properties of gaseous hydrogen and deuterium at low temperatures are complicated, not only owing to the failure of formula (3) but also owing to para-ortho separation. They will not be discussed here.

Turning now to the vibrational degree of freedom, we use another characteristic temperature Θ_v related to a characteristic vibrational frequency ν and wave number ν/c by

$$\Theta_v = \frac{h\nu}{k} = 1.4385 \frac{\nu}{c} \text{ deg. cm.} \tag{4.30.4}$$

and $\lambda_v(T)$ is then given by

$$\lambda_v(T) = 1 - e^{-\Theta_v/T}. \tag{4.30.5}$$

In Table 4.2 values Θ_v are given * for the various molecules. We see that at ordinary temperatures $T \ll \Theta_v$ and $\lambda_v(T)$ consequently does not differ much from unity except at high temperatures.

TABLE 4.2

Characteristic temperatures Θ_r for rotation and Θ_v for vibration of typical diatomic molecules.

Formula	Θ_r deg.	$\Theta_v/10^2$ deg.	σ
H_2	85.0	59.8	2
D_2	42.5	43.0	2
N_2	2.84	33.5	2
O_2	2.06	22.4	2
CO	2.74	30.8	1
NO	2.42	27.0	1
HCl	15.0	41.5	1
HBr	12.0	36.8	1
HI	9.2	32.1	1
Cl_2	0.346	7.96	2
Br_2	0.116	4.62	2
I_2	0.054	3.07	2

By substituting (1), (3) and (5) into (4.16.10) we obtain

$$\mu^\dagger = RT \log \lambda^\dagger = H^0 - RT \log \frac{T^{\frac{7}{2}}}{\Theta^{\dagger\frac{5}{2}} \Theta_r \sigma}$$

$$-RT \log \left(1 + \frac{1}{3}\frac{\Theta_r}{T} + \frac{1}{15}\frac{\Theta_r^2}{T^2}\right) + RT \log (1 - e^{-\Theta_v/T}). \tag{4.30.6}$$

---

* Values of ν taken from Herzberg, *Molecular Spectra of Diatomic Molecules*. Cf. Fowler and Guggenheim, *Statistical Thermodynamics* (1939) p. 90; Slater, *Introduction to Chemical Physics* (1939) p. 142.

If we expand the second logarithm, we obtain a constant term $-\frac{1}{3}R\Theta_r$ which may be absorbed into H^0. The next term in this expansion is $\frac{1}{90}\Theta_r^2/T^2$ and further terms are negligible. We thus obtain

$$\mu^\dagger = H^0 - RT\log\frac{T^{\frac{7}{2}}}{\Theta^{\dagger\frac{5}{2}}\Theta_r\sigma} - \frac{1}{90}\frac{R\Theta_r^2}{T} + RT\log(1-e^{-\Theta_v/T}), \quad (4.30.7)$$

wherein the term $R\Theta_r^2/90\,T$ is in practice negligible. Omitting this term and substituting (7) into (4.16.2) we obtain

$$\mu = H^0 - RT\log\frac{T^{\frac{7}{2}}}{\Theta^{\dagger\frac{5}{2}}\Theta_r\sigma} + RT\log(1-e^{-\Theta_v/T})$$
$$+ RT\log\frac{P}{P^\dagger} + BP. \quad (4.30.8)$$

From this we derive immediately

$$S_m = \frac{7}{2}R + R\log\frac{T^{\frac{7}{2}}}{\Theta^{\dagger\frac{5}{2}}\Theta_r\sigma} - R\log(1-e^{-\Theta_v/T}) + \frac{R\,\Theta_v/T}{e^{\Theta_v/T}-1}$$
$$- R\log\frac{P}{P^\dagger} - P\frac{dB}{dT}, \quad (4.30.9)$$

$$H_m = H^0 + \frac{7}{2}RT + \frac{R\,\Theta_v}{e^{\Theta_v/T}-1} + \left(B - T\frac{dB}{dT}\right)P, \quad (4.30.10)$$

$$C = R\left\{\frac{7}{2} + \frac{(\Theta_v/2T)^2}{\sinh^2(\Theta_v/2T)}\right\} - T\frac{d^2B}{dT^2}P. \quad (4.30.11)$$

§ 4.31 Polyatomic Linear Molecules

The formulae of the preceding section require only slight modification to apply to polyatomic linear molecules. We continue to write $\lambda^\dagger$ in the form (4.30.1) and the rotational factor $\lambda_r(T)$ is precisely the same as for diatomic molecules. Typical values of Θ_r are given in Table 4.3, from which we see that in practice $T \gg \Theta_r$. If the linear molecule contains a atoms, there will be $3a-5$ independent vibrational modes. Each such mode has a characteristic frequency ν with corresponding characteristic temperature Θ_v and each contributes a factor of the form (4.30.5) to $\lambda_v(T)$. Values of Θ_v are given * for typical molecules in Table 4.3.

We thus deduce

$$\mu^\dagger = H^0 - RT\log\frac{T^{\frac{7}{2}}}{\Theta^{\dagger\frac{5}{2}}\Theta_r\sigma} - \frac{1}{90}\frac{R\Theta_r^2}{T} + RT\sum_{\Theta_v}\log(1-e^{-\Theta_v/T}), \quad (4.31.1)$$

wherein the summation extends over $3a-5$ characteristic temperatures Θ_v not necessarily all different. Omitting the negligible term in Θ_r^2 we obtain for the several thermodynamic functions

$$\mu = H^0 - RT\log\frac{T^{\frac{7}{2}}}{\Theta^{\dagger\frac{5}{2}}\Theta_r\sigma} + RT\sum_{\Theta_v}\log(1-e^{-\Theta_v/T})$$
$$+ RT\log\frac{P}{P^\dagger} + BP, \quad (4.31.2)$$

---

* Values of ν taken from Herzberg, *Infra-red and Raman Spectra*, (1945). C.f. Fowler and Guggenheim, *Statistical Thermodynamics* (1939) p. 112.

$$S_m = \tfrac{7}{2} R + R \log \frac{T^{\frac{7}{2}}}{\Theta^{\dagger\frac{5}{2}} \Theta_r \sigma} - R \sum_{\Theta_v} \log (1 - e^{-\Theta_v/T})$$

$$+ R \sum_{\Theta_v} \frac{\Theta_v/T}{e^{\Theta_v/T} - 1} - R \log \frac{P}{P^\dagger} - P \frac{dB}{dT}. \qquad (4.31.3)$$

$$H_m = H^0 + \tfrac{7}{2} RT + R \sum_{\Theta_v} \frac{\Theta_v}{e^{\Theta_v/T} - 1} + \left(B - T \frac{dB}{dT} \right) P. \qquad (4.31.4)$$

$$C = R \left\{ \tfrac{7}{2} + \sum_{\Theta_v} \frac{(\Theta_v/2T)^2}{\sinh^2 (\Theta_v/2T)} \right\} - T \frac{d^2B}{dT^2} P. \qquad (4.31.5)$$

Each Σ denotes summation over $3a - 5$ terms for molecules composed of a atoms.

TABLE 4.3

Characteristic temperature Θ_r for rotation and Θ_v for vibration of typical polyatomic linear molecules.

Formula	Θ_r deg.	$\Theta_v /10^2$ deg.	σ
OCO	0.56	9.60 9.60 20.0 33.8	2
NNO	0.60	8.47 8.47 18.5 32.0	1
HCCH	1.68	8.80 8.80 10.5 10.5 28.4 47.3 48.5	2

§ 4.32 Polyatomic Non-Linear Molecules

A polyatomic non-linear molecule containing a atoms has 3 rotational degrees of freedom and $3a - 6$ vibrational degrees of freedom. We still write $\lambda^\dagger$ in the form (4.30.1), but the rotational factor $\lambda_r(T)$ is now given by

$$\lambda_r(T) = \frac{\sigma \Theta_r^{\frac{3}{2}}}{\pi^{\frac{1}{2}} T^{\frac{3}{2}}}, \qquad (T \gg \Theta_r) \qquad (4.32.1)$$

omitting terms smaller by an order Θ_r/T, since the contribution of such terms can be absorbed into H^0, and neglecting terms smaller by an order Θ_r^2/T^2. In (1) the symmetry number σ is defined as the number of indistinguishable orientations of the molecule. For example σ is 1 for NOCl,

2 for OH_2, 3 for NH_3, 4 for C_2H_4, 6 for BF_3, 12 for CH_4 and 12 for C_6H_6. The characteristic temperature Θ_r is now defined by

$$\Theta_r = \frac{h^2}{8\,\pi^2\,(I_1\,I_2\,I_3)^{\frac{1}{3}}\,k} = \frac{39.60\ \text{deg.}}{10^{40}\,(I_1\,I_2\,I_3)^{\frac{1}{3}}/\text{g.cm.}^2},\qquad (4.32.2)$$

where I_1, I_2, I_3 are the three principle moments of inertia.

The vibrational factor $\Theta_v(T)$ is of the same form as for linear molecules except that there are $3a-6$ factors instead of $3a-5$.

We thus obtain for the several thermodynamic functions

$$\mu = H^0 - RT\log\frac{\pi^{\frac{1}{2}}\,T^4}{\Theta^{\dagger\frac{5}{2}}\,\Theta_r^{\frac{3}{2}}\,\sigma} + RT\sum_{\Theta_v}\log\left(1-e^{-\Theta_v/T}\right)$$

$$+ RT\log\frac{P}{P^\dagger} + BP,\qquad (4.32.3)$$

$$S_m = 4\,R + R\log\frac{\pi^{\frac{1}{2}}\,T^4}{\Theta^{\dagger\frac{5}{2}}\,\Theta_r^{\frac{3}{2}}\,\sigma} - R\sum_{\Theta_v}\log\left(1-e^{-\Theta_v/T}\right)$$

$$+ R\sum_{\Theta_v}\frac{\Theta_v/T}{e^{\Theta_v/T}-1} - R\log\frac{P}{P^\dagger} - P\frac{dB}{dT},\qquad (4.32.4)$$

$$H_m = H^0 + 4\,RT + R\sum_{\Theta_v}\frac{\Theta_v}{e^{\Theta_v/T}-1} + \left(B - T\frac{dB}{dT}\right)P,\qquad (4.32.5)$$

$$C = R\left\{4 + \sum_{\Theta_v}\frac{(\Theta_v/2T)^2}{\sinh^2(\Theta_v/2T)}\right\} - T\frac{d^2B}{dT^2}P.\qquad (4.32.6)$$

Each Σ denotes summation over $3a-6$ terms for molecules composed of a atoms.

Values of Θ_r and Θ_v for some typical non-linear molecules are given[*] in Table 4.4. Even for OH_2, the molecule having the smallest moments of

TABLE 4.4

Characteristic temperatures Θ_r for rotation and Θ_v for vibration of typical non-linear molecules

Formula	Θ_r deg.	$\Theta_v/100$ deg.	σ
NOCl		9.1 13.2 26.2	1
OH_2	22.2	22.9 52.5 54.0	2
NH_3	12.3	13.7 23.4 23.4 48.0 49.1 49.1	3

[*] Values of ν taken from Herzberg, *Infra-red and Raman Spectra*, (1945). C.f. Fowler and Guggenheim, *Statistical Thermodynamics* (1939) pp. 113—114.

TABLE 4.5

Contributions of a single harmonic oscillator to the several thermodynamic quantities expressed as functions of

$$x = \frac{h\nu}{kT} = \frac{\Theta_v}{T}$$

x	$-\mu/RT$ $= -\log(1-e^{-x})$	H_m/RT $= \dfrac{x}{e^x-1}$	$S_m/R \cdot$ $= \dfrac{H_m-\mu}{RT}$	C/R $= \dfrac{(\frac{1}{2}x)^2}{\sinh^2(\frac{1}{2}x)}$
.01	4.610	0.995	5.605	1.000
.05	3.021	0.975	3.996	1.000
.1	2.352	0.951	3.303	0.999
.2	1.708	0.903	2.611	0.997
.3	1.350	0.857	2.208	0.993
.4	1.110	0.813	1.923	0.987
.5	0.933	0.771	1.704	0.979
.6	0.796	0.730	1.526	0.971
.7	0.686	0.691	1.377	0.960
.8	0.597	0.653	1.249	0.948
.9	0.522	0.617	1.138	0.935
1.0	0.459	0.582	1.041	0.921
1.1	0.405	0.549	0.954	0.905
1.2	0.358	0.517	0.876	0.888
1.3	0.318	0.487	0.805	0.870
1.4	0.283	0.458	0.741	0.852
1.5	0.252	0.431	0.683	0.832
1.6	0.226	0.405	0.630	0.811
1.7	0.202	0.380	0.582	0.790
1.8	0.181	0.356	0.537	0.769
1.9	0.162	0.334	0.496	0.747
2.0	0.145	0.313	0.458	0.724
2.1	0.131	0.293	0.424	0.701
2.2	0.117	0.274	0.392	0.678
2.3	0.106	0.256	0.362	0.655
2.4	0.095	0.239	0.335	0.632
2.5	0.086	0.224	0.309	0.609
2.6	0.077	0.209	0.286	0.586
2.7	0.070	0.195	0.264	0.563
2.8	0.063	0.181	0.244	0.540
2.9	0.057	0.169	0.225	0.518
3.0	0.051	0.157	0.208	0.496
3.2	0.042	0.136	0.178	0.454
3.4	0.034	0.117	0.151	0.413
3.6	0.028	0.101	0.129	0.374
3.8	0.023	0.087	0.110	0.338
4.0	0.018	0.075	0.093	0.304
4.5	0.011	0.051	0.062	0.230
5.0	0.007	0.034	0.041	0.171
5.5	0.004	0.023	0.027	0.125
6.0	0.002	0.015	0.017	0.090
6.5	0.002	0.010	0.013	0.064
7.0	0.001	0.006	0.007	0.045

inertia, the condition $T \gg \Theta_r$ for formula (1) is satisfied at all practical temperatures. The contributions of each vibrational mode to the several thermodynamic quantities may be read from Table 4.5, which gives the contributions to $-\mu/RT$, to H_m/RT, to S_m/RT and to C/R all as functions of Θ_v/T.

§ 4.33   Electronic Contributions

We have hitherto tacitly ignored any possible contribution to the thermo-dynamic functions due to the electronic degrees of freedom. The contri-bution to μ, S_m and H_m is in fact zero for the vast majority of chemical substances not having a free valency; the electronic contributions may then be ignored. In particular this condition is fulfilled by the following molecules.

(a)   The monatomic molecules He, Ne, A, Kr, Xe, Zn, Cd, Hg.

(b)   The diatomic molecules H_2, D_2, Li_2, Na_2, K_2, N_2, F_2, Cl_2, Br_2, I_2, CO, HCl, HBr, HI.

(c)   The polyatomic inorganic molecules OH_2, SH_2, NH_3, PH_3, CH_4, CO_2, N_2O, CS_2, SO_2.

(d)   All organic molecules, including those containing double or triple bonds, other than those classed as free radicals.

The one notably exceptional molecule, which according to its chemical behaviour is regarded as having no free valencies, is O_2. Whereas the normal states of all the molecules mentioned above are singlets, the normal state of O_2 is $^3\Sigma$. As a result of this, λ contains an extra factor $\frac{1}{3}$, while μ contains an extra term $- RT \log 3$ and S_m contains an extra term $R \log 3$. As long as we are considering only gaseous oxygen these extra factors and terms, being constant, are physically irrelevant. It is only when we come to consider the equilibrium between gaseous oxygen and solid oxygen or chemical equilibria between oxygen and other gases that these extra contributions become physically significant.

There are also electronic contributions in the case of molecules having a single free valency. This has the form of an extra factor $\frac{1}{2}$ in λ, an extra term $- RT \log 2$ in μ and an extra term $R \log 2$ in S_m in the case of all the following molecules

(a)   The univalent atoms Li, Na, K, Tl.

(b)   Organic free radicals such as CH_3 and $C(C_6H_5)_3$.

On the other hand in the case of the free halogen atoms the electronic contributions are not so simple *. The contribution to λ is an extra factor

$$(4 + 2 e^{-\Theta_e/T})^{-1}, \qquad (4.33.1)$$

where Θ_e is an electronic characteristic temperature. The values of Θ_e are as follows

Cl	$\Theta_e = 1.28 \times 10^3$ °K
Br	$\Theta_e = 5.2 \times 10^3$ °K
I	$\Theta_e = 10.9 \times 10^3$ °K

---

* See Fowler and Guggenheim, *Statistical Thermodynamics* (1939) p. 201.

We see that for temperatures up to 1000 °K, it is only in the case of Cl that the second term in (1) is not negligible. For Br and I the factor in λ reduces effectively to $\frac{1}{4}$. The corresponding terms in μ and S_m are of course $-RT \log 4$ and $R \log 4$ respectively.

We have still to mention the odd molecule NO. The extra factor in λ is

$$\tfrac{1}{2} (1 + e^{-\Theta_e/T})^{-1}, \tag{4.33.2}$$

with $\Theta_e = 178$ °K. Thus at very low temperatures this factor is effectively $\frac{1}{2}$ and at very high temperatures it is effectively $\frac{1}{4}$. As the temperature is raised there are especially sharp increases in S_m and in H_m in the neighbourhood of 178 °K.

In conclusion we may mention that even in the case of the most stable saturated molecules, there is in principle an electronic factor in λ of the form

$$(1 + \varpi e^{-\Theta_e/T})^{-1}, \tag{4.33.3}$$

where ϖ is a small integer, but the characteristic temperature Θ_e is so large that this factor differs insignificantly from unity.

§ 4.34   Pressure Dependence for Condensed Phases

We turn now from gases to condensed phases and shall later consider the equilibrium between a condensed phase and a gas. As we shall see in § 4.48, there are conditions of temperature and pressure called critical at which all distinction between gas and liquid disappears, but except at conditions close to the critical there is a rather sharp contrast between the properties of a gas and a liquid. The contrast between gas and solid is always a sharp one.

Whereas the isothermal compressibility $\varkappa$ of a gas is at least roughly equal to the reciprocal of the pressure, the isothermal compressibility of a solid and that of a liquid, except near the critical temperature, is much smaller than that of a gas and is nearly independent of the pressure. For a condensed phase, whether solid or liquid, we may therefore usually assume

$$-\frac{1}{V}\left(\frac{\partial V}{\partial P}\right) = \varkappa = \text{constant}, \qquad (T \text{ const.}). \tag{4.34.1}$$

We can integrate (1) at constant temperature to obtain

$$V = V^\dagger e^{-\varkappa P}, \qquad (T \text{ const.}), \tag{4.34.2}$$

where $V^\dagger$ is the limiting value of V at vanishing pressure and of course depends on the temperature. Since moreover at all ordinary pressures $\varkappa P \ll 1$, we may, without loss of accuracy, replace (2) by the more convenient relation

$$V = V^\dagger (1 - \varkappa P), \tag{4.34.3}$$

or for one mole

$$V_m = V_m^\dagger (1 - \varkappa P). \tag{4.34.4}$$

We can integrate again with respect to P at constant T and obtain, using (1.36.6),

$$\mu = \mu^\dagger + PV_m^\dagger (1 - \tfrac{1}{2} \varkappa P) = \mu^\dagger + P[V_m]. \qquad (4.34.5)$$

where $\mu^\dagger$ is the limiting value of μ at vanishing pressure and depends only on the temperature, while $[V_m]$ denotes the value of V_m at a pressure equal to $\tfrac{1}{2} P$.

For typical liquids $\varkappa$ is about 10^{-4} atm.$^{-1}$ and for many solids is even smaller. Hence even at pressures of many atmospheres, the terms in $\varkappa P$ may usually be neglected.

Multiplying (4) by P and subtracting from (5) we obtain

$$F_m = \mu^\dagger + \tfrac{1}{2} \varkappa P^2 V_m^\dagger, \qquad (4.34.6)$$

where the term containing $\varkappa$ is again almost always negligible.

According to the definition of the coefficient of thermal expansion α,

$$\frac{dV^\dagger}{dT} = \alpha^\dagger V^\dagger, \qquad (4.34.7)$$

where $\alpha^\dagger$ is the value of α for vanishing pressure. At ordinary temperatures not near the critical α is nearly independent of temperature and is about 10^{-3} deg.$^{-1}$, so that for many purposes the variation of volume with temperature is negligible.

At temperatures well below the critical, V_m in a typical liquid or solid is between 10 and 100 cm^3/mole, so that at atmospheric pressure PV_m is usually less than 0.1 atm. litre. whereas at ordinary temperatures RT is about 20 atm. litre. Thus for a condensed phase at atmospheric pressure PV_m is usually less than and often much less than 1 % of RT. For this reason PV_m is for many purposes negligible and it is then unnecessary to distinguish between the values of μ and F_m or between the values of H_m and U_m.

If we differentiate (5) with respect to T, we obtain

$$S_m = -\frac{d\mu^\dagger}{dT} - \alpha P[V_m] = -\frac{d\mu^\dagger}{dT} - \alpha P V_m^\dagger (1 - \tfrac{1}{2} \varkappa P), \qquad (4.34.8)$$

where α must strictly be given its value at a pressure equal to $\tfrac{1}{2} P$, but usually the variation of α with pressure may be ignored. At ordinary pressures and even at quite high pressures the last term in (8) will be negligible and we may write

$$S_m = -\frac{d\mu^\dagger}{dT} - \alpha P V_m^\dagger. \qquad (4.34.9)$$

From (9) and (5) we obtain

$$H_m = \mu^\dagger - T\frac{d\mu^\dagger}{dT} + P V_m^\dagger (1 - \tfrac{1}{2} \varkappa P - \alpha T), \qquad (4.34.10)$$

where the terms containing P and particularly those containing $\varkappa$ and α will usually be negligible.

§ 4.35   Temperature Dependence for Liquids

We have seen that the dependence of the thermodynamic properties of condensed phases on the pressure is simple and usually unimportant. We have now to consider how these properties depend on the temperature.

As regards liquids there is nothing fundamental or general that can be said except that μ can often be represented over quite a wide range of temperature by an empirical relation of the form

$$\mu = A-(B-C)T-CT \log T + PV_m, \qquad (A, B, C \text{ const.}), \qquad (4.35.1)$$

where we have neglected the compressibility. From (1) it follows that neglecting thermal expansion

$$S_m = B + C \log T, \qquad\qquad (B, C \text{ const.}), \qquad (4.35.2)$$

$$H_m = A + CT + PV_m, \qquad\quad (A, C \text{ const.}). \qquad (4.35.3)$$

According to this empirical approximation the molar heat capacity C is independent of the temperature. We have already mentioned in § 4.05 that for many liquids, in particular water, C is nearly independent of the temperature.

The approximate constancy of C and the consequent validity of relations of the form (1), (2), (3) also hold for many solids at ordinary and higher temperatures, but not at low temperatures. This accident has in the past caused undue importance to be attached to the heat capacity, in contrast to the heat function H and the entropy S. The only real importance of C is that it is the connecting link between H and S, as explained in § 4.05. This link is especially simple when C is independent of T, but this occurrence, however frequent, is of no fundamental importance.

§ 4.36   Crystals at Very Low Temperatures

It is predicted by statistical theory and borne out by experiment that at very low temperatures the heat function of a crystalline solid varies linearly with the fourth power of the absolute temperature. That is to say, neglecting the small dependence on pressure,

$$H_m = H_m^0 + \tfrac{1}{4} a T^4, \qquad\qquad (\text{small } T), \qquad (4.36.1)$$

where a is a constant and H_m^0 is the limiting value of H_m as $T \to 0$. Correspondingly we have for the entropy

$$S_m = S_m^0 + \tfrac{1}{3} a T^3, \qquad\qquad (\text{small } T), \qquad (4.36.2)$$

where S_m^0 is the limiting value of S_m as $T \to 0$. The formulae (1) and (2) are not independent, but are related through the thermodynamic formula (4.04.2)

$$T \, dS = dH, \qquad\qquad (\text{const. } P). \qquad (4.36.3)$$

From (1) and (2) it immediately follows that

$$\mu = H_m^0 - T S_m^0 - \tfrac{1}{12} a T^4, \qquad (\text{small } T). \qquad (4.36.4)$$

8

We have not stated how small T must be for these formulae to hold, nor is it possible to make any precise statement since the requirement is different for different substances. For most substances investigated these formulae appear to be at least approximately valid at temperatures below 20 °K and for many substances at temperatures below 40 °K.

We shall see later that a comparison between the constant S_m^0 in (2) and the constant $d\mu^+/dT$ occurring in the formula for the molar entropy of a gas is of considerable interest. For this reason it is important to be able to extrapolate experimental data on the entropy from the lowest experimental temperature down to 0 °K. For this purpose one determines a suitable value of the constant a from the relation (1) by plotting H against T^4 in the lowest temperature range in which experimental measurements have been made. This value of a is then used in (2) to give experimental values of $S(T)-S(0)$. Provided the experimental data extend below 20 °K, the contribution to S from this extrapolation is usually so small that a very accurate estimate of a is not required.

Actually the most important feature of the formulae of this section is not their precise form, still less the value of a, but the fact that S tends rapidly towards a constant value as T decreases. This behaviour is in striking contrast with the formulae for the entropy of gases at ordinary temperatures which contain terms in log T.

§ 4.37 Crystals at Intermediate Temperatures. Debye's Model.

In the previous section we have described the thermodynamic behaviour of crystals at very low temperatures. In § 4.35 we mentioned briefly that at ordinary and higher temperatures the behaviour of many solids, as well as liquids, is represented at least approximately by the formulae of that section corresponding to a temperature-independent heat capacity. In the intermediate temperature range the heat capacity increases, but its rate of increase falls rather rapidly. There is no precise quantitative theory except for the simplest crystals consisting of monatomic molecules. Even for these the accurate theory is so extremely complicated as to be of little practical use and it is in fact usually replaced by a much simpler approximation due to Debye.

We shall not here describe Debye's model, still less discuss * its inadequacy, but shall give the formulae which follow from it. The formulae contain apart from the temperature T, two parameters namely the energy U_m^0 of the crystal at $T = 0$ and a characteristic temperature Θ_D. Both these parameters U_m^0 and Θ_D are functions of the molar volume V_m, but are independent of the temperature. In considering Debye's model it is therefore expedient to regard as independent variables T, V instead of the usually more practically convenient T, P. We accordingly begin by writing down Debye's formula for the molar free energy F_m of a crystal

$$F_m = U_m^0 - T S_m^0 + 3RT \int_0^{\Theta_D} \log(1 - e^{-\theta/T}) \frac{3\theta^2}{\Theta_D^3} d\theta. \qquad (4.37.1)$$

* See Blackman, *Rep. Progress. Phys.* (1942) 8 11.

wherein we repeat that U_m^0 and Θ_D are functions of V_m whereas S_m^0 on the other hand is a constant independent of V_m, as well as of T, and depends only on the arbitrary zero of entropy.

From (1) we could derive the pressure by the relation

$$P = -\left(\frac{\partial F}{\partial V}\right)_T = -\left(\frac{\partial F_m}{\partial V_m}\right)_T. \tag{4.37.2}$$

We have however seen in § 4.34 that the thermodynamic properties of a condensed phase, in particular a crystal, are nearly independent of the pressure; more precisely $PV_m \ll RT$. We may consequently regard the pressure as negligible and replace (2) by the condition

$$\left(\frac{\partial F_m}{\partial V_m}\right)_T = 0, \tag{4.37.3}$$

which gives an equilibrium relation between U^0 and Θ_D. From (1) and (3) we find that this relation is

$$\frac{\partial U_m^0}{\partial V_m} = 3R\frac{\partial \Theta_D}{\partial V_m}\int_0^{\Theta_D}\frac{1}{e^{\theta/T}-1}\frac{3\,\theta^3\,d\theta}{\Theta_D^4}. \tag{4.37.4}$$

From (1) we can derive formulae for the other thermodynamic functions, in particular

$$U_m - U_m^0 = 3R\int_0^{\Theta_D}\frac{1}{e^{\theta/T}-1}\frac{3\,\theta^3\,d\theta}{\Theta_D^3}, \tag{4.37.5}$$

$$S_m - S_m^0 = -3R\int_0^{\Theta_D}\left\{\log(1-e^{-\theta/T}) - \frac{\theta/T}{e^{\theta/T}-1}\right\}\frac{3\,\theta^2\,d\theta}{\Theta_D^3}, \tag{4.37.6}$$

$$C_V = 3R\int_0^{\Theta_D}\frac{(\theta/2T)^2}{\sinh^2(\theta/2T)}\frac{3\,\theta^2\,d\theta}{\Theta_D^3} \tag{4.37.7}$$

We may note that at very low temperatures; $T \ll \Theta_D$ and we may without sensible error replace the upper limits of integration in the above formulae by ∞. We thus obtain

$$U_m = U_m^0 + 3R\frac{T^4}{\Theta_D^3}\int_0^{\infty}\frac{3\,\xi^3\,d\xi}{e^\xi-1} = U_m^0 - 3R\frac{T^4}{\Theta_D^3}\frac{\pi^4}{5}, \tag{4.37.8}$$

which, in view of the negligible difference between U_m and H_m is in agreement with (4.36.1) if

$$\tfrac{1}{4}a = \frac{3\pi^4}{5}\frac{R}{\Theta_D^3}. \tag{4.37.9}$$

While we shall not here discuss the extent of agreement or disagreement to be expected between these formulae and the behaviour of real crystals, we shall however devote some space to the consideration of how the comparison can most directly be made. Let us therefore consider which quantities are most directly measurable, bearing in mind that with all condensed phases it is convenient to make measurements at constant pressure but extremely difficult to make measurements at constant volume.

The usual calorimetric measurements determine directly how H depends on T. Provided these measurements have been carried to a low enough temperature, the extrapolation to $T = 0$ can be performed as described in § 4.36 so that we know $H_m(T) - H_m^0$ as a function of T. Then by using the relation (4.36.3) we can *without any further experimental data* compute $S_m(T) - S_m^0$. We can now compare this experimental quantity with the right side of (4.37.6), which is tabulated as a function of Θ_D/T. We thus obtain for each temperature T a value of Θ_D which fits the experimental value of $S_m - S^0$. These values of Θ_D will neither be constant in practice, nor according to Debye's model. For we are considering data at constant pressure, consequently at varying volume and, as the volume varies, so Θ_D varies. In fact as the volume increases, theory predicts that Θ_D should steadily decrease. If then it is found that as T increases, the value of Θ_D determined as described above slowly, but steadily decreases then we may say that at least there is no contradiction between the experimental data and the model. If on the other hand as T increases, the value of Θ_D thus determined increases or fluctuates, then we may say with certainty that the experimental data are in disagreement with the model.

We give typical illustrations of this method of comparison in Tables 4.6 and 4.7 for gold [*] and magnesium [**] respectively. We observe that for gold Θ_D rises from 163° to 173° and then falls again to 167°. For magnesium Θ_D decreases steadily from 360° to 318°. In a few cases, such as copper and lead, Θ_D varies even less than in the case of gold. In other cases, notably lithium, Θ_D varies by nearly 20 %.

We would emphasize that the entropy is the only simple thermodynamic function for which we have both a closed formula and an experimental value obtainable from a single set of calorimetric measurements performed at constant pressure. In spite of the directness and simplicity of the above method of comparison, it is not generally used. The usual procedure is, from the experimental measurements of H as a function of T, first to compute $dH/dT = C_P$; then by measured, or estimated values of a and $\varkappa$ to use formula (4.09.3) to compute C_V from C_P; lastly to compare the C_V so calculated with formula (7). There are two objections to this procedure as compared with that recommended. In the first place the computation of C_P from H involves a differentiation and so increases any experimental errors, whereas the computation of S from H involves a differentiation followed by an integration, which helps to smooth out the errors introduced by the differentiation. In the second place the computation of C_V from C_P by means of (4.09.3) requires either several other pieces of experimental data or else some guess work, neither of which is required if one makes comparisons of entropy. When the value of C_V, thus computed or estimated,

---

    * Clusius and Harteck, *Zeit. Physik. Chem.* (1928) **134** 243.
   ** Clusius and Vaughen, *J. Am. Chem. Soc.* (1930) **52** 4686

TABLE 4.6

Comparison of molar entropy of gold with Debye's formula

T °K	$(S_m - S_m^0)/R$ expt.	$\dfrac{\Theta_D}{T}$	Θ_D deg.
15	0.06	10.90	163
20	0.14	8.25	165
30	0.385	5.57	167
40	0.705	4.225	167
50	1.05	3.39	170
60	1.40	2.87	172
70	1.73	2.45	171
80	2.03	2.15	172
90	2.32	1.91	172
100	2.58	1.72	172
120	3.07	1.44	173
140	3.49	1.23	172
160	3.87	1.075	172
180	4.22	0.95	171
200	4.53	0.855	171
300	5.77	0.555	167

TABLE 4.7

Comparison of molar entropy of magnesium with Debye's formula

T °K	$(S_m - S_m^0)/R$ expt.	$\dfrac{\Theta_D}{T}$	$\dfrac{\Theta_D}{\text{deg.}}$
20	0.01	18.0	360
30	0.05	11.5	345
40	0.13	8.38	335
50	0.26	6.53	326
60	0.41	5.41	324
80	0.77	4.03	322
100	1.15	3.22	322
120	1.52	2.68	322
140	1.87	2.30	322
160	2.20	2.00	320
180	2.50	1.78	320
200	2.76	1.61	322
300	7.77	1.06	318

is compared with formula (7) we can calculate at each temperature a value of Θ_D which fits. Just as in the comparison of entropies, these values of Θ_D should, if the model is good, decrease slowly and steadily as the temperature, and so the volume, increases. There appears to be a widespread, but mistaken belief that Θ_D should be independent of temperature in spite of the thermal expansion.

Quite apart from the change in Θ_D due to thermal expansion, variations of Θ_D with temperature are to be expected owing to the inadequacy of Debye's model. In view of all the complications in the lattice theory Debye's theory is remarkable not in the extent of its failure, but rather in the extent of its success [*].

§ 4.38 Corresponding Temperatures of Crystals

We have seen that Debye's model is only an approximate representation of a simple crystal of monatomic molecules and further that even if it were an accurate representation, the characteristic temperature Θ_D should still vary with temperature owing to thermal expansion. Nevertheless it is an experimental fact that Debye's formulae with constant Θ_D do give a remarkably good approximate representation over a wide temperature range of the actual behaviour of many simple crystals, especially metals crystallizing in the cubic system. For such substances the values of $S - S^0$, of $(H - H^0)/T$ and consequently of $(\mu - \mu^0)/T$ or of $Y - Y^0$ are universal functions of T/Θ_D. Thus several important thermodynamic properties of different crystals have the same value when T/Θ_D has the same value. Temperatures of different substances such that T/Θ_D has the same value are called *corresponding temperatures*. The principle that certain thermodynamic properties have equal values for different substances at corresponding temperatures is called a *principle of corresponding temperatures*. It is to be observed that this principle for simple crystals makes no reference to the pressure, which is tacitly assumed to be low and to have no appreciable effect on the values of the properties under discussion. In § 4.53 we shall discuss a more interesting principle of corresponding temperatures and corresponding pressures for liquids and gases.

§ 4.39 Comparison of Debye's Functions with Einstein's

Debye's model was preceded by a simpler model due to Einstein leading to the simpler formulae

$$F_m = U_m^0 - T S_m^0 + 3 RT \log (1 - e^{-\Theta_E/T}), \qquad (4.39.1)$$

$$U_m - U_m^0 = 3 R \, \Theta_E/(e^{\Theta_E/T} - 1), \qquad (4.39.2)$$

$$S_m - S_m^0 = - 3 R \{\log (1 - e^{-\Theta_E/T}) - \Theta_E/T (e^{\Theta_E/T} - 1)\}, \quad (4.39.3)$$

$$C_V = 3 R \, \frac{(\Theta_E/2T)^2}{\sinh^2 (\Theta_E/2T)}. \qquad (4.39.4)$$

where Θ_E is Einstein's characteristic temperature.

---

[*] See Blackman, *Rep. Progress. Phys.* (1942) 8 11.

By comparing Debye's formulae with Einstein's we observe that the former contain integrals from zero to Θ_D where the latter contains merely simple functions of Θ_E. Thus Θ_E in a sense represents an average Θ covering the range from 0 to Θ_D. Thus at any given temperature the value of Θ_E which fits is always smaller than the value of Θ_D which fits.

If one tries to fit the experimental data by Einstein's formulae with a constant Θ_E one fails completely at the lowest temperatures, but at higher temperatures there is little to choose between Einstein's formulae and Debye's, provided the value chosen for Θ_E is suitably adjusted. In fact when $T > \frac{1}{3}\Theta_D$ the values of $U_m - U_m^0$ calculated from Debye's formula do not differ appreciably from the values calculated from Einstein's formula provided one uses for Θ_E the value given by $\Theta_E = 0.73\ \Theta_D$. Similarly when $T > \frac{1}{3}\Theta_D$ the values of $S_m - S_m^0$ calculated from Debye's formula do not differ appreciably from the values calculated from Einstein's formula provided one takes $\Theta_E = 0.71\ \Theta_D$. The comparison is shown in Table 4.8.

TABLE 4.8

Comparison of Einstein's formulae with Debye's assuming
$$\Theta_E = 0.73\ \Theta_D \text{ for energies}$$
and $\Theta_E = 0.71\ \Theta_D$ *for entropies*

$\dfrac{\Theta_D}{T}$	$\dfrac{U_m - U_m^0}{3RT}$		$\dfrac{S_m - S_m^0}{3R}$	
	Debye	Einstein	Debye	Einstein
0.1	.964	.963	3.64	3.64
0.2	.929	.929	2.945	2.95
0.4	.860	.861	2.26	2.26
0.6	.794	.797	1.85	1.86
0.8	.733	.736	1.575	1.58
1.0	.675	.679	1.36	1.37
1.2	.620	.625	1.19	1.19
1.4	.571	.575	1.045	1.045
1.6	.525	.527	0.925	0.925
1.8	.482	.483	0.825	0.820
2.0	.442	.442	0.735	0.730
2.2	.405	.403	0.657	0.650
2.4	.371	.368	0.590	0.580
2.6	.339	.334	0.529	0.518
2.8	.310	.304	0.476	0.463
3.0	.284	.276	0.429	0.414

The slight difference of about 2 % between the best values of Θ_E corresponding to a given Θ_D in the cases of the energy and the entropy is a measure of the accuracy lost by the substitution. If one takes $\Theta_E = 0.72\,\Theta_D$, the difference between the values calculated by the two formulae for the free energy are even less than for the energy and the entropy. Since in any case the experimental data cannot be fitted exactly by a constant value of Θ_D, considerable simplification can often be attained without significant loss of accuracy by using Einstein's formulae rather than Debye's provided one is concerned only with temperatures greater than $\frac{1}{3}\,\Theta_D$. At lower temperatures Debye's formulae should be used rather than Einstein's.

§ 4. 40 Equilibrium between Two Phases

Having discussed the thermodynamic properties of a single phase, we now turn to consider two phases in equilibrium. If we denote the two phases by superscripts α and β, the condition for equilibrium between the two phases is according to (1. 45. 5)

$$\mu^\alpha = \mu^\beta, \tag{4.40.1}$$

or according to (4. 15. 7)

$$\lambda^\alpha = \lambda^\beta, \tag{4.40.2}$$

Since in any single phase of a pure substance the temperature T and pressure P may be varied independently and μ or λ may be regarded as a function of T, P, we may therefore regard (1) or (2) as expressing a relation between T and P for equilibrium between the two phases. It follows that when the two phases are in equilibrium, the temperature T and pressure P are not independently variable but either determines the other. We accordingly say that a single phase of one component has two *degrees of freedom* but a pair of phases of one component has only one *degree of freedom*.

§ 4. 41 Relation between Temperature and Pressure for Two Phase Equilibrium

We now proceed to determine how the equilibrium pressure between two phases α and β depends on the temperature T. Differentiating (4. 40. 1) we have

$$d\mu^\alpha = d\mu^\beta. \tag{4.41.1}$$

or

$$\frac{\partial \mu^\alpha}{\partial T}\,dT + \frac{\partial \mu^\alpha}{\partial P}\,dP = \frac{\partial \mu^\beta}{\partial T}\,dT + \frac{d\mu^\beta}{\partial P}\,dP \tag{4.41.2}$$

Using (1. 36. 5) and (1. 36. 6), we obtain

$$-S_m^\alpha\,dT + V_m^\alpha\,dP = -S_m^\beta\,dT + V_m^\beta\,dP. \tag{4.41.3}$$

or

$$(V_m^\beta - V_m^\alpha)\,dP = (S_m^\beta - S_m^\alpha)\,dT. \tag{4.41.4}$$

Formula (4) can also be obtained more directly from Maxwell's relation (3.04.3)

$$\left(\frac{\partial P}{\partial T}\right)_V = \left(\frac{\partial S}{\partial V}\right)_T \qquad (4.41.5)$$

We apply this relation to a system consisting of the two phases α and β in equilibrium with each other. Since for this equilibrium to persist P is completely determined by T and is independent of V, we may replace the partial differential coefficient $(\partial P/\partial T)_V$ by dP/dT. Moreover at constant temperature, and incidentally also constant pressure, S and V can only change through some quantity of substance passing from the phase α to the phase β or conversely. Thus the ratio of the changes in S and in V is independent of the quantity transferred from the one phase to the other. If then we denote by the symbol Δ the increase of any property when one mole passes from the phase α to the phase β, we have

$$\left(\frac{\partial S}{\partial V}\right)_T = \frac{\Delta S}{\Delta V}. \qquad (4.41.6)$$

and so (5) becomes

$$\frac{dP}{dT} = \frac{\Delta S}{\Delta V}. \qquad (4.41.7)$$

which is the same as (4) in slightly different notation.

Since we may rewrite (4.40.1) as

$$H_m^\alpha - T S_m^\alpha = H_m^\beta - T S_m^\beta, \qquad (4.41.8)$$

it follows immediately that

$$T \Delta S = T(S_m^\beta - S_m^\alpha) = H_m^\beta - H_m^\alpha = \Delta H. \qquad (4.41.9)$$

This relation has an obvious physical meaning, the same as that of (4.04.3). If one mole passes isothermally from the phase α to the phase β, the heat q absorbed is equal to ΔH because the process occurs at constant pressure and it is also equal to $T \Delta S$ because, the system being in equilibrium throughout, the change is reversible.

If we now substitute from (9) into (7), we obtain

$$\frac{dP}{dT} = \frac{\Delta H}{T \Delta V} = \frac{H_m^\beta - H_m^\alpha}{T(V_m^\beta - V_m^\alpha)}, \qquad (4.41.10)$$

which is known as *Clapeyron's relation*. This can also be obtained more directly by starting from

$$\frac{\mu^\alpha}{T} = \frac{\mu^\beta}{T} \qquad (4.41.11)$$

instead of (4.40.1). Differentiating (11) we obtain

$$\frac{\partial (\mu^\alpha/T)}{\partial T} dT + \frac{1}{T} \frac{\partial \mu^\alpha}{\partial P} dP = \frac{\partial (\mu^\beta/T)}{\partial T} dT + \frac{1}{T} \frac{\partial \mu^\beta}{\partial P} dP, \quad (4.41.12)$$

and so using (1.36.9) and (1.36.6)

$$-\frac{H_m^\alpha}{T^2}\,dT + \frac{V_m^\alpha}{T}\,dP = -\frac{H_m^\beta}{T^2}\,dT + \frac{V_m^\beta}{T}\,dP. \qquad (4.41.13)$$

whence (10) follows immediately. We have given these alternative derivations of (10) because of its great importance, as the prototype of other similar formulae in systems of more than one component.

§ 4.42   Clapeyron's Relation Applied to Two Condensed Phases

Let us consider the application of Clapeyron's relation to the equilibrium between a solid and a liquid. Using the superscripts S and L to denote these two phases, we have for the variation of the equilibrium pressure with the equilibrium temperature according to (4.41.10)

$$\frac{dP}{dT} = \frac{H_m^L - H_m^S}{T(V_m^L - V_m^S)} = \frac{\triangle_f H}{T(V_m^L - V_m^S)} = \frac{\triangle_f S}{V_m^L - V_m^S}. \qquad (4.42.1)$$

where $\triangle_f H$ is the *molar heat of fusion* and $\triangle_f S$ is the *molar entropy of fusion*. Since fusion is always an endothermic process, the numerator of (1) is always positive, but the denominator may have either sign. It is negative for water, but positive for most substances. Thus the melting point of ice is decreased by increase of pressure, but that of most solids is increased.

The application of Clapeyron's relation to the equilibrium between two solid phases is analogous. In (1) we need only make the superscript L denote the phase stable at the higher temperature and S the phase stable at the lower temperature, so that $H_m^L - H_m^S$ is positive. The sign of dP/dT will then be the same as that of $V_m^L - V_m^S$.

For condensed phases, both V_m^L and V_m^S are small and their difference is much smaller. Usually a pressure of some hundred atmospheres is required to change the freezing-point by a single degree. As an illustrative example, let us consider water. We have

$$-\frac{dP}{dT} = \frac{22 \text{ joule/mole deg.}}{(19.6-18.0)\,\text{cm.}^3/\text{mole}} = \frac{22}{1.6}\,\frac{\text{joule}}{\text{cm.}^3\text{deg.}}$$

$$= \frac{220}{1.6}\,\frac{\text{atm.}}{\text{deg.}} = 140\,\frac{\text{atm.}}{\text{deg.}}. \qquad (4.42.2)$$

As a second example, let us take sodium. We have

$$\frac{dP}{dT} = \frac{7.1 \text{ joule/mole deg.}}{(24.6-24.2)\,\text{cm.}^3/\text{mole}} = \frac{7.1}{0.4}\,\frac{\text{joule}}{\text{cm.}^3\text{ deg.}}$$

$$= \frac{71}{0.4}\,\frac{\text{atm.}}{\text{deg.}} = 180\,\frac{\text{atm.}}{\text{deg.}}. \qquad (4.42.3)$$

Hence as long as the pressure does not exceed one or two atmospheres, the freezing-point may for many purposes be regarded as unaffected by the pressure.

§ 4.43 Clapeyron's Relation Applied to Vapour Equilibrium

Let us now consider the equilibrium between a liquid and a gaseous phase. Using the superscripts L for the liquid and G for the gas we have according to (4.41.10)

$$\frac{dP}{dT} = \frac{H_m^G - H_m^L}{T(V_m^G - V_m^L)}. \qquad (4.43.1)$$

This exact relation can be transformed by making two approximations. In the first place we neglect the second virial coefficient of the gas and treat it as perfect. In the second place we neglect the molar volume of the liquid compared with that of the vapour. With these approximations we have

$$V_m^G - V_m^L \simeq V_m^G \simeq RT/P. \qquad (4.43.2)$$

Substituting (2) into (1), we obtain

$$\frac{1}{P}\frac{dP}{dT} = \frac{H_m^G - H_m^L}{RT^2} = \frac{\triangle_e H}{RT^2}, \qquad (4.43.3)$$

where $\triangle_e H$ is the *molar heat of evaporation*.

It will later prove convenient to have a symbol other than P to denote equilibrium vapour pressure of a condensed phase and for this purpose we shall use p. We accordingly write in place of (3)

$$\frac{d\log p}{dT} = \frac{\triangle_e H}{RT^2}, \qquad (4.43.4)$$

or

$$\frac{d\log p}{d(1/T)} = -\frac{\triangle_e H}{R}. \qquad (4.43.5)$$

It follows from (5) that if we plot $\log p$ against $1/T$ the curve so obtained has at each point a slope equal to $-\triangle_e H/R$. Actually $\triangle_e H$ varies so slowly with the temperature that this curve is nearly a straight line.

Formula (5) incidentally provides a method, rarely if ever mentioned, for determining the molar mass in the vapour. For by measuring p at several known temperatures we can use (5) to calculate $\triangle_e H$. We can then make direct calorimetric measurements to determine what mass of liquid is converted to vapour when a quantity of heat equal to $\triangle_e H$ is absorbed. This mass is then one mole of vapour.

The treatment of equilibrium between a solid and its vapour is precisely analogous. The vapour pressure p of the solid is related to the temperature by

$$\frac{d\log p}{d(1/T)} = -\frac{\triangle_s H}{R}, \qquad (4.43.6)$$

where $\triangle_s H$ is the *molar heat of sublimation*.

§ 4. 44 Heat Capacities of Two Phases in Equilibrium

Consider two phases of a single component in mutual equilibrium. Let the equilibrium pressure, which will depend on the temperature, be denoted by P_{Eq}. Suppose now that we isolate a portion of either of these phases and change its temperature, not at constant pressure, but adjusting the pressure to the value P_{Eq} corresponding to two phase equilibrium at each temperature. The quantity of heat absorbed in this phase will evidently be proportional to the number of moles in the phase and, for a small temperature increase dT proportional to dT. We may therefore write for either of the two phases

$$q = n\, C_{Eq}\, dT, \qquad (4.44.1)$$

where n is the number of moles in the phase and C_{Eq} is the *molar heat capacity at two phase equilibrium*. Since moreover the change is reversible we may write instead of (1)

$$T\, dS = n\, C_{Eq}\, dT, \qquad (4.44.2)$$

or

$$dS_m = C_{Eq}\, dT/T. \qquad (4.44.3)$$

But for the change in question

$$dS_m = \left\{ \left(\frac{\partial S_m}{\partial T} \right)_P + \left(\frac{\partial S_m}{\partial P} \right)_T \frac{dP}{dT} \right\} dT. \qquad (4.44.4)$$

Comparing (3) with (4) we see that

$$C_{Eq} = T \left\{ \left(\frac{\partial S_m}{\partial T} \right)_P + \left(\frac{\partial S_m}{\partial P} \right)_T \frac{dP}{dT} \right\} = C_P - a\, V_m\, T \frac{dP}{dT}, \qquad (4.44.5)$$

using the definition (4.05.2) of C_P and Maxwell's relation (3.04.4). Now substituting from (4.41.10) into (5) we obtain

$$C_{Eq} = C_P - a\, V_m\, \frac{\triangle H}{\triangle V}, \qquad (4.44.6)$$

where $\triangle$ denotes the increase in H when one mole passes isothermally from the one phase to the other; as regards sign the same convention must of course be used for $\triangle H$ and $\triangle V$.

§ 4. 45 Heat Capacities at Saturation

The most important application of the formulae of the previous section is to the equilibrium between a liquid and its vapour. The quantities C_{Eq} are then called the *molar heat capacities at saturation* and are denoted by C_{sat}. If we neglect the second virial coefficient of the gas and also neglect the molar volume of the liquid compared with that of the gas, formula (4.44.6) becomes

$$C_{sat} = C_P - a\, \frac{PV_m}{RT}\, \triangle_e H \qquad (4.45.1)$$

where $\triangle_e H$ is the molar heat of evaporation.

Formula (1) is applicable either to the vapour or to the liquid, but the importance of the second term on the right is very different in the two cases. For the vapour we have, still neglecting the second virial coefficient

$$a = T^{-1}, \qquad PV_m = RT,$$ (4. 45. 2)

so that, using the superscript G for the gas,

$$C_{sat}^G = C_P^G - \frac{\Delta_e H}{T} = C_P^G - \Delta_e S.$$ (4. 45. 3)

The second term on the right may be numerically greater than the first, in which case C_{sat}^G is negative. For example for steam at its normal boiling-point

$$C_P = 34 \text{ joule/mole deg.,}$$

$$\Delta_e S = \frac{\Delta_e H}{T} = \frac{40.6 \text{ Kjoule/mole}}{373 \text{ deg.}} = 109 \text{ joule/mole deg.,}$$

so that

$$C_{sat}^G = (34 - 109) \text{ joule/mole deg.} = -75 \text{ joule/mole deg.}$$

and we see that the heat capacity of steam at saturation is negative.

For the liquid phase on the other hand the second term on the right of (1) is incomparably smaller than for the gas both because a is smaller and because V_m is smaller by a factor of something like 10^3 or more. Consequently for the liquid phase we may neglect this term and replace (1) by

$$C_{sat}^L = C_P^L,$$ (4. 45. 4)

where the superscript L denotes the liquid phase.

The formulae of this section may also be applied to the equilibrium conditions between solid and vapour. Formula (3) is then applicable to the vapour and formula (4) for the solid.

§ 4. 46 Temperature Dependence of Heats of Evaporation and of Fusion

Consider any phase change such as evaporation or fusion and let the symbol Δ denote the increase in any property when one mole passes isothermally from the one phase to the other in the direction such that ΔH is positive, i.e. from liquid to gas or from solid to liquid. Then we have

$$\Delta H/T = \Delta S.$$ (4. 46. 1)

Differentiating with respect to T, varying P so as to maintain equilibrium, we have

$$\frac{d}{dT}\left(\frac{\Delta H}{T}\right) = \frac{d}{dT}\Delta S = \Delta \frac{dS}{dT} = \frac{\Delta C_{Eq}}{T},$$ (4. 46. 2)

or

$$\frac{d}{dT}\Delta H - \frac{\Delta H}{T} = \Delta C_{Eq}.$$ (4. 46. 3)

For equilibrium between liquid and vapour, $C_{Eq} = C_{sat}$ is given by (4. 45. 3) for the vapour and by (4. 45. 4) for the liquid. Substituting these into (3) we obtain

$$\frac{d}{dT} \triangle_e H = C_P^G - C_P^L. \qquad (4.\,46.\,4)$$

the terms $\triangle_e H/T$ on either side cancelling. Formula (4) involves the several approximations mentioned in § 4. 45. It is formally similar to the exact formula for a process taking place between pressure limits independent of the temperature.

To obtain the temperature coefficient of a heat of fusion, we have to go back to (4. 44. 6), which we rewrite in the form

$$C_{Eq} = C_P - \left(\frac{\partial V_m}{\partial T}\right)_P \frac{\triangle_f H}{\triangle_f V}. \qquad (4.\,46.\,5)$$

where $\triangle_f$ denotes the increase of a molar quantity on fusion. Substituting (5) into (3), we obtain

$$\frac{d}{dT} \triangle_f H = \triangle_f C_P + \frac{\triangle_f H}{T} - \triangle_f H \left(\frac{\partial \log \triangle_f V}{\partial T}\right)_P. \qquad (4.\,46.\,6)$$

a formula due to Planck [*]. The last term on the right will usually be very small compared with the second and may then be neglected. We then obtain the approximation

$$\frac{d}{dT} \triangle_f H = \triangle_f C_P + \frac{\triangle_f H}{T} \qquad (4.\,46.\,7)$$

Of the two terms on the right, either may be numerically greater. We thus have a formula not even approximately of the same form as the formula for a process taking place between pressure limits independent of the temperature.

Evidently the formulae of this section may *mutatis mutandis* be applied to the equilibrium between two solid phases.

§ 4. 47 Triple Point

We have seen that the equilibrium condition for a single component between two phases α and β

$$\mu^\alpha(T, P) = \mu^\beta(T, P) \qquad (4.\,47.\,1)$$

is equivalent to a relation between P and T which can be represented by a curve on a $P-T$ diagram. Similarly the equilibrium between the phases α and γ can be represented by a curve on a $P-T$ diagram. If these two curves cut, at the point of intersection we shall have

$$\mu^\alpha(T, P) = \mu^\beta(T, P) = \mu^\gamma(T, P). \qquad (4.\,47\,2)$$

and the three phases α, β, γ will be in mutual equilibrium. This point of intersection is called a *triple-point* and the values of T and P at the triple

---

[*] Planck. *Ann. d. Physik* (1887) **30**, 574

point are called the *triple-point temperature* and the *triple-point pressure*.

We have seen that a single component in one phase has two degrees of freedom since temperature and pressure can be varied independently and that two phases in mutual equilibrium have only one degree of freedom since the temperature and pressure are mutually dependent. We now see that three phases can exist in mutual equilibrium only at a particular temperature and particular pressure. Thus three phases of a single component in mutual equilibrium have no degrees of freedom.

In Fig. 4.3 the conditions of mutual equilibrium for H_2O are shown * on the $P-T$ diagram.

Triple-points can also exist for two solid phases and one liquid phase

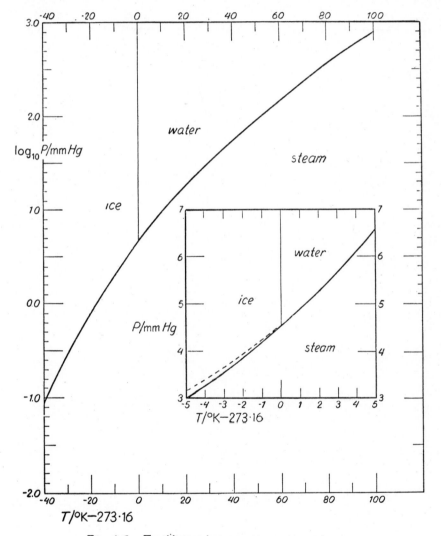

Fig. 4.3. Equilibrium between ice, water and steam.

----

* From Landolt–Börnstein *Tables*.

or for two solid phases and a vapour phase or three solid phases. More rarely we may have two liquid phases and a vapour phase or a solid phase. A triple-point can occur in a region where all three phases are metastable. Fig. 4.4 shows the conditions of equilibrium for sulphur *. There are three stable triple points

T_1: equilibrium between monoclinic, liquid and vapour

T_2: equilibrium between rhombic, monoclinic and liquid

T_3: equilibrium between rhombic, monoclinic and vapour

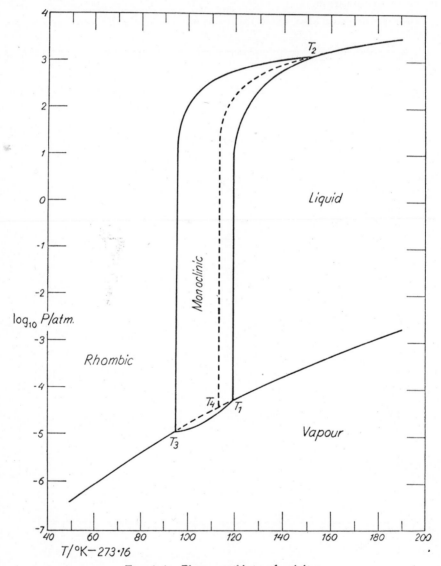

Fig. 4.4. Phase equilibria of sulphur.

---

* From Landolt–Börnstein *Tables*.

and one metastable triple-point

T_4: equilibrium between rhombic, liquid and vapour all three phases phases being metastable and the monoclinic being the stable form.

§ 4.48 Critical Point

The $P - V_m$ isotherms of all pure substances divide into two classes according as the temperature lies above or below a *critical temperature* T_c. Examples of each class for carbon dioxide * are shown in Fig. 4.5.

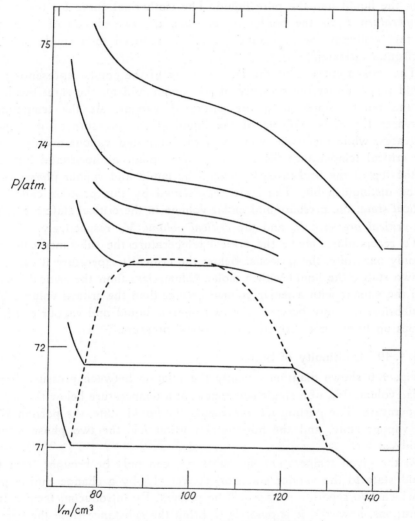

Fig. 4.5. Isotherms of carbon dioxide.

When the molar volume is sufficiently large both classes approximate to the rectangular hyperbolae $PV_m = RT$ of a perfect gas. As the molar

---

* Michels, Blaisse and Michels, *Proc. Roy. Soc.* A (1937) **160** 367.

volume diminishes, the form of the two classes is quite different. At temperatures greater than the critical, there is a smooth regular variation along the whole isotherm, which can be expressed mathematically by saying that it is a single analytic curve or expressed physically by saying that throughout the isotherm there is a single gaseous phase. At temperatures below the critical on the other hand, the isotherm consists of three analytically distinct parts separated by discontinuities of the slope. The middle portion is a horizontal straight line. These parts represent respectively the pure vapour, the saturated vapour in equilibrium with the liquid and the pure liquid. The isothermal curve for the *critical temperature* T_c is the borderline between the two classes of isotherms. In this isotherm the horizontal portion is reduced to a single point of horizontal inflexion.

The broken curve is on the left the locus of the points representing the liquid phase under the pressure of its vapour and on the right the locus of the points representing the saturated vapour. As the temperature increases the molar volume of the liquid at the pressure of its vapour increases, while the molar volume of the saturated vapour decreases. At the critical temperature the isotherm has a point of horizontal inflexion at the top of the broken curve where the liquid and vapour phases cease to be distinguishable. The state represented by this point is called the *critical state*; the pressure and molar volume in the critical state are called the *critical pressure* P_c and the *critical volume* V_c respectively.

To recapitulate, above the critical temperature the substance can exist in only one state, the gaseous. Below the critical temperature it can exist in two states, the liquid with a molar volume less than the critical volume and the vapour with a molar volume greater than the critical volume. The equilibrium pressure between the two phases, liquid and vapour can have values up to but not exceeding the critical pressure.

§ 4.49   Continuity of State

Fig. 4.6 shows diagrammatically the relation between pressure P and molar volume V_m of a single component at a temperature below the critical temperature. The portion KL represents the liquid state, the portion VW the vapour state, and the horizontal portion LV the two phase system liquid-vapour.

At the given temperature the substance can only be brought from the liquid state to the vapour state, or, conversely, by a change during part of which two separate phases will be present. By introducing temperature alterations, however, it is possible to bring the substance from the vapour state represented by W to the liquid state represented by K by a continuous change throughout which there is never more than one phase present. It is only necessary to raise the temperature above the critical temperature, keeping the volume sufficiently greater than the critical volume, then compress the fluid to a volume below the critical volume, keeping the temperature above the critical temperature, and finally cool the liquid to its original temperature, keeping the volume sufficiently below the critical volume. This possibility of continuity between the liquid and vapour states was first realized by James Thomson, and he suggested that the portions

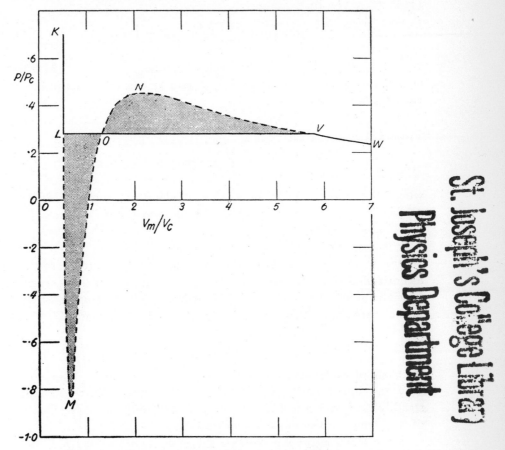

Fig. 4.6. Continuity between liquid and gas phases.

KL and *VW* of the isotherm are actually parts of one smooth curve, such as *KLMONVW*. In point of fact, states corresponding to the portion *VN* are realizable as *supersaturated* vapour, and under certain circumstances the same may be true of the portion *LM* representing *superheated* liquid. Each of these portions represents states stable with respect to infinitesimal variations, but unstable relative to the two phase system liquid + saturated vapour. The portion of the curve *MON*, on the other hand, represents states absolutely unstable, since here

$$\frac{\partial V_m}{\partial P} > 0, \qquad (4.49.1)$$

and, according to (4.02.4), such states are never realizable.

Although the states represented by points on the curve *LMONV* are unstable, either relatively or absolutely, still they are equilibrium states. It follows that the sequence of states represented by the curve $LMONV$ corresponds to a reversible process. The change in the chemical potential μ of the fluid in passing through this sequence of states is, according to (1.36.6), given by

$$\mu^G - \mu^L = \int \left(\frac{\partial \mu}{\partial P} \right)_T dP = \int V_m \, dP, \qquad (4.49.2)$$

where the integrals are to be evaluated along the curve LMONV. But, since the two states represented by L and G can exist in equilibrium with each other, we have

$$\mu^G = \mu^L. \qquad (4.49.3)$$

From (2) and (3) we deduce

$$\int V_m \, dP = 0, \qquad (4.49.4)$$

where the integral is to be evaluated along the curve $LMONV$. The geometrical significance of (4) is that the two shaded surfaces LMO and ONV are of equal area.

It is instructive to consider *continuity of state* in terms of the free energy F. Imagine F to be plotted as vertical coordinate against T and V as horizontal Cartesian coordinates. The resulting locus is a curved surface. Consider now cross-sections of this surface by planes $T = $ const. Examples of these are shown diagrammatically in Fig. 4.7 and since

$$\left(\frac{\partial F}{\partial V} \right)_T = -P, \qquad (4.49.5)$$

the slope of each curve at each point is equal to $-P$.

In the upper curve we see that as V increases, the negative slope steadily decreases numerically and so P decreases steadily. This is typical of any temperature above the critical.

In the lower curve we see that there are two portions $K'L'$ and $V'W'$ in which the negative slope decreases steadily as V increases and these are joined by a straight line $L'V'$ touching $K'L'$ at L' and touching $V'W'$ at V'. These three portions correspond to liquid, to vapour and to a two-phase liquid-vapour system. This is typical of a temperature below the critical. The broken portion of curve $L'M'$ represents superheated liquid and the broken portion $V'N'$ represents supersaturated vapour. We see immediately that all states represented by these portions of curve are metastable, for any point on either of them lies above a point of the same volume V on the straight line $L'V'$ This means that the free energy of the superheated liquid or supersaturated vapour is greater than a system of the same volume consisting of a mixture of liquid L' and vapour V'.

The portions of curve $L'M'$ and $N'V'$ have curvature concave upwards so that

$$\frac{\partial P}{\partial V} = -\frac{\partial^2 F}{\partial V^2} < 0. \qquad (4.49.6)$$

Hence according to (4. 02. 4) they represent states internally stable, though metastable with respect to a two phase mixture. If however we wish to unite these two portions into a single smooth curve, the middle portion

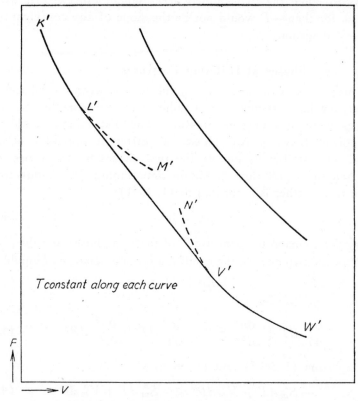

Fig. 4. 7.   Stable and metastable isotherms.

would necessarily have a curvature concave downwards. This would correspond to a positive value of $\partial P/\partial V$ and so to unstable states and we saw in § 1. 43 that such states are never realizable. It may therefore be argued that no physical significance could be attached to this part of the $F—T—V$ surface. Nevertheless, if the realizable parts $K'L'M'$ and $N'V'W'$ of the surface could be represented by the *same analytical function*, it would be reasonable from a mathematical point of view to consider the complete surface. Having constructed such a surface and considering a section corresponding to a particular temperature below the critical, we could then plot $P = -\partial F/\partial V$ against V and so construct a curve such as that in Fig. 4. 6. From this construction it follows of necessity that in Fig. 4. 6 the area below the broken curve $LMONV$ and the area below the straight line LV are both equal to the height of L' above V' in Fig. 4. 7. Consequently these two areas are equal. From this it follows immediately that the two shaded areas are equal as already proved. Since the portion MON of the curve cannot be realized experimentally, instead of saying that the two phase equilibrium is determined by the condition of equality of the two shaded areas, it is perhaps more correct to say that L and V being known the connecting portion of the curve *must* be sketched in such a manner as to make the two shaded areas equal; otherwise it would be nonsensical, for then $-P$ would not be the slope of any conceivable curve on the $F-V$ diagram.

§ 4.50   Two Phases at Different Pressures

In our previous considerations of equilibrium between two phases of one component, we have assumed the equilibrium to be complete so that the two phases were at the same pressure. The distribution equilibrium of one component between two phases at different pressures is also of theoretical interest. Let us denote the two phases by the superscripts α and β. Then the equilibrium condition determining the change from the one phase to the other is according to (1.46.1)

$$\mu^\alpha = \mu^\beta. \tag{4.50.1}$$

If we vary the common temperature T of the two phases and the pressures P^α and P^β of the two phases, the condition for maintenance of equilibrium is

$$d\mu^\alpha = d\mu^\beta, \tag{4.50.2}$$

or

$$\frac{\partial \mu^\alpha}{\partial T} dT + \frac{\partial \mu^\alpha}{\partial P^\alpha} dP^\alpha = \frac{\partial \mu^\beta}{\partial T} dT + \frac{\partial \mu^\beta}{\partial P^\beta} dP^\beta. \tag{4.50.3}$$

Substituting from (1.36.5) and (1.36.6) we obtain

$$- S_m^\alpha dT + V_m^\alpha dP^\alpha = - S_m^\beta dT + V_m^\beta dP^\beta, \tag{4.50.4}$$

or

$$V_m^\beta dP^\beta - V_m^\alpha dP^\alpha = (S_m^\beta - S_m^\alpha) dT = \underset{\alpha \to \beta}{\triangle} S\, dT, \tag{4.50.5}$$

where $\underset{\alpha \to \beta}{\triangle}$ is used to denote the increase of a quantity when one mole passes from the phase α to the phase β.

Since we may rewrite (1) as

$$H_m^\alpha - T S_m^\alpha = H_m^\beta - T S_m^\beta, \tag{4.50.6}$$

it follows immediately that

$$T \underset{\alpha \to \beta}{\triangle} S = T(S_m^\beta - S_m^\alpha) = H_m^\beta - H_m^\alpha = \underset{\alpha \to \beta}{\triangle} H, \tag{4.50.7}$$

just as for two phases at the same pressure. In fact formula (4.41.9) is a special example of (7) and the physical significance is the same in both cases.

If we now substitute from (7) into (5) we obtain

$$V_m^\beta dP^\beta - V_m^\alpha dP^\alpha = \underset{\alpha \to \beta}{\triangle} H\, dT/T. \tag{4.50.8}$$

It is evident that two of the three quantities T, P^α, P^β are independent and so the system has two degrees of freedom. The most important application of these formulae is to the equilibrium between a liquid and its vapour. We then use the superscript L for the liquid and G for the vapour. We also use P to denote the pressure on the liquid and p the pressure of the vapour. In this notation (8) becomes

$$V_m^G \, dp - V_m^L \, dP = \frac{\Delta_e H}{T} \, dT, \tag{4.50.9}$$

where $\Delta_e H$ is the molar heat of evaporation. According to the definition of fugacity $p^\star$ and (4.22.5), we may replace (9) by

$$RT \, d \, \log p^\star - V_m^L \, dP = \frac{\Delta_e H}{T} \, dT. \tag{4.50.10}$$

In particular at constant temperature we have for the dependence of the fugacity of the gas on the external pressure P on the liquid

$$\left(\frac{\partial \log p^\star}{\partial P} \right)_T = \frac{V_m^L}{RT}. \tag{4.50.11}$$

If we treat the vapour as a perfect gas, we may replace $p^\star$ by p.

If, on the other hand, we maintain constant the pressure P on the liquid, we obtain from (10) for the dependence of the gas fugacity on the temperature

$$\frac{d \log p^\star}{dT} = \frac{\Delta_e H}{RT^2}, \qquad \text{(const. } P), \tag{4.50.12}$$

or if we treat the vapour as a perfect gas

$$\frac{d \log p}{dT} = \frac{\Delta_e H}{RT^2}, \qquad \text{(const. } P), \tag{4.50.13}$$

or

$$\frac{d \log p}{d(1/T)} = -\frac{\Delta_e H}{R} \qquad \text{(const. } P). \tag{4.50.14}$$

It is instructive to compare (14) with (4.43.5). The latter involves neglecting the molar volumes of the liquid compared with that of the vapour, but the former involves no such approximation. The difference between the exact formula (14) and the approximate formula (4.43.5) is negligible owing to the fact that in order to affect the saturated vapour pressure p appreciably by change of the hydrostatic pressure P at constant temperature, one requires according to (11) pressures considerably greater than the vapour pressure itself.

The direct experimental application of these formulae would require the separation of the liquid from the vapour by a membrane permeable to the vapour, but not to the liquid. This is difficult to achieve, though not impossible. Consequently the formulae have not much direct practical importance. They have nevertheless a real importance, which will become clear when we consider systems of two or more components. We shall find that these formulae remain true in the presence of another component gas insoluble in the liquid, provided we interpret p as the *partial pressure* of the vapour when mixed with the inert gas. We cannot profitably say more at this stage, but we shall return to this point in § 5.21.

§ 4.51 Fugacity of a Condensed Phase

In § 4.22 we defined the fugacity of a gaseous pure substance in terms of its absolute activity λ. We now define the fugacity of a pure substance in any condensed phase as being equal to the fugacity in the gas phase with which it is in equilibrium. Evidently when two condensed phases are in equilibrium with each other the fugacities must be equal in the two phases.

With this extended definition we may regard formula (4.50.10), namely

$$d \log p^\star = \frac{\triangle_e H}{RT^2}\, dT + \frac{V_m^L}{RT}\, dP \qquad (4.51.1)$$

as expressing the dependence of the fugacity $p^\star$ of a liquid on the temperature T and the external pressure P. A precisely analogous equation applies to a solid.

§ 4.52 Van der Waals' and Dieterici's Equations of State

Many attempts have been made in the past to represent the equation of state of gas and liquid throughout the whole $P-V-T$ domain by an analytical formula. It is now known that it is not possible so to represent the experimental data accurately except by complicated and unwieldy formulae of little interest. On the other hand the distinction between liquid and gas and the existence of a critical point can be deduced *qualitatively* from various quite simple equations of state. Of these we shall mention the two simplest, namely the equation of van der Waals, already referred to in § 4.20,

$$\left(P + \frac{a}{V_m^2}\right)(V_m - b) = RT, \qquad (4.52.1)$$

and the equation of Dieterici

$$P(V_m - b) = RT\, e^{-a/RTV_m}. \qquad (4.52.2)$$

At low pressures, both these equations reduce to

$$V_m = \frac{RT}{P} + b - \frac{a}{RT}, \qquad (4.52.3)$$

neglecting second order small terms. We have already discussed formula (3) in § 4.20. It is equivalent to writing for the second virial coefficient B

$$B = b - \frac{a}{RT} \qquad (4.52.4)$$

We saw in § 4.18 that fair agreement with the experimental data at high temperatures can be obtained by suitable choice of a and b. This is about the sum total of agreement between these equations of state and reality. Nor has either equation any theoretical basis outside this range of low pressures and high temperatures.

It is now well known that neither van der Waals' nor Dieterici's equation can be made to fit the experimental data over any wide domain of T, P. It might however be hoped that by regarding a, b as slowly varying functions of T, P it would be possible to represent the experimental data over a small region by suitably chosen values of a and b. There is in fact a widespread belief that a and b can be so chosen as to represent the actual behaviour at the critical point. We shall now show that this belief has some measure of justification in the case of Dieterici's equation, but none whatever in the case of van der Waals' equation.

We have seen in § 4.48 that at the critical point the isotherm on the $P-V$ diagram is a point of horizontal inflexion. We therefore have the critical conditions

$$\left(\frac{\partial P}{\partial V}\right)_T = 0, \tag{4.52.5}$$

$$\left(\frac{\partial^2 P}{\partial V^2}\right)_T = 0. \tag{4.52.6}$$

If we substitute (1) into (5) and (6) we obtain

$$-\frac{RT_c}{(V_c-b)^2} + \frac{2a}{V_c^3} = 0, \tag{4.52.7}$$

$$\frac{2RT_c}{(V_c-b)^3} - \frac{6a}{V_c^4} = 0. \tag{4.52.8}$$

From these we obtain immediately

$$b = \tfrac{1}{3} V_c, \qquad a = \tfrac{9}{8} RT_c V_c. \tag{4.52.9}$$

Substituting (9) into (1) we obtain van der Waals' equation in the alternative form

$$\left(P + \frac{9}{8}\frac{RT_c V_c}{V_m^2}\right)(V_m - \tfrac{1}{3} V_c) = RT. \tag{4.52.10}$$

In particular by setting $V_m = V_c$ and $T = T_c$ we obtain for P_c

$$P_c = \frac{3}{8}\frac{RT_c}{V_c}, \tag{4.52.11}$$

or

$$\frac{P_c V_c}{RT_c} = \tfrac{3}{8}. \tag{4.52.12}$$

Adopting a similar procedure with Dieterici's equation, we substitute

(2) into (5) and (6). After some simple algebraic reduction we obtain

$$\frac{a}{RT_c} = \frac{V_c^2}{V_c - b} = \frac{V_c^3}{2(V_c - b)^3},$$ (4. 52. 13)

whence

$$b = \tfrac{1}{2} V_c, \qquad a = 2 RT_c V_c.$$ (4. 52. 14)

Substituting (14) into (2), we obtain Dieterici's equation in the alternative form

$$P(V_m - \tfrac{1}{2} V_c) = RT e^{-2T_c V_c / T V_m}.$$ (4. 52. 15)

In particular by setting $V_m = V_c$ and $T = T_c$ we obtain for P_c

$$P_c = \frac{2 RT_c}{V_c} e^{-2},$$ (4. 52. 16)

or

$$\frac{P_c V_c}{RT_c} = 2 e^{-2}.$$ (4. 52. 17)

Thus for the value of the ratio $P_c V_c / RT_c$ we have according to van der Waals' equation 0.375 and according to Dieterici's equation 0.271. We shall see in § 4.53 that for the gases with the simplest molecules the experimental value of this ratio is nearly 0.29. For the majority of non-polar substances the experimental values lie between 0.25 and 0.30. We see then that in this respect Dieterici's equation gives at least a rough representation of the observed relation between $P_c V_c$ and T_c, whereas van der Waals' equation does not.

Unfortunately one sometimes meets the statement that van der Waals' constants a and b were computed from the critical data. Such a statement is at least ambiguous, if not nonsensical; for as van der Waals' equation gives a false value of $P_c V_c / RT_c$ one can evidently obtain various inconsistent sets of values for a, b according as these are computed from P_c, V_c or from P_c, T_c or from V_c, T_c.

§ 4.53 Corresponding States

The *principle of corresponding states* asserts that for a group of similar substances the equation of state can be written in the form

$$\frac{P}{P_c} = \varphi \left(\frac{T}{T_c}, \frac{V_m}{V_c} \right),$$ (4. 53. 1)

where φ is the same function for all the substances of the group.

Since according to (4. 52. 10) and (4. 52. 12) van der Waals' equation of state can be written in the form

$$\left(\frac{P}{P_c} + 3 \frac{V_c^2}{V_m^2} \right) \left(\frac{V_m}{V_c} - \frac{1}{3} \right) = \frac{8}{3} \frac{T}{T_c}.$$ (4. 53. 2)

It follows that a group of substances all conforming to this equation would obey the principle of corresponding states. Since however no such substances exist, this is of no physical interest. The like may be said of Dieterici's equation which can be written in the form

$$\frac{P}{P_c}\left(\frac{V_m}{V_c} - \frac{1}{2}\right) = \tfrac{1}{2} e^{2-2T_c V_c / T V_m}. \qquad (4.53.3)$$

or in fact of any other proposed equation of state containing just two adjustable parameters.

Although, as we have already mentioned, it is not possible to express the equation of state in any simple analytical form, the principle of corresponding states is obeyed with a useful degree of accuracy by a considerable number of substances. It is in fact obeyed with a high degree of accuracy by the three inert elements A, Kr, Xe and to a somewhat lower degree of accuracy by these substances together with Ne, N_2, O_2, CO and CH_4. It would be misleading to try to divide substances into two groups, those which do and those which do not obey the principle. One should rather say that various types of substance obey the principle to a greater or less extent according to their nature. One can at least roughly group substances into the following classes such that generally speaking substances in any class obey the principle rather less well than those in the preceding class and rather better than those in the following class.

(1) The inert heavy elements A, Kr, Xe
(2) The inert lighter elements Ne, He
(3) Non-polar or almost non-polar diatomic molecules, such as N_2, O_2, CO
(4) Lighter non-polar diatomic molecule H_2
(5) Highly symmetrical, non-polar and slightly polarizable molecules, such as CH_4
(6) Less symmetrical non-polar and slightly polarizable molecules such as CO_2
(7) Highly symmetrical, non-polar but polarizable molecules such as CCl_4
(8) Less symmetrical, non-polar but polarizable molecules such as CS_2
(9) Slightly polar small molecules such as COS, $CHCl_3$
(10) Larger slightly polar molecules, such as esters, ketones
(11) Strongly polar molecules such as nitro-compounds
(12) Molecules which form hydrogen bonds, such as OH_2
(13) Molecules which react chemically, such as NO_2.

We shall now review briefly * some of the experimental data which show directly or indirectly how well the substances Ne, A, Kr, Xe, N_2, O_2, CO, CH_4 obey an equation of state of the common form (1).

In Table 4.9 the first row gives the molecular weights, the next three

---

* Guggenheim, *J. Chem. Phys.* (1945) **13** 253; compare Pitzer, *J. Chem. Phys.* (1939) **7** 583.

TABLE 4.9
Corresponding states of gases and liquids

	Formula	Ne	A	Kr	Xe	N_2	O_2	CO	CH_4
1	M	20.18	39.94	83.7	131.3	28.02	32.00	28.00	16.03
2	$T_c/°K$	44.8	150.7	209.4	289.8	126.0	154.3	133.0	190.3
3	$V_c/cm.^3\,mole^{-1}$	41.7	75.3	92.1	113.7	90.2	74.5	93.2	98.8
4	$P_c/atm.$	26.9	48.0	54.1	58.2	33.5	49.7	34.5	45.7
5	$P_c V_c/RT_c$	0.305	0.292	0.290	0.278	0.292	0.292	0.294	0.289
6	$T_B/°K$	121	411.5			327		~345	491
7	T_B/T_c	2.70	2.73			2.59		2.6	2.58
8	$T_s/°K\ (p=P_c/50)$	25.2	86.9	122.0	167.9	74.1	90 1	78.9	110.5
9	T_s/T_c	0.563	0.577	0.582	0.580	0 588	0.583	0.593	0.581
10	$\Delta_e H/R°K$	224	785	1086	1520	671	820	727	1023
11	$\Delta_e H/RT_s$	8.9	9.04	8.91	9.06	9.06	9.11	9.22	9.26
12	$V_m/cm.^3$		28.1	34.1	42.7				
13	V_m/V_c		0.374	0.371	0.376				

rows the critical temperatures T_c, critical volumes V_c and critical pressures P_c. The fifth row gives values of $P_c V_c/RT_c$ which according to the principle should have a universal value. All the values lie close to 0.29.

In Fig. 4.8 all the experimental data on the second virial coefficients

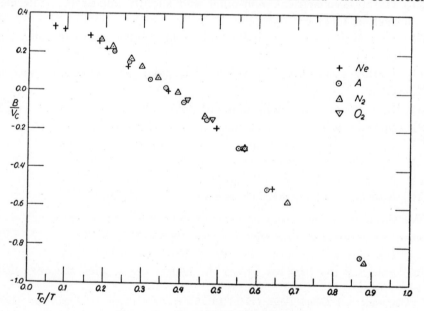

Fig. 4.8. Second virial coefficients.

of these substances are shown in the form of B/V_c plotted against T_c/T. It will be seen that the data for the four substances are roughly fitted by the same curve. The Boyle temperature T_B at which the second virial coefficient changes sign is given in the sixth row of Table 4.9 and in the seventh row are given values of T_B/T_c. All these values lie near 2.7.

If ϱ^L denotes the density of the liquid and ϱ^G that of the vapour in mutual equilibrium at the temperature T, while ϱ_c denotes the density at the critical point, then according to the principle of corresponding states one should expect ϱ^L/ϱ_c and ϱ^G/ϱ_c to be common functions of T/T_c. How nearly this is the case is shown in Fig. 4.9. The curve in the diagram

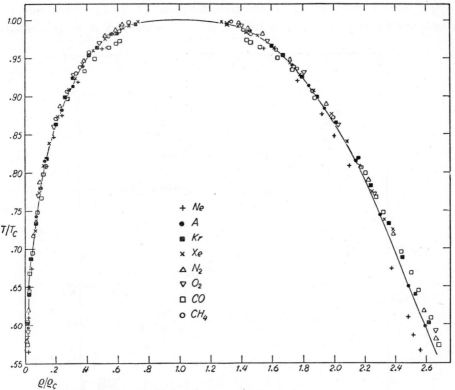

Fig. 4.9. Reduced densities of coexisting liquid and gas phases.

is drawn according to the empirical formulae

$$\frac{\varrho^L + \varrho^G}{2\varrho_c} = 1 + \frac{3}{4}\left(1 - \frac{T}{T_c}\right). \qquad (4.53.4)$$

$$\frac{\varrho^L - \varrho^G}{\varrho_c} = \frac{7}{2}\left(1 - \frac{T}{T_c}\right)^{\frac{1}{3}}. \qquad (4.53.5)$$

It is a pure accident that the data can be represented by formulae with such simple numerical coefficients. These formulae as displayed above are of high relative accuracy, but if used to compute ϱ^G the percentage inaccuracy increases with decrease of temperature and becomes serious below $T \simeq 0.65\ T_c$. It is therefore not recommended to use these formulae for computing values of ϱ^G. There are however occasions when one requires relatively accurate values, not of ϱ^G itself, but of $(\varrho^L - \varrho^G)/\varrho_c$; on such occasions formula (5), in view of its extreme simplicity and surprisingly high accuracy, has much to recommend it. An example of its use will occur in § 4. 74.

At temperatures considerably below the critical temperature, say $T < 0.65\ T_c$, it is better to consider the equilibrium vapour pressure p instead of ϱ^G. According to the principle of corresponding states one should expect p/P_c to be a common function of T/T_c. That this is approximately the case is seen from Fig. 4. 10 where log p/P_c is plotted

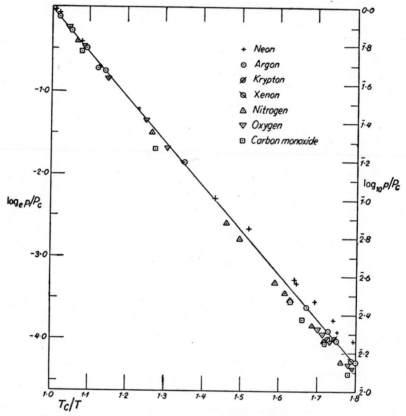

Fig. **4. 10**. Relation between vapour pressure and temperature.

against T_c/T for the several substances. It is clear that the relation is nearly linear, so that we may write

$$\log_e \frac{p}{P_c} = A - B\frac{T_c}{T}, \qquad (4.53.6)$$

where $A,\ B$ are constants having nearly the same values for the several substances. In the diagram the straight line which best fits the data for argon has been drawn. For this line

$$A = 5.29, \quad B = 5.31, \qquad \text{(triple-point to critical point)}. \quad (4.53.7)$$

The fact that A is nearly but not exactly equal to B, means that the relation (6) holds nearly but not quite up to the critical temperature. A formula of the type (6) has a theoretical basis at low temperatures, where the vapour does not differ significantly from a perfect gas and the molar heat of evaporation is nearly independent of the temperature. Under these conditions $\Delta_e H/R = BT_c$. At higher temperatures where the vapour pressure is greater, neither of these conditions holds; the vapour deviates appreciably from a perfect gas and $\Delta_e H$ decreases, becoming zero at $T = T_c$. At such temperatures formula (6) is empirical, but remains surprisingly accurate owing to a compensation between the two deviations.

In the temperature range between the triple-point and the normal boiling-point a formula of the type (6) becomes almost if not quite as accurate as the experimental data, but the best values for the constants A, B over this temperature range are not the same as the best values for the whole range from triple-point to critical point. For argon an excellent fit of the experimental data between the triple-point and the normal boiling-point is attained with the values

$$A = 5.13, \quad B = 5.21. \qquad \text{(temperatures below N.B.P.)}. \quad (4.53.8)$$

In this temperature range the molar heat of evaporation $\Delta_e H$ is sensibly constant and has the value given by

$$\frac{\Delta_e H}{R} = 5.21 \, T_c. \qquad (4.53.9)$$

In the eighth row of Table 4.9 are given the temperatures T_s at which the vapour pressure has a value one fiftieth of the critical pressure. In the ninth row are given values of the ratio T_s/T_c. These are all close to 0.58.

In the tenth row of this table are given values of $\Delta_e H$ the molar heat of evaporation in the low temperature range where it is nearly independent of the temperature. In the eleventh column are given values of $\Delta_e H/RT_s$. All these values lie near to 9.0. Since $\Delta_e H/T$ is the entropy of evaporation, this aspect of the principle of corresponding states may be formulated thus: the entropy of evaporation at *corresponding temperatures*, e.g. temperatures at which the vapour pressure is one fiftieth the critical pressure, has a common value. The older rule of Trouton that substances should have the same entropy of evaporation at their *normal boiling-points* is not in accord with the principle of corresponding states and is in somewhat less good agreement with the facts.

In the twelfth row of the table are given values of V_m the molar volume of the liquid at temperatures just above the triple point and in the thirteenth row values of the ratio V_m/V_c. These values are all near to 0.375.

§ 4.54 Corresponding States of Solids

The principle of corresponding states has a much more restricted applicability to solids. It however applies with high accuracy to the group of the inert elements Ne, A, Kr, Xe. The relevant data for comparison are given in Table 4.10. In the first three rows are given values of T_c, V_c and P_c.

TABLE 4.10

Corresponding states of solids

	Formula	Ne	A	Kr	Xe
1	$T_c/°K$	44.8	150.7	209.4	289.8
2	$V_c/cm.^3\ mole^{-1}$	41.7	75.3	92.1	113 7
3	$P_c/atm.$	26.9	48 0	54.1	58.2
4	$T_t/°K$	24.6	83 8	116 0	161.3
5	T_t/T_c	0.549	0.557	0 553	0.557
6	$\triangle_f H/R°K$	40.3	141.3	196.2	276
7	$\triangle_f H/RT_c$	1.64	1.69	1 69	1.71
8	$P_t/atm.$	0.425	0.682	0.721	0.810
9	$100\,P_t/P_c$	1.58	1.42	1.33	1.39
10	$V^L/cm.^3$		28.14	34.13	42.68
11	$V^S/cm.^3$		24.61	29 65	37.09
12	V^L/V^S		1.144	1.151	1.151

In the fourth row are given values of the triple point temperature T_t and in the fifth row values of the ratio T_t/T_c. All these values are near to 0.555.

In the sixth row are given values of the molar heat of fusion $\triangle_f H$ divided by R and in the seventh row values of the entropy of fusion $\triangle_f H/T_t$ divided by R. These are all near to 1.69.

In the eighth row are given values of P_t the triple point pressure and in the ninth row values of the ratio $100\,P_t/P_c$. These are all near to 1.4.

Finally in the tenth and eleventh rows are given the molar volumes V^L and V^S of the liquid and, solid respectively both at the triple point. In the twelvth row are given the ratios V^L/V^S, all near to 1.15.

§ 4.55 Energy and Entropy Constants

In § 4.16 and § 4.29—4.33 we discussed in some detail the thermodynamic functions of gases. As well as directly measurable quantities such as T, P, B and certain characteristic temperatures Θ_r, Θ_v, Θ_e all well defined properties of the molecules, these formulae contained two further constants H^0 and $\Theta^\dagger$ which we have as yet hardly discussed at all. To be precise the molar heat function H_m contains the additive constant H^0, which we shall now write as $H_m^G(0)$ to show that it refers to the gas phase, while the molar entropy S_m contains the additive constant $-\frac{5}{2} R \log \Theta^\dagger$. The chemical potential μ consequently involves both these constants.

In § 4.36 we described the behaviour of the thermodynamic functions of a crystal at very low temperatures. We saw that the molar heat content H_m contains an additive constant H_m^0, which we shall now write as $H_m^S(0)$ to contrast it with $H_m^G(0)$. Similarly the molar entropy contained an additive constant S_m^0. It will be convenient to define a number o by the relation

$$S_m^0 = R \log o. \qquad (4.55.1)$$

The chemical potential of a crystal consequently involves both the constants $H_m^S(0)$ and S_m^0 or o.

As long as we are concerned only with one single phase, the relevant constants are without any physical significance. It is when we come to compare two phases, that we must be careful to assign values to the constants corresponding to the same conventions.

As regards the heat function constants $H_m^G(0)$ and $H_m^S(0)$ there is little to be said except that when referred to the same energy zero, as they must be if we wish to compare them at all, $H_m^G(0) - H_m^S(0)$ is the value of the molar heat of sublimation of the crystal extrapolated to the absolute zero of temperature. If the heat of sublimation $\triangle_s H$ has been measured at the temperature T, we have

$$\triangle_s H(T) = H_m^G(T) - H_m^S(T). \qquad (4.55.2)$$

Direct calorimetric measurements on the crystal lead to an experimental value of

$$H_m^S(T) - H_m^S(T_0), \qquad (4.55.3)$$

where T_0 is some very low temperature. A small extrapolation, according to formula (4.36.1) leads to a value of

$$H_m^S(T_0) - H_m^S(0). \qquad (4.55.4)$$

Theoretical information concerning the nature of the gaseous molecules, or alternatively calorimetric measurements together with an extrapolation to $T = 0$ in accordance with the theory of the various types of gaseous molecules, gives a value of

$$H_m^G(T) - H_m^G(0). \qquad (4.55.5)$$

10

By adding the quantities (2), (3), (4) and subtracting the quantity (5) we can obtain the value of

$$H_m^G(0) - H_m^S(0). \tag{4.55.6}$$

We turn now to the more interesting entropy constants $-\frac{5}{2} R \log \Theta^\dagger$ and $R \log o$. We described in detail in § 4.04 how to determine experimentally the entropy difference between any two states of a single substance. In particular we can determine experimentally the value of

$$S_m^G(T) - S_m^S(T_0), \tag{4.55.7}$$

where T_0 is some very low temperature. Knowing the values of all the terms in $S_m^G(T)$ except the constant $-\frac{5}{2} R \log \Theta^\dagger$ and extrapolating $S_m^S(T_0)$ to $T_0 \to 0$ in accordance with formula (4.36.2), we thus obtain an experimental value of

$$R \log \Theta^{\dagger \frac{5}{2}} o. \tag{4.55.8}$$

This quantity will be discussed in the following sections.

§ 4.56   Entropy Constants of Monatomic Substances

We begin by considering monatomic substances, since such complications' as occasionally occur for other types of molecules are entirely absent for these. We shall discuss in turn the possible contributions of the various degrees of freedom to the quantity (4.55.8) namely

$$R \log \Theta^{\dagger \frac{5}{2}} o. \tag{4.56.1}$$

Firstly as regards any intra-nuclear degrees of freedom, in particular that due to nuclear spin, their contributions to the solid and to the gas are the same and consequently they make no contribution to (1).

Secondly as regards the electronic degrees of freedom, any contribution in the gaseous state has been allowed for as described in § 4.33 and is not contained in the $\Theta^\dagger$ term. In the solid at low temperatures we may safely assert that there is no electronic contribution.

There remain only the translational degrees of freedom. In the solid these account for the terms which are represented approximately by the temperature dependent terms in Debye's formulae. At very low temperatures they are represented more accurately by the term $\frac{1}{3} a T^3$ in (4.36.2) and they tend to zero as $T \to 0$. Consequently they contribute nothing to (1). There remains only the contribution of the translational degrees of freedom in the gas and this gives by comparison of (2.17.7) with (4.29.4)

$$\Theta^{\dagger \frac{5}{2}} o = \frac{h^3 P^\dagger}{(2 \pi m)^{\frac{3}{2}} k^{\frac{5}{2}}} \tag{4.56.2}$$

where h is Planck's constant, k is Boltzmann's constant, m is the mass of one molecule (atom) and $P^\dagger$ is the arbitrary standard pressure occurring in the formulae of § 4.29. Obviously $\Theta^\dagger$ must depend on $P^\dagger$ in such a manner that the value of any thermodynamic function at a given pressure P is independent of the arbitrary choice of $P^\dagger$

For a substance which in the gaseous state has monatomic molecules formula (2) is generally valid and is independent of any conventional zero of entropy. We now replace the invariant relation (2) by the conventional pair of relations

$$\Theta^{+\frac{5}{2}} = \frac{h^3 P^\dagger}{(2\pi m)^{\frac{3}{2}} k^{\frac{5}{2}}},$$ (4. 56. 3)

$$o = 1.$$ (4. 56. 4)

Formula (4) is equivalent to the convention

$$S_m^S (0) = 0.$$ (4. 56. 5)

These formulae correspond to the following conventional definition of zero entropy. The entropy of a monatomic substance is conventionally defined to be zero in a state such that

(a)   the contributions to the entropy from the translational and electronic degrees of freedom are zero;

(b)   the contributions due to any intranuclear degrees of freedom including spin are ignored, this being allowable only because the contributions are, under terrestial conditions, independent of temperature and the state of the substance.

This conventional choice of zero entropy has proved convenient and is widely used. Unfortunately some authors use the expression *absolute entropy* to denote the value of the entropy according to the convention (5) or some closely related convention. Such terminology is misleading and should be avoided. The only rational system of entropies to which one might reasonably apply the epithet *absolute* would be one referred to certain standard states of the fundamental particles, protons, neutrons and electrons of which matter consists. It is hardly necessary to state that the use of such a system is not at present feasible owing to lack of data on the entropy changes associated with nuclear transmutations. Even if feasible, it is doubtful whether it would serve any useful purpose in the field of terrestial physics and chemistry.

To recapitulate, the convention (5) is, at least for terrestial conditions, the most convenient, but it is in no sense absolute. We shall accordingly refer to the entropy values conforming to the convention (5) as the *conventional entropy values*.

§ 4. 57 Effect of Isotopes

In the previous section· we tacitly ignored any possible effect due to the substance being a mixture of isotopes. When this is the case there are two possible effects on the entropy. The first effect is the obvious one that the term $\frac{3}{2}R \log m$ in the entropy must be replaced by the suitably weighted sum

$$\tfrac{3}{2} R \, \Sigma_i \, x_i \log m_i.$$ (4. 57. 1)

where x_i is the mole fraction of the particular isotope i having an atomic mass m_i. Similarly the constant $H_m^G(0)$ occurring in H_m and in μ, but not in S_m, must be replaced by the weighted sum

$$\Sigma_i \, x_i \, H_i^G \, (0). \tag{4.57.2}$$

The second effect is that any phase, whether solid, liquid or gaseous consisting of a mixture of isotopes in mole fractions x_i has an entropy per mole exceeding the entropy per mole of similar phases of the pure isotopes at the same temperature and pressure and this excess is

$$-R \, \Sigma_i \, x_i \log x_i, \tag{4.57.3}$$

which is always a positive quantity since $x_i < 1$.

We shall meet formula (3) for *entropies of mixing* again in Chapter 5 and Chapter 6. In the present connection we need only note that as long as the solid and the gas have the same isotopic composition, the two terms of the form (3) cancel and so contribute nothing to $\Theta^\dagger$.

§ 4.58   Numerical Values in Entropy Constant

We shall now insert numerical values into (4.56.3), taking as our standard pressure $P^\dagger = 1$ atmosphere. We have then

$$h = 6.624 \times 10^{-27} \text{ erg sec.,}$$
$$k = 1.380_5 \times 10^{-16} \text{ erg deg.}^{-1},$$
$$P^\dagger = 1.013 \times 10^6 \text{ erg cm.}^{-3},$$
$$m = M \times 1.660 \times 10^{-24} \text{ g.,}$$

where M is the conventional *molecular weight*, or *atomic weight* since we are here considering monatomic molecules. Using these values we obtain

$$\Theta^{\dagger \frac{5}{2}} \, M^{\frac{3}{2}} = 39.03 \text{ deg.}^{\frac{5}{2}} = (4.33_1 \text{ deg.})^{\frac{5}{2}}, \qquad (P^\dagger = 1 \text{ atm.}). \tag{4.58.1}$$

Inserting this in formulae (4.29.2), (4.29.3) and (4.29.4), we obtain [*]

$$\log \lambda^\dagger = \frac{\mu^\dagger}{RT} = \frac{H^0}{RT} - \tfrac{5}{2} \log \frac{T}{4.33_1 \text{ deg.}} - \tfrac{3}{2} \log M, \quad (P^\dagger = 1 \text{ atm.}) \tag{4.58.2}$$

$$\log \lambda = \frac{\mu}{RT} = \frac{H^0}{RT} - \tfrac{5}{2} \log \frac{T}{4.33_1 \text{ deg.}} - \tfrac{3}{2} \log M + \log \frac{P}{\text{atm.}} + \frac{PB}{RT}. \tag{4.58.3}$$

$$\frac{S_m}{R} = \tfrac{5}{2} + \tfrac{5}{2} \log \frac{T}{4.33_1 \text{ deg.}} + \tfrac{3}{2} \log M - \log \frac{P}{\text{atm.}} - \frac{P}{R} \frac{dB}{dT}$$

$$= \tfrac{5}{2} \log \frac{T}{1.59_3 \text{ deg.}} + \tfrac{3}{2} \log M - \log \frac{P}{\text{atm.}} - \frac{P}{R} \frac{dB}{dT}. \tag{4.58.4}$$

Formula (4) has probably the most convenient form for purposes of calculation. It can also be written as

$$\frac{S_m}{R} = -1.16_5 + \tfrac{3}{2} \log M + \tfrac{5}{2} \log \frac{T}{\text{deg.}} - \log \frac{P}{\text{atm.}} - \frac{P}{R} \frac{dB}{dT}. \tag{4.58.5}$$

---

[*]   We recall that H^0 is the same quantity as is denoted by $H_m^G(0)$ in § 4.55.

or more conveniently as

$$\frac{S_m}{R} = 10.35 + \tfrac{3}{2}\log M + \tfrac{5}{2}\log\frac{T}{100\,\text{deg.}} - \log\frac{P}{\text{atm.}} - \frac{P}{R}\frac{dB}{dT}. \quad (4.58.6)$$

The corresponding formulae for μ/RT are

$$\frac{\mu}{RT} = \frac{H^0}{RT} - 3.66_5 - \tfrac{3}{2}\log M - \tfrac{5}{2}\log\frac{T}{\text{deg.}} + \log\frac{P}{\text{atm.}} + \frac{PB}{RT}, \quad (4.58.7)$$

$$\frac{\mu}{RT} = \frac{H^0}{RT} + 7.85 - \tfrac{3}{2}\log M - \tfrac{5}{2}\log\frac{T}{100\,\text{deg.}} + \log\frac{P}{\text{atm.}} + \frac{PB}{RT}. \quad (4.58.8)$$

Formulae (6) and (8) are of a form such that the numerical calculations can be completed with adequate accuracy by slide-rule.

§ 4.59 Entropy Constants of Diatomic and Polyatomic Substances

As explained in § 4.55 calorimetric measurements yield experimental values of

$$R\log\Theta^{+\frac{5}{2}}o. \quad (4.59.1)$$

Just as for substances with monatomic molecules we continue to assume that

$$\Theta^{+\frac{5}{2}} = \frac{h^3 P^\dagger}{(2\pi m)^{\frac{3}{2}} k^{\frac{5}{2}}}, \quad (4.59.2)$$

precisely as in (4.56.3). This corresponds to a conventional definition of zero entropy which includes our previous convention for monatomic molecules as a special case. This conventional choice of states of zero entropy is the following:

(a)   the contributions to the entropy from the translational and electronic degrees of freedom are zero;

(a')   the contributions to the entropy from the rotational and internal vibrational degrees of freedom are zero;

(b)   the contributions due to any intranuclear degrees of freedom including spin are ignored, this being allowable only because the contributions are, under terrestial conditions, independent of temperature and the state of the substance;

(c)   isotopic composition is ignored, this being allowable in so far as it is the same in all phases being compared.

For monatomic molecules the conditions (a') were automatically satisfied and were therefore not mentioned. In the case of hydrogen the assumption (b) is subject to certain restrictions which we shall consider in § 4.64.

Precisely as in the case of monatomic molecules, the convention described is convenient and generally used. We shall refer to entropy values thus fixed as *conventional entropy values* and shall avoid the misleading expression *absolute entropy*.

Applying the convention (2) to the experimental values of (1), we obtain conventional values of o which we shall discuss in the next section.

§ 4. 60   Zero-entropies of Crystals

It is found that the conventional values of o obtained as described in the preceding section are in almost all cases unity but that there are exceptions. We shall consider first the physical meaning of

$$o = 1 \qquad\qquad (4.60.1)$$

and then the physical meaning of the exceptions.

We recall that o was defined by (4. 55. 1)

$$S_m^0 = R \log o \qquad\qquad (4.60.2)$$

and that S_m^0 is obtained from experimental values of S at low temperatures by extrapolation according to (4. 36. 2). Provided the experimental data reach down to below 20 °K, the term

$$S_m(T) - S_m^0 = \tfrac{1}{3} a T^3 \qquad\qquad (4.60.3)$$

is so small that no appreciable error arises either from an error in the precise form of the relation assumed between S and T or from an inaccurate value of a. There is however a far more serious hidden assumption implied in the extrapolation, namely that the relation (3) does not completely break down at some temperature below that to which the experimental data extend. Owing to the possibility of this occurrence and the impossibility of a complete experimental disproof, it is well to remember that S_m^0, which we shall call the *zero-entropy* of the crystal, is the entropy smoothly *extrapolated to* $T = 0$ and is not necessarily the entropy *at* $T = 0$. Whereas obviously there is at any given date no experimental answer as to what happens in the temperature range still inaccessible to experiment, statistical theory can tell us when, if ever, it is reasonable to expect complications of the kind described. It in fact tells us that in most cases it is reasonably safe to assume that such possible complications are absent. It also tells us where to expect exceptions. One important exception, namely hydrogen, will be discussed in § 4. 64.

The condition $o = 1$ found for most crystals means that the conventional zero-entropy of the crystal is zero. According to the convention chosen in § 4. 59 this means that the contributions to the entropy from the translational, electronic, rotational and internal vibrational degrees of freedom are all zero. In other words disregarding intranuclear degrees of freedom and isotopic composition, we may say that no other degrees of freedom contribute anything to the entropy. Statistical theory tells us that this corresponds to the crystal being in a perfectly ordered state, provided we disregard intranuclear degrees of freedom and isotopic composition. Thus a combination of statistical theory with experimental data tells us that as the temperature decreases, most crystals tend towards a state of perfect order apart from intranuclear phenomena and isotopic composition. More strictly we should say that this is how the crystal appears to behave judging by the experimental data in the region of 20 °K down to 10 °K.

§ 4.61 Simple Typical Exceptions

We shall now consider the exceptions to the general rule $o = 1$. The two simplest are CO and NNO. In both cases the experimental evidence is that $o > 1$ and within the experimental accuracy $o = 2$. The statistical interpretation of a value 2 for o, is that instead of perfect order in the crystal, there are two possible orientations for each molecule and the molecules are randomly distributed among these two orientations. This is what one should expect to happen in the case of a linear molecule whose field of force is nearly but not quite symmetrical so that the molecule can be reversed end for end without an appreciable energy change. Statistical theory tells us that the equilibrium distribution of directions will remain random down to temperatures at which kT is comparable with the energy difference in the two orientations. At temperatures where kT is much smaller than the energy difference in the orientation, then only one orientation will be stable, but at such low temperatures it may well be that the molecules have not sufficient energy to turn round. In simple words when the crystal is so cold that the molecules have a preference for one orientation they have too little energy (are too "cold") to change their orientations. Such a crystal at the lowest temperatures will remain in a state with $o = 2$ and this state is metastable with respect to the ideal unrealizable state of ordered orientation with $o = 1$. It is believed that this is a true description of the behaviour of crystalline CO and NNO at the lowest temperatures. It is interesting to note that the SCO molecule is not sufficiently symmetrical to behave in this way and the experimental data are consistent with $o = 1$.

The case of NO is somewhat more complicated. It is suggested that at the lowest temperatures the molecular unit is $\begin{smallmatrix} NO \\ ON \end{smallmatrix}$ and that owing to the similarity between N and O atoms the two orientations $\begin{smallmatrix} NO \\ ON \end{smallmatrix}$ and $\begin{smallmatrix} ON \\ NO \end{smallmatrix}$ have nearly equal energies. There would then be a random distribution over these two orientations. This would lead to a value of $o = 2$ for the molecular unit N_2O_2; the corresponding value of o expressed in terms of the molecule NO is $2^{\frac{1}{2}}$ and this value is in agreement with experiment within the estimated accuracy.

The only other well established case of $o > 1$ believed due to simple orientational randomness is that of ice. To account for the experimental data the following assumptions are made:

(1)   In ice each oxygen atom has two hydrogens attached to it at distances about 0.95 Å forming a molecule, the HOH angle being about 105° as in the gas molecule.

(2)   Each HOH molecule is oriented so that its two H atoms are directed approximately towards two of the four O atoms which surround it tetrahedrally.

(3)   The orientations of adjacent HOH molecules are such that only one H atom lies approximately along each O—O axis.

(4)   Under ordinary conditions the interaction of non-adjacent molecules is not such as to stabilize appreciably any one of the many configurations satisfying the preceding conditions relative to the others.

On these assumptions Pauling [*] calculated that theoretically $o = \frac{3}{2}$. Experimentally this value is accurately verified for both H_2O and D_2O.

§ 4.62   Numerical Values in Formulae for Linear Molecules

For linear molecules, including diatomic molecules, the formula for $\mu^\dagger$ is the same as (4.58.2) for monatomic molecules. When we substitute this into the formulae of § 4.31 we obtain

$$\log \lambda = \frac{\mu}{RT} = \frac{H^0}{RT} - \tfrac{5}{2}\log \frac{T}{4.33_1 \text{ deg.}} - \tfrac{3}{2}\log M - \log \frac{T}{\Theta_r \sigma}$$
$$+ \sum_{\Theta_v} \log (1 - e^{-\Theta_v/T}) + \log \frac{P}{\text{atm.}} + \frac{PB}{RT}, \qquad (4.62.1)$$

$$\frac{S_m}{R} = \tfrac{7}{2} + \tfrac{5}{2}\log \frac{T}{4.33_1 \text{ deg.}} + \tfrac{3}{2}\log M + \log \frac{T}{\Theta_r \sigma}$$

$$- \sum_{\Theta_v} \log (1 - e^{-\Theta_v/T}) + \sum_{\Theta_v} \frac{\Theta_v/T}{e^{\Theta_v/T}-1} - \log \frac{P}{\text{atm.}} - \frac{P}{R}\frac{dB}{dT}$$

$$= \tfrac{5}{2}\log \frac{T}{1.06_8 \text{ deg.}} + \tfrac{3}{2}\log M + \log \frac{T}{\Theta_r \sigma} - \sum_{\Theta_v} \log (1 - e^{-\Theta_v/T})$$

$$+ \sum_{\Theta_v} \frac{\Theta_v/T}{e^{\Theta_v/T}-1} - \log \frac{P}{\text{atm.}} - \frac{P}{R}\frac{dB}{dT}. \qquad (4.62.2)$$

For diatomic molecules each $\sum\limits_{\Theta_v}$ reduces to a single term.

§ 4.63   Numerical Values in Formulae for Non-Linear Molecules

For polyatomic non-linear molecules the formula (4.58.2) for $\mu^\dagger$ still holds. When we substitute this into the formulae of § 4.32, we obtain

---

[*] Pauling, *J. Am. Chem. Soc.* (1935) **57** 2680.

$$\log \lambda = \frac{\mu}{RT} = \frac{H^0}{RT} - \tfrac{5}{2} \log \frac{T}{4.33_1 \text{ deg.}} - \tfrac{3}{2} \log M - \log \frac{\pi^{\frac{1}{2}} T^{\frac{3}{2}}}{\Theta_r^{\frac{3}{2}} \sigma}$$

$$+ \sum_{\Theta_v} \log (1 - e^{-\Theta_v/T}) + \log \frac{P}{\text{atm.}} + \frac{PB}{RT}, \qquad (4.63.1)$$

$$\frac{S_m}{R} = 4 + \tfrac{5}{2} \log \frac{T}{4.33_1 \text{ deg.}} + \tfrac{3}{2} \log M + \log \frac{\pi^{\frac{1}{2}} T^{\frac{3}{2}}}{\Theta_r^{\frac{3}{2}} \sigma}$$

$$- \sum_{\Theta_v} \log (1 - e^{-\Theta_v/T}) + \sum_{\Theta_v} \frac{\Theta_v/T}{e^{\Theta_v/T} - 1} - \log \frac{P}{\text{atm.}} - \frac{P}{R} \frac{dB}{dT}$$

$$= \tfrac{5}{2} \log \frac{T}{0.696_1 \text{ deg.}} + \tfrac{3}{2} \log M + \log \frac{T^{\frac{3}{2}}}{\Theta_r^{\frac{3}{2}} \sigma} - \sum_{\Theta_v} \log (1 - e^{-\Theta_v/T})$$

$$+ \sum_{\Theta_v} \frac{\Theta_v/T}{e^{\Theta_v/T} - 1} - \log \frac{P}{\text{atm.}} - \frac{P}{R} \frac{dB}{dT}. \qquad (4.63.2)$$

As an example of the use of these formulae let us calculate the molar entropy of steam at a temperature 373.16 °K and a pressure of one atmosphere. The molecular weight of water is $M = 18.02$ so that

$$4 + \tfrac{5}{2} \log \frac{T}{4.33_1 \text{ deg.}} + \tfrac{3}{2} \log M = 4 + \tfrac{5}{2} \log \frac{373.16}{4.33_1} + \tfrac{3}{2} \log 18.02$$

$$= 4 + 11.14 + 4.34 = 19.48$$

The rotational characteristic temperature of OH_2 is $\Theta_r = 22.2$ deg. and the symmetry number is $\sigma = 2$, so that

$$\log \frac{\pi^{\frac{1}{2}} T^{\frac{3}{2}}}{\Theta_r^{\frac{3}{2}} \sigma} = \log \left\{ \frac{\pi^{\frac{1}{2}}}{2} \left(\frac{373.16}{22.2} \right)^{\frac{3}{2}} \right\} = 4.11$$

The vibrational characteristic temperatures Θ_v are 2290°, 5250° and 5400°. For the contribution of the first we have

$$- \log (1 - e^{-2290/373}) + \frac{2290/373}{e^{2290/373} - 1} = 0.002 + 0.014 = 0.02$$

The contributions from the other two frequencies are negligible.

Since we are interested in the entropy at a pressure of one atmosphere, we have

$$- \log \frac{P}{\text{atm.}} = 0.$$

The correction term involving the second virial coefficient is negligible.

Adding the several contributions we obtain

$$\frac{S_m}{R} = 19.48 + 4.11 + 0.02 = 23.61,$$

$$(T = 373.16° \text{ K}, \quad P = 1 \text{ atm}). \qquad (4.63.3)$$

Let us now compare this with the experimental value of $(S_m - S_m^0)/R$ determined calorimetrically. From the calculation made in § 4.04 we have

$$S_m^G(373.16\,^\circ K, 1\,\text{atm.}) - S_m^S(0) = (38.09 + 21.99 + 23.52 + 108.95)$$

$$\text{joule/mole deg.}$$

$$= 192.55 \text{ joule/mole deg.}$$

and dividing by $R = 8.3140$ joule/mole deg.

$$\frac{S_m^G(373.16\,^\circ K) - S_m^S(0)}{R} = \frac{192.55}{8.3140} = 23.16. \qquad (4.63.4)$$

Subtracting (4) from (3) we obtain

$$S_m^S(0)/R = S_m^0/R = \log o = 0.45 \qquad (4.63.5)$$

in good agreement with Pauling's theoretical value discussed at the end of § 4.61

$$\log o = \log \tfrac{3}{2} = 0.41. \qquad (4.63.6)$$

§ 4.64   The Exceptional Case of Hydrogen

Hydrogen is exceptional in several respects. This is due partly to its molecule having such a small moment of inertia with a consequently high value of the rotational characteristic temperature $\Theta_r = 85.0^\circ$. It is also partly due to the molecule's having an exceptionally small field of force so that even at very low temperatures it still rotates in the crystal. We shall not here go into the theory [*] of the behaviour of hydrogen as this would take us too far afield. We shall merely state the facts sufficiently to show how the various thermodynamic formulae must be used so as to obtain correct results.

For the sake of consistency we define our conventional zero of entropy precisely as for all other molecules, so that formula (4.59.2) is valid for the gas. As regards the physical meaning of this convention the statements (a), (a') and (c) of § 4.59 hold without any alteration, but statement (b) should be modified as follows:

(b)   the contributions due to any intranuclear degrees of freedom other than resultant nuclear spin are ignored and the contribution due to the spin of the two nuclei in a hydrogen molecule is taken to be the same as if the nuclei were present in independent atoms. Any actual deviation from this will then appear in o.

We shall first consider the gas. The usual formulae for gases with diatomic molecules are applicable only at temperatures large compared with Θ_r, and consequently for H_2 they are only valid above about 300 °K.

As the temperature decreases from 300 °K to about 45 °K, the temperature dependent term in the molar heat function H_m decreases from the usual value $\tfrac{7}{2} RT$ for a diatomic gas to the value $\tfrac{5}{2} RT$ usually associated with a monatomic gas. At the same time the conventional molar entropy

---

[*]   Fowler and Guggenheim, *Statistical Thermodynamics* (1939) § 531.

decreases from the usual form for a diatomic gas to a value which except for a constant term recalls that of a monatomic gas. To be precise

$$\frac{\mu}{RT} = \frac{H^0}{RT} - \tfrac{5}{2}\log\frac{T}{\Theta^\dagger} - \tfrac{3}{4}\log 3 + \log\frac{P}{P^\dagger} + \frac{PB}{RT}. \quad (T < 45\,^\circ K) \quad (4.64.1)$$

$$\frac{S_m}{R} = \tfrac{5}{2} + \tfrac{5}{2}\log\frac{T}{\Theta^\dagger} + \tfrac{3}{4}\log 3 - \log\frac{P}{P^\dagger} - \frac{P}{R}\frac{dB}{dT}. \quad (T < 45\,^\circ K), \quad (4.64.2)$$

$$\frac{H_m}{RT} = \frac{H^0}{RT} + \tfrac{5}{2} + \frac{P}{R}\left(B - T\frac{dB}{dT}\right). \qquad (T < 45\,^\circ K). \quad (4.64.3)$$

The constant term $\tfrac{3}{4}\log 3$ in (2) is due to the fact that hydrogen behaves as a mixture of $\tfrac{1}{4}$ parahydrogen with a molar rotational entropy zero at low temperatures and $\tfrac{3}{4}$ orthohydrogen with a molar rotational entropy $R\log 3$ at low temperatures.

Turning now to the crystal, let us first ignore any experimental data below 12 °K and extrapolate smoothly the data between 20 °K and 12 °K in the usual way. We thus obtain well determined values of

$$S_m^G(T) - S_m^S(0) = S_m^G(T) - R\log o. \qquad (4.64.4)$$

We may use either the usual formula for $S_m^G(T)$ with $T > 300\,^\circ K$ or alternatively formula (2) for $S_m^G(T)$ with $T < 45\,^\circ K$; by either procedure we obtain a value for o agreeing within the experimental error with

$$\log o = \tfrac{3}{4}\log 3. \qquad (4.64.5)$$

We notice that the conventional zero-entropy of the crystal obtained by smooth extrapolation from 12 °K is the same as the conventional entropy in the gas below 45 °K.

This would complete the picture of ordinary hydrogen were it not for the existence of experimental data on the crystal between 12 °K and 2 °K. In this range the entropy decreases with anomalous rapidity In fact the heat capacity not only is anomalously greater than corresponds to the form aT^3, but it actually increases as the temperature decreases below 6 °K. On theoretical grounds it is quite clear that the ortho-molecules are somehow beginning to "line up" with a consequent decrease of entropy. There can be little doubt that if these experimental data extended to still lower temperatures the heat capacity would eventually become normal again after there had been a total loss of molar entropy $\tfrac{3}{4}R\log 3$. If we then determined $S_m^S(0)$ from here instead of by extrapolation from 12 °K, we should find

$$o = 1. \qquad (4.64.6)$$

Up to this point we have assumed that the crystal, like the gas, consists of the ordinary metastable mixture of $\tfrac{1}{4}$ parahydrogen and $\tfrac{3}{4}$ orthohydrogen. For this mixture the contributions of nuclear spin to the entropy are normal and so their conventional omission leads to no complications. If however the crystalline hydrogen were converted to stable pure para-hydrogen there would be a decrease in the contributions to the molar entropy, from the nuclear spins and from the mixing of the para and ortho-molecules, from $R \log 4$ to $R \log 1$, which would manifest itself as

$$o = \tfrac{1}{4}. \tag{4.64.7}$$

The conventional zero-entropy of stable parahydrogen is

$$S_m^0 = -R \log 4, \qquad \text{(para-hydrogen)} \tag{4.64.8}$$

and is thus negative.

For deuterium D_2 the general picture is similar with several differences of detail. The gas behaves like other diatomic gases at temperatures exceeding $200\,°K$. Between this temperature and about $25\,°K$, the temperature dependent term in the molar heat function H_m decreases to the value $\tfrac{5}{2} RT$ usually associated with a monatomic gas and there is of course a corresponding drop in the molar entropy. To be precise

$$\frac{\mu}{RT} = \frac{H^0}{RT} - \tfrac{5}{2} \log \frac{T}{\Theta^\dagger} - \tfrac{1}{3} \log 3 + \log \frac{P}{P^\dagger} + \frac{PB}{RT}, \quad (T < 25\,°K), \tag{4.64.9}$$

$$\frac{S_m}{R} = \tfrac{5}{2} + \tfrac{5}{2} \log \frac{T}{\Theta^\dagger} + \tfrac{1}{3} \log 3 - \log \frac{P}{P^\dagger} - \frac{P}{R} \frac{dB}{dT}, \quad (T < 25\,°K), \tag{4.64.10}$$

$$\frac{H_m}{RT} = \frac{H^0}{RT} + \tfrac{5}{2} + \frac{P}{R} \left(B - T \frac{dB}{dT} \right), \qquad (T < 25\,°K). \tag{4.64.11}$$

The constant term $\tfrac{1}{3} \log 3$ in (10) is due to the fact that D_2 behaves as a mixture of $\tfrac{2}{3}$ orthodeuterium with a molar rotational entropy zero at low temperatures and $\tfrac{1}{3}$ paradeuterium with a molar rotational entropy $R \log 3$ at low temperatures.

For the crystal similarly, if one extrapolates in the usual way from a temperature between $20\,°K$ and $10\,°K$ one obtains

$$S_m^S(0)/R = S_m^0/R = \log o = \tfrac{1}{3} \log 3. \tag{4.64.12}$$

There are as yet no experimental data at low enough temperatures to show the disappearance of this entropy.

For the ordinary metastable mixture of $\tfrac{2}{3}$ orthodeuterium and $\tfrac{1}{3}$ para-deuterium, the contributions of nuclear spin to the entropy are normal and so their conventional omission leads to no complications. When however the crystalline deuterium is converted to stable pure ortho-deuterium there is a decrease in the contributions to the molar entropy of the nuclear spins and the mixing of the ortho and para molecules from $R \log 9$ to $R \log 6$. If we assume that at the lowest temperatures the molecules line up, as we know to be the case with H_2, this will manifest itself as

$$o = \tfrac{6}{9} = \tfrac{2}{3}. \tag{4.64.13}$$

The conventional zero-entropy of stable orthodeuterium is

$$S_m^0 = R \log \tfrac{2}{3}. \qquad (4.64.14)$$

which is thus negative.

§ 4.65   Effect of Isotopes

In § 4.57 we considered two possible effects due to the presence of isotopes in a monatomic substance. In the case of a diatomic or polyatomic substance there are three possible effects, which we shall now consider.

The first effect, as in the case of monatomic substances, is that $\log M$ must be replaced by the suitably weighted sum

$$\Sigma_i \, x_i \log M_i, \qquad (4.65.1)$$

where x_i is the mole fraction of the particular isotope i having a conventional molecular weight M_i. Similarly $\log \Theta_r$ must be replaced by

$$\Sigma_i \, x_i \log \Theta_{ri}, \qquad (4.65.2)$$

where Θ_{ri} is the value of Θ_r for the particular isotope i. The terms in Θ_v must similarly be replaced by suitably weighted averages. It should not be necessary to give details, especially since in almost all cases it is sufficiently accurate to replace these averaging rules by the simpler rules of replacing

$$M \text{ by } \Sigma_i \, x_i \, M_i \qquad (4.65.3)$$

$$\Theta_r \text{ by } \Sigma_i \, x_i \, \Theta_{ri}, \qquad (4.65.4)$$

$$\Theta_v \text{ by } \Sigma_i \, x_i \, \Theta_{vi}. \qquad (4.65.5)$$

It is only in the cases of H_2, D_2 and possibly other very light molecules containing H, D, that these simpler averaging rules may not always be sufficiently accurate.

The term H^0 occurring in H_m and in μ, but not in S_m, must likewise be replaced by the weighted average

$$\Sigma_i \, x_i \, H_i^0 \qquad (4.65.6)$$

The second effect is that any phase whether solid, liquid or gaseous, consisting of a mixture of isotopic molecules in mole fractions x_i, has an entropy per mole exceeding the entropy per mole of similar phases of the pure isotopes at the same temperature and pressure and this excess is

$$-R \, \Sigma_i \, x_i \log x_i, \qquad (4.65.7)$$

which is always positive since $x_i < 1$. As long as the solid and gas have same isotopic composition, the two terms of the form (7) cancel and so contribute nothing to $\Theta^{+\frac{5}{2}} o$.

The third effect to be considered is that associated with difference in symmetry. Let us consider the particular example of Cl_2. There are three kinds of molecules $^{35}Cl \, ^{35}Cl$, $^{37}Cl \, ^{37}Cl$ and $^{35}Cl \, ^{37}Cl$. For the molecules $^{35}Cl \, ^{35}Cl$ and $^{37}Cl \, ^{37}Cl$ the symmetry number σ is 2, while for the molecule

^{35}Cl ^{37}Cl it is 1. In the crystal, on the other hand, o for ^{35}Cl ^{37}Cl will have the value 2 because each molecule can be reversed to give a physically distinct state of the crystal of effectively equal energy, whereas for ^{35}Cl ^{35}Cl and ^{37}Cl ^{37}Cl there are not two distinguishable orientations of effectively equal energy and so o is 1. Thus the product σo has the same value 2 for all three types of molecules. Ignoring the isotopic composition means then assigning to ^{35}Cl ^{37}Cl a fictitious value of $\sigma = 2$ instead of $\sigma = 1$ and to o a fictitious value $o = 1$ instead of $o = 2$. When we compare the entropy of the gas and the crystal, and it is only in such comparisons that the values assigned to S_m have any significance, the two errors cancel.

It is instructive to compare the relative behaviours of CO and N_2 with those of ^{35}Cl ^{37}Cl and ^{37}Cl ^{37}Cl. We saw in § 4. 61 that for CO the value of o is 2 while of course $\sigma = 1$. We should however obtain correct results if we assumed as for N_2 that $o = 1$ with $\sigma = 2$, using this *effective symmetry number* because CO is an *effectively symmetrical* molecule.

The same principle holds in more complicated cases. For example comparing the isotopic molecules CH_4, CH_3D, CH_2D_2 we see that for the first $\sigma = 12$, $o = 1$, for the second $\sigma = 3$, $o = 4$ and for the third $\sigma = 2$, $o = 6$ so that in all three cases the product σo is 12.

§ 4. 66 Third Principle of Thermodynamics and Nernst's Heat Theorem

We recall our formulation of the third principle in § 1. 63, which we now repeat.

By the standard methods of statistical thermodynamics it is possible to derive for certain entropy changes general formulae which cannot be derived from the zeroth, first or second principles of classical thermodynamics.

In the present chapter we have had three distinct examples of this type.

In the first place we have quoted a result of completely general validity for the entropy constant of gases at sufficiently high temperatures, namely the formula (4. 56. 3) or (4. 59. 2) for $\Theta^\dagger$.

In the second place we have quoted a result of completely general validity for the increase of entropy when isotopes, or for that matter any other very similar molecules, are mixed at constant temperature and pressure.

In the third place we have quoted a result concerning the conventional zero-entropy of a crystal, namely that o is usually but not always unity.

This last result, in the form quoted, is not altogether satisfactory because it admits exceptions without indicating how or when these occur. It is therefore desirable to try to replace this statement by a more definite statement not admitting exceptions. The following statement fulfils these requirements.

If $\triangle S$ denotes the increase in entropy in any isothermal change which we represent symbolically by

$$\alpha \to \beta, \qquad\qquad (4.\,66.\,1)$$

and we extrapolate $\triangle S$ to $T = 0$ smoothly in the usual way, then if the states α and β are both internally stable, or if any kind of internal metastability present is not affected by the change $\alpha \to \beta$,

$$\underset{T \to 0}{Lt}\, \triangle S = 0. \qquad\qquad (4.\,66.\,2)$$

If on the other hand α is internally metastable, while β is stable, so that the change $\alpha \to \beta$ removes the metastability, then

$$\underset{T \to 0}{Lt}\, \triangle S < 0 \qquad\qquad (4.\,66.\,3)$$

The case where α is stable and β metastable does not arise, since the change $\alpha \to \beta$ would then be impossible. The above statements constitute an amended form [*] of a theorem first stated by Nernst and usually known as *Nernst's Heat Theorem*.

We shall now verify that the behaviour already described of crystals in the limit $T \to 0$ is in accord with the above general statement.

We observe that the several exceptional crystals for which o is not unity are in fact in internally metastable states with some form of randomness of arrangement of the molecules. If by any means it were possible to change such a crystal to the stable completely ordered modifications o would be reduced from a value greater than unity to the value unity and so (3) is satisfied.

Examples of changes satisfying (2) are allotropic changes such as

$$\text{white tin} \to \text{grey tin}$$

$$\text{monoclinic sulphur} \to \text{rhombic sulphur}$$

In each of these examples, although at low temperatures and ordinary pressures the first form is metastable with respect to the second, both forms are completely stable with respect to internal changes. In each case for both phases $o = 1$ and so the equality (2) is obeyed.

Another interesting example is that of helium, the only substance which remains liquid down to $T = 0$. The liquid is changed to solid under pressure. The relation between the pressure and freezing temperature is shown in Fig. 4.11, from which it is clear that

$$\underset{T \to 0}{Lt}\, \frac{dP}{dT} = 0. \qquad\qquad (4.\,66.\,4)$$

But according to the Clapeyron relation (4.41.10) this is equivalent to

$$\underset{T \to 0}{Lt}\, \frac{\triangle S}{\triangle V} = 0. \qquad\qquad (4.\,66.\,5)$$

---

[*] See Simon, *Erg. d. Exakt. Naturwiss.* 9 222 (1930).

But ΔV is certainly finite and so (5) implies

$$\underset{T \to 0}{Lt}\, \triangle S = 0. \tag{4.66.6}$$

The most numerous and important examples of the relation (2) are

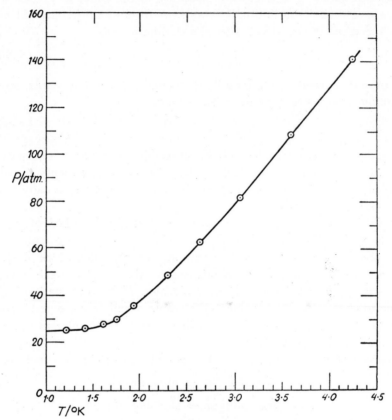

Fig. 4.11.   Melting-curve of helium.

those of chemical reactions between solid phases, for example

$$Ag + I \to AgI$$

These will be discussed in § 7.14.

§ 4.67   Thermal Expansion at Low Temperatures

It is an experimental fact that the coefficient of thermal expansion of all solids and of liquid helium tend towards zero as the temperature is decreased. But according to Maxwell's relation (3.04.4), this implies that

$$\underset{T \to 0}{Lt}\left(\frac{\partial S}{\partial P}\right)_T = 0. \tag{4.67.1}$$

If we integrate this from P^I to P^{II}, we obtain

$$\underset{T \to 0}{Lt}\{S(T, P^{II}) - S(T, P^I)\} = 0, \tag{4.67.2}$$

which is in accordance with the general relation (4.66.2).

This is the only example of the application of (4.66.2) to a simple physical change which we can discuss at this stage. In Chapter XIII we shall consider an interesting application to variation of the strength of an applied magnetic field.

§ 4.68   Unattainability of Absolute Zero

The general laws formulated in the preceding sections concerning the behaviour of matter extrapolated to $T = 0$ are equivalent to the following principle *:

It is impossible by any procedure, no matter how idealized, to reduce the temperature of any system to the absolute zero in a finite number of operations.

We shall now prove this equivalence. Let us consider any process (e.g. change of volume, change of external field, allotropic change) denoted formally by

$$\alpha \to \beta. \tag{4.68.1}$$

We shall use the superscripts α and β to denote properties of the system in the states α and β respectively. Then the molar entropies of the system in these two states depend on the temperature according to the formulae

$$S_m^\alpha = S_m^{0\alpha} + \int_0^T \frac{C^\alpha}{T}\, dT, \tag{4.68.2}$$

$$S_m^\beta = S_m^{0\beta} + \int_0^T \frac{C^\beta}{T}\, dT, \tag{4.68.3}$$

where $S_m^{0\alpha}$, $S_m^{0\beta}$ are the limiting values of S_m^α, S_m^β for $T \to 0$. It is known from quantum theory that both the integrals converge. Suppose now that we start with the system in the state α at the temperature T' and that we can make the process $\alpha \to \beta$ take place adiabatically. Let the final temperature after the system has reached the state β be T''. We shall now consider the possibility or impossibility of T'' being zero. From the second principle of thermodynamics we know that for an adiabatic process defined by its initial and final states the entropy increases if there is any irreversible change and remains constant if the change is completely reversible. It is therefore clear that the chances of attaining as low a final T as possible are most favourable when the change is completely reversible. We need therefore consider only such changes. For a reversible adiabatic change (1) we have then by (2) and (3)

$$S_m^{0\alpha} + \int_0^{T'} \frac{C^\alpha}{T}\, dT = S_m^{0\beta} + \int_0^{T''} \frac{C^\beta}{T}\, dT. \tag{4.68.4}$$

---

* See Simon, *Science Museum Handbook* **3** (1937) p. 61. All earlier discussions are unnecessarily restricted.

Compare Fowler and Guggenheim, *Statistical Thermodynamics* (1939) § 538.

11

If T'' is to be zero, we must then have

$$S_m^{0\beta} - S_m^{0\alpha} = \int_0^{T'} \frac{C^\alpha}{T} \, dT. \tag{4.68.5}$$

Now if $S_m^{0\beta} - S_m^{0\alpha} > 0$ it will always be possible to choose an initial T' satisfying (5) and by making the process $\alpha \to \beta$ take place from this initial T' it will be possible to reach $T'' = 0$. From the premise of the unattainability of $T = 0$ we can therefore conclude that

$$S_m^{0\beta} \leqq S_m^{0\alpha} \tag{4.68.6}$$

Similarly we can show that if we can make the reverse process take place reversibly and adiabatically then we could reach $T'' = 0$ from an initial temperature T' satisfying

$$S_m^{0\alpha} - S_m^{0\beta} = \int_0^{T'} \frac{C^\beta}{T} \, dT. \tag{4.68.7}$$

Further if $S_m^{0\alpha} - S_m^{0\beta} > 0$, we can always choose an initial T' satisfying (7). From the unattainability of $T = 0$ we can therefore conclude that

$$S_m^{0\alpha} \leqq S_m^{0\beta}. \tag{4.68.8}$$

From (6) and (8) we deduce

$$S_m^{0\alpha} = S_m^{0\beta}, \tag{4.68.9}$$

which is precisely formula (4.66.2) of Nernst's Heat Theorem.

We can also show conversely that given (9), neither the process $\alpha \to \beta$ nor the reverse process $\beta \to \alpha$ can be used to reach $T = 0$. For, assuming (9) to be true, we now have for the adiabatic process $\alpha \to \beta$ the initial temperature T' and the final temperature T'' related by

$$\int_0^{T'} \frac{C^\alpha}{T} \, dT = \int_0^{T''} \frac{C^\beta}{T} \, dT. \tag{4.68.10}$$

To reach $T'' = 0$ we should require

$$\int_0^{T'} \frac{C^\alpha}{T} \, dT = 0. \tag{4.68.11}$$

But, since $C^\alpha > 0$ always, for any non-zero T', it is impossible to satisfy (11). Hence the process $\alpha \to \beta$ can not be used to reach $T = 0$. The proof for the reverse process $\beta \to \alpha$ is exactly similar.

In the above argument we have assumed that the states α and β are connected by reversible paths. If all the phases concerned are phases in complete internal equilibrium the changes concerned must presumably be regarded as reversible. If any phase occurs naturally in metastable internal equilibrium, a process affecting it may or may not disturb the frozen metastability. If it does not disturb it, then the change may still be regarded as reversible, but otherwise it will be a natural irreversible change. We shall now verify that by using internally metastable phases we are still unable to reach $T = 0$. In fact as foreshadowed above the irreversibility involved makes the task more difficult.

Suppose for example that α is internally metastable, while β is internally stable. Then according to (4. 66. 3) of Nernst's Heat Theorem

$$S_m^{0\alpha} > S_m^{0\beta}. \tag{4.68.12}$$

But the change $\alpha \to \beta$ is a natural irreversible process and the opposite change is impossible; hence the adiabatic change $\alpha \to \beta$ takes place with increase of entropy, so that

$$S_m^{0\alpha} + \int_0^{T'} \frac{C^\alpha}{T} \, dT < S_m^{0\beta} + \int_0^{T''} \frac{C^\beta}{T} \, dT. \tag{4.68.13}$$

Thus to attain $T'' = 0$, we must have

$$\int_0^{T'} \frac{C^\alpha}{T} \, dT < S_m^{0\beta} - S_m^{0\alpha} < 0 \tag{4.68.14}$$

using (12). But since $C^\alpha > 0$ always, it is impossible to satisfy (14) and so we again find it impossible to reach $T = 0$.

We shall revert to the subject of the unattainability of $T = 0$ at the end of Chapter XIII on magnetic systems.

§ 4.69 Interfacial Layers

We complete this chapter by a consideration of interfacial layers. In a one component system we cannot usually have more than one liquid phase and so we need consider only the interfaces between a liquid and its vapour. The interfacial tension of such an interface is usually called the *surface tension of the liquid*.

As we have seen in § 4.40 a one component system with two bulk phases has one degree of freedom. We may accordingly treat the temperature as the independent variable; the pressure is then determined by the temperature. Thus the properties of the interfacial layer, in particular the surface tension will be completely determined by the temperature. Our main task is therefore to consider how the surface tension depends on the temperature.

§ 4.70 Temperature Dependence of Surface Tension

We begin with formula (1. 55. 3)

$$- d\gamma = S^\sigma dT - \tau dP + \Gamma d\mu, \tag{4.70.1}$$

where we have dropped the subscript u in S^σ, which we henceforth assume to refer to unit area.

From the equilibrium between the liquid phase, denoted by the superscript L, and the gas phase, denoted by the superscript G, we have as in § 4.41

$$d\mu = - S_m^L \, dT + V_m^L \, dP = - S_m^G \, dT + V_m^G \, dP. \tag{4.70.2}$$

When we eliminate $d\mu$ and dP from (1) and (2) we obtain

$$-\frac{d\gamma}{dT} = (S^\sigma - \Gamma S_m^L) - (\tau - \Gamma V_m^L)\frac{S_m^G - S_m^L}{V_m^G - V_m^L}. \qquad (4.70.3)$$

This formula relates the temperature coefficient of the surface tension to certain entropy changes. Before we examine this formula in any detail, we shall show how it can be transformed to another relation involving energy changes instead of entropy changes.

For the two bulk phases we have as usual

$$\mu = G_m^L = U_m^L - TS_m^L + PV_m^L, \qquad (4.70.4)$$

$$\mu = G_m^G = U_m^G - TS_m^G + PV_m^L. \qquad (4.70.5)$$

For the surface layer we have by applying to unit area the formulae of § 1.54

$$\Gamma\mu = G^\sigma = U^\sigma - TS^\sigma + P\tau - \gamma. \qquad (4.70.6)$$

We now use (4), (5) and (6) to eliminate S_m^L, S_m^G and S^σ from (3). We obtain

$$-T\frac{d\gamma}{dT} = (U^\sigma - \Gamma U_m^L) + P(\tau - \Gamma V_m^L) - \gamma$$

$$-(\tau - \Gamma V_m^L)\frac{U_m^G - U_m^L}{V_m^G - V_m^L} - P(\tau - \Gamma V_m^L). \qquad (4.70.7)$$

The terms containing P cancel and (7) reduces to

$$\gamma - T\frac{d\gamma}{dT} = (U^\sigma - \Gamma U_m^L) - (\tau - \Gamma V_m^L)\frac{U_m^G - U_m^L}{V_m^G - V_m^L}. \qquad (4.70.8)$$

§ 4.71 Invariance of Relations

We recall that according to the definition in § 1.51 of a surface phase the properties associated with it depend on the position of the boundaries AA' and BB' in Fig. 1.2. We shall henceforth refer to these as the $L\sigma$ and the $G\sigma$ boundaries respectively. Since the precise placing of these boundaries is partly arbitrary, the values assigned to such quantities as τ, Γ, S^σ, U^σ are also arbitrary. We can nevertheless verify that our formulae are invariant with respect to shifts of either or both of the boundaries. It is hardly necessary to mention that the intensive variables T, P and μ are unaffected by shifts of either boundary. It is also clear from the definition of γ in § 1.52 that its value is invariant.

Let us now consider a shift of the plane boundary $L\sigma$ through a distance $\delta\tau$ away from the gas phase. Then Γ becomes increased by the number of moles in a cylinder of liquid of height $\delta\tau$, of cross-section unity and consequently of volume $\delta\tau$. Thus Γ becomes increased by $\delta\tau/V_m^L$. It follows immediately that $\tau - \Gamma V_m^L$ remains invariant. Similarly S^σ becomes increased by the entropy in a cylinder of liquid of volume $\delta\tau$, that is to say by an amount $S_m^L \delta\tau / V_m^L$. It follows immediately that $S^\sigma - \Gamma S_m^L$ remains invariant. Precisely similar considerations show that $U^\sigma - \Gamma U_m^L$ remains invariant.

We have now to consider a similar shift of the $G\sigma$ boundary through a distance $\delta\tau$ away from the liquid phase. Then Γ is increased by $\delta\tau / V_m^G$, and so $(\tau - \Gamma V_m^L)$ is increased by $(V_m^G - V_m^L)\,\delta\tau / V_m^G$. Similarly $(S^\sigma - S_m^L)$ is increased by $(S_m^G - S_m^L)\,\delta\tau / V_m^G$. When we insert these values into (4.70.3) we see that the resulting variation vanishes. The same holds for (4.70.8).

§ 4.72   Simplifying Approximation

The formulae of § 4.70 are strictly accurate and involve no assumptions or approximations concerning the structure of the interfacial layer. We shall see that they can be greatly simplified by making use of our knowledge concerning this layer.

In § 4.34 we mentioned that, at temperatures well below the critical, PV_m^L is small compared with RT and may usually be ignored. In the interfacial layer the density is comparable to that in the liquid phase so that τ/Γ is comparable to V_m^L and negligible compared with V_m^G. Consequently the terms containing the factor $(\tau - \Gamma V_m^L)/(V_m^G - V_m^L)$ may be neglected. Formulae (4.70.3) and (4.70.8) then reduce to

$$-\frac{d\gamma}{dT} = S^\sigma - \Gamma S_m^L, \qquad (4.72.1)$$

$$\gamma - T\frac{d\gamma}{dT} = U^\sigma - \Gamma U_m^L \qquad (4.72.2)$$

respectively.

It is worth noticing that the right side of (1) is the entropy of unit area of surface less the entropy of the same material content of liquid and the right side of (2) is the energy of unit area of surface less the energy of the same material content of liquid. More pictorially we may say that when unit area of surface is created isothermally and reversibly, the work done on the system is γ, the heat absorbed by the system is the right side of (1) multiplied by T, and the increase of energy, the sum of these two quantities, is equal to the right side of (2).

If however we are making the above simplifying approximations, then by making them at an earlier stage we can considerably simplify the derivations. We accordingly replace (4.70.1) by the approximation

$$-d\gamma = S^\sigma dT + \Gamma d\mu, \qquad (4.72.3)$$

and (4.70.2) by the approximation

$$d\mu = -S_m^L\,dT = -S_m^G\,dT + RT\,d\log P. \qquad (4.72.4)$$

Eliminating $d\mu$ from (3) and (4) we obtain immediately

$$-d\gamma = (S^\sigma - \Gamma S_m^L)\,dT \qquad (4.72.5)$$

in agreement with (1).

Furthermore we replace (4. 70. 4) by the approximation

$$\mu = U_m^L - TS_m^L,$$

(4. 72. 6)

and (4. 70. 6) by the approximation

$$\Gamma\mu = U^\sigma - TS^\sigma - \gamma.$$

(4. 72. 7)

Eliminating S^σ and S_m^L from (5), (6) and (7) we recover (2).

We conclude this discussion with a warning against indiscriminately using the simplified formulae of this section in the neighbourhood of the critical point. The necessary condition for their use is that

$$\tau/\Gamma - V_m^L \ll V_m^G - V_m^L.$$

(4. 72. 8)

In the neighbourhood of the critical temperature V_m^L becomes nearly as great as V_m^G and this condition may no longer be taken for granted.

§ 4. 73 Vapour Pressure of Small Drops

Fig. 4. 12 represents a small spherical drop and a portion of liquid in

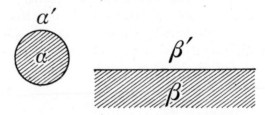

Fig. 4. 12. Vapour pressure of droplet.

bulk both at the same temperature. We denote the interiors of these liquid phases by α, β respectively and the vapour immediately outside them by α', β' respectively. Let us assume that the external pressures $P^{\alpha'}$ and $P^{\beta'}$ are equal, that is

$$P^{\alpha'} = P^{\beta'}.$$

(4. 73. 1)

Then, according to (1. 56. 10) the pressure P^α at the interior α of the drop is greater than that P^β of the liquid in bulk, according to

$$P^\alpha - P^\beta = \frac{2}{r}\gamma.$$

(4. 73. 2)

But according to (4. 50. 11) the fugacity $p^\star$ is related to the pressure P by

$$\frac{d \log p^\star}{dP} = \frac{V_m^L}{RT}.$$

(4. 73. 3)

If then we neglect the compressibility of the liquid, the fugacity $p^{\star\alpha}$ of the liquid in the drop is related to the fugacity $p^{\star\beta}$ of the liquid in bulk by

$$RT \log \frac{p^{\star\alpha}}{p^{\star\beta}} = (P^\alpha - P^\beta) V_m^L.$$

(4. 73. 4)

Comparing (2) and (4) we find

$$RT \log \frac{p^{*\alpha}}{p^{*\beta}} = \frac{2}{r} \gamma V_m^L. \tag{4.73.5}$$

If we neglect deviations of the vapour from a perfect gas, we may replace fugacities p^* by vapour pressures p and so obtain

$$RT \log \frac{p^{\alpha}}{p^{\beta}} = \frac{2}{r} \gamma V_m^L. \tag{4.73.6}$$

We see then that at the same external pressure the small drop always has a greater fugacity and vapour pressure than the bulk liquid. Vapour will distil from the drop to the liquid and as the drop becomes smaller its vapour pressure increases still more. Thus small drops are essentially metastable relative to the liquid in bulk.

§ 4.74 Empirical Temperature Dependence of Surface Tension

Since the surface tension of a liquid decreases with increasing temperature and vanishes at the critical point, the simplest possible form of empirical relation between γ and T is

$$\gamma = \gamma_0 \left(1 - \frac{T}{T_c} \right)^{1+r}, \tag{4.74.1}$$

where γ_0 and r are constants. For the substances having the simplest and most symmetrical molecules such as Ne, A, N_2, O_2 excellent agreement with the experimental data is obtained with $r = 2/9$ as is shown in Table 4.11. The data at the foot of this table will be discussed in § 4.75.

The reason for the particular choice $r = 2/9$ will be explained shortly. Ferguson[*] in a review of the experimental data for ten esters and four other organic compounds found $r = 0.210 \pm 0.015$, which does not differ significantly from the value 2/9 adopted above. Van der Waals at a much earlier date suggested the value $r = 0.234$, but accurate experimental data do not support this value.

Another type of formula relates the surface tension γ to the coexisting molar volumes V^L of the liquid and V^G of the vapour. The simplest satisfactory formula of this type is the following

$$\gamma y^{-\frac{2}{3}} \propto (1 - T/T_c) \tag{4.74.2}$$

where y is defined by

$$y = \frac{1}{V_m^L} - \frac{1}{V_m^G}. \tag{4.74.3}$$

or

$$y V_c = \frac{\varrho^L - \varrho^G}{\varrho_c}. \tag{4.74.4}$$

---

[*] Ferguson, *Trans. Faraday Soc.* (1923) **19** 407; *Proc. Phys. Soc.* (1940) **52** 759.

TABLE 4. 11

$$\gamma = \gamma_0 \left(1 - T/T_c\right)^{11/9}.$$

Ne			A			N₂			O₂		
$T_c = 44.8$ °K $\gamma_0 = 15.1$ dyne/cm.			$T_c = 150.7$ °K $\gamma_0 = 36.31$ dyne/cm.			$T_c = 126.0$ °K $\gamma_0 = 28.4$ dyne/cm.			$T_c = 154.3$ °K $\gamma_0 = 38.4$ dyne/cm.		
T °K	γ/dyne cm.$^{-1}$		T °K	γ/dyne cm.$^{-1}$		T °K	γ/dyne cm.$^{-1}$		T °K	γ/dyne cm.$^{-1}$	
	calc.	obs.		calc.	obs.		calc.	obs.		calc.	obs
24.8	5.64	5.61	85.0	13.16	13.19	70.0	10.54	10.53	70.0	18.34	18.35
25.7	5.33	5.33	87.0	12.67	12.68	75.0	9.40	9.39	75.0	17.02	17.0
26.6	5 02	4.99	90.0	11.95	11.91	80.0	8.29	8.27	80.0	15.72	15.73
27.4	4.75	4.69				85.0	7.20	7.20	85.0	14.44	14.5
28.3	4.45	4.44				90.0	6.14	6.16	90.0	13 17	13.23
$V_c = 41.7$ cm.³/mole $\gamma_0 V_c^{\frac{2}{3}} T_c^{-1} =$ 4.05 erg deg.$^{-1}$ mole$^{-\frac{2}{3}}$			$V_c = 75.3$ cm.³/mole $\gamma_0 V_c^{\frac{2}{3}} T_c^{-1} =$ 4.3 erg deg.$^{-1}$ mole$^{-\frac{2}{3}}$			$V_c = 90.2$ cm.³/mole $\gamma_0 V_c^{\frac{2}{3}} T_c^{-1} =$ 4.5 erg deg.$^{-1}$ mole$^{-\frac{2}{3}}$			$V_c = 74.5$ cm.³/mole $\gamma_0 V_c^{\frac{2}{3}} T_c^{-1} =$ 4.4 erg deg.$^{-1}$ mole$^{-\frac{2}{3}}$		

This formula, due to Katayama *, is a striking improvement over the older and less accurate formula of Eötvos, which contained V^L instead of y^{-1}. This was shown by Katayama for various organic compounds and we shall now verify that this is also the case for the substances having the simplest molecules.

In § 4. 53 we verified that the substances having the simplest molecules follow with a high degree of accuracy formula (4. 53. 5), namely

$$\frac{\varrho^L - \varrho^G}{\varrho_c} = \frac{7}{2} \left(1 - \frac{T}{T_c}\right)^{\frac{1}{3}}. \qquad (4.74.5)$$

Using the definition (4) of y, this can be written

$$y \propto \left(1 - \frac{T}{T_c}\right)^{\frac{1}{3}}. \qquad (4.74.6)$$

If we now eliminate y between (2) and (6), we obtain

$$\gamma \propto \left(1 - \frac{T}{T_c}\right)^{1\frac{2}{9}}, \qquad (4.74.7)$$

of the form (1) with $r = 2/9$. It follows that the verification of (7) in Table 4. 11 and the verification of (5) in Fig. 4. 9 together constitute a verification of (2).

If instead of eliminating y between (2) and (6), we eliminate T/T_c between the same formulae we obtain

$$\gamma \propto y^{3\frac{2}{7}}. \qquad (4.74.8)$$

* Katayama, *Science Reports Tôhoku Imperial University* (1916) 4 373.

The better known relation of McLeod * with an index 4 instead of $3\frac{2}{5}$ is less accurate, at least for the substances having the simplest molecules. Actually for the half dozen organic compounds considered by McLeod it is clear that γ in fact varies as some power of y less than 4.

§ 4. 75 Corresponding States Applied to Surface Tensions

The principle of corresponding states, so far as applicable at all to surfaces, can on physical grounds be expected to hold only for substances having the simplest and most symmetrical molecules.

According to the principle it is clear from dimensional considerations that $\gamma_0 \ V_c^{\frac{2}{3}} \ T_c^{-1}$ should be a common function of T/T_c for substances obeying the principle. In particular, if these substances obey (4. 74. 1), then $\gamma_0 \ V_c^{\frac{2}{3}} \ T_c^{-1}$ should have a common value. The data ** at the bottom of Table 4. 11 show that this is in fact the case within about $\pm 2\%$ for A, N_2, O_2, while the value for Ne deviates by rather less than 10 %.

---

* McLeod, *Trans. Faraday Soc.* (1923) **19** 38.
** For details see Guggenheim, *J. Chem. Phys.* (1945) **13** 259.

CHAPTER V

SYSTEMS OF TWO NON-REACTING COMPONENTS

§ 5.01 Introduction

As soon as we turn from systems of one component to systems of more than one component we introduce the possibility of new degrees of freedom associated with differences in composition. For example we can have two liquid phases of different composition in equilibrium with each other.

There are no differences of principle between the treatment of systems of two components on the one hand and systems of more than two components on the other. Nevertheless a separate chapter is being devoted to the former not because any emphasis is placed on the number *two*, but rather because formulae for a specified number, e.g. two, of components are in many respects more definite and therefore simpler than formulae for an unspecified number of components.

It is assumed throughout this chapter that the two species do not react chemically with each other. Consideration of chemical reactions is postponed to Chapter VII.

§ 5.02 Partial Molar Volumes

If we make up a mixture of n_1 moles of a substance 1 having a molar mass M_1 and n_2 moles of a substance 2 having a molar mass M_2 then owing to the conservation of mass it is evident that the mass M of the mixture is given by

$$M = n_1 M_1 + n_2 M_2. \qquad (5.02.1)$$

It would be desirable to have similar relations for other extensive properties such as volume V and entropy S, but as these are not necessarily conserved on mixing the situation is not so simple. One might define V_1 as having the same value as in the pure substance and then use the relation

$$V = n_1 V_1 + n_2 V_2 \qquad (5.02.2)$$

as a definition of V_2. But such a convention would be unsymmetrical with respect to the species 1 and 2, and is therefore objectionable. We accordingly have to proceed by a less obvious path.

We define quantities V_1, V_2 by the relations

$$V_1 = \left(\frac{\partial V}{\partial n_1}\right)_{T,P,n_2}, \qquad (5.02.3)$$

$$V_2 = \left(\frac{\partial V}{\partial n_2}\right)_{T,P,n_1}, \qquad (5.02.4)$$

so that for the most general change in the homogeneous mixture of the species 1 and 2

$$dV = \alpha V dT - \varkappa V dP + V_1 dn_1 + V_2 dn_2. \qquad (5.02.5)$$

and for the variations in content at constant temperature and constant pressure

$$dV = V_1 dn_1 + V_2 dn_2, \qquad (\text{const. } T, P). \qquad (5.02.6)$$

At constant temperature and pressure V is homogeneous of the first degree in n_1, n_2 and so V_1, V_2 are homogeneous of zero degree in n_1, n_2. This means physically that if we increase n_1 and n_2 in the same ratio, then V is also increased in the same ratio while V_1, V_2 remain constant. If then we consider a variation at constant relative composition, that is to say constant n_1/n_2, we may write

$$dn_1 = n_1 d\xi, \quad dn_2 = n_2 d\xi, \quad dV = V d\xi. \qquad (5.02.7)$$

Substituting (7) into (6), we obtain

$$V d\xi = n_1 V_1 d\xi + n_2 V_2 d\xi. \qquad (5.02.8)$$

Now dividing throughout by $d\xi$, or alternatively integrating from $\xi = 0$ to $\xi = 1$, we obtain

$$V = n_1 V_1 + n_2 V_2. \qquad (5.02.9)$$

which is of the desired form (2). We have thus achieved our object of attaining this relation by means of a symmetrical definition of V_1 and V_2. We call V_1 the *partial molar volume* of the species 1 and V_2 the *partial molar volume* of the species 2.

§ 5.03   Other Partial Molar Quantities

Corresponding to any extensive property X, the partial molar quantities X_1, X_2 are defined precisely as in the case of volume, that is to say

$$X_1 = \left(\frac{\partial X}{\partial n_1} \right)_{T, P, n_2}, \qquad (5.03.1)$$

$$X_2 = \left(\frac{\partial X}{\partial n_2} \right)_{T, P, n_1}. \qquad (5.03.2)$$

By reasoning precisely analogous to that in the case of volume, we can then deduce

$$X = n_1 X_1 + n_2 X_2. \qquad (5.03.3)$$

It is not necessary to write down relations of this form for each extensive property. We shall merely give a table of some important examples.

X	X_1	X_2
V	V_1	V_2
S	S_1	S_2
U	U_1	U_2
F	F_1	F_2
H	H_1	H_2
G	G_1	G_2
C	C_1	C_2
C_v	C_{v1}	C_{v2}

It is perhaps worth while drawing attention here to the fact that the quantity X need not be a thermodynamic property of the system. It is only required that X shall be an extensive property. We shall merely mention one example of such a non-thermodynamic property. If r denotes the refractive index of a mixture of two substances, we define the *total refractivity* R of the system by

$$R = \frac{r^2 - 1}{r^2 + 2} V, \tag{5.03.4}$$

so that R is clearly an extensive property. We then define *partial molar refractivities* in the usual way by

$$R_1 = \left(\frac{\partial R}{\partial n_1}\right)_{T, P, n_2}, \tag{5.03.5}$$

$$R_2 = \left(\frac{\partial R}{\partial n_2}\right)_{T, P, n_1}, \tag{5.03.6}$$

and it then follows as usual that

$$R = n_1 R_1 + n_2 R_2. \tag{5.03.7}$$

The reason for choosing this particular example is the following. There are theoretical grounds for expecting R to be an approximately additive quantity, in which case R_1, R_2 would be independent of the composition of the mixture and have the same values as for the two pure substances. This is more or less supported by experiment. There are however theoretical grounds for expecting in certain cases deviations from simple additivity and this is also confirmed by experiment. The quantitative theoretical discussion of such deviations from simple additivity could be improved by the use of the *partial molar refractivities* defined as above.

§ 5.04 Relations Between Several Partial Molar Quantities

Since the partial molar quantities are defined from extensive properties by simple differentiation, it follows that they are interrelated in a manner similar to the extensive properties from which they are derived. In particular we have

$$F_1 = U_1 - TS_1, \tag{5.04.1}$$

$$H_1 = U_1 + PV_1, \tag{5.04.2}$$

$$\mu_1 = G_1 = U_1 - TS_1 + PV_1, \tag{5.04.3}$$

$$S_1 = -\left(\frac{\partial G_1}{\partial T}\right)_P = -\left(\frac{\partial \mu_1}{\partial T}\right)_P, \tag{5.04.4}$$

$$V_1 = \left(\frac{\partial G_1}{\partial P}\right)_T = \left(\frac{\partial \mu_1}{\partial P}\right)_T, \tag{5.04.5}$$

$$H_1 = G_1 - T\left(\frac{\partial G_1}{\partial T}\right)_P = -T^2\left(\frac{\partial [G_1/T]}{\partial T}\right)_P, \tag{5.04.6}$$

$$F_1 = G_1 - P \left(\frac{\partial G_1}{\partial P} \right)_T,$$ (5.04.7)

$$U_1 = G_1 - T \left(\frac{\partial G_1}{\partial T} \right)_P - P \left(\frac{\partial G_1}{\partial P} \right)_T,$$ (5.04.8)

$$C_1 = T \left(\frac{\partial S_1}{\partial T} \right)_P = \left(\frac{\partial H_1}{\partial T} \right)_P$$ (5.04.9)

All differentiations in the above are performed at constant composition. A precisely similar set of relations of course holds for the partial molar quantities of the species 2.

§ 5.05   Variations of Partial Molar Quantities with Composition

If we differentiate the relation (5.02.9) we obtain

$$dV = n_1 dV_1 + V_1 dn_1 + n_2 dV_2 + V_2 dn_2,$$ (5.05.1)

and comparing this with (5.02.5) we derive

$$-aV \, dT + \varkappa V \, dP + n_1 \, dV_1 + n_2 \, dV_2 = 0.$$ (5.05.2)

In particular at constant temperature and pressure

$$n_1 dV_1 + n_2 dV_2 = 0, \qquad \text{(const. } T, P\text{)}.$$ (5.05.3)

Similarly for any other pair of partial molar quantities X_1, X_2 we can derive

$$n_1 dX_1 + n_2 dX_2 = 0, \qquad \text{(const. } T, P\text{)}.$$ (5.05.4)

§ 5.06   Use of Mole Fractions

The relative composition of any phase is conveniently described by the *mole fractions* as defined in § 1.37. In a phase containing two components, the mole fractions x_1, x_2 are defined by

$$x_1 = \frac{n_1}{n_1 + n_2}, \qquad x_2 = \frac{n_2}{n_1 + n_2}$$ (5.06.1)

and satisfy the identity

$$x_1 + x_2 = 1.$$ (5.06.2)

We shall use as independent variable x_2 and shall drop the subscript 2. We accordingly write

$$x_2 = x, \qquad x_1 = 1 - x.$$ (5.06.3)

Formula (5.05.4) is then equivalent to

$$(1-x) \left(\frac{\partial X_1}{\partial x} \right)_{T,P} + x \left(\frac{\partial X_2}{\partial x} \right)_{T,P} = 0,$$ (5.06.4)

or more briefly

$$(1-x) \frac{\partial X_1}{\partial x} + x \frac{\partial X_2}{\partial x} = 0,$$ (5.06.5)

it being understood that the other independent variables throughout are T, P unless any statement is made to the contrary.

§ 5.07 Mean Molar Quantities

Corresponding to any extensive property X, the *mean molar quantity* X_m in a phase of two components is defined by

$$(n_1 + n_2) X_m = X. \tag{5.07.1}$$

The various thermodynamic mean molar quantities are interrelated in the same manner as the extensive quantities from which they are derived. In particular

$$F_m = U_m - TS_m, \tag{5.07.2}$$

$$H_m = U_m + PV_m, \tag{5.07.3}$$

$$G_m = U_m - TS_m + PV_m, \tag{5.07.4}$$

$$S_m = - \frac{\partial G_m}{\partial T}, \tag{5.07.5}$$

$$H_m = G_m - T \frac{\partial G_m}{\partial T}, \tag{5.07.6}$$

$$F_m = G_m - P \frac{\partial G_m}{\partial P}, \tag{5.07.7}$$

$$U_m = G_m - T \frac{\partial G_m}{\partial T} - P \frac{\partial G_m}{\partial P}, \tag{5.07.8}$$

$$C_m = T \frac{\partial S_m}{\partial T} = \frac{\partial H_m}{\partial T} \tag{5.07.9}$$

In all the above differentiations the independent variables are T, P, x; thus in all of them x is kept constant.

§ 5.08 Relations Between Partial Molar and Mean Molar Quantities

If we apply the relation (5.03.3) to a phase containing in all one mole, we obtain

$$X_m = (1 - x) X_1 + x X_2. \tag{5.08.1}$$

Differentiating (1) with respect to x, taking account of (5.06.4) we find

$$\frac{\partial X_m}{\partial x} = X_2 - X_1. \tag{5.08.2}$$

From (1) and (2) we deduce

$$X_1 = X_m - x \frac{\partial X_m}{\partial x}, \tag{5.08.3}$$

$$X_2 = X_m + (1 - x) \frac{\partial X_m}{\partial x}. \tag{5.08.4}$$

Formulae (3) and (4) have a simple geometrical interpretation shown in Fig. 5.1. The abscissa is x, increasing from zero at O representing the pure component 1 to unity at O' representing the pure component 2. Suppose the curve APB to be a plot of the mean molar quantity X_m as ordinate and P

to be any point on it. Let the tangent QPR to this curve at P cut the O and O' ordinates at Q and R respectively. Then from (3) and (4) we see

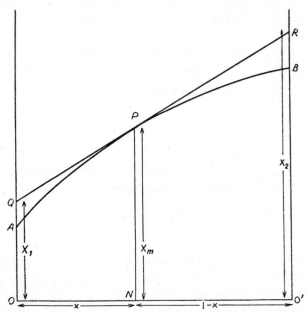

Fig. **5.1.** Relation between partial molar quantities and mean molar quantity.

that the partial molar quantities X_1 and X_2 for the composition at P are represented by OQ and $O'R$ respectively.

It is clear from this construction or otherwise that for either pure component the *partial molar quantity* is equal to the *mean molar quantity*, becoming in fact the *molar quantity* used in the preceding chapter.

§ 5.09 Partial Molar Quantities at High Dilution

By writing (5.06.5) in the form

$$\frac{\partial X_1}{\partial x} \bigg/ \frac{\partial X_2}{\partial x} = -\frac{x}{1-x}, \qquad (5.09.1)$$

we make the interesting observation that as $x \to 0$ either $\dfrac{\partial X_1}{\partial x} \to 0$ or $\dfrac{\partial X_2}{\partial x} \to \infty$. Both alternatives occur. We shall find later that as $x \to 0$, $\dfrac{\partial V_1}{\partial x}$, $\dfrac{\partial U_1}{\partial x}$, $\dfrac{\partial H_1}{\partial x}$, $\dfrac{\partial C_1}{\partial x}$ all tend towards zero, while $\dfrac{\partial S_2}{\partial x}$, $\dfrac{\partial F_2}{\partial x}$, $\dfrac{\partial G_2}{\partial x}$ all tend towards infinity.

In the limit $x \to 1$, we of course meet the converse behaviour corresponding to interchange of the species 1 and 2.

§ 5.10 Gibbs-Duhem Relation

All our considerations concerning partial molar quantities X_1, X_2 are valid when X is any extensive property. In particular if we take X to be the Gibbs function G, we have according to (5.06.5)

$$(1-x)\frac{\partial G_1}{\partial x} + x\frac{\partial G_2}{\partial x} = 0. \qquad (5.10.1)$$

Now from the fundamental relation (1.31.6) applied to a phase with two components

$$dG = -SdT + VdP + \mu_1\,dn_1 + \mu_2\,dn_2, \qquad (5.10.2)$$

we see that

$$G_1 = \mu_1, \qquad (5.10.3)$$

$$G_2 = \mu_2. \qquad (5.10.4)$$

Substituting (3) and (4) into (1) we obtain

$$(1-x)\frac{\partial \mu_1}{\partial x} + x\frac{\partial \mu_2}{\partial x} = 0, \qquad (5.10.5)$$

which is the Gibbs–Duhem relation already derived in § 1.38.

It is worth noting that since formula (1) follows from the fact that G is an extensive property and from the definitions of G_1 and G_2, it is clear that in deriving the Gibbs–Duhem relation (5) thermodynamic considerations come in only through the use of (3) and (4).

If we take X_m in (5.08.3) and (5.08.4) to be G_m, we have

$$\mu_1 = G_m - x\frac{\partial G_m}{\partial x}, \qquad (5.10.6)$$

$$\mu_2 = G_m + (1-x)\frac{\partial G_m}{\partial x}. \qquad (5.10.7)$$

§ 5.11   Binary Gaseous Mixtures

In considering a mixture of two gases it is convenient to begin with the independent variables T, V and transform to the variables T, P later. We accordingly begin by describing the free energy F.

We recall that for a single gas containing n moles the free energy F is according to (4.23.5)

$$F = n\mu^\dagger - nRT + nRT \log\frac{nRT}{P^\dagger V} + \frac{n^2 RTB}{V}, \qquad (5.11.1)$$

neglecting virial coefficients beyond the second. Statistical mechanics shows that the term containing B is due to interactions of pairs of molecules, whereas the higher virial coefficients, which we are neglecting, are connected with simultaneous interactions involving more than two molecules. The remaining terms in (1) are those of a perfect gas in which the molecules are treated as independent.

The extension of (1) to a mixture containing n_1 moles of species 1 and n_2 moles of species 2 is

$$F = n_1 \left\{ \mu_1^\dagger - RT + RT \log \frac{n_1 RT}{P^\dagger V} \right\}$$
$$+ n_2 \left\{ \mu_2^\dagger - RT + RT \log \frac{n_2 RT}{P^\dagger V} \right\}$$
$$+ \frac{RT}{V} \left\{ n_1^2 B_{11} + 2 n_1 n_2 B_{12} + n_2^2 B_{22} \right\}. \qquad (5.11.2)$$

In (2) the term in B_{11} takes account of interactions between pairs of molecules of type 1, B_{22} between pairs of molecules of type 2 and B_{12} between pairs of molecules one of each type. These three coefficients, as well as $\mu_1^\dagger, \mu_2^\dagger$ depend only on the temperature. We recall that $P^\dagger$ denotes some standard pressure, whose choice of course affects the values of $\mu_1^\dagger, \mu_2^\dagger$.

From (2) we derive immediately

$$P = - \left(\frac{\partial F}{\partial V} \right)_{T, n_1, n_2} = (n_1 + n_2) \frac{RT}{V}$$
$$+ \frac{RT}{V^2} \left\{ n_1^2 B_{11} + 2 n_1 n_2 B_{12} + n_2^2 B_{22} \right\}. \qquad (5.11.3)$$

$$\mu_1 = \left(\frac{\partial F}{\partial n_1} \right)_{T, V, n_2} = \mu_1^\dagger + RT \log \frac{n_1 RT}{P^\dagger V} + \frac{2RT}{V} (n_1 B_{11} + n_2 B_{12}). \qquad (5.11.4)$$

$$\mu_2 = \left(\frac{\partial F}{\partial n_2} \right)_{T, V, n_1} = \mu_2^\dagger + RT \log \frac{n_2 RT}{P^\dagger V} + \frac{2RT}{V} (n_1 B_{12} + n_2 B_{22}). \qquad (5.11.5)$$

The absolute activities are given by

$$\log \lambda_1 = \log \lambda_1^\dagger + \log \frac{n_1 RT}{P^\dagger V} + \frac{2}{V} (n_1 B_{11} + n_2 B_{12}), \qquad (5.11.6)$$

$$\log \lambda_2 = \log \lambda_2^\dagger + \log \frac{n_2 RT}{P^\dagger V} + \frac{2}{V} (n_1 B_{12} + n_2 B_{22}), \qquad (5.11.7)$$

where

$$\lambda_1^\dagger = e^{\mu_1^\dagger / RT}, \qquad \lambda_2^\dagger = e^{\mu_2^\dagger / RT}. \qquad (5.11.8)$$

§ 5.12   Change of Variable from V to P

Formula (5.11.3) expresses P as a power series in V^{-1}, which is quadratic because we are neglecting smaller terms of higher order. We can invert this into a formula for V as a power series in P and obtain to the same degree of accuracy

$$\frac{V}{n_1 + n_2} = \frac{RT}{P} + \frac{n_1^2 B_{11} + 2 n_1 n_2 B_{12} + n_2^2 B_{22}}{(n_1 + n_2)^2}. \qquad (5.12.1)$$

Substituting (1) into (5.11.4) we obtain to the same order of accuracy

$$\mu_1 = \mu_1^\dagger + RT \log \frac{n_1}{n_1 + n_2} + RT \log \frac{P}{P^\dagger}$$
$$+ P \left\{ B_{11} - \left(\frac{n_2}{n_1 + n_2} \right)^2 (B_{11} - 2B_{12} + B_{22}) \right\}. \quad (5.12.2)$$

Similarly

$$\mu_2 = \mu_2^\dagger + RT \log \frac{n_2}{n_1 + n_2} + RT \log \frac{P}{P^\dagger}$$
$$+ P \left\{ B_{22} - \left(\frac{n_1}{n_1 + n_2} \right)^2 (B_{11} - 2B_{12} + B_{22}) \right\}. \quad (5.12.3)$$

For the absolute activities we have

$$\log \lambda_1 = \log \lambda_1^\dagger + \log \frac{n_1}{n_1 + n_2} + \log \frac{P}{P^\dagger}$$
$$+ \frac{P}{RT} \left\{ B_{11} - \left(\frac{n_2}{n_1 + n_2} \right)^2 (B_{11} - 2 B_{12} + B_{22}) \right\}. \quad (5.12.4)$$

$$\log \lambda_2 = \log \lambda_2^\dagger + \log \frac{n_2}{n_1 + n_2} + \log \frac{P}{P^\dagger}$$
$$+ \frac{P}{RT} \left\{ B_{22} - \left(\frac{n_1}{n_1 + n_2} \right)^2 (B_{11} - 2 B_{12} + B_{22}) \right\}. \quad (5.12.5)$$

For the Gibbs function we have

$$G = n_1 \mu_1 + n_2 \mu_2$$
$$= n_1 \mu_1^\dagger + n_2 \mu_2^\dagger + (n_1 + n_2) RT \log \frac{P}{P^\dagger}$$
$$+ n_1 RT \log \frac{n_1}{n_1 + n_2} + n_2 RT \log \frac{n_2}{n_1 + n_2}$$
$$+ P \left\{ n_1 B_{11} + n_2 B_{22} - \frac{n_1 n_2}{(n_1 + n_2)} (B_{11} - 2 B_{12} + B_{22}) \right\}. \quad (5.12.6)$$

For the entropy we have

$$S = -\left(\frac{\partial G}{\partial T} \right)_P = -n_1 \frac{d\mu_1^\dagger}{dT} - n_2 \frac{d\mu_2^\dagger}{dT} - (n_1 + n_2) R \log \frac{P}{P^\dagger}$$
$$- n_1 R \log \frac{n_1}{n_1 + n_2} - n_2 R \log \frac{n_2}{n_1 + n_2}$$
$$- P \left\{ n_1 \frac{dB_{11}}{dT} + n_2 \frac{dB_{22}}{dT} - \frac{n_1 n_2}{(n_1 + n_2)} \frac{d}{dT} (B_{11} - 2 B_{12} + B_{22}) \right\}. \quad (5.12.7)$$

and for the heat function

$$H = G + TS = n_1 \left(\mu_1^\dagger - T \frac{d\mu_1^\dagger}{dT} \right) + n_2 \left(\mu_2^\dagger - T \frac{d\mu_2^\dagger}{dT} \right)$$

$$+ P\, n_1 \left(B_{11} - T \frac{dB_{11}}{dT} \right) + P\, n_2 \left(B_{22} - T \frac{dB_{22}}{dT} \right)$$

$$- P \frac{n_1 n_2}{(n_1 + n_2)} \left(1 - T \frac{d}{dT} \right) (B_{11} - 2 B_{12} + B_{22}). \qquad (5.12.8)$$

The partial molar entropies are

$$S_1 = \left(\frac{\partial S}{\partial n_1} \right)_{T,P} = - \frac{\partial \mu_1}{\partial T} = - \frac{d\mu_1^\dagger}{dT} - R \log \frac{n_1}{n_1 + n_2} - R \log \frac{P}{P^\dagger}$$

$$- P \left\{ \frac{dB_{11}}{dT} - \left(\frac{n_2}{n_1 + n_2} \right)^2 \frac{d}{dT} (B_{11} - 2 B_{12} + B_{22}) \right\}, \qquad (5.12.9)$$

and similarly for S_2.

§ 5.13 Partial Pressures and Fugacities

The *partial pressures* p_1 and p_2 are defined by

$$p_1 = \frac{n_1}{n_1 + n_2} P, \qquad p_2 = \frac{n_2}{n_1 + n_2} P. \qquad (5.13.1)$$

The fugacities p_1^* and p_2^* are defined by

$$\frac{p_1^*}{\lambda_1} = \text{const.}, \qquad \frac{p_2^*}{\lambda_2} = \text{const.}, \qquad (T \text{ const.}), \qquad (5.13.2)$$

$$\frac{p_1^*}{p_1} \to 1, \qquad \frac{p_2^*}{p_2} \to 1 \quad \text{as} \quad P \to 0, \qquad (\text{all } T). \qquad (5.13.3)$$

From (1), (2), (3), (5.12.4), (5.12.5) it follows that

$$\log p_1^* = \log p_1 + \frac{P}{RT} \left\{ B_{11} - \left(\frac{n_2}{n_1 + n_2} \right)^2 (B_{11} - 2 B_{12} + B_{22}) \right\}. \qquad (5.13.4)$$

$$\log p_2^* = \log p_2 + \frac{P}{RT} \left\{ B_{22} - \left(\frac{n_1}{n_1 + n_2} \right)^2 (B_{11} - 2 B_{12} + B_{22}) \right\}. \qquad (5.13.5)$$

§ 5.14 Idealized Binary Gaseous Mixtures

Experimental data on the coefficient B_{12} are almost entirely lacking. In their absence it is usual to assume

$$B_{12} = \tfrac{1}{2} (B_{11} + B_{22}). \qquad (5.14.1)$$

There is no theoretical, nor experimental basis for (1), but in the absence of any information it is as good a guess as any other for B_{12}. The physical assumption which (1) represents is closely allied to the physical assumption which leads to a liquid mixture being *ideal* in the sense to be defined in

§ 5. 29. We shall accordingly refer to a binary gaseous mixture assumed to obey (1) as an *idealized mixture*.

For an idealized mixture we deduce from (1) and (5.11.3)

$$P = (n_1 + n_2) \frac{RT}{V} + (n_1 + n_2) \frac{RT}{V^2} \{ n_1 B_{11} + n_2 B_{22} \}. \quad (5.14.2)$$

Hence the partial pressures defined by (5.13.1) and (5.13.2) are

$$p_1 = n_1 \frac{RT}{V} \left\{ 1 + \frac{n_1 B_{11} + n_2 B_{22}}{V} \right\}. \quad (5.14.3)$$

$$p_2 = n_2 \frac{RT}{V} \left\{ 1 + \frac{n_1 B_{11} + n_2 B_{22}}{V} \right\}, \quad (5.14.4)$$

whereas according to (5.13.4), (5.13.5) the fugacities become

$$\log p_1^* = \log p_1 + \frac{PB_{11}}{RT}, \quad (5.14.5)$$

$$\log p_2^* = \log p_2 + \frac{PB_{22}}{RT}. \quad (5.14.6)$$

According to (5) and (6) the ratio of the fugacity p_1^* to the partial pressure p_1 in the idealized mixture is the same as in the pure single gas at the same total pressure P. This is the empirical relation often assumed for purposes of calculation. It is equivalent to the assumption (1), which we repeat has neither theoretical nor experimental basis.

§ 5.15 Binary Perfect Gas with T, V as Variables

At low pressures it is often allowable to ignore all the terms containing B_{11}, B_{12}, B_{22}. Under these conditions we say that we are regarding the gas as a *perfect gas*.

For the free energy of a perfect gas we have according to (5.11.2)

$$F = n_1 \left\{ \mu_1^\dagger - RT + RT \log \frac{n_1 RT}{P^\dagger V} \right\}$$

$$+ n_2 \left\{ \mu_2^\dagger - RT + RT \log \frac{n_2 RT}{P^\dagger V} \right\}. \quad (5.15.1)$$

Thus the free energy of a perfect gas containing two components is just the sum of the free energies at the same temperature of the two separate gases each occupying the same volume V as the mixture.

For the entropy we deduce from (1)

$$S = -\left(\frac{\partial F}{\partial T} \right)_{V, n_1, n_2} = -n_1 \left\{ \frac{d\mu_1^\dagger}{dT} + R \log \frac{n_1 RT}{P^\dagger V} \right\}$$

$$- n_2 \left\{ \frac{d\mu_2^\dagger}{dT} + R \log \frac{n_2 RT}{P^\dagger V} \right\} \quad (5.15.2)$$

so that the entropy is also the sum of the entropies of the two separate gases at the same temperature each occupying the same volume V as the mixture.

The energy is given by

$$U = F + TS = n_1 \left\{ \mu_1^\dagger - T\frac{d\mu_1^\dagger}{dT} - RT \right\} + n_2 \left\{ \mu_2^\dagger - T\frac{d\mu_2^\dagger}{dT} - RT \right\}. \quad (5.15.3)$$

from which we observe that the energies are both additive and independent of the volume at a given temperature.

The pressure is given by

$$P = -\left(\frac{\partial F}{\partial V}\right)_{T,n_1,n_2} = (n_1 + n_2)\frac{RT}{V}. \quad (5.15.4)$$

and the partial pressures are

$$p_1 = n_1 \frac{RT}{V}. \quad (5.15.5)$$

$$p_2 = n_2 \frac{RT}{V}. \quad (5.15.6)$$

We thus see that in a binary perfect gas the partial pressure of either component is the same as if it occupied the same volume at the same temperature in the absence of the other gas. This is *Dalton's Law of partial pressures*.

Finally in a perfect gas the fugacity is the same as the partial pressure and consequently the condition for equilibrium across a membrane permeable to the species 1, but not the species 2, becomes

$$p_1^\alpha = p_1^\beta \quad (5.15.7)$$

where the superscripts α, β refer to the two sides of the membrane.

§ 5.16 Binary Perfect Gas with T, P as Variables

If we wish to use the more usual independent variables T, P we must turn to the formulae of § 5.12. Omitting all terms containing B_{11}, B_{12}, B_{22} we obtain as the formulae for a perfect gas

$$G = n_1 \left\{ \mu_1^\dagger + RT \log \frac{P}{P^\dagger} + RT \log \frac{n_1}{n_1 + n_2} \right\}$$

$$+ n_2 \left\{ \mu_2^\dagger + RT \log \frac{P}{P^\dagger} + RT \log \frac{n_2}{n_1 + n_2} \right\}. \quad (5.16.1)$$

$$\mu_1 = \mu_1^\dagger + RT \log \frac{P}{P^\dagger} + RT \log \frac{n_1}{n_1 + n_2} = \mu_1^\dagger + RT \log \frac{p_1}{P^\dagger}. \quad (5.16.2)$$

$$\mu_2 = \mu_2^\dagger + RT \log \frac{P}{P^\dagger} + RT \log \frac{n_2}{n_1 + n_2} = \mu_2^\dagger + RT \log \frac{p_2}{P^\dagger}. \quad (5.16.3)$$

$$\lambda_1 = \lambda_1^\dagger \frac{p_1}{P^\dagger}. \quad (5.16.4)$$

$$\lambda_2 = \lambda_2^\dagger \frac{p_2}{p^\dagger},$$

(5. 16. 5)

$$S = -n_1 \left\{ \frac{d\mu_1^\dagger}{dT} + R \log \frac{P}{P^\dagger} + R \log \frac{n_1}{n_1 + n_2} \right\}$$

$$\qquad - n_2 \left\{ \frac{d\mu_2^\dagger}{dT} + R \log \frac{P}{P^\dagger} + R \log \frac{n_2}{n_1 + n_2} \right\}.$$

(5. 16. 6)

Whereas we saw in the preceding section that at given T, V the thermodynamic functions of a perfect gas are additive, we see that this is by no means the case for the thermodynamic functions at given T, P. The entropy contains the extra terms

$$-R \left\{ n_1 \log \frac{n_1}{n_1 + n_2} + n_2 \log \frac{n_2}{n_1 + n_2} \right\}.$$

(5. 16. 7)

usually called the *entropy of mixing*. The same extra terms occur in J and Y. Correspondingly G and F contain the extra terms

$$RT \left\{ n_1 \log \frac{n_1}{n_1 + n_2} + n_2 \log \frac{n_2}{n_1 + n_2} \right\}.$$

(5. 16. 8)

We also note the interesting result that for a perfect gas each μ can be expressed as a function of temperature and partial pressure independent of the total pressure and of the partial pressure of the other component.

The volume, the heat function and the energy are given by

$$V = \frac{\partial G}{\partial P} = (n_1 + n_2) \frac{RT}{P}$$

(5. 16. 9)

$$H = G + TS = n_1 \left(\mu_1^\dagger - T \frac{d\mu_1^\dagger}{dT} \right) + n_2 \left(\mu_2^\dagger - T \frac{d\mu_2^\dagger}{dT} \right),$$

(5. 16. 10)

$$U = H - PV = n_1 \left(\mu_1^\dagger - T \frac{d\mu_1^\dagger}{dT} - RT \right) + n_2 \left(\mu_2^\dagger - T \frac{d\mu_2^\dagger}{dT} - RT \right).$$

(5. 16. 11)

We note that at given T, P the volumes are additive, while at given T the heat functions and energies are additive and independent of the pressure.

For the partial molar quantities, other than G_1, G_2 which are the same as μ_1, μ_2 respectively, we have

$$S_1 = \frac{\partial S}{\partial n_1} = -\frac{\partial \mu_1}{\partial T} = -\frac{d\mu_1^\dagger}{dT} - R \log \frac{P}{P^\dagger} - R \log \frac{n_1}{n_1 + n_2}$$

$$\qquad = -\frac{d\mu_1^\dagger}{dT} - R \log \frac{p_1}{p^\dagger},$$

(5. 16. 12)

$$V_1 = \frac{\partial V}{dn_1} = \frac{RT}{P},$$

(5. 16. 13)

$$H_1 = G_1 + TS_1 = \mu_1^{\dagger} - T \frac{d\mu_1^{\dagger}}{dT} \qquad (5.16.14)$$

$$U_1 = H_1 - PV_1 = \mu_1^{\dagger} - T \frac{d\mu_1^{\dagger}}{dT} - RT, \qquad (5.16.15)$$

and analogous relations for S_2, V_2, H_2, U_2.

From (14) and (15) it follows that the partial molar heat capacities are equal to the molar heat capacities of the pure components.

§ 5.17   Introduction to Binary Liquids

We now turn to liquid mixtures of two components and the equilibrium between such phases and other phases, gaseous, liquid or solid. We begin by certain general considerations applying to all such liquid mixtures. We shall next consider a special class of such mixtures, called *ideal*, which exhibit an especially simple behaviour. We shall then show how the behaviour of non-ideal mixtures can conveniently be compared and correlated with that of ideal mixtures. The procedure will be illustrated in greater detail for a class of mixtures called *regular*.

A homogeneous mixture of two components is often called a *solution*, one of the components being called the *solvent*, the other the *solute*. From a thermodynamic point of view there is complete symmetry between the two components of a mixture and there is no distinction between *solvent* and *solute*, and it is largely a matter of convention which is called which. In practice it is usual to designate by the term *solvent* the species present in the greater proportion, but this is not a rigid rule. We shall for the most part avoid using the terms except in connection with certain phenomena, such as osmotic equilibrium, which themselves create a dissymetry between the two components.

§ 5.18   Use of Activities and Fugacities

All the equilibrium properties of the two components 1 and 2 are determined by their respective chemical potentials μ_1 and μ_2. In our consideration of liquid mixtures, we shall be particularly concerned with a comparison of the equilibrium properties of the mixture with those of the pure components. Consequently we shall be concerned not so much with μ_1, μ_2 themselves as with the differences

$$\mu_1 - \mu_1^0, \qquad (5.18.1)$$

$$\mu_2 - \mu_2^0, \qquad (5.18.2)$$

where the superscript 0 denotes the value for the pure liquid at the same temperature and pressure.

We recall the definition * of absolute activities λ_1, λ_2 in § 4.15, namely

$$\mu_1 = R T \log \lambda_1, \qquad (5.18.3)$$

$$\mu_2 = R T \log \lambda_2. \qquad (5.18.4)$$

---

* Fowler and Guggenheim, *Statistical Thermodynamics* (1939) p. 66.

Up to the present we have mentioned absolute activities from time to time and sometimes given formulae for them with the object of gradually familiarizing the reader with them. We have however hitherto made little use of absolute activities. Henceforth we shall make considerably increasing use of them, for they are in fact most convenient in the treatment of mixtures.

Continuing to use the superscript 0 to refer to the pure liquid, we have

$$\mu_1 - \mu_1^0 = RT \log \frac{\lambda_1}{\lambda_1^0}, \tag{5.18.5}$$

$$\mu_2 - \mu^2 = RT \log \frac{\lambda_2}{\lambda_2^0}, \tag{5.18.6}$$

from which we see that instead of considering the quantities (1) and (2) we can equally usefully, and incidentally more compactly consider the quantities

$$\lambda_1/\lambda_1^0 \quad \text{and} \quad \lambda_2/\lambda_2^0. \tag{5.18.7}$$

These ratios are sometimes called the *relative activities* * sometimes merely *activities* and are then denoted by the symbols a_1 and a_2. Since however *relative activities* are also sometimes defined according to different conventions and such different uses of the same name lead to dangerous confusion, we shall avoid their use. We accordingly continue to use explicitly the *absolute activities* λ_1, λ_2, λ_1^0, λ_2^0.

Incidentally we may mention that the name *absolute activities* * is due to the need of avoiding any possible confusion with the *relative activities* (7). This use of the word *absolute* has nothing to do with any implication of absoluteness in the conventional choice of zero states of either energy or entropy.

It is worth while drawing attention to the connection of absolute activities with the Planck function Y. According to (4.15.10) applied to a phase of two components, we have

$$dY = \frac{H}{T^2} dT - \frac{V}{T} dP - R \log \lambda_1 \, dn_1 - R \log \lambda_2 \, dn_2. \tag{5.18.8}$$

Hence according to the definition of partial molar quantities in § 5.03, just as

$$G_1 = \mu_1, \qquad G_2 = \mu_2. \tag{5.18.9}$$

so also

$$Y_1 = -R \log \lambda_1, \qquad Y_2 = -R \log \lambda_2. \tag{5.18.10}$$

From this digression we return to consider the quantities (7) and particularly to consider their experimental determination. For the equili-

---

* Introduced by G N Lewis who denoted them first by ξ and later by a. See Lewis, *Proc. Am. Ac. Sci.* (1907) **43** 259; *Zeit. Physik. Chem.* (1907) **61** 129.

brium of the species 1 between any two phases α and β we have according to (4. 15. 7) the simple condition

$$\lambda_1^\alpha = \lambda_1^\beta,$$ (5. 18. 11)

and in particular for the equilibrium between a liquid phase L and a gas phase G

$$\lambda_1^L = \lambda_1^G.$$ (5. 18. 12)

From (12) and (5. 13. 2) it follows that the ratio of the absolute activities of the species 1 in any two phases α, β not necessarily in mutual equilibrium, is equal to the ratio of the fugacities of the species in the gas phases in equilibrium with α, β respectively.

We now define the *fugacity* p_i^* of a species i in any phase, liquid or otherwise, as equal to the fugacity in the gas phase in equilibrium with it. We then have for the species 1 in any two phases α and β

$$\frac{\lambda_1^\alpha}{\lambda_1^\beta} = \frac{p_1^{*\alpha}}{p_1^{*\beta}}.$$ (5. 18. 13)

If the pressure in the gas phase is not too high, we can usually treat the gas as if perfect. The fugacities p^* then become equal to the partial vapour pressures p. According to this approximation (13) reduces to

$$\frac{\lambda_1^\alpha}{\lambda_1^\beta} = \frac{p_1^\alpha}{p_1^\beta}.$$ (5. 18. 14)

An important application of (13) is to the comparison between the absolute activity λ_1 of 1 in a liquid mixture and its absolute activity λ_1^0 in the pure liquid at the same temperature. Then we have

$$\frac{\lambda_1}{\lambda_1^0} = \frac{p_1^*}{p_1^{*0}}$$ (5. 18. 15)

or if we treat the gas as perfect

$$\frac{\lambda_1}{\lambda_1^0} = \frac{p_1}{p_1^0}.$$ (5. 18. 16)

We shall sometimes require (16) in the differential form

$$d \log \lambda_1 = d \log p_1, \qquad \text{(const. } T). \qquad$$ (5. 18. 17)

There are, of course, corresponding relations for the component 2.

§ 5. 19 Conventional Notation

For the sake of brevity and simplicity we shall henceforth, except when stated to the contrary, treat all vapours as perfect gases. We shall accordingly throughout assume in accordance with (5. 18. 16)

$$\lambda_1/\lambda_1^0 = p_1/p_1^0.$$ (5. 19. 1)

If ever the approximation of treating the vapours as perfect gases is not adequate, it is merely necessary to replace the partial vapour pressures p by the fugacities p^*.

§ 5. 20 Duhem-Margules Relation

Substituting (5.18.3) and (5.18.4) into the Gibbs–Duhem relation (5.10.5) we obtain it in the alternative form

$$(1-x)\frac{\partial \log \lambda_1}{\partial x} + x\frac{\partial \log \lambda_2}{\partial x} = 0, \qquad \text{(const. } T, P\text{).} \qquad (5.20.1)$$

Differentiating (5.19.1) logarithmically with respect to x at constant T, P we obtain

$$\frac{\partial \log \lambda_1}{\partial x} = \frac{\partial \log p_1}{\partial x}. \qquad (5.20.2)$$

Substituting this and the similar relation for the component 2 into (1), we obtain

$$(1-x)\frac{\partial \log p_1}{\partial x} + x\frac{\partial \log p_2}{\partial x} = 0, \quad \text{(const. } T, P\text{).} \qquad (5.20.3)$$

This important relation is called the *Duhem–Margules relation* [*]. It follows from this relation that if p_1 and p_2 are plotted against x, the shape of either curve completely determines the shape of the other. An example of this interrelation [**] between the pair of curves is shown in Fig. 5.2 and Table 5.1, where the subscript 1 denotes water and 2 ethyl alcohol.

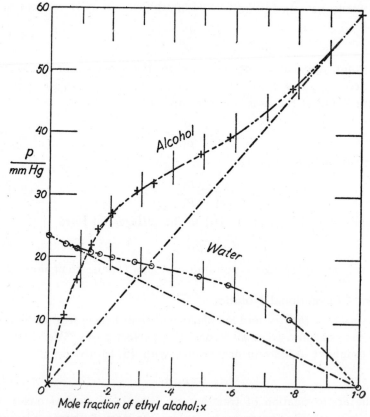

Fig. 5. 2. Illustration of Duhem–Margules relation.

[*] Margules, *Sitzungsber. K. Akad. Wiss. Wien* (1895) **104** 1258—1260.
[**] See Adam and Guggenheim, *Proc. Roy. Soc. A.* (1933) **139** 231.

TABLE 5.1

Verification of Duhem–Margules relation for mixtures of water and ethyl alcohol at 25° C

x	$\dfrac{p_1}{mm.\,Hg.}$	$\dfrac{p_2}{mm.\,Hg.}$	$-(1-x)\dfrac{\partial \log p_1}{\partial x}$ $= x\dfrac{\partial \log p_2}{\partial x}$
0	23.75	0.0	1.00
0.1	21.7	17.8	0.76
0.2	20.4	26.8	0.41
0.3	19.4	31.2	0.37
0.4	18.35	34.2	0.355
0.5	17.3	36.9	0.41
0.6	15.8	40.1	0.53
0.7	13.3	43.9	0.655
0.8	10.0	48.3	0.77
0.9	5.5	53.3	0.915
1.0	0.0	59.0	1.00

§ 5.21 Effect of External Pressure

Applying the cross-differentiation identity (3.01.7) to (5.18.8), we obtain

$$-R\left(\frac{\partial \log \lambda_1}{\partial P}\right)_{T,\,n_1,\,n_2} = \frac{\partial}{\partial P}\frac{\partial Y}{\partial n_1} = \frac{\partial}{\partial n_1}\frac{\partial Y}{\partial P}$$

$$= -\frac{1}{T}\left(\frac{\partial V}{\partial n_1}\right)_{T,\,P,\,n_2} = -\frac{V_1}{T}, \qquad (5.21.1)$$

and using (5.18.17)

$$\frac{\partial \log p_1}{\partial P} = \frac{\partial \log \lambda_1}{\partial P} = \frac{V_1}{RT}, \qquad \text{(const. } T,\,x\text{).} \qquad (5.21.2)$$

Neglecting compressibility, which is justifiable for any liquid phase at ordinary pressures, and integrating (2) we obtain

$$\log \frac{p_1(P)}{p_1(0)} = \log \frac{\lambda_1(P)}{\lambda_1(0)} = \frac{PV_1}{RT}. \qquad (5.21.3)$$

Just as for a pure liquid $PV_1 \ll RT$ even at pressures of several atmospheres. Consequently for pressures not exceeding about one atmosphere, we may with sufficient accuracy regard λ_1 and p_1 as independent of the pressure P.

We shall accordingly usually neglect the dependence of the absolute activity λ_1 and the vapour pressure p_1 in the liquid mixture on the total pressure P, except when we are particularly interested in high values of P as when we come to consider osmotic equilibrium in § 5.27.

All that has been said concerning the species 1 of course applies equally to the species 2.

Although the effect of varying the total pressure on a liquid phase is usually negligible, it is important to clarify what exactly we mean by such an effect. In theory the total pressure on a condensed phase in equilibrium with saturated vapour might be varied by separating the liquid from the vapour by a piston permeable to the vapour but not to the liquid. Such an arrangement has however little practical importance, but in practice an analogous result is obtainable by addition to the gas phase of an inert gas insoluble in the liquid. For we have seen in § 5.16 that in a mixture of two perfect gases the absolute activity of each is at a given temperature determined completely by its partial pressure and is unaffected by the partial pressure of the other gas. In § 6.12 we shall see that this remains true in a perfect gas mixture of any number of components. Consequently if we add an inert gas insoluble in the liquid, this may be regarded not as a component of the system under discussion, but merely as part of the apparatus used to fix the pressure on the liquid phase. What has just been said applies equally to a pure liquid as to a liquid mixture of two, or for that matter more than two, components.

§ 5.22   Equilibrium Between Liquid and Vapour

Let us now consider from a very general point of view the equilibrium conditions between a liquid mixture of two components and the vapour phase.

Each phase by itself has evidently three degrees of freedom, which we can take as given by the three independent variables T, P, x. Alternatively if we use the four variables T, P, μ_1, μ_2 these are not independent, but are connected by the Gibbs–Duhem relation

$$S\,dT - V\,dP + n_1\,d\mu_1 + n_2\,d\mu_2 = 0. \qquad (5.22.1)$$

If we now consider two phases, say liquid and vapour, in mutual equilibrium then the variables T, P, μ_1, μ_2 are connected by two Gibbs–Duhem relations, one for each phase. Thus, using L to denote liquid and G to denote gas,

$$S^L\,dT - V^L\,dP + n_1^L\,d\mu_1 + n_2^L\,d\mu_2 = 0, \qquad (5.22.2)$$

$$S^G\,dT - V^G\,dP + n_1^G\,d\mu_1 + n_2^G\,d\mu_2 = 0. \qquad (5.22.3)$$

The term $V^L dP$ in (2) is, as explained in the previous section, usually negligible, but in the present connection nothing is gained by its omission.

It is convenient to rewrite (2) and (3) in terms of a single mole of each phase. Thus

$$S_m^L\,dT - V_m^L\,dP + (1-x^L)\,d\mu_1 + x^L\,d\mu_2 = 0, \qquad (5.22.4)$$

$$S_m^G\,dT - V_m^G\,dP + (1-x^G)\,d\mu_1 + x^G\,d\mu_2 = 0. \qquad (5.22.5)$$

It is hardly necessary to point out that we need not attach superscripts to the variables T, P, μ_1, μ_2 since at equilibrium each of these has the same value in both phases.

From (4) and (5) we could, if we wished, eliminate any one of the quantities dT, dP, $d\mu_1$, $d\mu_2$ thus obtaining a single relation between the other three. Whether we do this or not, it is clear, as we have two independent relations between four variables, that only two of these variables are independent. We conclude that a system of two phases and two components in equilibrium has *two degrees of freedom*. If for example we specify the values of T and x^L, then all other quantities in particular P and x^G are thereby fixed.

§ 5.23 Mixtures with Stationary Vapour Pressures and Boiling-Points

We have seen that for equilibrium between liquid and vapour the two equations (5.22.4) and (5.22.5) must be satisfied simultaneously. This leads, as we shall see, to particularly simple and interesting results when the relative compositions of the two phases happen to be the same, that is to say when

$$x^L = x^G. \qquad (5.23.1)$$

If we subtract (5.22.4) from (5.22.5) we obtain

$$(S_m^G - S_m^L)\,dT - (V_m^G - V_m^L)\,dP + (x^L - x^G)(d\mu_1 - d\mu_2) = 0 \quad (5.23.2)$$

Let us now consider variations of pressure and composition at constant temperature. Then (2) becomes

$$(V_m^G - V_m^L)\frac{dP}{dx} = (x^L - x^G)\left(\frac{d\mu_1}{dx} - \frac{d\mu_2}{dx}\right), \qquad \text{(const. } T\text{).} \qquad (5.23.3)$$

Hence under the particular conditions described by (1), we have

$$(V_m^G - V_m^L)\frac{dP}{dx} = 0, \qquad \text{(const. } T\text{),} \qquad (5.23.4)$$

where x denotes either x^L or x^G, and since $V_G^m \neq V_m^L$,

$$dP/dx = 0, \qquad \text{(const. } T\text{).} \qquad (5.23.5)$$

This tells us that whenever the relative compositions of the liquid and vapour in mutual equilibrium at a given temperature are identical, the equilibrium pressure is a maximum or minimum at the given temperature. Similarly if we consider variations of temperature and composition at constant pressure, (2) becomes

$$-(S_m^G - S_m^L)\frac{dT}{dx} = (x^L - x^G)\left(\frac{d\mu_1}{dx} - \frac{d\mu_2}{dx}\right), \qquad \text{(const. } P\text{),} \qquad (5.23.6)$$

and under the conditions described by (1)

$$(S_m^G - S_m^L)\frac{dT}{dx} = 0, \qquad \text{(const. } P) \qquad (5.23.7)$$

where x denotes either x^L or x^G. Since $S_m^G \neq S_m^L$, it follows that

$$dT/dx = 0, \qquad \text{(const. } P). \qquad (5.23.8)$$

This tells us that whenever the relative compositions of the liquid and vapour in mutual equilibrium at a given pressure are identical, the equilibrium temperature is a minimum or maximum at the given pressure.

These striking conclusions seem quite natural when expressed by diagrams. For example Fig. 5.3 shows the boiling-point T plotted against

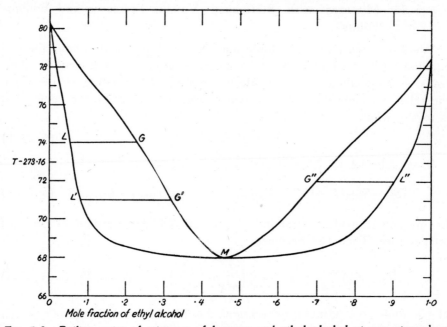

Fig. **5.3**. Boiling point of mixtures of benzene and ethyl alcohol at one atmosphere.

compositions of the two phases. For instance the points L and G represent the liquid and gas phases in equilibrium at one temperature; L', G' is another such pair and L'', G'' another. The point M represents liquid and gas of the same composition and in this example the equilibrium temperature or boiling-point is a minimum.

§ 5.24   Temperature Coefficients

Applying the cross-differentiation relation (3.01.7) to (5.18.8), we obtain

$$-R\left(\frac{\partial \log \lambda_1}{\partial T}\right)_{P, n_1, n_2} = \frac{\partial}{\partial T}\frac{\partial Y}{\partial n_1} = \frac{\partial}{\partial n_1}\frac{\partial Y}{\partial T} = \frac{1}{T^2}\left(\frac{\partial H}{\partial n_1}\right)_{T, P, n_2} = \frac{H_1}{T^2}. \qquad (5.24.1)$$

or more briefly

$$\frac{\partial \log \lambda_1}{\partial T} = -\frac{H_1}{RT^2}, \qquad \text{(const. } P, x\text{).} \qquad (5.24.2)$$

There is obviously a similar relation for the component 2.

If we apply (2) to the liquid mixture and to the pure liquid component and subtract, we obtain

$$\frac{\partial \log (\lambda_1/\lambda_1^0)}{\partial T} = -\frac{H_1 - H_1^0}{RT^2}, \qquad \text{(const. } P, x\text{).} \qquad (5.24.3)$$

and using (5.19.1)

$$\frac{\partial \log (p_1/p_1^0)}{\partial T} = -\frac{H_1 - H_1^v}{RT^2}, \qquad \text{(const. } P, x\text{).} \qquad (5.24.4)$$

§ 5.25 Equilibrium Between Liquid Mixture and Pure Solid Phase

Let us now consider the equilibrium between the liquid mixture and the pure solid 1. We are assuming that the pressure is either constant or irrelevant. We use the superscript S to denote the solid phase, the superscript 0 for the pure liquid and no superscript for the liquid mixture. Then for equilibrium between the liquid mixture and the pure solid at the temperature T

$$\lambda_1(T) = \lambda_1^S(T). \qquad (5.25.1)$$

If T^0 denotes the corresponding equilibrium temperature for the pure liquid, that is to say the *freezing-point* of the pure liquid, we have correspondingly

$$\lambda_1^0(T^0) = \lambda_1^S(T^0), \qquad (5.25.2)$$

which can be rewritten in the form

$$\lambda_1^0(T) = \frac{\lambda_1^0(T)}{\lambda_1^0(T^0)} \lambda_1^S(T^0). \qquad (5.25.3)$$

Taking logarithms of (1) and (3) and subtracting we obtain

$$\log \frac{\lambda_1^0(T)}{\lambda_1(T)} = \log \frac{\lambda_1^0(T)}{\lambda_1^0(T^0)} - \log \frac{\lambda_1^S(T)}{\lambda_1^S(T^0)}. \qquad (5.25.4)$$

Now applying the integrated form of (5.24.2) to the pure solid and pure liquid in turn, we have

$$\log \frac{\lambda_1^S(T)}{\lambda_1^S(T^0)} = -\int_{T^0}^{T} \frac{H_1^S}{RT^2} \, dT, \qquad (5.25.5)$$

$$\log \frac{\lambda_1^0(T)}{\lambda_1^0(T^0)} = -\int_{T^0}^{T} \frac{H_1^0}{RT^2} \, dT. \qquad (5.25.6)$$

Substituting (5) and (6) into (4) we obtain

$$\log \frac{\lambda_1^0(T)}{\lambda_1(T)} = -\int_{T^0}^{T} \frac{H_1^0 - H_1^S}{RT^2} \, dT. \tag{5.25.7}$$

We note that the quantity $H_1^0 - H_1^S$ is the *molar heat of fusion* of the species 1.

Further procedure depends on the accuracy aimed at. We can always expand the molar heat of fusion $(H_1^0 - H_1^S)$ as a power series in $T - T^0$. insert into (7) and then perform the integration explicitly. If we have to use many terms the procedure may be tedious, but is always straightforward. Usually it will be adequate to write

$$H_1^0(T) - H_1^S(T) = H_1^0(T^0) - H_1^S(T^0) + (C^0 - C^S)(T - T^0) \tag{5.25.8}$$

and treat $C^0 - C^S$ as constant. In all cases we can write the result in the form

$$\log \frac{\lambda_1^0(T)}{\lambda_1(T)} = \frac{[\triangle_f H_i^0]}{R} \left(\frac{1}{T} - \frac{1}{T^0} \right). \tag{5.25.9}$$

where $[\triangle_f H_i^0]$ denotes the value of the molar heat of fusion $\triangle_f H_1^0$ for the pure substance averaged over the reciprocal temperature interval $1/T^0$ to $1/T$. Since $\triangle_f H_1^0$ is always positive and λ_1^0/λ_1 is always greater than unity, it follows that $T < T^0$. Thus the freezing-point of the solution is always less than that of the pure solvent.

§ 5.26 Equilibrium with Vapour of Pure Component

We shall now consider the equilibrium between the liquid mixture and the gas phase in the case that the component 2 has a negligible vapour pressure. We describe such a component as *nonvolatile*. We accordingly regard the gas phase as consisting entirely of the component 1 and we use the superscript G to denote this phase.

We then proceed to consider the equilibrium between the two phases at a given pressure precisely as in the case of equilibrium with a pure solid phase studied in the previous section. The steps of the argument are precisely analogous and we obtain eventually the relation

$$\log \frac{\lambda_1^0(T)}{\lambda_1(T)} = \frac{[\triangle_e H_i^0]}{R} \left(\frac{1}{T^0} - \frac{1}{T} \right). \tag{5.26.1}$$

where $[\triangle_e H_i^0]$ denotes the value of the molar heat of evaporation $\triangle_e H_1^0$ for the pure liquid averaged over the reciprocal temperature interval $1/T$ to $1/T^0$. Since $\triangle_e H_1^0$ is always positive and $\lambda_1^0/\lambda_1 > 1$, it follows that $T > T^0$. Thus the boiling-point of the solution at a given pressure is greater than that of the pure solvent.

§ 5. 27   Osmotic Equilibrium

Suppose we have two liquid mixtures α and β, both containing the two species 1 and 2, separated by a membrane permeable to 1 but not to 2. In this connection we shall follow the customary practice of calling the permeant species 1 the *solvent* and the nonpermeant species 2 the *solute*. We assume that the two phases are at the same temperature, but not necessarily at the same pressure. The condition that the two phases should be in equilibrium with respect to the solvent species 1 is

$$\lambda_1^\alpha = \lambda_1^\beta, \tag{5.27.1}$$

or if we use (5. 19. 1)

$$p_1^\alpha = p_1^\beta. \tag{5.27.2}$$

For these relations to be satisfied it will generally be necessary for the two phases to be at different pressures. There is then equilibrium with respect to the solvent species 1, but not with respect to the solute species 2 nor is there hydrostatic equilibrium between the two phases, the difference of pressure being balanced by a force exerted by the membrane. A partial equilibrium of this kind is called *osmotic equilibrium* of the solvent species 1.

By using the relation (5. 21. 2)

$$\frac{\partial \log p_1}{\partial P} = \frac{\partial \log \lambda_1}{\partial P} = \frac{V_1}{RT}, \qquad \text{(const. } T, x\text{),} \tag{5.27.3}$$

we can determine the pressure difference $P^\alpha - P^\beta$ required to preserve osmotic equilibrium.

We shall use the notation $p_1(P, x)$ to denote the value of the partial vapour pressure p_1 in a phase of composition x at a pressure P. We do not refer to the temperature as this is assumed constant throughout. The condition (2) for osmotic equilibrium becomes in this notation

$$p_1(P^\alpha, x^\alpha) = p_1(P^\beta, x^\beta). \tag{5.27.4}$$

Dividing both sides of (4) by $p_1(P^\beta, x^\alpha)$ and taking logarithms, we obtain

$$\log \frac{p_1(P^\alpha, x^\alpha)}{p_1(P^\beta, x^\alpha)} = \log \frac{p_1(P^\beta, x^\beta)}{p_1(P^\beta, x^\alpha)}. \tag{5.27.5}$$

If we integrate (3) from P^β to P^α and substitute the result on the left side of (5) we find

$$\frac{1}{RT} \int_{P^\beta}^{P^\alpha} V_1^\alpha \, dP = \log \frac{p_1(P^\beta, x^\beta)}{p_1(P^\beta, x^\alpha)}. \tag{5.27.6}$$

In order to evaluate the integral in (6) it is for most purposes sufficient to ignore compressibility and treat V_1 as independent of P. In case greater refinement should be desired, we can obtain all the accuracy that can ever be required by assuming that V_1 varies linearly with P. We then obtain

$$\frac{[V_1^\alpha]}{RT}(P^\alpha - P^\beta) = \log \frac{p_1(P^\beta, x^\beta)}{p_1(P^\beta, x^\alpha)}, \tag{5.27.7}$$

13

where the symbol $[V_1^\alpha]$ denotes the value of V_1^α at a pressure equal to the mean of P^α and P^β.

Formula (7) is the general relation determining the pressure difference across the membrane at osmotic equilibrium. The case of greatest interest is when the phase β consists of the pure solvent. The pressure difference $P^\alpha - P^\beta$ is then called the *osmotic pressure* and is denoted by Π. We can in this case replace the superscript β by 0 and drop the superscript α. We thus have

$$\frac{\Pi[V_1]}{RT} = \log \frac{p_1^0(P)}{p_1(P)}. \tag{5.27.8}$$

or if, as is usually the case, we may ignore compressibility

$$\frac{\Pi V_1}{RT} = \log \frac{p_1^0(P)}{p_1(P)}. \tag{5.27.9}$$

If moreover the pressure P on the pure solvent is roughly atmospheric, then regardless of how great Π may be we may as explained in § 5.21 regard p_1 and p_1^0 as essentially independent of P. Formula (9) can then be simplified to

$$\frac{\Pi V_1}{RT} = \log \frac{p_1^0}{p_1}. \tag{5.27.10}$$

from which we see that provided the pressure P on the pure solvent is low, the osmotic pressure Π does not depend significantly on P.

If instead of dividing both sides of (4) by $p_1(P^\beta, x^\alpha)$, we divide both sides by $p_1(P^\alpha, x^\beta)$ and otherwise proceed in the same way, we obtain instead of (7)

$$\frac{[V_1^\beta]}{RT}(P^\alpha - P^\beta) = \log \frac{p_1(P^\alpha, x^\beta)}{p_1(P^\alpha, x^\alpha)} \tag{5.27.11}$$

and instead of (8)

$$\frac{\Pi[V_1^0]}{RT} = \log \frac{p_1^0 \, \Pi}{p_1(P+\Pi)}. \tag{5.27.12}$$

It can be shown that the alternative formulae (8) and (12) are fully equivalent. On the whole formula (8) is the more useful.

§ 5.28   Pressure on Semi-permeable Membrane

The osmotic pressure is by definition a pressure that must be applied to the solution to bring it into a certain equilibrium condition. It is not a pressure exerted by the solution or part of the solution at its normal low pressure. It is, in fact, analogous to the freezing-point of a solution, which has no relation to the actual temperature of the solution, but is the temperature to which it must be brought to reach a certain equilibrium state. The osmotic pressure is nevertheless sometimes defined as the pressure exerted on a membrane, permeable only to the solvent, separating the solution from pure solvent. This definition, unless carefully qualified, is incorrect. Another definition sometimes given is the pressure exerted by the solute molecules on a membrane permeable only to the solvent. This definition is still more incorrect than the last. The truth as regards the pressure on the membrane is as follows. When the solution is at the same pressure, e.g. atmospheric, as the solvent, there will be a resultant flow of solvent through the membrane from the solvent to the solution, but the resultant pressure on the membrane itself is negligibly small, and may be in either direction. If, however, the solution is subjected to a certain high external pressure, the flow of solvent through the membrane is equal in either direction; there is then osmotic equilibrium and the excess pressure on the solution over the pressure of the solvent is by definition the osmotic pressure. Under conditions of osmotic equilibrium, but only under these conditions, is the external pressure difference required to prevent the membrane from moving equal to the osmotic pressure.

§ 5. 29   Ideal Mixtures

In order to obtain more detailed information concerning the equilibrium properties of binary liquid mixtures, it is necessary to know or assume something about the dependence of the chemical potentials μ_1, μ_2 or the absolute activities λ_1, λ_2 on the composition of the mixture. Thermodynamic considerations alone cannot predict the form of this dependence, but only impose the restriction of the Gibbs–Duhem relation. According to (5. 20. 1), one form in which this relation can be written is

$$\frac{\partial \log \lambda_1}{\partial \log (1-x)} = \frac{\partial \log \lambda_2}{\partial \log x}, \tag{5. 29. 1}$$

from which we see that one possible solution is

$$\lambda_1 = (1-x)\, \lambda_1^0, \tag{5. 29. 2}$$

$$\lambda_2 = x\, \lambda_2^0, \tag{5. 29. 3}$$

where, as usual, the superscript ^{0} refers to the pure liquid.

We call mixtures obeying the relations (2) and (3) *ideal mixtures*. We shall devote considerable attention to such mixtures and this for several reasons.

In the first place the behaviour of ideal solutions is the simplest conceivable either from a mathematical or from a physical aspect.

In the second place statistical theory predicts that mixtures of two very similar species, in particular two isotopes, will be ideal.

In the third place it is found experimentally that ideal mixtures do exist. As a typical example we may mention chlorobenzene and bromobenzene; another example is ethylene bromide and propylene bromide.

In the fourth place although most real mixtures are not ideal, in many cases the resemblances between a real mixture and an ideal mixture are more striking than the differences.

In the fifth place the ideal mixture is the most convenient standard with which to compare any real mixture.

Ideal solutions were first clearly defined and studied by G. N. Lewis [*] and by Washburn [**]

§ 5. 30   Thermodynamic Functions of Ideal Mixtures

From the formulae (5. 29. 2) and (5. 29. 3) we can immediately derive formulae for all the thermodynamic functions of an ideal mixture. In particular we have, using the superscript ^{0} to refer to the pure liquids,

$$\mu_1 = RT \log \lambda_1 = \mu_1^0 + RT \log (1-x)$$
$$= RT \log \lambda_1^0 + RT \log (1-x), \tag{5. 30. 1}$$

$$\mu_2 = RT \log \lambda_2 = \mu_2^0 + RT \log x$$
$$= RT \log \lambda_2^0 + RT \log x, \tag{5. 30. 2}$$

$$G_m = (1-x)\,\mu_1 + x\,\mu_2$$
$$= (1-x)\,\mu_1^0 + x\,\mu_2^0 + RT \left\{ (1-x) \log (1-x) + x \log x \right\}. \tag{5. 30. 3}$$

$$Y_m/R = -(1-x) \log \lambda_1^0 - x \log \lambda_2^0$$
$$- (1-x) \log (1-x) - x \log x, \tag{5. 30. 4}$$

$$S_m = -(1-x) \frac{d\mu_1^0}{dT} - x \frac{d\mu_2^0}{dT} - R \left\{ (1-x) \log (1-x) + x \log x \right\}. \tag{5. 30. 5}$$

$$H_m = (1-x) \left(\mu_1^0 - T \frac{d\mu_1^0}{dT} \right) + x \left(\mu_2^0 - T \frac{d\mu_2^0}{dT} \right). \tag{5. 30. 6}$$

$$V_m = (1-x) \frac{\partial \mu_1^0}{\partial P} + x \frac{\partial \mu_2^0}{\partial P}. \tag{5. 30. 7}$$

$$S_1 = -\frac{\partial \mu_1}{\partial T} = -\frac{d\mu_1^0}{dT} - R \log (1-x). \tag{5. 30. 8}$$

$$S_2 = -\frac{\partial \mu_2}{\partial T} = -\frac{d\mu_2^0}{dT} - R \log x. \tag{5. 30. 9}$$

$$H_1 = \mu_1^0 - T \frac{d\mu_1^0}{dT} = H_1^0. \tag{5. 30. 10}$$

$$H_2 = \mu_2^0 - T \frac{d\mu_2^0}{dT} = H_2^0. \tag{5. 30. 11}$$

$$V_1 = \frac{\partial \mu_1^0}{\partial P} = V_1^0 \tag{5. 30. 12}$$

$$V_2 = \frac{\partial \mu_2^0}{\partial P} = V_2^0. \tag{5. 30. 13}$$

[*] Lewis, *J. Am. Chem. Soc.* (1908) **30** 668.

[**] Washburn, *Z. Physik. Chem.* (1910) **74** 537.

§ 5. 31   Mixing Properties of Ideal Mixtures

From (5.30.12) and (5.30.13) we see that the partial molar volumes in an ideal mixture are independent of the composition. Hence on mixing at constant temperature and pressure there is no change of volume.

From (5.30.10) and (5.30.11) we see that the partial molar heat functions of an ideal mixture are independent of the composition. Hence on mixing at constant temperature and pressure there is no absorption or emission of heat.

From (5.30.5) we see by comparison with (5.16.7) that at constant temperature and pressure the *entropy of mixing* is of precisely the same form as in a binary mixture of perfect gases. This is also true for the mixing terms in Y, G, J, F.

It must be emphasized that this similarity between ideal liquid mixtures and perfect gaseous mixtures as regards dependence of the thermodynamic properties on the composition holds only when the other independent variables are T and P. There are no correspondingly simple relations in terms of the variables T and V, which incidentally are an inconvenient set of independent variables for any phase other than a gas.

There is, of course, no similarity between liquid and gaseous mixtures as regards dependence of properties on the pressure. For example, in a perfect gaseous mixture

$$\frac{\partial \mu_1}{\partial P} = V_1 = \frac{RT}{P} \qquad (5.31.1)$$

while in a liquid ideal mixture

$$\frac{\partial \mu_1}{\partial P} = \frac{\partial \mu_1^0}{\partial P} = V_1 = V_1^\dagger (1 - \varkappa P) \simeq V_1^\dagger. \qquad (5.31.2)$$

§ 5. 32   Partial Vapour Pressures

From formulae (5.29.2) and (5.29.3) together with (5.19.1) we have immediately

$$p_1/p_1^0 = 1 - x, \qquad (5.32.1)$$

$$p_2/p_2^0 = x. \qquad (5.32.2)$$

Thus if the partial vapour pressures, or more strictly the fugacities, of the two components of an ideal mixture are plotted against the mole fraction of either, one obtains two straight lines. The experimental data [*] for the mixture ethylene bromide and propylene bromide at the temperature 85 °C are shown in Fig. 5.4. We see that this mixture is ideal.

The direct proportionality between partial vapour pressure and mole fraction described by formulae (1) and (2) is called *Raoult's Law*.

---

[*]   Von Zawidzki, *Z. Physik. Chem.* (1900) **35** 129.

For the dependence of vapour pressures on the temperature, we have from (1) and (4. 50. 13)

$$\left(\frac{\partial \log p_1}{\partial T}\right)_x = \frac{d \log p_1^0}{dT} = \frac{\Delta_e H_1^0}{RT^2}. \qquad (5. 32. 3)$$

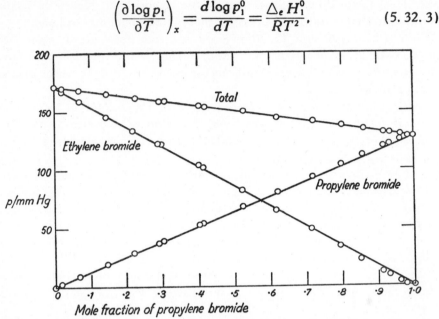

Fig. **5. 4.** Partial and total vapour pressures of mixtures of ethylene bromide and propylene bromide at 85° C.

where $\Delta_e H_1^0$ is the molar heat of evaporation of the pure liquid. We can write (3) in the equivalent form

$$\left\{\frac{\partial \log p_1}{\partial (1/T)}\right\}_x = -\frac{\Delta_e H_1^0}{R}. \qquad (5. 32. 4)$$

There are of course analogous formulae for the component 2.

§ 5. 33   Equilibrium Between Ideal Liquid Mixture and Pure Solid Phase

To obtain the formula relating the composition of an ideal binary mixture to the temperature at which it is in equilibrium with the pure solid phase 1, we have merely to substitute (5. 29. 2) into (5. 25. 9). We thus obtain

$$-\log (1-x) = \frac{[\Delta_f H_1^0]}{R}\left(\frac{1}{T} - \frac{1}{T^0}\right), \qquad (5. 33. 1)$$

where we recall that T^0 is the freezing-point of the pure substance 1 and $[\Delta_f H_1^0]$ denotes the molar heat of fusion $\Delta_f H_1^0$ of the species 1 averaged over the reciprocal temperature interval $1/T^0$ to $1/T$.

Since the heat of fusion is always positive and $0 < x < 1$, it follows that $T < T^0$, as already mentioned in § 5. 25.

§ 5. 34   Equilibrium Between Ideal Solution and Vapour of Pure Solvent

We consider next an ideal solution of a non-volatile solute and obtain a formula relating the boiling-point T, at a specified pressure, to the composition. We use formula (5. 26. 1) and substitute from (5. 29. 2). We thus obtain immediately

$$-\log{(1-x)} = \frac{[\triangle_e H_1^0]}{R}\left(\frac{1}{T^0}-\frac{1}{T}\right),\qquad (5.34.1)$$

wherein we recall that T denotes the boiling-point of the mixture, T^0 the boiling-point of the pure liquid 1 at the same pressure and $[\triangle_e H_1^0]$ denotes the value of the molar heat of evaporation $\triangle_e H_1^0$ of the pure liquid 1 averaged over the reciprocal temperature range $1/T$ to $1/T^0$.

Since the heat of evaporation is always positive and x can only be positive, it follows from (1) that $T > T^0$. Thus the boiling-point of the solution is higher than that of the pure liquid.

§ 5. 35   Osmotic Pressure of Ideal Solution

To obtain the formula for the osmotic pressure Π of an ideal solution, regarding the component 1 as solvent we have merely to substitute (5. 32. 1) into (5. 27. 8). We thus obtain

$$\frac{\Pi[V_1]}{RT} = -\log{(1-x)},\qquad (5.35.1)$$

wherein we recall that $[V_1]$ denotes the value of V_1 averaged between the pressures of the two phases in osmotic equilibrium. When we neglect compressibility (1) simplifies to

$$\frac{\Pi V_1}{RT} = -\log{(1-x)}.\qquad (5.35.2)$$

There is of course an analogous relation for osmotic equilibrium with respect to the species 2.

§ 5. 36   Non-ideal Mixtures

We have already mentioned that most mixtures are not ideal, but it is customary to correlate the thermodynamic properties of each real mixture with those of an ideal mixture. This is achieved formally by the introduction of certain coefficients to express quantitatively the discrepancies between the properties of the real solution and an ideal solution. The most important such coefficients are the *activity coefficients* first used by G. N. Lewis * and the *osmotic coefficients* first used by Bjerrum **. These will be defined in turn.

---

* The earliest use of the expression activity coefficient which the author has been able to find is by Noyes and Bray, *J. Am. Chem. Soc.* (1911) **33** 1646. These authors however attribute it to G. N. Lewis.

** Bjerrum, *Fysisk Tidskrift* (1916) **15** 66; *Zeit. Elektrochem.* (1918) **24** 325.

§ 5.37 Activity Coefficients

The activity coefficients f_1 and f_2 of the two components are defined by

$$\lambda_1/\lambda_1^0 = p_1/p_1^0 = (1-x)\,f_1, \qquad (5.37.1)$$

$$\lambda_2/\lambda_2^0 = p_2/p_2^0 = x\,f_2. \qquad (5.37.2)$$

It is evident that each activity coefficient is unity in the respective pure substance.

We recall that in case the vapours may not be treated as perfect gases we must replace the vapour pressures p in these and all formulae by the fugacities $p^\star$.

Comparing (1), (2) with (5.29.2), (5.29.3) we see at once that in an ideal mixture both the activity coefficients f_1 and f_2 are unity. Thus we may use $\log f_1$ and $\log f_2$ as measures of deviations from ideality.

§ 5.38 Osmotic Coefficients

If we regard the species 1 as the solvent then its osmotic coefficient g_1 is defined by

$$\log \frac{\lambda_1}{\lambda_1^0} = \log \frac{p_1}{p_1^0} = g_1 \log (1-x). \qquad (5.38.1)$$

Comparing (1) with (5.29.2) we see that in an ideal mixture g_1 is unity and we may accordingly use $1-g_1$ as a measure of deviation from ideality.

The osmotic coefficient g_1 and the activity coefficient f_1 of the species 1 are seen by comparison of (1) with (5.37.1) to be related by

$$g_1 \log (1-x) = \log (1-x) + \log f_1. \qquad (5.38.2)$$

or

$$(g_1 - 1) \log (1-x) = \log f_1. \qquad (5.38.3)$$

If alternatively we choose to regard the species 2 as solvent there is an analogous definition of g_2 with corresponding relation to f_2. We shall however always regard the species denoted by 1 as the solvent and shall accordingly never use g_2.

§ 5.39 Relation between Two Activitiy Coefficients

If we take the Gibbs–Duhem relation in the form (5.20.1)

$$(1-x)\frac{\partial \log \lambda_1}{\partial x} + x\frac{\partial \log \lambda_2}{\partial x} = 0, \qquad \text{(const. } T, P\text{)}, \quad (5.39.1)$$

and substitute (5.37.1) and (5.37.2) we obtain

$$(1-x)\frac{\partial \log f_1}{\partial x} + x\frac{\partial \log f_2}{\partial x} = 0, \qquad \text{(const. } T, P\text{)}, \quad (5.39.2)$$

all other terms cancelling.

Formula (2) may be rewritten in the integrated form

$$\log f_2 = \int_x^1 \frac{1-x}{x} \, d\log f_1, \qquad \text{(const. } T, P\text{)}. \quad (5.39.3)$$

This formula enables us to compute the activity coefficient of the species 2 at a mole fraction x provided we know the activity coefficient of the other species 1 at *all* compositions intermediate between a mole fraction x and the pure liquid 2.

§ 5.40 Behaviour at High Dilutions

By rewriting (5.39.2) in the form

$$\frac{\partial \log f_1}{\partial x} \bigg/ \frac{\partial \log f_2}{\partial x} = -\frac{x}{1-x}, \qquad (5.40.1)$$

we see immediately that in the limit of vanishing x *either*

$$\frac{\partial \log f_1}{\partial x} \to 0 \quad \text{as} \quad x \to 0, \qquad (5.40.2)$$

or

$$\frac{\partial \log f_2}{\partial x} \to \infty \quad \text{as} \quad x \to 0. \qquad (5.40.3)$$

Statistical theory tells us that the second alternative (3) cannot occur unless there are long range forces between the molecules of species 2. Thus this alternative could occur in solutions of electrolytes and in Chapter IX we shall see that it does occur. But for mixtures of non-electrolytes, such as we are here concerned with, only the former alternative (2) occurs. If further we assume that $\log f_1$ can be expressed as an integral power series in x, the lowest power of x which can occur will be x^2.

§ 5.41 Illustrative Symmetrical Formulae

As an instructive exercise we shall now consider some simple possible formulae for activity coefficients without at this stage considering which of them are physically important. We begin by rewriting (5.39.2) in the form

$$\frac{1}{x} \frac{\partial \log f_1}{\partial x} = -\frac{1}{1-x} \frac{\partial \log f_2}{\partial x}. \qquad (5.41.1)$$

From (1) we see immediately that we can write the general solution in the form

$$\log f_1 = \int x \, \varphi(x) \, dx, \qquad (5.41.2)$$

$$\log f_2 = -\int (1-x) \, \varphi(x) \, dx, \qquad (5.41.3)$$

where $\varphi(x)$ is an arbitrary function of x. The simplest and most interesting solutions are those having symmetry with respect to x and $(1-x)$, that is to say those such that

$$\varphi(x) = \varphi(1-x).\qquad (5.41.4)$$

If we restrict ourselves to integral power series in x, then the most general form of $\varphi(x)$ satisfying (4) is

$$\varphi(x) = \Sigma_s A_s \{x(1-x)\}^{s-1},\qquad (5.41.5)$$

where each A_s is independent of x, but in general depends on T.

For the reasons given in § 5.40 we are here only interested in formulae for $\log f_1$ in which the lowest power of x is greater than 1; that is to say, if integral, not less than 2. Consequently the lowest value of s of physical interest is $s = 1$. We shall now consider the terms corresponding to $s = 1, 2, 3$ in turn.

We first set all $A_s = 0$ except A_1. If we then substitute (4) into (2) and integrate, we obtain

$$\log f_1 = A_1 \tfrac{1}{2} x^2.\qquad (5.41.6)$$

Similarly (3) gives

$$\log f_2 = A_1 \tfrac{1}{2}(1-x)^2.\qquad (5.41.7)$$

This particular behaviour describes a class of systems called *regular solutions*, which will be discussed in §§ 5.49 — 5.53.

Similarly by setting all $A_s = 0$ except A_2, we obtain as another possible symmetrical solution

$$\log f_1 = A_2 \{\tfrac{1}{3} x^3 - \tfrac{1}{4} x^4\},\qquad (5.41.8)$$
$$\log f_2 = A_2 \{\tfrac{1}{3}(1-x)^3 - \tfrac{1}{4}(1-x)^4\};\qquad (5.41.9)$$

and again by setting all $A_s = 0$ except A_3

$$\log f_1 = A_3 \{\tfrac{1}{4} x^4 - \tfrac{2}{5} x^5 + \tfrac{1}{6} x^6\},\qquad (5.41.10)$$
$$\log f_2 = A_3 \{\tfrac{1}{4}(1-x)^4 - \tfrac{2}{5}(1-x)^5 + \tfrac{1}{6}(1-x)^6\}.\qquad (5.41.11)$$

We can of course also obtain symmetrical solutions by linear combinations of (6), (8), (10) or (7), (9), (11). We could further obtain still other symmetrical solutions by using higher values of s, but we shall not pursue this subject any further since up to the present there has been no extensive use of such formulae other than (6) and (7).

§ 5.42   Illustrative Unsymmetrical Formulae

As a further illustrative example we shall consider some possible formulae of a quite different type having a pronounced dissymmetry with respect to the two species. In an ideal solution the mean molar Gibbs function is given by (5.30.3). The corresponding formula for the Gibbs function G of the whole mixture is

$$G = n_1 \mu_1^0 + n_2 \mu_2^0 + RT \left\{ n_1 \log \frac{n_1}{n_1 + n_2} + n_2 \log \frac{n_2}{n_1 + n_2} \right\}.\qquad (5.42.1)$$

Let us now by contrast consider a non-ideal mixture in which G is given by

$$G = n_1 \mu_1^0 + n_2 \mu_2^0 + RT \left\{ n_1 \log \frac{n_1}{n_1 + r n_2} + n_2 \log \frac{r n_2}{n_1 + r n_2} \right\}. \quad (5.42.2)$$

where r is a constant parameter. We obtain for μ_1, μ_2 by differentiating (2) with respect to n_1, n_2 respectively

$$\mu_1 = \mu_1^0 + RT \left\{ \log \frac{n_1}{n_1 + r n_2} + \frac{(r-1) n_2}{n_1 + r n_2} \right\}. \quad (5.42.3)$$

$$\mu_2 = \mu_2^0 + RT \left\{ \log \frac{r n_2}{n_1 + r n_2} - \frac{(r-1) n_1}{n_1 + r n_2} \right\}. \quad (5.42.4)$$

The formula for G_m corresponding to formula (2) for G is

$$G_m = (1-x) \mu_1^0 + x \mu_2^0 + RT \left\{ (1-x) \log \frac{1-x}{1+(r-1)x} + x \log \frac{rx}{1+(r-1)x} \right\}. \quad (5.42.5)$$

Substituting (5) into (5.10.6) and (5.10.7), we obtain

$$\mu_1 = \mu_1^0 + RT \left\{ \log \frac{1-x}{1+(r-1)x} + \frac{(r-1)x}{1+(r-1)x} \right\}. \quad (5.42.6)$$

$$\mu_2 = \mu_2^0 + RT \left\{ \log \frac{rx}{1+(r-1)x} - \frac{(r-1)(1-x)}{1+(r-1)x} \right\}. \quad (5.42.7)$$

which are equivalent to (3) and (4) respectively. We see at once that the identity

$$G_m = (1-x) \mu_1 + x \mu_2 \quad (5.42.8)$$

is satisfied.

Corresponding to (6) and (7) we have for the absolute activities λ_1, λ_2

$$\lambda_1 = \lambda_1^0 \frac{1-x}{1+(r-1)x} \exp \left\{ \frac{(r-1)x}{1+(r-1)x} \right\}. \quad (5.42.9)$$

$$\lambda_2 = \lambda_2^0 \frac{rx}{1+(r-1)x} \exp \left\{ -\frac{(r-1)(1-x)}{1+(r-1)x} \right\}. \quad (5.42.10)$$

Comparing (5.37.1) and (5.37.2) with (5) and (6) respectively we obtain for the activity coefficients

$$\log f_1 = \log \frac{1}{1+(r-1)x} + 1 - \frac{1}{1+(r-1)x}. \quad (5.42.11)$$

$$\log f_2 = \log \frac{r}{1+(r-1)x} + 1 - \frac{r}{1+(r-1)x}. \quad (5.42.12)$$

It can be verified that (11) and (12) satisfy identically relation (5.39.2).

In solutions so dilute with respect to the component 2 that $(r-1)x < 1$ we can expand in powers of $y \equiv (r-1)x$ obtaining

$$\log f_1 = -\tfrac{1}{2} y^2 + \tfrac{2}{3} y^3 - \tfrac{3}{4} y^4 + \dots, \qquad [y \equiv (r-1)x < 1]. \quad (5.42.13)$$

$$\log f_2 = \log r - (r-1) + (r-1) y - (r-\tfrac{1}{2}) y^2 + (r-\tfrac{1}{3}) y^3 - \dots,$$
$$[y \equiv (r-1)x < 1]. \quad (5.42.14)$$

We emphasize that the convergence of these series requires that $y \equiv (r-1) \, x < 1$; the condition $x < 1$ is not sufficient.

We shall consider a possible application of these formulae in § 5.54.

§ 5.43   Temperature Dependence of Activity Coefficients

By substituting (5.37.1) into (5.24.3) or (5.24.4) we obtain

$$\frac{\partial \log f_1}{\partial T} = -\frac{H_1 - H_1^0}{RT^2}, \qquad \text{(const. } P, x). \qquad (5.43.1)$$

The quantity $H_1 - H_1^0$ occurring in (1) is the heat required to be absorbed so as to keep the temperature unchanged when one mole of the pure liquid 1 is added to a large excess of the mixture. We shall call this the *partial molar heat of mixing* of the species 1. An analogous definition applies to the species 2.

§ 5.44   Pressure Dependence of Activity Coefficients

Applying (5.21.2) to the mixture and the pure liquid in turn, we obtain

$$\frac{\partial \log (p_1/p_1^0)}{\partial P} = \frac{V_1 - V_1^0}{RT}, \qquad \text{(const. } T, x). \qquad (5.44.1)$$

Substituting (5.37.1) into (1) we find

$$\frac{\partial \log f_1}{\partial P} = \frac{V_1 - V_1^0}{RT}, \qquad \text{(const. } T, x). \qquad (5.44.2)$$

This effect of pressure on activity coefficients is usually, if not always, negligible.

§ 5.45   Equilibrium of Liquid Mixture with Pure Solid Phase

For the condition of equilibrium between a liquid mixture and the pure solid phase, we obtain by substituting (5.37.1) and (5.38.1) into (5.25.9)

$$-\log \{(1-x) f_1\} \equiv -g_1 \log (1-x) = \frac{[\Delta_f H_1^0]}{R} \left(\frac{1}{T} - \frac{1}{T^0} \right). \qquad (5.45.1)$$

wherein f_1 and g_1 denote the values at the freezing temperature T. Thus, provided the molar heat of fusion $\Delta_f H_1^0$ of the pure substance is known, comparison of the freezing-point T of the solution with the freezing-point T^0 of the pure solvent provides directly values of the activity coefficient f_1 or the osmotic coefficient g_1 at the temperature T. If values of f_1 or g_1 are required at any other temperature a correction has to be applied by using (5.43.1).

§ 5.46   Boiling-Point of Solution of Non-volatile Solute

To obtain the relation between the boiling-point T of a solution of a non-volatile solute 2 in a solvent 1 and the composition of this solution, we substitute (5.37.1) and (5.38.1) into (5.26.1). We find

$$-\log\{(1-x)f_1\} \equiv -g\log(1-x) = \frac{[\triangle_e H_1^0]}{R}\left(\frac{1}{T^0}-\frac{1}{T}\right), \qquad (5.46.1)$$

wherein f_1 and g_1 denote the values at the boiling-point T. Thus, if the molar heat of evaporation $\triangle_e H_1^0$ of the pure solvent is known, comparison of the boiling-point T of the solution with the boiling-point T^0 of the pure solvent gives directly values of the activity coefficient f_1 or the osmotic coefficient g_1 at the temperature T. If values of f_1 or g_1 are required at any other temperature a correction has to be applied using (5.43.1).

§ 5.47   Osmotic Pressure

We obtain a general formula for the osmotic pressure, regarding the species 1 as solvent, by substituting (5.37.1) and (5.38.1) into (5.27.8). Thus

$$\frac{\Pi[V_1]}{RT} = -\log\{(1-x)f_1\} \equiv -g_1\log(1-x). \qquad (5.47.1)$$

Comparing (1) with (5.35.1) we observe that the actual osmotic pressure differs from its ideal value by the factor g_1. This explains the name *osmotic coefficient*. Reference to formula (5.45.1) suggests however that the name *freezing-point coefficient* would be equally appropriate.

The values of f_1 and g_1 to be used in (1) are those at the pressure P on the pure solvent at osmotic equilibrium. Alternatively instead of using (5.27.8) we may use (5.27.12) and then obtain

$$\frac{\Pi[V_1^0]}{RT} = -\log\{(1-x)f_1\} \equiv -g_1\log(1-x), \qquad (5.47.2)$$

wherein V_1^0 is the molar volume of the pure solvent, while f_1, g_1 now have the values appropriate to the pressure $P+\Pi$ on the solution at osmotic equilibrium. Usually the differences between the quantities in the two formulae (1) and (2) will be small, if not negligible.

§ 5.48   Internal Stability with Respect to Composition

In § 4.01 and § 4.02 we discussed the thermal and hydrostatic conditions of internal stability respectively. In a system of a single component these are the only kinds of internal stability to be considered. In a phase of two components we have also to consider the condition that the phase should not split into two phases with different compositions.

We can conveniently study this problem by reference to a plot of the mean molar Gibbs function G_m against mole fraction x at given T, P. Examples of such a plot are shown in Fig. 5.5, which in appearance reminds one of Fig. 4.7. If now we imagine a phase of composition x to split into two, one of slightly greater and the other of slightly smaller x, the new value of G_m is then given by a point on the straight line joining the two points repre-

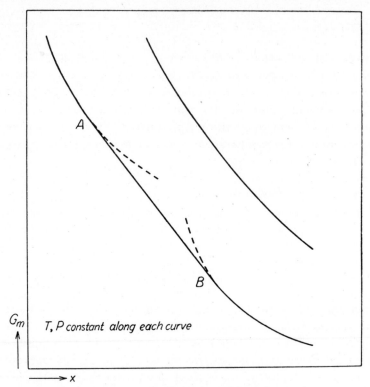

Fig. **5.5**. Stable and metastable isotherms.

senting the two new phases. If this point lies above the one representing the original phase, the system will revert to its original state which is stable. In the contrary case the original phase is unstable. It is then clear from the diagram that while the upper curve represents phases all stable, the phases represented by the dotted portion of the lower curve between A and B are metastable with respect to a mixture of phases represented by A and B.

At constant temperature and pressure according to (1.33.4)

$$dG = \mu_1 \, dn_1 + \mu_2 \, dn_2, \qquad (\text{const. } T, P). \qquad (5.48.1)$$

Hence for one mole, setting

$$n_1 = 1 - x, \qquad (5.48.2)$$

$$n_2 = x, \qquad (5.48.3)$$

we have

$$dG_m = (\mu_2 - \mu_1) \, dx, \qquad (5.48.4)$$

so that the slope of the curve at any point is equal to $\mu_2 - \mu_1$. We may note that formula (4) is a special case of the general relation (5.08.2).

As the two phases A and B are in mutual equilibrium they have equal values of μ_1, μ_2 and consequently of $\mu_2 - \mu_1$, in agreement with the fact that the straight line AB touches the curve at A and B.

It can happen that at some temperatures the behaviour corresponds to a curve such as the upper one in the diagram, while at other temperatures, usually lower ones, the behaviour corresponds to a curve such as the lower one in the diagram. There will then be some temperature, called the *critical temperature of mixing*, at which the change in type of behaviour takes place. At temperatures one side of this critical temperature the two liquids are miscible in all proportions; at temperatures the other side of the critical temperature the miscibility is limited, only phases to the left of A or to the right of B being stable.

We shall now determine the conditions at the critical temperature. The lower curve in Fig. 5.5 is concave upwards in the stable regions and in the dotted metastable regions. In these parts of the curve

$$\frac{\partial^2 G_m}{\partial x^2} > 0. \qquad (5.48.5)$$

If we imagine the two dotted curves joined into a single curve then in the middle there must be a part of the curve convex upwards corresponding to completely unstable phases. Hence between A and B there are two points of inflexion C and D where

$$\frac{\partial^2 G_m}{\partial x^2} = 0 \qquad \text{(at } C \text{ and } D\text{).} \qquad (5.48.6)$$

At the temperature of critical mixing these two points merge into a single point at which, as well as (6),

$$\frac{\partial^3 G_m}{\partial x^3} = 0. \qquad (5.48.7)$$

Owing to (4) the condition (6) may be written

$$\frac{\partial \mu_1}{\partial x} = \frac{\partial \mu_2}{\partial x}, \qquad (5.48.8)$$

and the condition (7)

$$\frac{\partial^2 \mu_1}{\partial x^2} = \frac{\partial^2 \mu_2}{\partial x^2}. \qquad (5.48.9)$$

We also have from the Gibbs–Duhem relation (5.10.5)

$$(1-x)\frac{\partial \mu_1}{\partial x} + x\frac{\partial \mu_2}{\partial x} = 0, \qquad (5.48.10)$$

and differentiating again with respect to x

$$(1-x)\frac{\partial^2 \mu_1}{\partial x^2} - \frac{\partial \mu_1}{\partial x} + x\frac{\partial^2 \mu_2}{\partial x^2} + \frac{\partial \mu_2}{\partial x} = 0. \qquad (5.48.11)$$

It follows from (8) and (10) that at the point of critical mixing

$$\frac{\partial \mu_1}{\partial x} = \frac{\partial \mu_2}{\partial x} = 0. \tag{5.48.12}$$

and so from (9) and (11)

$$\frac{\partial^2 \mu_1}{\partial x^2} = \frac{\partial^2 \mu_2}{\partial x^2} = 0. \tag{5.48.13}$$

In terms of absolute activities (12) and (13) become

$$\frac{\partial \log \lambda_1}{\partial x} = \frac{\partial \log \lambda_2}{\partial x} = 0, \tag{5.48.14}$$

$$\frac{\partial^2 \log \lambda_1}{\partial x^2} = \frac{\partial^2 \log \lambda_2}{\partial x^2} = 0. \tag{5.48.15}$$

If we substitute (5.37.1) and (5.37.2) into (14) and (15) we obtain the conditions at the point of critical mixing in the form

$$\frac{\partial \log f_1}{\partial x} - \frac{1}{1-x} = \frac{\partial \log f_2}{\partial x} + \frac{1}{x} = 0, \tag{5.48.16}$$

$$\frac{\partial^2 \log f_1}{\partial x^2} - \frac{1}{(1-x)^2} = \frac{\partial^2 \log f_2}{\partial x^2} - \frac{1}{x^2} = 0. \tag{5.48.17}$$

The use of these formulae will be illustrated in § 5.53.

§ 5.49 Regular Solutions

We turn now to a class of mixtures called *regular mixtures* or *regular solutions* defined by the properties

$$\log f_1 = \frac{w}{RT} x^2, \tag{5.49.1}$$

$$\log f_2 = \frac{w}{RT} (1-x)^2, \tag{5.49.2}$$

wherein w is not merely independent of the composition but also of the temperature. We notice that (1) and (2) are examples of (5.41.6) and (5.41.7) wherein we set

$$A_1 = \frac{2w}{RT}. \tag{5.49.3}$$

The name *regular solution* was first used by Hildebrand [*]. We shall devote considerable attention to these mixtures for several reasons.

In the first place the behaviour of regular mixtures is one of the simplest conceivable, after ideal mixtures, either from a mathematical or from a physical aspect.

In the second place statistical theory predicts that any mixture of two

---

[*] Hildebrand, *J. Am. Chem. Soc.* (1929) **51** 69.

kinds of non-polar molecules of similar simple shape should obey certain laws, called the laws of *strictly regular solutions* *, to which the formulae for *regular solutions* are a useful approximation.

In the third place the experimental work of Hildebrand ** has shown that a considerable number of binary mixtures show a behaviour which can be represented either accurately or approximately by the laws of regular solutions.

§ 5.50 Heats of Mixing in Regular Solutions

Differentiating (5.49.1) with respect to T we obtain

$$\frac{\partial \log f_1}{\partial T} = -\frac{w}{RT^2} x^2,$$

(5.50.1)

and comparing with (5.43.1) we see that

$$H_1 - H_1^0 = w\, x^2.$$

(5.50.2)

Thus the partial molar heat of mixing of the species 1 into the solution is wx^2 and similarly that of the species 2 is $w\,(1-x)^2$.

In particular by making x tend towards unity in (2) we see that w is the heat required to maintain constant temperature when one mole of the species 1 is transferred from the pure liquid 1 into a large amount of the pure liquid 2. The same quantity w is also equal to the heat required to maintain constant temperature when one mole of the species 2 is transferred from the pure liquid 2 into a large amount of the pure liquid 1.

It is an essential property of regular mixtures as defined by Hildebrand that this quantity w is independent of the temperature.

§ 5.51 Partial Vapour Pressures of Regular Solutions

From (5.49.1) and (5.37.1) it follows immediately that the partial vapour pressure, or strictly the fugacity, of the component 1 is given by

$$p_1 = p_1^0 (1-x) \exp\{x^2\, w/RT\}.$$

(5.51.1)

Similarly

$$p_2 = p_2^0\, x \exp\{(1-x)^2\, w/RT\}.$$

(5.51.2)

For solutions very dilute with respect to the species 2, when $x \ll 1$, formula (2) approximates to

$$p_2 = p_2^0\, e^{w/RT}\, x, \qquad (x \ll 1).$$

(5.51.3)

This direct proportionality between p_2 and x for small values of x is called *Henry's Law* and it holds not only for regular solutions but also when the activity coefficients have a more complicated form.

---

* See Fowler and Guggenheim, *Statistical Thermodynamics* (1939) §§ 818—819.

** Hildebrand, *Solubility of Non-electrolytes* (1936).

There is, of course a corresponding formula for solutions very dilute with respect to 1

$$p_1 = p_1^0 \, e^{w/RT} (1 - x), \qquad (1 - x \ll 1). \tag{5.51.4}$$

We shall revert to *Henry's Law* in Chapter VII.

§ 5.52   Osmotic Pressure in Regular Solutions

Substituting (5.51.1) into (5.27.8) we obtain for the osmotic pressure Π in a regular solution, regarding the component 1 as the solvent,

$$\frac{\Pi [V_1]}{RT} = - \log (1 - x) - \frac{w}{RT} x^2. \tag{5.52.1}$$

From (1) and (5.47.1) we see that the osmotic coefficient in a regular solution, regarding the species 1 as solvent, is given by

$$g_1 - 1 = \frac{w \, x^2}{RT \log (1 - x)}. \tag{5.52.2}$$

When $x \ll 1$ formula (2) may be approximated by

$$g_1 - 1 = - \frac{w}{RT} x, \qquad (x \ll 1). \tag{5.52.3}$$

There are of course similar formulae in which the component 2 is regarded as the solvent.

§ 5.53   Critical Mixing in Regular Solutions

In Fig. 5.6 p_1/p_1^0 and p_2/p_2^0 have been plotted against x for $w/RT = 1$ and $w/RT = -2$. We see that when w is positive, the curves lie above the straight lines representing Raoult's law for ideal solutions; this situation is sometimes called a *positive deviation* from Raoult's law. On

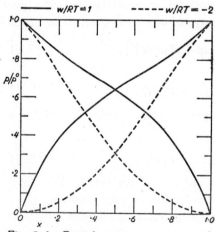

Fig. 5.6. Partial vapour pressures of regular solutions; (complete mixing).

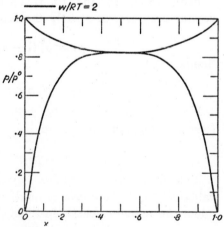

Fig. 5.7. Partial vapour pressures of regular solutions; (temperature of critical mixing).

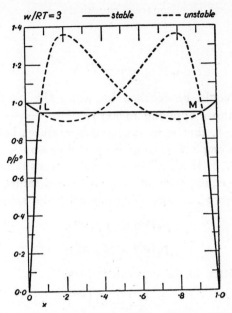

Fig. 5.8. Partial vapour pressures of regular solutions; (incomplete mixing).

the other hand when w is negative, both curves lie below the straight line of the ideal solution and this situation is sometimes described as a *negative deviation* from Raoult's law.

Fig. 5.7 gives similar plots for $w/RT = 2$. We shall show that this is the temperature of critical mixing. According to (5.48.16) and (5.48.17) the conditions of critical mixing are determined by

$$\frac{\partial \log f_1}{\partial x} = \frac{1}{1-x}, \qquad (5.53.1)$$

$$\frac{\partial^2 \log f_1}{\partial x^2} = \frac{1}{(1-x)^2}. \qquad (5.53.2)$$

these conditions together corresponding to a horizontal inflexion in the curves p/p^0 plotted against x.

For a regular solution f_1 is given by (5.49.1)

$$\log f_1 = \frac{w}{RT} x^2. \qquad (5.53.3)$$

Substituting this into (1) and (2) we obtain

$$\frac{w}{RT} 2x = \frac{1}{1-x}, \qquad (5.53.4)$$

$$\frac{w}{RT} 2 = \frac{1}{(1-x)^2}. \qquad (5.53.5)$$

The solution of these simultaneous equations is

$$x = \tfrac{1}{2},\tag{5.53.6}$$

$$\frac{w}{RT} = 2.\tag{5.53.7}$$

The same result could be reached by using the conditions applying to $\log f_2$ instead of those applying to $\log f_1$.

When $w/RT > 2$, that is to say at temperatures below that of critical mixing, there is incomplete mixing. A typical example, namely $w/RT = 3$, is shown in Fig. 5.8. If x', x'' denote the compositions of the two liquid phases in mutual equilibrium at a given temperature T, below that of critical mixing, then x', x'' are determined by the simultaneous equations

$$p_1(x') = p_1(x''),\tag{5.53.8}$$

$$p_2(x') = p_2(x'').\tag{5.53.9}$$

These may be written in the equivalent form

$$\frac{p_1(x')}{p_1^0} = \frac{p_1(x'')}{p_1^0},\tag{5.53.10}$$

$$\frac{p_2(x')}{p_2^0} = \frac{p_2(x'')}{p_2^0}.\tag{5.53.11}$$

For a regular mixture there is complete symmetry between p_1/p_1^0 as a function of x and p_2/p_2^0 as a function of $(1 - x)$. It follows from this symmetry that

$$x' + x'' = 1,\tag{5.53.12}$$

and consequently

$$\frac{p_2(x')}{p_2^0} = \frac{p_2(1 - x'')}{p_2^0} = \frac{p_1(x'')}{p_1^0} = \frac{p_1(x')}{p_1^0}.\tag{5.53.13}$$

Hence x', x'' are determined by the intersections of the two curves. These are the points L, M in Fig. 5.8. The curves between L and M represent solutions either metastable near L, M or completely unstable towards the middle of the diagram.

§ 5.54 Mixtures of Large and Small Molecules

We noticed in § 5.31 that if two species form an ideal mixture, then they mix isothermally without increase or decrease of the heat function. Zero heat of mixing is thus a necessary condition for two species to form an ideal mixture, but it is not a sufficient condition. Statistical mechanics indicates as a further necessary condition that the two kinds of molecules should not differ greatly in size. It is accordingly of interest to consider the properties of mixtures of two kinds of molecules sufficiently similar to mix in all proportions without any heat of mixing, but differing widely in size. This is a complicated problem in statistical mechanics which has not been solved completely. It is probable that the shapes of the molecules matter as well as their sizes. However, ignoring such complications, there are reasons for believing that departures from the laws of ideal mixtures due to wide differences in size between the two species of molecule can be at least semi-quantitatively described by means of relatively simple formulae in which the only new parameter is the ratio of the molecular volumes.

If r denotes the ratio of the volume of a molecule of type 2 to that of a molecule of type 1, then subject to various restrictions and approximations which we shall not here go into, we may write for the Gibbs function of a mixture containing n_1 moles of 1 and n_2 moles of 2,

$$G = n_1\,\mu_1^0 + n_2\,\mu_2^0 + RT\left\{n_1 \log \frac{n_1}{n_1 + rn_2} + n_2 \log \frac{rn_2}{n_1 + rn_2}\right\}. \quad (5.54.1)$$

The reader will recognize (1) as formula (5.42.2) the consequences of which have already been studied in § 5.42 as an exercise. We accordingly recall some of these consequences without proof. For the vapour pressures and absolute activities we have

$$\frac{p_1}{p_1^0} = \frac{\lambda_1}{\lambda_1^0} = \frac{1-x}{1 + (r-1)x} \exp\left\{\frac{(r-1)\,x}{1 + (r-1)\,x}\right\}, \quad (5.54.2)$$

$$\frac{p_2}{p_2^0} = \frac{\lambda_2}{\lambda_2^0} = \frac{rx}{1 + (r-1)x} \exp\left\{-\frac{(r-1)(1-x)}{1 + (r-1)\,x}\right\}. \quad (5.54.3)$$

For the activity coefficients we have correspondingly

$$\log f_1 = \log \frac{1}{1 + (r-1)\,x} + 1 - \frac{1}{1 + (r-1)\,x}, \quad (5.54.4)$$

$$\log f_2 = \log \frac{r}{1 + (r-1)\,x} + 1 - \frac{r}{1 + (r-1)\,x}. \quad (5.54.5)$$

We notice that when $r = 1$, we have $f_1 = f_2 = 1$ and we recover the formulae of ideal mixtures. Of especial interest is the opposite case where r differs greatly from unity. Since replacing r by $1/r$ is mathematically equivalent to interchanging the names 1 and 2 of the two components, it will suffice to consider only the alternative $r > 1$. If now we denote the *volume fraction* of the component 2 by v, defined by

$$v = \frac{rx}{1 + (r-1)\,x}, \quad (5.54.6)$$

formulae (2) and (3) may be written

$$\frac{p_1}{p_1^0} = \frac{\lambda_1}{\lambda_1^0} = (1 - v) \exp\left\{\left(1 - \frac{1}{r}\right) v\right\}. \quad (5.54.7)$$

$$\frac{p_2}{p_2^0} = \frac{\lambda_2}{\lambda_2^0} = v \exp\left\{-(r-1)(1-v)\right\}, \quad (5.54.8)$$

respectively.

These formulae with $r > 1$ are relevant to solutions of rubber and synthetic polymers in certain organic solvents. Such solutions show pronounced deviations from Raoult's law, which can be represented at least approximately * by formula (7) due to Flory **.

Even so it should be noted that Raoult's law is valid in the limit $v \to 0$, when (7) reduces to

$$1 - \frac{p_1}{p_1^0} = 1 - \frac{\lambda_1}{\lambda_1^0} \to \frac{v}{r} \to x. \tag{5.54.9}$$

§ 5.55 Interfacial Layers in Binary Systems

We shall now consider the thermodynamics of interfacial layers between two bulk phases each containing the same two components. There are two cases to distinguish: first an interface between a liquid binary mixture and its vapour, when the interfacial tension is called the *surface tension*; second an interface between two liquid layers containing in different proportions two incompletely miscible components.

We shall first discuss the liquid-vapour interface using an approximation, sufficient for most if not all practical applications. We shall next give a similar approximate treatment of a liquid-liquid interface. Finally we shall give an accurate treatment applicable in principle to either type of interface, but of small practical use.

§ 5.56 Liquid-Vapour Interface

We begin with formula (1.55.3) applied to a system of two components 1 and 2. Thus

$$-d\gamma = S^\sigma \, dT - \tau \, dP + \Gamma_1 \, d\mu_1 + \Gamma_2 \, d\mu_2, \tag{5.56.1}$$

where we have dropped the subscript u in S_u^σ which we used in Chapter IV to denote entropy per unit area of the interfacial layer. At the same time in the liquid phase we have according to (5.04.4) and (5.04.5)

$$d\mu_1 = -S_1 \, dT + V_1 \, dP + \frac{\partial \mu_1}{\partial x} \, dx, \tag{5.56.2}$$

$$d\mu_2 = -S_2 \, dT + V_2 \, dP + \frac{\partial \mu_2}{\partial x} \, dx, \tag{5.56.3}$$

where we have omitted superscripts from quantities relating to the liquid phase.

In our initial treatment of a liquid-vapour interface we shall make approximations similar to those used in § 4.72 for a single component interface.

In the first place we assume that PV_1 and PV_2 are in the liquid phase so small compared with RT that they may be neglected.

---

* See Gee, *J. de Phys.* (1947) **44** 66.
** Flory, *J. Chem. Phys.* (1941) **9** 660; (1942) **10** 51.

In the second place we assume that the two geometrical surfaces separating the interfacial phase from the two bulk phases are placed so near to each other that terms in $P\tau$ may also be neglected. We accordingly replace (1), (2), (3) by

$$-d\gamma = S^\sigma dT + \Gamma_1 d\mu_1 + \Gamma_2 d\mu_2, \qquad (5.56.4)$$

$$d\mu_1 = -S_1 dT + \frac{\partial \mu_1}{\partial x} dx, \qquad (5.56.5)$$

$$d\mu_2 = -S_2 dT + \frac{\partial \mu_2}{\partial x} dx. \qquad (5.56.6)$$

Substituting (5) and (6) into (4) we obtain

$$-d\gamma = (S^\sigma - \Gamma_1 S_1 - \Gamma_2 S_2) dT + \left(\Gamma_1 \frac{\partial \mu_1}{\partial x} + \Gamma_2 \frac{\partial \mu_2}{\partial x}\right) dx. \qquad (5.56.7)$$

The system of two components in liquid and vapour has two degrees of freedom. There are consequently two independent variables, for which we choose T and x. Formula (7) thus expresses variations of the surface tension γ in terms of variations dT and dx of the two independent variables.

Since the quantities $\partial \mu_1/\partial x$ and $\partial \mu_2/\partial x$ on the right of (7) are related by the Gibbs–Duhem relation (5.10.5)

$$(1-x)\frac{\partial \mu_1}{\partial x} + x\frac{\partial \mu_2}{\partial x} = 0, \qquad (5.56.8)$$

we can use this relation to eliminate either of them. If for example we eliminate $\partial \mu_1/\partial x$ we obtain

$$-d\gamma = (S^\sigma - \Gamma_1 S_1 - \Gamma_2 S_2) dT + \left(\Gamma_2 - \frac{x\Gamma_1}{1-x}\right)\frac{\partial \mu_2}{\partial x}\partial x. \qquad (5.56.9)$$

By this elimination we have unavoidably destroyed the symmetry between the components 1 and 2.

§ 5.57 Invariance of Relations

We recall that according to the definition in § 1.51 and § 1.56 of a surface phase the properties associated with it depend on the positions of the boundaries AA' and BB' in Figs. 1.2 and 1.3. As in § 4.71 we shall henceforth refer to the boundary between surface layer and liquid as $L\sigma$ and that between surface layer and gas as $G\sigma$. Since the precise positions assigned to these geometrical boundaries is partly arbitrary, the values assigned to such quantities as Γ_1, Γ_2, S^σ are also arbitrary. We can nevertheless verify that our formulae are invariant with respect to shifts of either or both of these boundaries. It is hardly necessary to mention that the intensive variables T, μ_1, μ_2 are unaffected by shifts of either boundary. It is also clear from the definition of γ in § 1.52 and § 1.56 that its value is invariant.

Let us now consider a shift of the plane boundary $L\sigma$ a distance $\delta\tau$ away from the gas phase. Then Γ_1 becomes increased by the number of moles of the species 1 in a cylinder of liquid of height $\delta\tau$, of cross-section unity and so of volume $\delta\tau$. But the total number of moles in the volume $\delta\tau$ is $\delta\tau/V_m$ of which the number of species 1 is $(1-x)\,\delta\tau/V_m$. Similarly Γ_2 becomes increased by $x\delta\tau/V_m$. Consequently although shifting the boundary $L\sigma$ alters the values of Γ_1 and Γ_2, the quantity

$$\Gamma_2 - \frac{x\Gamma_1}{1-x} \qquad (5.57.1)$$

remains unchanged. The invariant quantity (1) is essentially the same as a quantity defined by Gibbs in a more abstract manner and denoted by him by the symbol $\Gamma_{2(1)}$.

Similarly when the boundary $L\sigma$ is shifted a distance $\delta\tau$ away from the gas phase, S^σ becomes increased by the entropy contained in a cylinder of liquid of volume $\delta\tau$, that is to say by an amount

$$S_m\,\delta\tau/V_m = \{(1-x)\,S_1 + x\,S_2\}\,\delta\tau/V_m.$$

At the same time $\Gamma_1 S_1$ is increased by $S_1(1-x)\,\delta\tau/V_m$ and $\Gamma_2 S_2$ by $S_2 x\,\delta\tau/V_m$. Consequently the quantity

$$S^\sigma - \Gamma_1 S_1 - \Gamma_2 S_2 \qquad (5.57.2)$$

occurring in (5.56.9) remains invariant.

With regard to a shift of the geometrical surface $G\sigma$, little need be said in the present connection. For our approximation of neglecting terms in $P\tau$, as we are doing, is equivalent to assuming that the quantity of matter per unit volume in the gas phase is negligible compared with that in unit volume of the surface layer. Consequently if we shifted the geometrical surface $G\sigma$ away from the liquid even to the extent of doubling the value of τ, the change in the physical content of the surface layer would be negligible and consequently the values of Γ_1, Γ_2, S^σ would not be appreciably affected.

§ 5.58 Temperature Coefficient of Surface Tension

If we apply formula (5.56.9) to variations of temperature at constant composition x, we obtain

$$-\frac{d\gamma}{dT} = S^\sigma - \Gamma_1 S_1 - \Gamma_2 S_2, \qquad \text{(const. } x\text{).} \quad (5.58.1)$$

This relation involving entropies can be transformed to one involving energies as follows. Since we are neglecting terms in PV_1 and PV_2 we replace (5.04.3) by the approximation

$$\mu_1 = U_1 - TS_1. \qquad (5.58.2)$$

and similarly

$$\mu_2 = U_2 - TS_2. \qquad (5.58.3)$$

Applying formula (1.54.6) to unit area and neglecting the term containing $V^\sigma = \tau A$, we have

$$\Gamma_1 \mu_1 + \Gamma_2 \mu_2 = F^\sigma - \gamma = U^\sigma - TS^\sigma - \gamma. \qquad (5.58.4)$$

We now use (2), (3), (4) to eliminate S^σ, S_1, S_2 from (1). We thus obtain

$$\gamma - T \frac{d\gamma}{dT} = U^\sigma - \Gamma_1 U_1 - \Gamma_2 U_2. \qquad (5.58.5)$$

It is worth noticing that the right side of (1) is the entropy of unit area of interface less the entropy of the same material content in the liquid phase. Likewise the right side of (5) is the energy of unit area of interface less the energy of the same material content in the liquid phase. More pictorially we may say that it is the energy which must be supplied to prevent any change of temperature when unit area of surface is formed from the liquid. It is sometimes called the surface energy per unit area, but this name belongs more properly to U^σ.

§ 5.59 Variations of Composition

If we apply (5.56.7) to a variation of composition at constant temperature we obtain

$$-\frac{d\gamma}{dx} = \Gamma_1 \frac{\partial \mu_1}{\partial x} + \Gamma_2 \frac{\partial \mu_2}{\partial x}, \qquad \text{(const. } T\text{)}. \qquad (5.59.1)$$

Alternatively using (5.56.9) we obtain the simpler, but less symmetrical relation

$$-\frac{d\gamma}{dx} = \left(\Gamma_2 - \frac{x\Gamma_1}{1-x} \right) \frac{\partial \mu_2}{\partial x}, \qquad \text{(const. } T\text{)}. \qquad (5.59.2)$$

Using (5.18.4) we obtain in terms of absolute activities

$$-\frac{d\gamma}{dx} = RT \left(\Gamma_2 - \frac{x\Gamma_1}{1-x} \right) \frac{\partial \log \lambda_2}{\partial x}, \qquad \text{(const. } T\text{)}, \qquad (5.59.3)$$

and using (5.18.17) we obtain in terms of the partial vapour pressure, or strictly the fugacity.

$$-\frac{d\gamma}{dx} = RT \left(\Gamma_2 - \frac{x\Gamma_1}{1-x} \right) \frac{\partial \log p_2}{\partial x}, \qquad \text{(const. } T\text{)}. \qquad (5.59.4)$$

From (4) we see that from measurements of p_2 and γ over a range of compositions, one can calculate the value of

$$\Gamma_2 - \frac{x\Gamma_1}{1-x}. \qquad (5.59.5)$$

As we saw in § 5. 57, this quantity is invariant with respect to shift in position of the geometrical boundary $L\sigma$ between the liquid and the interface. Values can be assigned to Γ_1 and Γ_2 individually only by adopting some more or less arbitrary convention. We shall illustrate this by a numerical example in the next section.

In the special case of an ideal solution formula (4) becomes

$$-\frac{d\gamma}{dx} = RT\left(\frac{\Gamma_2}{x} - \frac{\Gamma_1}{1-x}\right), \tag{5.59.6}$$

while for a regular solution

$$-\frac{d\gamma}{dx} = \left(\frac{\Gamma_2}{x} - \frac{\Gamma_1}{1-x}\right)\left\{RT - 2wx(1-x)\right\}. \tag{5.59.7}$$

§ 5. 60 Example of Water and Alcohol

We shall now consider the experimental data for mixtures of water and alcohol in order to illustrate the use of the formulae of the preceding section. The experimental data for the partial vapour pressures have already been given in Fig. 5. 2 and Table 5. 1, where we verified that they are consistent with the Duhem–Margules relation. In Table 5. 2 the first three columns repeat those of Table 5. 1, the subscript 1 denoting water and 2 alcohol. The fourth column gives experimental values of the surface tension γ. The fifth column gives values of $-p_2\,\partial\gamma/\partial p_2$ obtained by plotting γ against log p and measuring slopes. The sixth column gives values of

$$\Gamma_2 - \frac{x}{1-x}\,\Gamma_1, \tag{5.60.1}$$

calculated from (5. 59. 4), which can be rewritten in the form

$$-p_2\frac{\partial\gamma}{\partial p_2} = RT\left(\Gamma_2 - \frac{x\,\Gamma_1}{1-x}\right). \tag{5.60.2}$$

The values of the quantity (1) are given in the sixth column in moles/cm^2. In the seventh column the corresponding molecular quantity is given in molecules/Å^2.

As we have repeatedly emphasized, this is as far as one can go without making some non-thermodynamic convention. We shall now give an example of such a convention. Let us assume that the interfacial layer is unimolecular and that each molecule of water occupies a constant area of interface and likewise each molecule of alcohol. This assumption may be expressed by

$$A_1\,\Gamma_1 + A_2\,\Gamma_2 = 1. \qquad (A_1, A_2 \text{ const.}). \tag{5.60.3}$$

We may, if we like, call A_1, A_2 the *partial molar areas* of the two species in the interface. The essence of our assumption is not the definition of these quantities, but the assignment to them of definite constant values.

TABLE 5.2
Water-alcohol mixtures

Determination of $\Gamma_2 - \dfrac{x}{1-x}\Gamma_1$

x	$\dfrac{p_1}{\text{mm. Hg}}$	$\dfrac{p_2}{\text{mm. Hg}}$	$\dfrac{\gamma}{\text{erg cm.}^{-2}}$	$\dfrac{-p_2\dfrac{\partial\gamma}{\partial p_2}}{\text{erg cm.}^{-2}}$	$\dfrac{\Gamma_2-\dfrac{x}{1-x}\Gamma_1}{10^{-10}\text{ moles cm.}^{-2}}$	$\dfrac{\Gamma_2-\dfrac{x}{1-x}\Gamma_1}{10^{-2}\text{molecules }\overset{\circ}{A}^{-2}}$
0	23.75	0.0	72.2	0.0	0.0	0.0
0.1	21.7	17.8	36.4	15.6	6.3	3.8
0.2	20.4	26.8	29.7	16.0	6.45	3.9
0.3	19.4	31.2	27.6	14.6	5.9	3.6
0.4	18.35	34.2	26.35	12.6	5.1	3.1
0.5	17.3	36.9	25.4	10.5	4.25	2.6
0.6	15.8	40.1	24.6	8.45	3.4	2.06
0.7	13.3	43.9	23.85	7.15	2.9	1.75
0.8	10.0	48.3	23.2	6.2	2.5	1.5
0.9	5.5	53.3	22.6	5.45	2.2	1.33
1.0	0.0	59.0	22.0	5.2	2.1	1.27

TABLE 5.3
Water-alcohol mixtures

Values of Γ in 10^{-10} mole/cm.^{2} calculated from

$$A_1\Gamma_1 + A_2\Gamma_2 = 1$$

with $A_1 = 0.04 \times 10^{10}$ cm.^{2}/mole of water
$A_2 = 0.12 \times 10^{10}$ cm.^{2}/mole of alcohol

x	$\Gamma_2-\dfrac{x}{1-x}\Gamma_1$	Γ_2	Γ_1	$\dfrac{\Gamma_2}{\Gamma_1+\Gamma_2}$
0.0	0.0	0.0	25.0	0.00
0.05	5.9	6.2	6.4	0.49
0.1	6.3	6.8	4.6	0.60
0.2	6.45	7.25	3.25	0.69
0.3	5.9	7.25	3.25	0.69
0.4	5.1	7.25	3.25	0.69
0.5	4.25	7.3	3.1	0.70
0.6	3.4	7.45	2.65	0.74
0.7	2.9	7.65	2.0	0.79
0.8	2.5	7.9	1.3	0.86
0.9	2.2	8.1	0.7	0.94
1.0	2.1	8.35	0.0	1.00

which can neither be determined nor verified by thermodynamic means.
As an example we might assume

$$A_1 = 0.06 \times 10^{10} \text{ cm}^2/\text{mole},$$
$$A_2 = 0.12 \times 10^{10} \text{ cm}^2/\text{mole};$$ (5. 60. 4)

corresponding to

$$A_1/N = \ \ 7 \text{ Å}^2/\text{molecule},$$
$$A_2/N = 20 \text{ Å}^2/\text{molecule}.$$ (5. 60. 5)

The relation (3) with the values of A_1, A_2 given by (4) is sufficient to determine values of Γ_1, Γ_2 from the values of the expression (1) already given in Table 5.2. The results of the calculation are given in Table 5.3. The first column gives the mole-fraction x of alcohol, the second the values of the expression (1) taken from the previous table, the third and fourth columns the values of Γ_1, Γ_2 calculated by means of (3). The fifth column gives values of $\Gamma_2/(\Gamma_1 + \Gamma_2)$ which we may call the mole fraction of alcohol in the surface layer. As the mole fraction thus calculated, in the surface layer increases steadily with the mole fraction in the liquid, we may conclude that although the model on which the assumptions (3), (4), (5) were based is admittedly arbitrary, at least it does not lead to unreasonable or surprising results.

§ 5.61   Interface Between Two Binary Liquids

We turn now to consider the interface between two liquid phases of two components. Two such phases may or may not be regular, but they obviously cannot be ideal. In our initial treatment we shall make approximations similar to those in § 5.56.

We assume that in a liquid phase PV_1 and PV_2 are so small compared with RT that they may be neglected. This assumption now applies to both liquid phases. Just as in § 5.56 we also neglect terms in $P\tau$.

There is an important physical difference between the significance of our approximate treatment of a liquid-vapour interface in the previous sections and the approximate treatment we are now about to give of a liquid-liquid interface. In the case of the liquid-vapour system we took as independent variables the temperature and composition of the liquid phase. Since the system has two degrees of freedom, these determine the composition and pressure of the vapour phase. Moreover the consequent variations of pressure are significant in determining the thermodynamic properties of the vapour phase. In our present discussion of a liquid-liquid system we are assuming that the thermodynamic properties of all phases, that is both liquids and interface, are independent of the pressure. We are thus effectively suppressing variability of pressure as a possible degree of freedom. But when we do this, a single liquid binary phase has only two remaining degrees of freedom, so that we might take as variables either T, x which are independent or T, μ_1, μ_2 subject to the Gibbs–Duhem relation. Correspondingly in a system of two binary liquid phases the variables T, μ_1, μ_2 are subject to two Gibbs–Duhem relations, one in each phase. Thus the system has effectively only one degree of freedom instead of two. Hence the temperature completely determines the composition of both liquid phases and so also the properties of the interface.

We may alternatively describe the situation as follows. A binary liquid-liquid system, like a binary liquid-vapour system has two degrees of freedom. We may therefore take as independent variables T, P and these will then determine the composition of both phases and so also the properties of the interface. When however we use the approximation of treating the properties of every phase as effectively independent of P, then clearly all the equilibrium properties are completely determined by T.

We accordingly proceed to determine how the interfacial tension depends on the temperature.

§ 5.62 Temperature Dependence of Interfacial Tension

We begin with formula (5.56.4)

$$-d\gamma = S^\sigma\, dT + \Gamma_1 d\mu_1 + \Gamma_2 d\mu_2, \qquad (5.62.1)$$

which applies as well to a liquid-liquid as to a liquid-vapour interface. We also have a Gibbs–Duhem relation in each of the liquid phases. It is convenient to use these in the form, (1.38.3), with the term $V_m\, dP$ neglected. We have accordingly, denoting the two liquid phases by the superscripts α and β,

$$S_m^\alpha\, dT + (1 - x^\alpha)\, d\mu_1 + x^\alpha\, d\mu_2 = 0, \qquad (5.62.2)$$

$$S_m^\beta\, dT + (1 - x^\beta)\, d\mu_1 + x^\beta\, d\mu_2 = 0, \qquad (5.62.3)$$

wherein we have omitted the superscripts on T, μ_1, μ_2 since these have the same values throughout the system. We recall that S_m^α, S_m^β denote the mean molar entropies in the two phases.

To obtain the dependence of γ on the temperature, we have merely to eliminate $d\mu_1$, $d\mu_2$ from (1), (2), (3). We thus obtain

$$-\frac{d\gamma}{dT} = \frac{\begin{vmatrix} S^\sigma & S_m^\alpha & S_m^\beta \\ \Gamma_1 & 1 - x^\alpha & 1 - x^\beta \\ \Gamma_2 & x^\alpha & x^\beta \end{vmatrix}}{x^\beta - x^\alpha} = \frac{\begin{vmatrix} S^\sigma & S_m^\alpha & S_m^\beta \\ \Gamma_1 + \Gamma_2 & 1 & 1 \\ \Gamma_2 & x^\alpha & x^\beta \end{vmatrix}}{x^\beta - x^\alpha}. \qquad (5.62.4)$$

There seems to be no alternative simpler formula having as high an accuracy.

§ 5.63 Accurate Formulae

For the sake of completeness we shall now derive formulae, in principle applicable to any interface in a system of two components, in which we do not neglect the terms in $V dP$ or τdP. We however warn the reader that these formulae are too complicated to be of any practical use.

We accordingly revert to formula (5.56.1), namely

$$- d\gamma = S^\sigma dT - \tau pP + \Gamma_1 d\mu_1 + \Gamma_2 d\mu_2. \qquad (5.63.1)$$

and formulae (5.56.2) and (5.56.3) applied to each of the two phases α, β

$$d\mu_1^\alpha = - S_1^\alpha dT + V_1^\alpha dP + \frac{\partial \mu_1^\alpha}{\partial x^\alpha} dx^\alpha, \qquad (5.63.2)$$

$$d\mu_2^\alpha = - S_2^\alpha dT + V_2^\alpha dP + \frac{\partial \mu_2^\alpha}{\partial x^\alpha} dx^\alpha, \qquad (5.63.3)$$

$$d\mu_1^\beta = - S_1^\beta dT + V_1^\beta dP + \frac{\partial \mu_1^\beta}{\partial x^\beta} dx^\beta, \qquad (5.63.4)$$

$$d\mu_2^\beta = - S_2^\beta dT + V_2^\beta dP + \frac{\partial \mu_2^\beta}{\partial x^\beta} dx^\beta. \qquad (5.63.5)$$

We shall also use the Gibbs–Duhem relation in the form (5.10.5) in both the phases α, β

$$(1 - x^\alpha) \frac{\partial \mu_1^\alpha}{\partial x^\alpha} + x^\alpha \frac{\partial \mu_2^\alpha}{\partial x^\alpha} = 0. \qquad (5.63.6)$$

$$(1 - x^\beta) \frac{\partial \mu_1^\beta}{\partial x^\beta} + x^\beta \frac{\partial \mu_2^\beta}{\partial x^\beta} = 0. \qquad (5.63.7)$$

For any variations maintaining equilibrium, we have as usual

$$d\mu_1^\alpha = d\mu_1^\beta = d\mu_1. \qquad (5.63.8)$$
$$d\mu_2^\alpha = d\mu_2^\beta = d\mu_2. \qquad (5.63.9)$$

If we multiply (8) by $(1 - x^\beta)$, (9) by x^β, substitute from (2), (3) (4), (5) and add, we obtain using (7)

$$0 = - \{(1 - x^\beta)(S_1^\alpha - S_1^\beta) + x^\beta (S_2^\alpha - S_2^\beta)\} \, dT$$
$$+ \{(1 - x^\beta)(V_1^\alpha - V_1^\beta) + x^\beta (V_2^\alpha - V_2^\beta)\} \, dP$$
$$+ \left\{ (1 - x^\beta) \frac{\partial \mu_1}{\partial x^\alpha} + x^\beta \frac{\partial \mu_2}{\partial x^\alpha} \right\} dx^\alpha. \qquad (5.63.10)$$

If further we substitute (2), (3) into (1) we obtain

$$- d\gamma = (S^\sigma - \Gamma_1 S_1^\alpha - \Gamma_2 S_2^\alpha) \, dT - (\tau - \Gamma_1 V_1^\alpha - \Gamma_2 V_2^\alpha) \, dP$$
$$+ \left\{ \Gamma_1 \frac{\partial \mu_1}{\partial x^\alpha} + \Gamma_2 \frac{\partial \mu_2}{\partial x^\alpha} \right\} dx^\alpha. \qquad (5.63.11)$$

If we now eliminate dP between (10) and (11) we obtain

$$-d\gamma = \left(\Delta_{\alpha\sigma}S - \frac{\Delta_{\alpha\sigma}V \, \Delta_{\alpha\beta}S}{\Delta_{\alpha\beta}V} \right) dT$$

$$+ \left(\Gamma_1 + \frac{\Delta_{\alpha\sigma}V(1-x^\beta)}{\Delta_{\alpha\beta}V} \right) \frac{\partial\mu_1}{\partial x^\alpha} \, dx^\alpha$$

$$+ \left(\Gamma_2 + \frac{\Delta_{\alpha\sigma}V \, x^\beta}{\Delta_{\alpha\beta}V} \right) \frac{\partial\mu_2}{\partial x^\alpha} \, dx^\alpha \qquad (5.63.12)$$

wherein we have used the following abbreviations

$$\Delta_{\alpha\beta}S = (1-x^\beta)(S_1^\beta - S_1^\alpha) + x^\beta (S_2^\beta - S_2^\alpha), \qquad (5.63.13)$$

$$\Delta_{\alpha\beta}V = (1-x^\beta)(V_1^\beta - V_1^\alpha) + x^\beta (V_2^\beta - V_2^\alpha), \qquad (5.63.14)$$

$$\Delta_{\alpha\sigma}S = S^\sigma - \Gamma_1 S_1^\alpha - \Gamma_2 S_2^\alpha, \qquad (5.63.15)$$

$$\Delta_{\alpha\sigma}V = \tau - \Gamma_1 V_1^\alpha - \Gamma_2 V_2^\alpha. \qquad (5.63.16)$$

From these definitions we observe that $\Delta_{\alpha\beta}S$ is the entropy increase and $\Delta_{\alpha\beta}V$ the volume increase when one mole of the phase β is formed at constant temperature and constant pressure by taking the required amounts of the two components from the phase α. Likewise $\Delta_{\alpha\sigma}S$ is the entropy increase and $\Delta_{\alpha\sigma}V$ the volume increase when unit area of the surface layer σ is formed at constant temperature and constant pressure by taking the required amounts of the two components from the phase α.

Finally we can eliminate $\partial\mu_1/\partial x^\alpha$ (or $\partial\mu_2/\partial x^\alpha$) between (6) and (12). Thus

$$-d\gamma = \left(\Delta_{\alpha\sigma}S - \frac{\Delta_{\alpha\sigma}V \, \Delta_{\alpha\beta}S}{\Delta_{\alpha\beta}V} \right) dT$$

$$+ \left\{ \left(\Gamma_2 - \frac{x^\alpha \Gamma_1}{1-x^\alpha} \right) + \frac{\Delta_{\alpha\sigma}V(x^\beta - x^\alpha)}{\Delta_{\alpha\beta}V(1-x^\alpha)} \right\} \frac{\partial\mu_2}{\partial x^\alpha} \, dx^\alpha. \qquad (5.63.17)$$

We see from either (12) or (17) that the temperature coefficient of γ at constant composition of the phase α is

$$-\frac{d\gamma}{dT} = \Delta_{\alpha\sigma}S - \frac{\Delta_{\alpha\sigma}V \, \Delta_{\alpha\beta}S}{\Delta_{\alpha\beta}V}, \qquad \text{(const. } x^\alpha \text{).} \qquad (5.63.18)$$

This formula applies in principle to any interface. For a liquid-vapour interface we may assume that $\Delta_{\alpha\sigma}V/\Delta_{\alpha\beta}V$ is negligibly small and then (18) reduces to

$$-\frac{d\gamma}{dT} = \Delta_{\alpha\sigma}S, \qquad \text{(const. } x^\alpha \text{).} \qquad (5.63.19)$$

which is the same as (5.58.1). For a liquid-liquid interface formula (18), though strictly correct is of little use since the ratio $\Delta_{\alpha\sigma}V/\Delta_{\alpha\beta}V$ of two very small quantities is difficult, if not impossible, to estimate or measure.

§ 5.64   Insoluble Films

In our discussion of surface layers we have hitherto assumed implicitly that both the components were present to an appreciable extent in at least one of the bulk phases. During the past half century the experimental and theoretical work of Rayleigh, Pockels, Devaux, Marcelin, Langmuir and Adam * have brought into prominence surface phases of a quite different type. This work is concerned with the behaviour of minute quantities of various substances at the surface of a single underlying liquid, usually water. These substances are so slightly soluble in the liquid phase and so involatile that during the time of an experiment the quantity that can dissolve or evaporate is quite negligible compared with the quantity that remains at the surface. As regards the quantity at the surface phase, this is so small that the film is actually only one molecule thick.

The experimental and theoretical treatment most suitable for thermo-dynamic discussion is due to Adam. His experimental measurements are shown schematically in Fig. 5.9. Part of the liquid surface covered with

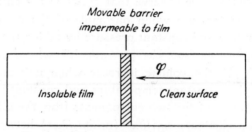

Fig. 5.9.   Experiment with insoluble film.

the insoluble film is separated from a clean surface by a movable barrier impermeable to the film. The quantity measured is the force per unit length of the barrier required to prevent the insoluble film from expanding. This quantity, which we shall denote by φ, is called the *spreading pressure* of the film. It is in a sense a *two-dimensional osmotic pressure*, inasmuch as it is the excess force per unit length or the *excess two-dimensional pressure* to which the surface film must be subjected in order that the film and the clean surface may be in equilibrium as regards the underlying liquid. For, obviously, as regards the underlying liquid there is equilibrium between the film and the homogeneous phase and likewise between the clean surface and the homogeneous phase. Consequently, there must be equilibrium between the film and the clean surface.

A surface phase σ of the type in question is completely defined by the nature of the underlying liquid, which we shall denote by the subscript 1, by the temperature T of the whole system, by the surface area A of the film, and by the number n_2 of moles of the species 2 present in the film

---

* For detailed references, see Adam, *Physics and Chemistry of Surfaces* (1941) Chapter II.

but insoluble in the underlying liquid 1. In our discussion of such a film we shall not consider variations of temperature. We accordingly omit the term in dT from (5.56.4) and write for the film

$$-d\gamma = \Gamma_1 \, d\mu_1 + \Gamma_2 \, d\mu_2, \quad (\text{const. } T). \qquad (5.64.1)$$

There are two significant differences between the present and previous applications of this formula. In the first place, since as regards the component 1 there is equilibrium between the layer and the pure underlying liquid having a well defined μ_1, clearly $d\mu_1$ vanishes and so (1) reduces to

$$-d\gamma = \Gamma_2 \, d\mu_2, \quad (\text{const. } T). \qquad (5.64.2)$$

In the second place since the component 2 is present only in the surface layer, Γ_2 has a well defined value invariant with respect to a shift in position of the geometrical surface defining the boundary of the interfacial layer. Γ_2 is in fact the total number of moles of the component 2 per unit area.

If now we denote by γ^0 the surface tension of the clean liquid on the other side of the barrier, the force per unit length which must be applied to the barrier to hold it stationary is evidently $\gamma^0 - \gamma$. It follows that the spreading pressure referred to above is

$$\varphi = \gamma^0 - \gamma, \qquad (5.64.3)$$

and so for variations in position of the barrier

$$d\varphi = -d\gamma. \qquad (5.64.4)$$

Substituting (4) into (2), we see that

$$d\varphi = \Gamma_2 \, d\mu_2. \qquad (5.64.5)$$

Owing to the assumed insolubility and involatility of the species 2, we cannot usefully replace μ_2 by its value in either the underlying liquid or in the vapour phase. In fact the determination of μ_2 in the film is best made by using formula (5).

§ 5.65 Two-dimensional Gases and Liquids

It was suggested by Langmuir and confirmed experimentally by Adam [*] that the films might be classified according to the relation between φ and Γ_2 as *two-dimensional gases, liquids and solids*. We shall henceforth drop the subscript 2.

In a two dimensional gas φ increases with Γ. Adam has shown both theoretically and experimentally that the limiting law for low values of Γ and φ is

$$\varphi = R \, T \, \Gamma. \qquad (5.65.1)$$

Substituting (1) into (5.64.5) we obtain

$$R \, T \, d\Gamma = \Gamma \, d\mu. \qquad (5.65.2)$$

---

[*] For details, see Adam, *Physics and Chemistry of Surfaces* (1941) p. 39.

which on integration gives

$$\mu' - \mu'' = RT \log \frac{\Gamma'}{\Gamma''} \qquad (5.65.3)$$

where the single and double dash refer to two different surface concentrations. Formula (3) recalls the formula for the dependence of the chemical potential of a three dimensional perfect gas on the number of moles per unit volume.

If we define the molar area A of the species 2 by

$$\Gamma A = 1, \qquad (5.65.4)$$

we can write (1) in the alternative form

$$\varphi A = RT, \qquad (5.65.5)$$

analogous to the equation of state of a perfect gas

$$P V_m = RT. \qquad (5.65.6)$$

In a two dimensional liquid film, by contrast with a two dimensional gaseous film, the molar area A decreases considerably less with increase of the pressure φ. If we write formally

$$A = A^\dagger (1 - \varkappa \varphi), \qquad (5.65.7)$$

where $A^\dagger$ is independent of φ, then the two-dimensional compressibility $\varkappa$ is small compared with $1/\varphi$, and varies much more slowly with the two-dimensional pressure than in the case of a two-dimensional gas. The value of $\varkappa$ may not, however, be assumed independent of the two-dimensional pressure.

Just as the external pressure on a liquid cannot be less than its vapour pressure, so there is a minimum value of φ for a two-dimensional liquid film. This is the *two-dimensional vapour pressure* p^σ of the liquid film. If we begin with a liquid film under compression and gradually decrease the pressure φ exerted on the barrier, the molar area A will increase only slowly, according to (7), until the pressure reaches the value p^σ, the two-dimensional vapour pressure. Further expansion of the film then takes place at the constant pressure p^σ. This is two-dimensional evaporation, and the film is no longer homogeneous, but partly liquid and partly vapour. When the area of the film has become so great that the film is completely gaseous, further expansion will be accompanied by a fall of pressure roughly according to (5).

§ 5.66   Binary Solid Solutions

We turn now to a brief consideration of solid phases containing two components, that is to say binary solid solutions. Much of the treatment of liquid solutions is directly applicable *mutatis mutandis* to solid solutions. Other parts of the treatment are obviously not applicable, in particular the following topics: equilibrium between a liquid mixture and a pure solid phase, osmotic equilibrium, interfacial tensions. Further the discussion of the boiling point of a solution of a non-volatile solute is of small importance for solid mixtures. Nor is the osmotic coefficient much used for a solid mixture.

There is a further difference between the treatments of liquid and of solid mixtures, a difference of degree or of emphasis rather than of kind. Most liquids are sufficiently volatile to have a conveniently measurable vapour pressure. Hence the partial vapour pressures of a liquid are usually readily measurable and so very real quantities. There is consequently a natural and reasonable tendency so far as possible to express most other equilibrium properties in terms of the partial vapour pressures. Whereas some solids also have readily measurable vapour pressures, many are effectively involatile. This being so, there is no particular merit in expressing other equilibrium properties in terms of the partial vapour pressures rather than in terms of the absolute activities. If then we compare, for example, the Gibbs–Duhem formula

$$(1 - x)\, d\mu_1 + x\, d\mu_2 = 0, \tag{5.66.1}$$

or its corrolary

$$(1 - x)\, d \log \lambda_1 + x\, d \log \lambda_2 = 0 \tag{5.66.2}$$

with the Duhem–Margules relation

$$(1 - x)\, d \log p_1 + x\, d \log p_2 = 0, \tag{5.66.3}$$

whereas these three relations are all equivalent, it is natural to place the emphasis on (3) in the case or liquids, but on (1) or (2) in the case of solids.

One of the great similarities between solids and liquids, in contrast to gases, is their insensitivity to pressure. For most purposes we may ignore the pressure. When we do this, a single phase of two components has two degrees of freedom, so that we may use as independent variables T, x. A pair of such phases in equilibrium has then only one degree of freedom, the composition of both phases being determined by the temperature.

We shall deal extremely briefly with the aspects of solid solutions which are parallel to those of liquid solutions. We shall often quote formulae without repeating derivations previously given for liquids.

§ 5.67   Stationary Melting-Points

In § 5.23 we proved that whenever the relative compositions of a liquid and vapour in mutual equilibrium at a given pressure are identical, the equilibrium temperature is a minimum or maximum at the given pressure. By precisely the same proof the same result can be derived for a solid and vapour in equilibrium.

Of greater practical interest is the equilibrium between solid and liquid phases. Using the superscripts S and L to refer to these two phases respectively, we can derive a formula analogous to (5.23.6), namely

$$(S_m^L - S_m^S)\frac{dT}{dx} = (x^L - x^S)\left(\frac{d\mu_1}{dx} - \frac{d\mu_2}{dx}\right). \tag{5.67.1}$$

where x denotes the mole fraction of the component 2 in either phase. Whereas formula (5.23.6) was deduced for constant pressure conditions, as far as (1) is concerned the pressure is practically irrelevant. If the liquid and solid phases have identical relative compositions, then

$$x^S = x^L, \tag{5.67.2}$$

and so (1) reduces to

$$(S_m^L - S_m^S)\frac{dT}{dx} = 0. \tag{5.67.3}$$

Since $S_m^L \neq S_m^S$, it follows that

$$dT/dx = 0. \tag{5.67.4}$$

Thus when the relative compositions of the solid and liquid in mutual equilibrium are identical, the equilibrium temperature is a minimum or maximum.

§ 5.68   Ideal Mixtures

A solid *ideal mixture* is defined in the same manner as in the case of liquids, namely by

$$\lambda_1 = \lambda_1^0 (1 - x) \tag{5.68.1}$$
$$\lambda_2 = \lambda_2^0 x, \tag{5.68.2}$$

where the superscript λ^0 denotes the pure solid phase. Actual examples of ideal mixtures are fewer among solids than among liquids, but the ideal mixture remains the convenient standard with which to compare a real mixture.

The thermodynamic functions and properties of ideal mixtures follow directly from (1), (2) as in the case of liquids. In particular the heat functions are additive; that is to say the molar heats of mixing are zero. On the other hand the *molar entropy of mixing* S_m is given by

$$S_m/R = - (1 - x) \log (1 - x) - x \log x. \tag{5.68.3}$$

Probably the most important application of this and related formulae is to isotopes, as in § 4.57.

§ 5.69   Non-ideal Mixtures

Any real mixture is conveniently compared with an ideal mixture by the formal use of activity coefficients f_1, f_2 defined by

$$\lambda_1 = \lambda_1^0 (1 - x) f_1. \tag{5.69.1}$$
$$\lambda_2 = \lambda_2^0 x f_2. \tag{5.69.2}$$

According to the Gibbs–Duhem relation (5.66.2) the two activity coefficients are interrelated by

$$(1-x)\frac{\partial \log f_1}{\partial x} + x\frac{\partial \log f_2}{\partial x} = 0. \qquad (5.69.3)$$

The temperature coefficients of the activity coefficients are related to the *partial molar heats of mixing* according to

$$\frac{\partial \log f_1}{\partial T} = -\frac{H_1 - H_1^0}{RT^2}, \qquad \text{(const. } x\text{),} \qquad (5.69.4)$$

$$\frac{\partial \log f_2}{\partial T} = -\frac{H_2 - H_2^0}{RT^2}, \qquad \text{(const. } x\text{).} \qquad (5.69.5)$$

The conditions for internal stability with respect to splitting into two phases, for the equilibrium between two phases and for the critical temperature of mixing are precisely analogous to those for liquid mixtures.

§ 5.70 Regular Mixtures

A *regular solid mixture* is defined precisely as a regular liquid mixture by

$$\log f_1 = \frac{w}{RT} x^2, \qquad (5.70.1)$$

$$\log f_2 = \frac{w}{RT} (1-x)^2, \qquad (5.70.2)$$

wherein w is independent not only of the composition but also of the temperature.

The partial molar heats of mixing are given by

$$H_1 - H_1^0 = w\, x^2, \qquad (5.70.3)$$
$$H_2 - H_2^0 = w\, (1-x)^2 \qquad (5.70.4)$$

respectively.

If w is positive, the critical temperature of mixing T_c is given by

$$T_c = \tfrac{1}{2}\, w/R. \qquad (5.70.5)$$

If on the other hand w is negative, the temperature T_λ determined by

$$T_\lambda = -\tfrac{1}{4}\, w/R \qquad (5.70.6)$$

is likewise of interest as the highest temperature at which what is called *long-range order* can persist. We merely mention this in passing, because of the formal similarity between (5) and (6). We shall revert to the subject in § 7.20 and § 7.21 where we shall see that the temperature given by (6) is under certain conditions that of a *transition of the second order*.

CHAPTER VI

SYSTEMS OF SEVERAL NON-REACTING COMPONENTS

§ 6. 01   Introduction to Systems of Several Components

In treating systems of several components instead of only two components we meet hardly any new principles. The main difference is that many formulae contain more terms or sums of terms in place of single terms. We shall accordingly to a large extent merely quote formulae without giving derivations, when these are exactly analogous to those for binary mixtures.

§ 6. 02   Partial Molar and Mean Molar Quantities

Corresponding to any extensive property X in a phase containing n_i moles of each species i, the partial molar quantities X_i are defined by

$$X_i = \left(\frac{\partial X}{\partial n_i}\right)_{P,T,n_j} \qquad (6.02.1)$$

where n_j denotes all the n's except n_i.

The corresponding mean molar quantity X_m is defined by

$$X_m = X / \Sigma_i\, n_i. \qquad (6.02.2)$$

These quantities satisfy the relations

$$\Sigma_i\, n_i\, X_i = X, \qquad (6.02.3)$$

$$\Sigma_i\, n_i\, dX_i = 0, \qquad (\text{const. } T, P). \qquad (6.02.4)$$

or the equivalent relations

$$\Sigma_i\, x_i\, X_i = X_m \qquad (6.02.5)$$

$$\Sigma_i\, x_i\, dX_i = 0, \qquad (\text{const. } T, P), \qquad (6.02.6)$$

were x_i is the mole fraction of i defined by

$$x_i = n_i / \Sigma_k\, n_k. \qquad (6.02.7)$$

§ 6. 03   Relations Between Several Partial Molar Quantities

To each relation between two or more extensive properties there corresponds a relation between the partial molar quantities and likewise one between the mean molar quantities. In particular using the independent variables T, P, n_i and bearing in mind that

$$G_i = \mu_i, \qquad (6.03.1)$$

we have the following important relations

$$F_i = U_i - TS_i, \qquad (6.03.2)$$

$$H_i = U_i + PV_i, \qquad (6.03.3)$$

$$\mu_i = G_i = U_i - TS_i + PV_i. \tag{6.03.4}$$

$$S_i = -\frac{\partial G_i}{\partial T} = -\frac{\partial \mu_i}{\partial T}. \tag{6.03.5}$$

$$V_i = \frac{\partial G_i}{\partial P} = \frac{\partial \mu_i}{\partial P}. \tag{6.03.6}$$

$$H_i = \mu_i - T\frac{\partial \mu_i}{\partial T} = -T^2 \frac{\partial (\mu_i/T)}{\partial T}. \tag{6.03.7}$$

$$F_i = \mu_i - P\frac{\partial \mu_i}{\partial P}. \tag{6.03.8}$$

$$U_i = \mu_i - T\frac{\partial \mu_i}{\partial T} - P\frac{\partial \mu_i}{\partial P}. \tag{6.03.9}$$

$$C_i = T\frac{\partial S_i}{\partial T} = \frac{\partial H_i}{\partial T}. \tag{6.03.10}$$

$$\log \lambda_i = \mu_i/RT. \tag{6.03.11}$$

$$\frac{\partial \log \lambda_i}{\partial T} = -\frac{H_i}{RT^2}. \tag{6.03.12}$$

§ 6.04   Mole Fractions as Independent Variables

It will often be convenient, particularly when dealing with condensed phases, to use as independent variables temperature, pressure and mole fractions. In all such cases we shall in a phase containing G components, choose as independent variables $x_2, x_3,\ldots$, that is to say

$$x_s, \qquad (2 \leqslant s \leqslant G). \tag{6.04.1}$$

We shall consistently use the subscript s to denote any of the integers 2, 3, ..., but not 1. The mole fraction of species 1 is then given in terms of the variables x_s by

$$x_1 = 1 - \Sigma_s x_s. \tag{6.04.2}$$

§ 6.05   Notation for Changes of Composition

Let I denote any intensive property of a phase and let I be considered as a function of T, P, x_s. Then the most general variation of I is of the form

$$dI = \frac{\partial I}{\partial T} dT + \frac{\partial I}{\partial P} dP + \Sigma_s \frac{\partial I}{\partial x_s} dx_s. \tag{6.05.1}$$

We find it convenient to define the operator D as follows

$$DI = \Sigma_s \frac{\partial I}{\partial x_s} dx_s, \tag{6.05.2}$$

so that, by using this notation, (1) becomes

$$dI = \frac{\partial I}{\partial T} dT + \frac{\partial I}{\partial P} dP + DI. \tag{6.05.3}$$

In words DI is the part of the variation of I due to all variations of composition when T, P are kept constant.

§ 6.06   Gibbs-Duhem Relation

If we apply the Gibbs–Duhem relation (1.38.2) to one mole of any phase, we have

$$S_m \, dT - V_m \, dP + (1 - \Sigma_s \, x_s) \, d\mu_1 + \Sigma_s \, x_s \, d\mu_s = 0. \quad (6.06.1)$$

Using (6.03.5), (6.03.6) and (6.05.2) we have

$$d\mu_1 = - S_1 \, dT + V_1 \, dP + D\mu_1, \quad (6.06.2)$$

$$d\mu_s = - S_s \, dT + V_s \, dP + D\mu_s. \quad (6.06.3)$$

Substituting (2) and (3) into (1), we obtain

$$\{ S_m - (1 - \Sigma_s \, x_s) \, S_1 - \Sigma_s x_s \, S_s \} \, dT$$
$$+ \{ V_m - (1 - \Sigma_s \, x_s) \, V_1 - \Sigma_s \, x_s \, V_s \} \, dP$$
$$+ (1 - \Sigma_s \, x_s) \, D\mu_1 + \Sigma_s \, x_s \, D\mu_s = 0. \quad (6.06.4)$$

But according to (6.02.5)

$$S_m = (1 - \Sigma_s \, x_s) \, S_1 + \Sigma_s \, x_s \, S_s, \quad (6.06.5)$$

$$V_m = (1 - \Sigma_s \, x_s) \, V_1 + \Sigma_s \, x_s \, V_s, \quad (6.06.6)$$

from which we see that the coefficients of dT and dP in (4) vanish. Thus (4) reduces to

$$(1 - \Sigma_s x_s) \, D\mu_1 + \Sigma_s x_s \, D\mu_s = 0. \quad (6.06.7)$$

This straightforward derivation of (7) is instructive, but unnecessarily complicated. For we could obtain (7) immediately by applying (1) to changes of composition at constant T, P so that

$$dT = 0, \quad dP = 0, \quad d\mu_1 = D\mu_1, \quad d\mu_s = D\mu_s. \quad (6.06.8)$$

In terms of absolute activities λ_1, formula (7) becomes

$$(1 - \Sigma_s x_s) \, D \log \lambda_1 + \Sigma_s x_s \, D \log \lambda_s = 0. \quad (6.06.9)$$

§ 6.07   Duhem-Margules Relation

Using the relation

$$D \log \lambda = D \log p \quad (6.07.1)$$

where p denotes a partial pressure, or strictly a fugacity, in (6.06.9) we obtain the *Duhem–Margules relation*

$$(1 - \Sigma_s \, x_s) \, D \log p_1 + \Sigma_s x_s \, D \log p_s = 0. \quad (6.07.2)$$

§ 6.08   Gibbs' Phase Rule

All the intensive properties of any single phase are evidently completely determined by its temperature, pressure and composition. Thus we may take as independent variables T, P, x_s. If there are G components, there are $G - 1$ quantities x_s and so there are clearly $G + 1$ degrees of freedom.

Alternatively we may, if we prefer, define the state of a single phase by the $G + 2$ quantities T, P, μ_1, μ_s which are however connected by the Gibbs–Duhem relation

$$(1 - \Sigma_s x_s)\, D\mu_1 + \Sigma_s x_s\, D\mu_s = 0. \tag{6.08.1}$$

If now we consider two such phases α and β in mutual equilibrium, we may evidently still define their states by T, P, μ_1, μ_s each of these variables having at equilibrium the same value in both phases. But these variables are now connected by two Gibbs–Duhem relations, one in each phase

$$(1 - \Sigma_s x_s^\alpha)\, D\mu_1^\alpha + \Sigma_s x_s^\alpha\, D\mu_s^\alpha = 0, \tag{6.08.2}$$

$$(1 - \Sigma_s x_s^\beta)\, D\mu_1^\beta + \Sigma_s x_s^\beta\, D\mu_s^\beta = 0. \tag{6.08.3}$$

Hence of these $G + 2$ variables, only G are now independent. In other words the system has G degrees of freedom.

This argument is readily increased to any number $\mathcal{P}$ of phases in equilibrium. If we define the state of the system by the $G + 2$ variables T, P, μ_1, μ_s these are connected by $\mathcal{P}$ Gibbs–Duhem relations, one in each phase. Thus the number of these variables which are independent is $G + 2 - \mathcal{P}$. In other words the number of degrees of freedom is $G + 2 - \mathcal{P}$ This is the famous *Phase Rule* of *Gibbs* [*].

If we consider a system containing only condensed phases, then for most purposes the pressure is irrelevant and may be ignored. Under these conditions the remaining $G + 1$ variables T, μ_1, μ_s are connected by $\mathcal{P}$ Gibbs–Duhem relations and so the system has $G + 1 - \mathcal{P}$ degrees of freedom.

The essence of the *phase rule* is that in a system of any number of components, whenever the number of phases is increased by one the number of degrees of freedom is decreased by one.

§ 6.09   Introduction to Gaseous Mixtures

In our treatment of systems of one component in Chapter IV and of two components in Chapter V, we made a point of discussing the behaviour of *real gases* and then at a later stage described *perfect gases* as an idealized limit to which real gases approach to a greater or less extent. In gaseous systems of more than two components the formulae are rather cumbrous, unless the gases are treated as perfect. We shall accordingly concentrate attention on the formulae for perfect gases, merely indicating how these have to be modified to take account of imperfections. By this stage the reader will have safely escaped the danger of labouring under the delusion that thermodynamic formulae are specially related to perfect gases.

§ 6.10   Perfect Gaseous Mixtures with T, V as Variables

The fundamental characteristic defining a perfect gaseous mixture is

---

[*]   Gibbs, *Collected Works* vol. 1 p. 96.

that, at given values of temperature and volume, the free energy of the mixture is the sum of those of the individual perfect gases each at the same temperature and occupying the same volume. Thus we have as the analogue of (5. 15. 1)

$$F = \Sigma_i n_i \left\{ \mu_i^\dagger - RT + RT \log \frac{n_i RT}{P^\dagger V} \right\}. \tag{6.10.1}$$

where $P^\dagger$ denotes a standard pressure and $\mu_i^\dagger$ is the value of μ_i of the pure gas i at the pressure $P^\dagger$.

From (1) follow immediately

$$S = - \Sigma_i n_i \left\{ \frac{d\mu_i^\dagger}{dT} + R \log \frac{n_i RT}{P^\dagger V} \right\}. \tag{6.10.2}$$

$$U = \Sigma n_i \left\{ \mu_i^\dagger - T \frac{d\mu_i^\dagger}{dT} - RT \right\}. \tag{6.10.3}$$

$$P = \Sigma_i n_i \frac{RT}{V}. \tag{6.10.4}$$

$$C_V = \Sigma_i n_i \left\{ - T \frac{d^2\mu_i^\dagger}{dT^2} - R \right\}. \tag{6.10.5}$$

Formula (4) expresses *Dalton's Law* of the additivity of pressures at constant temperature and volume.

Furthermore we have

$$\mu_i = RT \log \lambda_i = \mu_i^\dagger + RT \log \frac{n_i RT}{P^\dagger V}. \tag{6.10.6}$$

$$S_i = - \frac{d\mu_i^\dagger}{dT} - R \log \frac{n_i RT}{P^\dagger V}. \tag{6.10.7}$$

$$U_i = \mu_i^\dagger - T \frac{d\mu_i^\dagger}{dT} - RT. \tag{6.10.8}$$

while the partial pressures p_i defined by

$$p_i = \frac{n_i}{\Sigma_k n_k} P = x_i P \tag{6.10.9}$$

are given by

$$p_i = \frac{n_i}{V} RT. \tag{6.10.10}$$

§ 6. 11 Perfect Gaseous Mixture with T, P as Variables

Using (6. 10. 4) to transform from the variables T, V, n_i to the variables T, P, n_i we obtain for the partial molar quantities

$$G_i = \mu_i = \mu_i^\dagger + RT \log \frac{P}{P^\dagger} + RT \log \frac{n_i}{\Sigma_k n_k}. \tag{6.11.1}$$

$$S_i = -\frac{d\mu_i^\dagger}{dT} - R \log \frac{P}{P^\dagger} - R \log \frac{n_i}{\Sigma_k n_k}. \qquad (6.11.2)$$

$$H_i = \mu_i^\dagger - T \frac{d\mu_i^\dagger}{dT}. \qquad (6.11.3)$$

$$C_i = -T \frac{d^2\mu_i}{dT^2}, \qquad (6.11.4)$$

and for the most important extensive quantities

$$G = \Sigma_i n_i \left\{ \mu_i^\dagger + RT \log \frac{P}{P^\dagger} + RT \log \frac{n_i}{\Sigma_k n_k} \right\}, \qquad (6.11.5)$$

$$S = -\Sigma_i n_i \left\{ \frac{d\mu_i^\dagger}{dT} + R \log \frac{P}{P^\dagger} + R \log \frac{n_i}{\Sigma_k n_k} \right\}, \qquad (6.11.6)$$

$$V = \frac{RT}{P}. \qquad (6.11.7)$$

We observe that the entropy of the mixture exceeds that of the constituent gases each at the same temperature and same total pressure by

$$-R \Sigma_i n_i \log \frac{n_i}{\Sigma_k n_k}, \qquad (6.11.8)$$

the so-called *entropy of mixing*. The corresponding *molar entropy of mixing* is

$$-R \Sigma_i x_i \log x_i. \qquad (6.11.9)$$

§ 6.12 Absolute Activities and Partial Pressures

If we substitute the definition (6.10.9) of partial pressure into (6.11.1) we obtain for the relation between chemical potential and partial pressure in a perfect gaseous mixture

$$\mu_i = \mu_i^\dagger + RT \log \frac{p_i}{P^\dagger}. \qquad (6.12.1)$$

The corresponding relation between the absolute activity λ_i and the partial pressure p_i in a perfect gas is

$$\lambda_i = \lambda_i^\dagger \frac{p_i}{P^\dagger}, \qquad (6.12.2)$$

where $\lambda_i^\dagger$, defined by

$$\mu_i^\dagger = RT \log \lambda_i^\dagger, \qquad (6.12.3)$$

is the absolute activity of the pure gas at the standard pressure $P^\dagger$.

§ 6.13 Fugacities of Real Gases

The fugacity p_i^* of the component i is defined by

$$p_i^*/\lambda_i = \text{const.}, \qquad (T \text{ const.}), \quad (6.13.1)$$

$$p_i^*/p_i \to 1 \text{ as } P \to 0, \qquad (\text{all } T). \qquad (6.13.2)$$

Thus while for a real gas the relation (6.12.2) is an approximation, which becomes accurate in the limit of a perfect gas, the similar formula

$$\lambda_i = \lambda_i^\dagger \, \frac{p_i^*}{p^\dagger} \tag{6.13.3}$$

is exact by definition. The more nearly a gas i resembles a perfect gas the more close the fugacity p_i will be to the partial vapour pressure p_i.

§ 6.14   Second Virial Coefficients

The deviations between a real gaseous mixture and a perfect one are expressed by means of virial coefficients. The second virial coefficient which takes account of interactions between two molecules both of type i is denoted by B_{ii}; that which takes account of the interactions between two molecules one of type i, the other of a different type j is denoted by B_{ij}.

The free energy of a real gaseous mixture has the form

$$F = \Sigma_i \, n_i \left\{ \mu_i^\dagger - RT + RT \log \frac{n_i RT}{p^\dagger V} \right\}$$
$$+ \frac{RT}{V} \left\{ \Sigma_i \, n_i^2 \, B_{ii} + \underset{i \neq j}{\Sigma} \, 2 \, n_i \, n_j \, B_{ij} \right\}, \tag{6.14.1}$$

where all higher virial coefficients have been neglected.

All other thermodynamic functions can be derived immediately from (1), but we shall not give any further details.

Since experimental data concerning the mixed virial coefficients B_{ij} are almost non-existent, it may be necessary to guess values. The simplest guess is

$$B_{ij} = \tfrac{1}{2} \, (B_{ii} + B_{jj}). \tag{6.14.2}$$

When this assumption is made, formula (1) reduces to

$$F = \Sigma_i \, n_i \left\{ \mu_i^\dagger - RT + RT \log \frac{n_i RT}{p^\dagger V} + \frac{RT}{V} \, \Sigma_k \, n_k \, B_{kk} \right\}. \tag{6.14.3}$$

The physical significance of (2) is analogous to the assumption that any mixture of two liquids is ideal, an assumption known to be untrue. Consequently the use of (2) has in general no justification either theoretical or experimental.

§ 6.15   Solvent and Solute Species

Any phase of more than one component may be called a *solution*, but the name is applied especially to liquids and solids. In the case of a gaseous phase it is more usual to speak of a *gaseous mixture*. We shall now consider liquid solutions.

It is usual to denote one of the component of a solution as the *solvent* and to call all the remaining components the *solute* species. From a thermodynamic point of view there is no distinction between solvent and solute, and it is quite arbitrary which species is regarded as solvent. In practice, it is usual to designate by the term solvent that species present in greatest proportion in the solution which in the pure form exists in the liquid state at the temperature and pressure of the solution, or at least at temperatures and pressures not far removed from those of the solution.

When we use these terms, we shall call the species 1 the solvent and the remaining components s solute species. Thus we use as independent variables the mole fractions of the solute species.

§ 6.16 Stationary Boiling-Point

Just as for a binary mixture in § 5.23, it can be shown that when a liquid and its vapour have the same relative composition

$$(S_m^G - S_m^L)\, dT = (V_m^G - V_m^L)\, dP, \qquad (x_i^L = x_i^G), \qquad (6.16.1)$$

where as usual the superscripts G, L denote the gas and liquid phases respectively. From (1) we see that, for the given pressure, such a mixture has a stationary boiling-point. Likewise for the given temperature such a mixture has a stationary total vapour pressure.

§ 6.17 Freezing-Point.

Precisely as in § 5.25 the freezing-point T of a solution is related to the freezing-point T^0 of the pure solvent by

$$\log \frac{\lambda_1^0(T)}{\lambda_1(T)} = \frac{[\triangle_f H_1^0]}{R}\left(\frac{1}{T} - \frac{1}{T^0}\right), \qquad (6.17.1)$$

where $[\triangle_f H_1^0]$ denotes the molar heat of fusion for the pure substance averaged over the reciprocal temperature interval $1/T^0$ to $1/T$.

We can write (1) in the alternative form

$$\log \frac{p_1^0(T)}{p_1(T)} = \frac{[\triangle_f H_1^0]}{R}\left(\frac{1}{T} - \frac{1}{T^0}\right). \qquad (6.17.2)$$

§ 6.18 Boiling-Point

Provided all the solute species are effectively non-volatile, the boiling-point T of the solution is related to the boiling-point T^0 of the pure solvent as in § 5.26 by

$$\log \frac{\lambda_1^0(T)}{\lambda_1(T)} = \frac{[\triangle_e H_1^0]}{R}\left(\frac{1}{T^0} - \frac{1}{T}\right), \qquad (6.18.1)$$

where $[\triangle_e H_1^0]$ denotes the value of the molar heat of evaporation $\triangle_e H_1^0$ of the pure liquid averaged over the reciprocal temperature interval $1/T$ to $1/T^0$.

We can write (1) in the alternative form

$$\log \frac{p_1^0(T)}{p_1(T)} = \frac{[\triangle_e H_1^0]}{R}\left(\frac{1}{T^0} - \frac{1}{T}\right). \qquad (6.18.2)$$

§ 6.19 Osmotic Pressure

For the osmotic equilibrium with respect to the solvent species 1, if the pressure on the pure solvent is P and that on the solution is $P + \Pi$ then precisely as in § 5.27 we can derive for the osmotic pressure Π the alternative formulae

$$\frac{\Pi [V_1]}{RT} = \log \frac{p_1^0 (P)}{p_1 (P)},$$
(6.19.1)

$$\frac{\Pi [V_1^0]}{RT} = \log \frac{p_1^0 (P + \Pi)}{p_1 (P + \Pi)}.$$
(6.19.2)

Here $[V_1]$, $[V_1^0]$ denote the values of V_1, V_1^0 respectively averaged between the pressures P and $P + \Pi$.

§ 6.20 Ideal Solutions

A solution is said to be ideal if for every component i

$$\mu_i = \mu_i^0 + RT \log x_i,$$
(6.20.1)

or

$$\lambda_i = \lambda_i^0 x_i,$$
(6.20.2)

where the superscript 0 refers to the pure liquid. Each vapour pressure p_i, or strictly each fugacity, obeys *Raoult's law*

$$p_i = p_i^0 x_i.$$
(6.20.3)

It is readily verified that the Duhem–Margules relation

$$\Sigma_i x_i D \log p_i = 0$$
(6.20.4)

is satisfied.

From (1) we derive immediately

$$H_i = \mu_i^0 - T \frac{d\mu_i^0}{dT} = H_i^0.$$
(6.20.5)

We thus observe that the *partial molar heat of mixing* $H_i - H_i^0$ is zero.

We also derive from (1)

$$S_i = -\frac{d\mu_i^0}{dT} - R \log x_i = S_i^0 - R \log x_i,$$
(6.20.6)

$$S_m = -\Sigma_i x_i S_i^0 - R \Sigma_i x_i \log x_i$$
(6.20.7)

We observe that the *molar entropy of mixing*

$$- R \Sigma_i x_i \log x_i,$$
(6.20.8)

has the same value as for a perfect gas at constant temperature and constant pressure.

The thermodynamic properties of the solvent species 1 are expressed in terms of the mole fractions of the solute species s by

$$\mu_1 = \mu_1^0 + R T \log (1 - \Sigma_s x_s),$$
(6.20.9)

$$p_1 = p_1^0 (1 - \Sigma_s x_s).$$
(6.20.10)

§ 6.21   Freezing-Point of Ideal Solution

From (6.17.2) and (6.20.10) we derive the relation between the freezing-point T of an ideal solution and the freezing-point T^0 of the pure solvent

$$-\log(1-\Sigma_s x_s) = \frac{[\triangle_f H_1^0]}{R}\left(\frac{1}{T}-\frac{1}{T^0}\right). \qquad (6.21.1)$$

We need hardly mention that, provided the mixture is ideal, we may call any one of the components the solvent and apply formula (1) to the equilibrium with the pure solid phase of this component.

§ 6.22   Osmotic Pressure of Ideal Solution

For osmotic equilibrium with respect to the solvent species 1, if the pressure on the pure solvent is P and that on the solution $P + \varPi$ then by using (6.20.10) in (6.19.1) or (6.19.2) we obtain for the osmotic pressure $\varPi$

$$\frac{\varPi[V_1^0]}{RT} = -\log(1-\Sigma_s x_s), \qquad (6.22.1)$$

where $[V_1^0]$ denotes the molar volume of the solvent averaged between the pressures P and $P + \varPi$. We may note that in an ideal solution $V_1 = V_1^0$ and consequently $[V_1] = [V_1^0]$.

§ 6.23   Non-ideal Mixtures

In principle we could treat any liquid mixture by the method of the preceding chapter, that is to say by the use of activity coefficients f_i defined by

$$\lambda_i = \lambda_i^0 x_i f_i, \qquad (6.23.1)$$

and such a procedure is in fact useful and usual for a mixture of several liquids which resemble one another rather closely. The mixtures will then not deviate greatly from ideality and the activity coefficients f_i will not differ greatly from unity. When we proceed in this way, the partial vapour pressures are given by

$$p_i = p_i^0 x_i f_i \qquad (6.23.2)$$

and all other thermodynamic properties can be expressed formally in terms of the f_i s and their differential coefficients.

The procedure thus described, while formally correct, is not always useful. For some of the solute species may melt at temperatures considerably higher than that of the solution. It will then be impossible to measure and difficult to estimate such quantities as λ_1^0, p_1^0 relating to the pure substance in the liquid state, that is to say a state unrealizable at the temperature concerned. Incidentally this may be the case when there is only one solute. It is therefore often expedient to compare the thermodynamic properties of a real solution not with an ideal solution as defined in § 6. 20, but instead with a different standard called an *ideal dilute solution*. This procedure will be described in the following two sections.

§ 6. 24   Ideal Dilute Binary Solutions

Let us for a moment return to the consideration of a binary solution of a single solute s in a solvent 1. Statistical theory shows, and it is in fact physically almost obvious, that if we plot p_s against x the curve has a finite slope at the origin. In other words the tangent at the origin has a finite slope which we shall denote by h.

Expressing this mathematically

$$p_s/x \rightarrow h \text{ as } x \rightarrow 0, \qquad (h \text{ finite}). \qquad (6.24.1)$$

How closely the curve follows this tangent is a question to which thermodynamical considerations supply no answer. In the exceptional case of the ideal solution defined in § 5.29 the law (1) holds right up to $x = 1$ so that h is the same as p_s^0. However we can always define an imaginary solution whose $p_s - x$ curve is the tangent at the origin to the $p_s - x$ curve of the real solution. We accordingly define an *ideal dilute binary solution* by

$$p_s = h\,x, \qquad (h \text{ const.}). \quad (6.24.2)$$

This relation is called *Henry's Law*. It is a limiting law valid in the limit $x_s \rightarrow 0$ and more or less accurate for x_s finite.

§ 6. 25   Ideal Dilute Solutions

The definition of the previous section can immediately be extended to a solution of several solutes. An *ideal dilute solution* is one such that

$$p_s = h_s\,x_s \text{ for all } s, \qquad (h_s \text{ const.}). \quad (6.25.1)$$

Formula (1), of which (6. 24. 2) is the simplest example, is called *Henry's Law*.

From (1) it follows immediately that

$$\lambda_s/x_s = \text{const.}, \qquad (\text{all } s). \quad (6.25.2)$$

From (1) and (2) we can derive the thermodynamic properties of an *ideal dilute solution*. This we proceed to do in the following sections.

§ 6. 26   Mixing Properties of Ideal Dilute Solutions

According to (6. 03. 12)

$$H_s = -RT^2 \frac{\partial \log \lambda_s}{\partial T}, \qquad (6.26.1)$$

and according to (6. 03. 6) and (6. 03. 11)

$$V_s = RT \frac{\partial \log \lambda_s}{\partial P}. \qquad (6.26.2)$$

Comparing (6.25.2) with (1) and (2) we deduce that for a given solute species s in an ideal dilute solution in a given solvent 1, the values of H_s, V_s are independent of the composition.

Writing H for X in (6.02.6), since we have just seen that all H_s are independent of the composition it follows that such is also the case for H_1. Similarly we see that in all ideal dilute solutions in a given solvent 1, the partial molar volume V_1 of the solvent is independent of the composition.

We can summarize these properties by saying that two ideal dilute solutions in the same solvent mix at constant temperature and pressure without change in the heat function or of the volume.

§ 6.27   Raoult's Law for Ideal Dilute Solutions

The Duhem–Margules relation (6.07.2) may be written

$$D \log p_1 = - \frac{\Sigma_s x_s \, D \log p_s}{1 - \Sigma_s x_s}. \tag{6.27.1}$$

For an ideal dilute solution, according to (6.25.1)

$$x_s \, D \log p_s = x_s \, D \log x_s = dx_s. \tag{6.27.2}$$

Substituting (2) into (1), we obtain

$$D \log p_1 = - \frac{d \, \Sigma_s x_s}{1 - \Sigma_s x_s}. \tag{6.27.3}$$

Integrating (3) at constant T, P and noticing that

$$p_1 = p_1^0 \text{ when all } x_s = 0, \tag{6.27.4}$$

we obtain

$$\log p_1 = \log p_1^0 + \log (1 - \Sigma_s x_s), \tag{6.27.5}$$

or

$$p_1 = p_1^0 (1 - \Sigma_s x_s). \tag{6.27.6}$$

Comparing (6) with (6.20.10) we see that in an ideal dilute solution the vapour pressure of the solvent obeys precisely the same law, *Raoult's law*, as in an ideal solution. As a point of historical interest Raoult's law was formulated for *ideal dilute* solutions by Raoult long before *ideal* solutions had been defined by G. N. Lewis as in § 6.20.

§ 6.28   Freezing-point and Boiling-point of Ideal Dilute Solution

Since (6.27.6) has the identical form of (6.20.10), we obtain the same formula for the freezing-point T of an ideal dilute solution as previously obtained in § 6.21 for an ideal solution. Thus

$$- \log (1 - \Sigma_s x_s) = \frac{[\Delta_f H_1^0]}{R} \left(\frac{1}{T} - \frac{1}{T^0} \right). \tag{6.28.1}$$

where T^0 is the freezing-point of the pure solvent and $[\Delta_f H_1^0]$ is the value of the molar heat of fusion $\Delta_f H^0$ of the pure solvent averaged over the reciprocal temperature range $1/T^0$ to $1/T$.

16

Similarly the boiling-point T of an ideal dilute solution containing only involatile solute species is related to the boiling-point T^0 of the pure solvent by

$$- \log (1 - \Sigma_s \, x_s) = \frac{[\Delta_e H_1^0]}{R} \left(\frac{1}{T^0} - \frac{1}{T} \right). \qquad (6.28.2)$$

where $[\Delta_e H_1^0]$ is the value of the molar heat of evaporation $\Delta_e H_1^0$ of the pure solvent averaged over the reciprocal temperature range $1/T^0$ to $1/T$.

§ 6.29 Osmotic Pressure of Ideal Dilute Solution

If at osmotic equilibrium the pressure on the pure solvent is P and that on the solution $P + \Pi$, then by using (6.27.6) in (6.19.1) or (6.19.2) we obtain for the osmotic pressure Π

$$\frac{\Pi [V_1^0]}{RT} = - \log (1 - \Sigma_s \, x_s). \qquad (6.29.1)$$

where $[V_1^0]$ denotes the molar volume of the solvent averaged between the pressures P and $P + \Pi$. As we saw in § 6.26, we need not distinguish between V_1 in the solution and V_1^0 in the pure solvent.

§ 6.30 Distribution between Two Solvents

For the equilibrium as regards the solute species s between two solutions, both ideal dilute but in different solvents, we have the equilibrium condition

$$\lambda_s^\alpha = \lambda_s^\beta, \qquad (6.30.1)$$

or

$$p_s^\alpha = p_s^\beta, \qquad (6.30.2)$$

where α, β denote the two different solvents. Since both solutions are by supposition ideal dilute, we have by Henry's Law (6.25.1)

$$p_s^\alpha = h_s^\alpha x_s^\alpha, \qquad \text{(const. } T\text{)}, \qquad (6.30.3)$$

$$p_s^\beta = h_s^\beta x_s^\beta, \qquad \text{(const. } T\text{)}. \qquad (6.30.4)$$

Substituting (3) and (4) into (2), we obtain

$$\frac{x_s^\beta}{x_s^\alpha} = \frac{h_s^\alpha}{h_s^\beta} = \text{const.}, \qquad \text{(const. } T\text{)}. \qquad (6.30.5)$$

This relation is called *Nernst's Distribution Law* for ideal dilute solutions. h_s^α / h_s^β is called the *partition coefficient* for the solute species s between the two solvents α and β.

§ 6. 31   Temperature Coefficients for Solute Species

The dependence on temperature of the absolute activity λ_s of the solute species s is according to (6. 03. 12)

$$\frac{\partial \log \lambda_s}{\partial T} = -\frac{H_s}{RT^2},\tag{6.31.1}$$

and in an ideal dilute solution, according to (6. 25. 2) and (6. 05. 2)

$$D \log \lambda_s = d \log x_s.\tag{6.31.2}$$

Combining (1) and (2) we obtain

$$d \log \lambda_s^I = -\frac{H_s^I}{RT^2} dT + d \log x_s,\tag{6.31.3}$$

where we have used the superscript I to denote the ideal dilute solution. We ignore effects due to variations of the pressure on the solution.

In the gas phase G, on the other hand, we have

$$d \log \lambda_s^G = -\frac{H_s^G}{RT^2} dT + d \log p_s.\tag{6.31.4}$$

For equilibrium between the solution and the gas phase, we have the usual condition

$$\lambda_s^G = \lambda_s^I,\tag{6.31.5}$$

and so for variations maintaining equilibrium between the two phases

$$d \log \lambda_s^G = d \log \lambda_s^I.\tag{6.31.6}$$

Substituting (3) and (4) into (6) we find

$$d \log \frac{p_s}{x_s} = \frac{H_s^G - H_s^I}{RT^2} dT = \frac{\triangle_e H_s^I}{RT^2} dT,\tag{6.31.7}$$

where $\triangle_e H_s^I$ denotes the molar heat of evaporation of s from the ideal dilute solution. Comparing (6. 25. 1) with (7), we deduce for the temperature dependence of the coefficient h_s in Henry's law

$$\frac{d \log h_s}{dT} = \frac{H_s^G - H_s^I}{RT^2} = \frac{\triangle_e H_s^I}{RT^2}.\tag{6.31.8}$$

If we apply (8) to two phases α, β and subtract we obtain for the temperature dependence of the partition coefficient

$$\frac{d \log (h_s^\alpha / h_s^\beta)}{dT} = \frac{\triangle_{\alpha\beta} H_s^I}{RT^2},\tag{6.31.9}$$

where $\triangle_{\alpha\beta} H_s^I$ is the *molar heat of transfer* of the species s from the ideal dilute solution α to the ideal dilute solution β.

§ 6. 32   Temperature Coefficient for Solvent

The dependence on temperature of the vapour pressure of the solvent is similar to that of the solute species but there is a much simpler derivation. We have Raoult's law (6. 27. 6)

$$p_1 = p_1^0 (1 - \Sigma_s x_s),$$ (6. 32. 1)

so that, by use of (4. 43. 4),

$$\frac{\partial \log p_1}{\partial T} = \frac{d \log p_1^0}{dT} = \frac{\Delta_e H_1^0}{RT^2},$$ (6. 32. 2)

where $\Delta_e H_1^0$ is the molar heat of evaporation of the pure liquid.

§ 6. 33   Non-ideal Solutions

Having completed our description of ideal dilute solutions, we are now able to give a formal treatment of any solution by comparing it with an ideal dilute solution, making use of the fact that in the limit of infinite dilution all solutions become ideal dilute.

We shall first discuss the thermodynamic functions and equilibria relating particularly to the solvent, since their treatment is precisely the same as that used in the previous chapter. We shall then turn to the thermodynamic functions and equilibria relating to the solute species; their treatment will be different from that used previously.

§ 6. 34   Activity Coefficient and Osmotic Coefficient of Solvent

As far as the solvent is concerned the treatment is exactly the same as if we chose as standard an ideal solution instead of an ideal dilute solution. In fact as far as the solvent is concerned the standard is the same, namely the pure solvent. We accordingly introduce the activity coefficient f and osmotic coefficient g of the solvent, in exact analogy with § 5. 37 and § 5. 38, defined by

$$\lambda_1 / \lambda_1^0 = p_1 / p_1^0 = (1 - \Sigma_s x_s) f_1,$$ (6. 34. 1)

$$\log \frac{\lambda_1}{\lambda_1^0} = \log \frac{p_1}{p_1^0} = g_1 \log (1 - \Sigma_s x_s).$$ (6. 34. 2)

From (1) and (2) we see that f_1 and g_1 are related by the identity

$$\log f_1 = (g_1 - 1) \log (1 - \Sigma_s x_s).$$ (6. 34. 3)

§ 6. 35   Temperature Dependence

The dependence of the activity coefficient of the solvent on the temperature is in precise analogy with (5. 43. 1)

$$\frac{\partial \log f_1}{\partial T} = -\frac{H_1 - H_1^0}{RT^2},$$ (6. 35. 1)

where $H_1 - H_1^0$ is the heat required to be absorbed so as to keep the temperature unchanged when one mole of the pure liquid is added to a large excess of the solution. We call $H_1 - H_1^0$ the *partial molar heat of dilution* of the solution.

The temperature dependence of the osmotic coefficient g_1 is obtained by substituting (6.34.3) into (1)

$$\frac{\partial g_1}{\partial T} = -\frac{H_1 - H_1^0}{RT^2 \log(1 - \Sigma_s x_s)}. \qquad (6.35.2)$$

We observe that, if the partial molar heat of dilution is zero, then the activity coefficient and osmotic coefficient of the solvent have values independent of the temperature.

§ 6.36 Pressure Dependence

For most purposes the effect of changes of pressure on the activity coefficient and osmotic coefficient may be neglected. Nevertheless for the sake of completeness we quote the relation, precisely analogous to (5.44.2)

$$\frac{\partial \log f_1}{\partial P} = \frac{V_1 - V_1^0}{RT}. \qquad (6.36.1)$$

Comparing (6.34.3) with (1), we have

$$\frac{\partial g_1}{\partial P} = \frac{V_1 - V_1^0}{RT \log(1 - \Sigma_s x_s)} \qquad (6.36.2)$$

§ 6.37 Freezing-Point

For the relation between the freezing-point T of the solution and the freezing-point T^0 of the pure solvent we obtain by substituting (6.34.2) into (6.17.2)

$$-g_1 \log(1 - \Sigma_s x_s) = \frac{[\triangle_f H_1^0]}{R}\left(\frac{1}{T} - \frac{1}{T^0}\right), \qquad (6.37.1)$$

where $[\triangle_f H_1^0]$ is the value of the molar heat of fusion $\triangle_f H_1^0$ of the pure solvent averaged over the reciprocal temperature range $1/T^0$ to $1/T$. In (1) the osmotic coefficient g_1 must be given its value at the freezing-point of the solution. This value can be related to the value at any other temperature through (6.35.2).

§ 6.38 Boiling-Point

If all the solute species are non-volatile, the boiling-point T of a solution is related to the boiling-point T^0 of the pure solvent by (6.18.2). By substituting (6.34.2) into (6.18.2) we obtain

$$-g_1 \log(1 - \Sigma_s x_s) = \frac{[\triangle_e H_1^0]}{R}\left(\frac{1}{T^0} - \frac{1}{T}\right), \qquad (6.38.1)$$

where $[\triangle_e H_1^0]$ is the value of the molar heat of evaporation $\triangle_e H_1^0$ of the pure solvent averaged over the reciprocal temperature interval $1/T$ to $1/T^0$. The value of g_1 in (1) is that at the boiling-point of the solution. This can be related to the value at any other temperature through (6.35.2).

§ 6.39 Osmotic Pressure

If at osmotic equilibrium the pressure on the pure solvent is P and that on the solution $P + \Pi$, then by substituting (6.34.2) into (6.19.1) or (6.19.2) we obtain the alternative formulae

$$\frac{\Pi[V_1]}{RT} = - g_1(P) \log(1 - \Sigma_s x_s),$$ (6.39.1)

$$\frac{\Pi[V_1^0]}{RT} = - g_1(P + \Pi) \log(1 - \Sigma_s x_s),$$ (6.39.2)

where $[V_1]$, $[V_1^0]$ denote the value of V_1, V_1^0 respectively averaged between the pressures P and $P + \Pi$, while $g_1(P)$ and $g_1(P + \Pi)$ denote the values of g_1 at the pressures P and $P + \Pi$ respectively. The equivalence of (1) and (2) may be verified by means of (6.36.2). In many cases the distinction between the two is negligible.

§ 6.40 Activity Coefficients of Solute Species

We recall that in § 6.23 we mentioned that in principle we could define activity coefficients f_s by the relation

$$p_s = p_s^0 x_s f_s,$$ (6.40.1)

but we explained that such a procedure, while formally correct, would often not be useful. We accordingly define a different kind of *activity coefficient* γ_s by

$$p_s = h_s x_s \gamma_s. \qquad (h_s \text{ const.})$$ (6.40.2)

$$\gamma_s = \frac{p_s}{h_s x_s} \to 1 \text{ as } \Sigma_s x_s \to 0.$$ (6.40.3)

Whereas f_s would measure the deviation from *Raoult's law of an ideal solution*, γ_s measures the deviation from *Henry's law of an ideal dilute solution*.

The distinction between f_s and γ_s, in the simplest case of only one solute, can be clearly shown on a diagram. Fig. 6.1 shows the partial vapour pressures in mixtures of water and alcohol plotted against the mole fraction of alcohol. These mixtures were discussed in § 5.20, where the treatment was symmetrical with respect to the two components. We now arbitrarily decide to call water the *solvent* and alcohol the *solute*.

Consider now for example the solution in which the mole fraction x of alcohol is 0.2. On the ordinate $x = 0.2$ there are points marked $ABCDEFG$. The straight line OB represents Raoult's law for alcohol and corresponds to the behaviour of nearly pure alcohol. The straight line OG represents Henry's law for alcohol and corresponds to the behaviour of alcohol in very dilute solution in water. Consequently f_s and γ_s are given by

$$f_s = FA/BA = 2.27,$$

$$\gamma_s = FA/GA = 0.60.$$

Incidentally for the solvent water

$$f_1 = DA/CA = 1.074$$

$$g_1 = 1 + \frac{\log 1.074}{\log 0.80} = 1 - \frac{0.072}{0.223} = 0.68.$$

It is unfortunate that the name *activity coefficient* has been used both for f_s and for γ_s. It is to be hoped that eventually this name will be used for

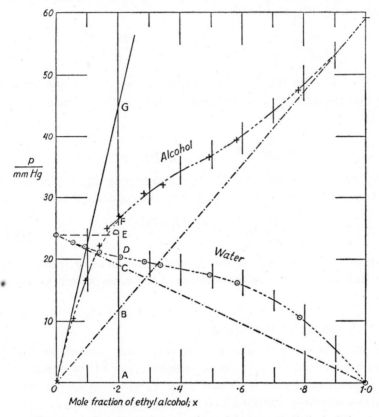

Fig. 6.1. Partial vapour pressures of water and ethyl alcohol.

only one of these quantities. One might perhaps call γ_s an *activity coefficient* and f_s a *fugacity coefficient*. However accepting the unfortunate situation as it is, we can minimize risk of confusion by using the distinct symbols f_s and γ_s consistently. We may also point out that when the deviations from Raoult's law are positive as in the water-alcohol mixtures f_s is greater than unity and γ_s is less than unity. In the contrary case of negative deviations f_s is less than unity and γ_s is greater than unity. The reason for this is that as the vapour pressure obeys Henry's law at one end and Raoult's law at the other, the whole curve is included between the straight lines OB of Raoult's law and OG of Henry's law.

§ 6. 41   Temperature Dependence of Activity Coefficients

If we compare two solutions in the same solvent at the same temperature, denoting the one by a single dash, the other by a double dash we have according to (6. 40. 2)

$$\frac{x'_s \gamma'_s}{x''_s \gamma''_s} = \frac{p'_s}{p''_s} = \frac{\lambda'_s}{\lambda''_s}. \qquad (6.41.1)$$

Differentiating (1) with respect to T, keeping both compositions constant and using (6. 03. 12) we obtain

$$\frac{\partial}{\partial T} \log \frac{\gamma'_s}{\gamma''_s} = \frac{\partial}{\partial T} \log \frac{\lambda'_s}{\lambda''_s} = -\frac{H'_s - H'_s}{RT^2}. \qquad (6.41.2)$$

Let us now choose for the solution denoted by two dashes one with $\Sigma_s x_s$ so small that the solution may be treated as ideal dilute. Then $\gamma''_s = 1$ and (2) reduces to

$$\frac{\partial}{\partial T} \log \gamma'_s = -\frac{H'_s - H^I_s}{RT^2}, \qquad (6.41.3)$$

where H^I_s denotes the value of H_s in a solution so dilute that it may be regarded as ideal dilute. We may now drop the redundant dash and obtain

$$\frac{\partial}{\partial T} \log \gamma_s = -\frac{H_s - H^I_s}{RT^2}. \qquad (6.41.4)$$

We observe that $H_s - H^I_s$ is the *partial molar heat of transfer* of the species s from an infinitely dilute solution in the same solvent to the actual solution.

§ 6. 42   Solubility of Pure Solid

If we consider several solutions in the same solvent at the same temperature all saturated with the same solid phase of the species s, then all these solutions have λ_s equal to the value of λ_s in the solid. Consequently all these solutions have the same value of $x_s \gamma_s$.

§ 6. 43   Distribution Between Two Solvents

For the equilibrium distribution of a solute species s between two solutions in different solvents, we have

$$\lambda^\alpha_s = \lambda^\beta_s, \qquad (6.43.1)$$

or

$$p^\alpha_s = p^\beta_s, \qquad (6.43.2)$$

where α, β denote the two different solvents. But according to (6. 40. 2) we have

$$p^\alpha_s = h^\alpha_s x^\alpha_s \gamma^\alpha_s, \qquad (6.43.3)$$

$$p^\beta_s = h^\beta_s x^\beta_s \gamma^\beta_s. \qquad (6.43.4)$$

Substituting (3) and (4) into (2) we obtain

$$\frac{x_s^\beta \gamma_s^\beta}{x_s^\alpha \gamma_s^\alpha} = \frac{h_s^\alpha}{h_s^\beta} = \text{const.,} \qquad (\text{const. } T). \qquad (6.43.5)$$

This is the extension of Nernst's distribution law to non-ideal solutions. According to (6.31.9) we have for the temperature dependence of the partition coefficient

$$\frac{d \log (h_s^\alpha / h_s^\beta).}{dT} = \frac{\triangle_{\alpha\beta} H_s^I}{RT^2}, \qquad (6.43.6)$$

where $\triangle_{\alpha\beta} H_s^I$ denotes the molar heat of transference of the species s from effectively infinite dilution in α to effectively infinite dilution in β.

It may happen that the solution α is so dilute as to be ideal dilute, while the solution β is not. In this case (5) reduces to

$$\frac{x_s^\beta \gamma_s^\beta}{x_s^\alpha} = \frac{h_s^\alpha}{h_s^\beta} = \text{const.,} \qquad (\alpha \text{ ideal dilute}). \qquad (6.43.7)$$

Under these conditions measurement of the distribution ratio x_s^β / x_s^α is a possible experimental method of determining γ_s^β.

§ 6.44   Relations Between Activity Coefficients

If we substitute (6.34.1) and (6.40.2) into the Duhem–Margules relation (6.07.2) we obtain

$$(1 - \Sigma_s x_s) D \log f_1 + \Sigma_s x_s D \log \gamma_s = 0. \qquad (6.44.1)$$

This important corollary of the Gibbs–Duhem relation is however not the only relation between the activity coefficients. Taking the fundamental relation (4.15.10)

$$dY = \frac{H}{T^2} dT - \frac{V}{T} dP - R \Sigma_i \log \lambda_i . dn_i, \qquad (6.44.2)$$

and, applying the cross-differentiation identity (3.01.7), we obtain

$$\frac{\partial \log \lambda_i}{\partial n_k} = \frac{\partial \log \lambda_k}{\partial n_i}. \qquad (6.44.3)$$

Rewriting formula (6.34.1) in terms of n's,

$$\frac{\lambda_1}{\lambda_1^0} = \frac{p_1}{p_1^0} = \frac{n_1}{n_1 + \Sigma_s n_s} f_1, \qquad (6.44.4)$$

and differentiating logarithmically

$$\frac{\partial \log \lambda_1}{\partial n_s} = - \frac{1}{n_1 + \Sigma_s n_s} + \frac{\partial \log f_1}{\partial n_s}. \qquad (6.44.5)$$

Similarly by writing (6.40.2) in terms of λ's and n's we derive

$$\lambda_s \propto \frac{n_s}{n_1 + \Sigma_s n_s} \gamma_s, \qquad (6.44.6)$$

and differentiating logarithmically

$$\frac{\partial \log \lambda_s}{\partial n_1} = -\frac{1}{1 + \Sigma_s\, n_s} + \frac{\partial \log \gamma_s}{\partial n_1}. \qquad (6.\,44.\,7)$$

Substituting (5) and (7) into (3), we obtain

$$\frac{\partial \log f_1}{\partial n_s} = \frac{\partial \log \gamma_s}{\partial n_1}. \qquad (6.\,44.\,8)$$

By similar methods we can deduce for any two solute species, such as 2 and 3

$$\frac{\partial \log \gamma_2}{\partial n_3} = \frac{\partial \log \gamma_3}{\partial n_2}. \qquad (6.\,44.\,9)$$

We do not propose to use the relations (8) and (9) synthetically, nor do we recommend that they should ever be so used. We however draw attention to their existence to emphasize the following point. If anyone were to suggest a series of purely empirical formulae expressing the γ's in terms of the x's or n's, then except by good fortune such formulae would not satisfy the relations (9) and consequently they would be physically impossible. Consequently the right procedure for solutions of several given solutes in a given solvent is not to guess formulae for the γ's and hope that they are possible ones, but rather to assume a formula for the Gibbs function G in terms of the n's, deduce from it formulae for μ_1 and the μ_s by differentiation, then by comparing these formulae with those in an ideal dilute solution deduce formulae for f_1 and the γ_s's; finally as a cross-check verify that these formulae in fact satisfy the relations (1), (8) and (9).

We shall illustrate by a simple example. Suppose we have a solvent 1 and two solute species 2 and 3. Then at dilutions so great that the solutions are ideal dilute the Gibbs function is of the form

$$G^I = n_1 \left\{ \mu_1^0 + RT \log \frac{n_1}{n_1 + n_2 + n_3} \right\}$$

$$+ n_2 \left\{ \mu_2^I + RT \log \frac{n_2}{n_1 + n_2 + n_3} \right\}$$

$$+ n_3 \left\{ \mu_3^I + RT \log \frac{n_3}{n_1 + n_2 + n_3} \right\}, \qquad (6.\,44.\,10)$$

where μ_1^0 is the chemical potential of the pure solvent, while μ_2^I, μ_3^I are functions of temperature only characteristic of the species 2, 3 respectively and of the solvent 1. We have also placed a superscript I in G^I to denote that this is the value of G for ideal dilute solutions. Let us now suppose that at less dilute solutions in the same solvent G has the form

$$G = G^I + RTA\,\frac{n_2\, n_3}{n_1 + n_2 + n_3}, \qquad (A \text{ const.}). \qquad (6.\,44.\,11)$$

We are not asserting that this form is the best representation for any particular solvent or solutes, but from a thermodynamic point of view it is a possible formula for G. Then from (11) we derive

$$\log f_1 = -A \frac{n_2 n_3}{(n_1 + n_2 + n_3)^2} = -A x_2 x_3. \qquad (6.44.12)$$

$$\log \gamma_2 = A \frac{n_3 (n_1 + n_3)}{(n_1 + n_2 + n_3)^2} = A x_3 (x_1 + x_3). \qquad (6.44.13)$$

$$\log \gamma_3 = A \frac{n_2 (n_1 + n_2)}{(n_1 + n_2 + n_3)^2} = A x_2 (x_1 + x_2). \qquad (6.44.14)$$

From the manner of derivation of f_1, γ_2, γ_3 from (11) the relations (8), (9) are automatically satisfied. The reader who is interested can readily verify this.

§ 6.45 Binary Solutions

Whereas in the case of more than one solute, formula (6.44.1) is best used as a check on the correctness of formulae for f_1, γ_s derived from an assumed formula for $G - G^I$, in the special case of a single solute it reduces to

$$(1 - x_s) d \log f_1 + x_s d \log \gamma_s = 0, \qquad (\text{const. } T), \qquad (6.45.1)$$

and in this case there are no other independent relations between f_1 and γ_s. It is true that there is the relation

$$\frac{\partial \log f_1}{\partial n_s} = \frac{\partial \log \gamma_s}{\partial n_1} \qquad (6.45.2)$$

but this can be derived from (1) as follows. Write $n_s / (n_1 + n_s)$ for x_s in (1) and multiply by $(n_1 + n_s)$, thus obtaining

$$n_1 d \log f_1 + n_s d \log \gamma_s = 0. \qquad (6.45.3)$$

From (3) we deduce

$$d \{ n_1 \log f_1 + n_s \log \gamma_s \} = \log f_1 \, dn_1 + \log \gamma_s \, dn_s. \qquad (6.45.4)$$

When we apply the cross-differentiation identity (3.01.7) to (4) we recover (2).

In the case of a binary solution any empirical formula for γ_s is a possible one from a purely thermodynamic point of view, though from other points of view only some kinds of formulae are reasonable. From such an assumed formula for γ_s one can then use (1) to obtain a formula for f_1, and conversely.

§ 6.46 Relation between Osmotic Coefficient and Activity Coefficients

By substituting (6.34.3) into (6.44.1) we obtain the relation between the osmotic coefficient g_1 of the solvent and the activity coefficients γ_s of the solutes

$$(1 - \Sigma_s x_s) \log (1 - \Sigma_s x_s) D g_1 + (1 - g_1) \Sigma_s dx_s + \Sigma_s x_s D \log \gamma_s = 0. \qquad (6.46.1)$$

This relation like (6.44.1) is useful only as a cross-check except in the case of only a single solute, when it reduces to

$$(1-x)\log(1-x)\,dg + (1-g)\,dx + x\,d\log\gamma = 0 \qquad (6.46.2)$$

where we have dropped the redundant subscripts 1 and s.

Transposing and integrating from 0 to x, we obtain

$$\log\gamma = -\int_0^x \frac{1-x}{x}\log(1-x)\,dg - \int_0^x \frac{1-g}{x}\,dx. \qquad (6.46.3)$$

If g has been determined at all mole fractions from 0 to x, we see that by using (3) we can in principle calculate γ for the solute at a mole fraction x. We shall however see that in practice the procedure is not necessarily as simple as would appear at first sight.

§ 6.47   Experimental Determination of g

The most accurate direct method of determining g experimentally is by measurements of freezing-point and use of formula (6.37.1), which for a single solute species we rewrite as

$$-g\log(1-x) = \frac{[\triangle_f H_1^0]}{RT^0 T}(T^0 - T). \qquad (6.47.1)$$

All the quantities $x, \triangle_f H_1^0, T^0, T$ can be measured and substitution of their values into (1) leads to experimental values of g.

Let us suppose that freezing-point measurements have been made so as to determine g over a range of steadily decreasing values of x and let us consider what results are to be expected.

Since we know that as $x \to 0$ so $g \to 1$, we may reasonably expect that $1-g$ can be expressed as a series of integral powers of x, say

$$1-g = Ax + Bx^2 + \ldots \qquad (6.47.2)$$

This is in fact the case for non-electrolytes and we may then hope to determine by a series of accurate freezing-point measurements the coefficients in such a formula as (2) so as to obtain a good fit. Formula (2) is not applicable to solutions of electrolytes; these will be discussed in Chapter IX.

Let us now consider what will happen if the measurements are extended down to gradually decreasing values of x. If the measurements are performed with sufficient care, we may expect to reach a range where all terms of (2) are negligible except the first. In this range $(1-g)/x$ has a constant value A and we may confidently and reasonably assume that this behaviour persists down to $x = 0$. Suppose however we tried to confirm this experimentally, let us examine what would happen.

We may reasonably assume that the experimental error in measuring $T^0 - T$ is at least roughly independent of x. Since, at low values of x, the value of $T^0 - T$ is itself roughly proportional to x, it follows that the fractional experimental error in g is inversely proportional to x. Hence according to (2) the fractional error in $1-g$ will be inversely proportional to x^2. It is therefore clear that by proceeding to experiment at smaller values of x, we eventually reach a stage where the experiments tell us nothing new.

The most reliable procedure is then to carry the experiments down to values of x where one finds experimentally

$$\frac{1-g}{x} = A, \qquad (A \text{ const.}), \qquad (6.47.3)$$

and then assume that this simple law persists down to $x = 0$.

We may mention that for solutions of non-electrolytes the limiting law (3) has not merely an empirical basis, but also a theoretical one based on statistical mechanics.

§ 6.48   Determination of γ from g

Let us now return to formula (6.46.3) and let us initially consider a value of x, say x', in the range where one finds experimentally

$$1-g = A x, \qquad (A \text{ const.}). \qquad (6.48.1)$$

Let us further suppose, for the sake of simplicity that $x' \ll 1$; in practice it will be possible to choose a value of x' satisfying these requirements. Then we may replace (6.46.3) by

$$\log \gamma (x') = \int_0^{x'} dg - \int_0^{x'} A \, dx = -2 \{1-g(x')\}, \qquad (6.48.1)$$

which gives $\gamma(x')$ explicitly in terms of $g(x')$.

Now suppose we want to calculate γ at a higher value of x. We break the range of integration in (6.46.3) at x', chosen as described above. We then have

$$\log \gamma = -2 \{1-g(x')\} - \int_{x'}^{x} \frac{1-x}{x} \log (1-x) \, dg - \int_{x'}^{x} \frac{1-g}{x} \, dx, \quad (6.48.2)$$

wherein the two integrals can be evaluated from the experimental data.

The important point emerging from this discussion is that we cannot calculate γ from experimental determinations of g, for example by freezing-point measurements, without making an assumption concerning g at low values of x. Since such an assumption has to be made anyway, it is just as well to make it explicitly and so obtain a closed formula for γ as well as for g in the range of small x. For solutions of non-electrolytes, with which we are here concerned, the usual and most reasonable assumption leads to

$$- \log \gamma = 2 (1-g), \qquad (x \ll 1). \qquad (6.48.3)$$

In Chapter IX, when we study solutions of electrolytes, we shall meet a quite different situation.

§ 6.49   Solid Solutions

Much of the treatment of liquid solutions is directly applicable *mutatis mutandis* to solid solutions. Other parts of the treatment are obviously not applicable, for example freezing-points, boiling-points and osmotic equilibrium.

On the other hand the definition of an *ideal dilute solid solution* by

$$\lambda_1 = \lambda_1^0 \, (1 - \Sigma_s \, x_s), \tag{6.49.1}$$

$$\lambda_s = k_s \, x_s, \qquad (k_s \text{ const.}) \tag{6.49.2}$$

is precisely analogous to that for liquid solutions, only the emphasis is on the absolute activities rather than on partial vapour pressures.

The definition of activity coefficients f_1, γ_s for real solutions by

$$\lambda_1 = \lambda_1^0 \, (1 - \Sigma_s \, x_s) \, f_1, \tag{6.49.3}$$

$$\lambda_s = k_s \, x_s \, \gamma_s \tag{6.49.4}$$

is precisely analogous to that for liquid solutions.

From the Gibbs–Duhem relation we deduce the relation between f_1 and the γ_s's

$$(1 - \Sigma_s \, x_s) \, D \log f_1 + \Sigma_s \, x_s \, D \log \gamma_s = 0, \tag{6.49.5}$$

and in particular for a single solute

$$(1 - x_s) \, d \log f_1 + x_s \, d \log \gamma_s = 0. \tag{6.49.6}$$

The distribution between two phases α, β having different solvents, whether solid or liquid, is determined by

$$\frac{x_s^\beta \, \gamma_s^\beta}{x_s^\alpha \, \gamma_s^\alpha} = \frac{h_s^\alpha}{h_s^\beta}. \tag{6.49.7}$$

§ 6.50   Temperature Dependence

The several relations for dependence on temperature correspond closely to those for liquid mixtures. In particular

$$\frac{\partial \log f_1}{\partial T} = - \frac{H_1 - H_1^0}{RT^2}, \tag{6.50.1}$$

where $H_1 - H_1^0$ is the *partial molar heat of dilution* of the solid solution. Likewise

$$\frac{\partial \log \gamma_s}{\partial T} = - \frac{H_s - H_s^I}{RT^2}, \tag{6.50.2}$$

where $H_s - H_s^I$ is the *partial molar heat of transfer* of the species s to the actual solution from an infinitely dilute solution in the same solid solvent.

§ 6.51.   Equilibrium between Two Phases of Same Composition

The law that when two different phases in mutual equilibrium have the same relative composition, that is $x_s^\alpha = x_s^\beta$ for all s, the equilibrium temperature is a minimum or a maximum holds equally well for two solid phases, two liquid phases or a solid phase and a liquid phase. In all these cases the pressure may usually be regarded as irrelevant.

The same law holds for equilibrium between a solid or a liquid phase and the gas phase, provided the pressure is kept constant.

§ 6.52 Surface Tension

We conclude this chapter with a brief discussion of interfacial layers, particularly those between a liquid and its vapour.

As described in §. 5.56 we shall neglect effects of pressure on the liquid phase and on the surface layer. We have then in analogy with (5.56.4), (5.56.5) and (5.56.6)

$$-d\gamma = S^\sigma dT + \Gamma_1 d\mu_1 + \Sigma_s \Gamma_s d\mu_s, \tag{6.52.1}$$

$$d\mu_1 = -S_1 dT + D\mu_1, \tag{6.52.2}$$

$$d\mu_s = -S_s dT + D\mu_s, \tag{6.52.3}$$

where (2) and (3) relate to the liquid phase *. We also have in the liquid phase the Gibbs–Duhem relation

$$(1 - \Sigma_s x_s) D\mu_1 + \Sigma_s x_s D\mu_s = 0. \tag{6.52.4}$$

Substituting (2) and (3) into (1) we obtain

$$-d\gamma = (S^\sigma - \Gamma_1 S_1 - \Sigma_s \Gamma_s S_s)dT + \Gamma_1 D\mu_1 + \Sigma_s \Gamma_s D\mu_s. \tag{6.52.5}$$

Now eliminating $D\mu_1$ between (4) and (5) we obtain finally

$$-d\gamma = (S^\sigma - \Gamma_1 S_1 - \Sigma_s \Gamma_s S_s)dT + \Sigma_s \left(\Gamma_s - \frac{x_s \Gamma_1}{1 - \Sigma_s x_s}\right) D\mu_s, \tag{6.52.6}$$

of which (5.56.9) is the simplest case.

By reasoning similar to that of § 5.57, one can verify the invariance of the coefficients of dT and $D\mu_s$ with respect to shifts of the geometrical surfaces bounding the surface layer.

§ 6.53 Temperature Coefficient of Surface Tension

For the temperature dependence of the surface tension at constant composition of the liquid, that is $D\mu_s = 0$ (all s), we obtain immediately from (6.52.6)

$$-\frac{d\gamma}{dT} = S^\sigma - \Gamma_1 S_1 - \Sigma_s \Gamma_s S_s \tag{6.53.1}$$

where the right side is the entropy of unit area of the surface layer less the entropy of the same material content in the liquid phase.

By proceeding as in § 5.58 one can transform (1) to the equivalent relation

$$\gamma - T\frac{d\gamma}{dT} = U^\sigma - \Gamma_1 U_1 - \Sigma_s \Gamma_s U_s. \tag{6.53.2}$$

---

* There should be no confusion between γ denoting surface tension and the activity coefficients γ_s.

where the right side is the energy which must be supplied, partly as work and partly as heat, to prevent any change of temperature when unit area of surface is formed from the liquid.

§ 6.54 Variations of Composition

For variations of composition at constant temperature (6.52.6) reduces to

$$-d\gamma = \Sigma_s \left(\Gamma_s - \frac{x_s \Gamma_1}{1 - \Sigma_s x_s} \right) D\mu_s,$$ (6.54.1)

or using

$$D\mu_s = R\,T\,D \log p_s,$$ (6.54.2)

$$-d\gamma = R\,T\,\Sigma_s \left(\Gamma_s - \frac{x_s \Gamma_1}{1 - \Sigma_s x_s} \right) D \log p_s.$$ (6.54.3)

Suppose for example there are two solutes 2 and 3, then we have

$$-\frac{d\gamma}{RT} = \left(\Gamma_2 - \frac{x_2 \Gamma_1}{1 - x_2 - x_3} \right) D \log p_2 + \left(\Gamma_3 - \frac{x_3 \Gamma_1}{1 - x_2 - x_3} \right) D \log p_3.$$ (6.54.4)

If then we measure γ, p_2, p_3 for three solutions of slightly differing composition we obtain two simultaneous equations for

$$\Gamma_2 - \frac{x_2 \Gamma_1}{1 - x_2 - x_3}$$ (6.54.5)

and

$$\Gamma_3 - \frac{x_3 \Gamma_1}{1 - x_2 - x_3}.$$ (6.54.6)

In general if there are $G-1$ solute species, one has to measure γ and all the p_s's in G solutions of slightly differing composition so as to obtain $G-1$ simultaneous equations determining the $G-1$ quantities

$$\Gamma_s - \frac{x_s \Gamma_1}{1 - \Sigma_s x_s}.$$ (6.54.7)

The expression (7) may be called the *surface excess per unit area* of the solute species s. The corresponding quantity for the solvent species 1 vanishes by definition. As we have repeatedly stressed, these quantities, in contrast to the individual Γ_s, are invariant with respect to shift of the boundary between the liquid phase and the surface phase and are therefore physically significant. The quantities (7) are the same as the quantities which Gibbs * denoted by $\Gamma_{s(1)}$, but his definition of these quantities was more abstract and more difficult to visualize.

§ 6.55 Interfacial Tension between Two Liquid Phases

For the interface between two liquid phases α, β neglecting dependence on pressure, we have

$$-d\gamma = S^s\,dT + \Gamma_1\,d\mu_1 + \Sigma_s \Gamma_s\,d\mu_s.$$ (6.55.1)

---

* Gibbs, *Collected Works*, vol. 1 pp. 234—235.

and the two Gibbs–Duhem relations

$$S_m^\alpha \, dT + (1 - \Sigma_s x_s^\alpha) \, d\mu_1 + \Sigma_s x_s^\alpha \, d\mu_s, \qquad (6.55.2)$$

$$S_m^\beta \, dT + (1 - \Sigma_s x_s^\beta) \, d\mu_1 + \Sigma_s x_s^\beta \, d\mu_s. \qquad (6.55.3)$$

If there are $G - 1$ solute species, there are $G + 1$ quantities dT, $d\mu_1$, $d\mu_s$ in (1) of which any two can be eliminated by using (2) and (3). Even in the simplest case of a single solute, we saw in § 5.62 that the result is complicated. With more than one solute, the results are more complicated and we shall not here pursue them.

§ 6.56   Vapour Pressure of Saturated Solution

Throughout this chapter and the previous one we have never yet considered any equilibrium involving more than two bulk phases, nor shall we do so in any detail. No new principles are involved and the methods already described are applicable. We shall confine ourselves to a single interesting example.

We consider the following problem. How does the vapour pressure of the solvent vary with the temperature in a solution kept saturated with a single non-volatile solid? Using the subscript 1 for the solvent, 2 for the solute and the superscripts G for the gas phase, S for the solid and none for the solution, we have for variations maintaining equilibrium

$$d \log \lambda_1 = d \log \lambda_1^G \qquad (6.56.1)$$

$$d \log \lambda_2 = d \log \lambda_2^S. \qquad (6.56.2)$$

Expanding these, we have

$$-\frac{H_1}{RT^2} \, dT + D \log \lambda_1 = -\frac{H_1^G}{RT^2} \, dT + d \log p_1. \qquad (6.56.3)$$

$$-\frac{H_2}{RT^2} \, dT + D \log \lambda_2 = -\frac{H_2^S}{RT^2} \, dT. \qquad (6.56.4)$$

Using $\triangle_e H$ to denote a heat of evaporation from the solution and $\triangle_f H$ to denote a heat of fusion into the solution, we can write (3) and (4) as

$$d \log p_1 = D \log \lambda_1 + \frac{\triangle_e H_1}{RT^2} \, dT, \qquad (6.56.5)$$

$$D \log \lambda_2 = \frac{\triangle_f H_2}{RT^2} \, dT. \qquad (6.56.6)$$

We now use the Gibbs–Duhem relation in the form

$$(1-x) D \log \lambda_1 + x D \log \lambda_2 = 0, \qquad (6.56.7)$$

to eliminate λ_1, λ_2 from (5), (6). We thus obtain

$$\frac{d \log p_1}{dT} = \frac{1}{RT^2} \left\{ \triangle_e H_1 - \frac{x}{1-x} \triangle_f H_2 \right\}. \qquad (6.56.8)$$

It is interesting to observe that the expression inside the curly brackets is equal and opposite to the *heat of formation* of the quantity of solution containing one mole of solvent from the gaseous solvent and from the solid solute.

17

CHAPTER VII

SYSTEMS OF CHEMICALLY REACTING SPECIES

§ 7.01 Notation and Terminology

We recall the notation introduced in § 1.49 and § 1.50 which we shall continue to use. We write

$$\Sigma \nu_A A \rightarrow \Sigma \nu_B B, \qquad (7.01.1)$$

meaning that at constant temperature ν_A moles of A in a well defined state and the like react to form ν_B moles of B in a well defined state and the like. In § 1.49 we gave examples to illustrate the meaning of A, B and of ν_A, ν_B. The coefficients ν_A, ν_B are always either small integers or simple rational fractions.

We stress the importance, before discussing any specific equilibrium, of writing down explicitly the formula of type (1) about which we are talking. For example to state that some constant describing the equilibrium between hydrogen and oxygen has a specified value is completely meaningless unless one states which of the following formulae one has in mind:

$$2H_2 + O_2 \rightarrow 2H_2O,$$
$$H_2 + \tfrac{1}{2}O_2 \rightarrow H_2O,$$
$$2H_2O \rightarrow 2H_2 + O_2,$$
$$H_2O \rightarrow H_2 + \tfrac{1}{2}O_2.$$

The constants corresponding to these four alternative formulae will all be different, but of course interrelated. It is also important to specify the state of each reacting species, e.g. H_2O (g) or H_2O (l), unless it is obvious as in the case of H_2 at ordinary temperatures which can only be H_2 (g).

We can measure the extent to which the process (1) takes place by the *degree of advancement* defined in § 1.50, such that a change of ξ to $\xi + d\xi$ means that $\nu_A d\xi$ moles of A and the like react to give $\nu_B d\xi$ moles of B and the like.

We also recall that the affinity of the process (1) is according to De Donder formally defined by

$$A = -\left(\frac{\partial F}{\partial \xi}\right)_{T, V^\alpha} = -\left(\frac{\partial G}{\partial \xi}\right)_{T, P^\alpha}, \qquad (7.01.2)$$

where V^α denotes the volume of each phase α and P^α the pressure of each phase α.

We then have the concise universal rule that in any natural process

$$A d\xi > 0, \quad \text{(natural)} \qquad (7.01.3)$$

and consequently for equilibrium

$$A = 0, \qquad \text{(equilibrium)}. \qquad\qquad (7.01.4)$$

This equilibrium condition is a concise method of stating that

$$\Sigma \nu_A \mu_A = \Sigma \nu_B \mu_B, \qquad \text{(equilibrium)}. \qquad\qquad (7.01.5)$$

This completes our recapitulation of the most important formulae of § 1.49 and § 1.50. We now recall the definition in § 4.15 of absolute activities λ by

$$\mu = R T \log \lambda, \qquad\qquad (7.01.6)$$

according to which (5) can be transcribed to

$$\frac{\Pi (\lambda_B)^{\nu_B}}{\Pi (\lambda_A)^{\nu_A}} = 1, \qquad \text{(equilibrium)}. \qquad\qquad (7.01.7)$$

We now introduce a new notation, leading to considerable condensation, of which we shall make much use.

Let I_A denote any intensive function relating to the species A, such as for example $\lambda_A, p_A, x_A, \gamma_A$ and similarly for I_B. Then we use the contracted notation $\Pi(I)$ defined by

$$\Pi (I) \equiv \frac{\Pi (I_B)^{\nu_B}}{\Pi (I_A)^{\nu_A}}. \qquad\qquad (7.01.8)$$

When in particular the I's have values corresponding to a state of chemical equilibrium, we shall call $\Pi(I)$ the *equilibrium product* of the I's.

Our first application of this notation is to (7), which we contract to

$$\Pi (\lambda) = 1, \qquad \text{(equilibrium)} \qquad\qquad (7.01.9)$$

and the general condition for chemical equilibrium can be stated in the form: *the equilibrium product of the absolute activities is unity.*

§ 7.02 Gaseous Equilibria

In studying gaseous equilibria we shall treat all gases as perfect. When this is not justifiable, it is only necessary to correct by replacing partial pressures by fugacities. As a matter of fact there are scarcely any experimental data on gaseous equilibria of sufficient accuracy for the distinction to be significant. In any case the lack of experimental data on second virial coefficients in gaseous mixtures makes it impossible to apply the correction in practice, even though the method is in principle straightforward.

We accordingly use formula (6.12.2)

$$\lambda_i = \lambda_i^\dagger \frac{p_i}{P^\dagger}, \qquad\qquad (7.02.1)$$

where we recall that $P^\dagger$ denotes an arbitrarily chosen standard pressure, for example one atmosphere, and $\lambda_i^\dagger$ denotes the value of λ_i for the pure single gas at the standard pressure. Thus $\lambda_i^\dagger$ is a function of temperature only. Substituting (1) into (7.01.9), we obtain as equilibrium condition

$$\Pi (p/P^\dagger) = K(T), \qquad (7.02.2)$$

where $K(T)$ is a function of temperature only, called the *equilibrium constant* and defined by

$$K^{-1} = \Pi (\lambda^\dagger). \qquad (7.02.3)$$

We shall consider these relations in greater detail in §§ 7.06—7.10.

§ 7.03 Heats of Reaction

Consider the process

$$\Sigma \nu_A A \to \Sigma \nu_B B, \qquad (7.03.1)$$

and let the operator $\triangle$ denote the excess of a final over an initial value corresponding to unit increase in the degree of advancement, the temperature remaining constant throughout.

If the process occurs at constant pressure then the heat absorbed is equal to $\triangle H$. For this reason $\triangle H$ is called the *heat of reaction at constant pressure* or sometimes just the *heat of reaction*.

If on the other hand the process occurs at constant volume the heat absorbed is equal to $\triangle U$, which is therefore called the *heat of reaction at constant volume*. This quantity is of little importance except for gas reactions, for which it is related to $\triangle H$ by

$$\triangle U = \triangle U - RT \triangle \Sigma \nu, \qquad (7.03.2)$$

neglecting terms involving the second virial coefficients.

We recall that for a perfect gas H is independent of the pressure and for a condensed phase the effect of variations of pressure is negligible. It is therefore usually unnecessary to specify the pressure when speaking of heats of reaction.

§ 7.04 Hess' Law

Since H is a function of the state of a system, $\triangle H$ is for successive processes at the same temperature an additive function. This property of $\triangle H$, known as *Hess' law*, is useful in enabling us to calculate $\triangle H$ for a reaction, difficult to produce quantitatively, from other reactions which give less difficulty. The following simple example will illustrate the point

C (graphite) $+ O_2$ (g) $\to CO_2$ (g), $- \triangle H = 393.5$ K joule
CO (g) $+ \frac{1}{2} O_2$ (g) $\to CO_2$ (g), $- \triangle H = 283.0$ K joule

In both the above cases $\triangle H$ is readily measurable. By subtraction we obtain

C (graphite) $+ \frac{1}{2} O_2$ (g) $\to$ CO (g), $- \triangle H = 110.5$ K joule,

a reaction difficult, if not impossible to study quantitatively.

Other numerous examples are the calculations of the *heats of formation* of organic compounds from the directly measured *heats of combustion*. A simple example is

$$CH_4\,(g) + 2\,O_2\,(g) \to CO_2\,(g) + 2\,H_2O\,(l), \qquad -\triangle H = 890.3\ \text{K joule}$$

$$C\,(\text{graphite}) + O_2\,(g) \to CO_2\,(g), \qquad -\triangle H = 393.5\ \text{K joule}$$

$$2\,H_2\,(g) + O_2\,(g) \to 2\,H_2O\,(l), \qquad -\triangle H = 571.6\ \text{K joule}$$

from which we immediately deduce

$$C\,(\text{graphite}) + 2\,H_2\,(g) \to CH_4\,(g), \qquad -\triangle H = \quad 74.8\ \text{K joule}$$

Unfortunately in calculating a heat of formation as the difference between much greater heats of combustion, since the experimental errors add up, there is considerable loss in percentage accuracy. Nevertheless this is the standard method of determining heats of formation of organic compounds from their elements.

Unfortunately some authors use the name *heat of reaction* for $-\triangle H$ instead of for $\triangle H$. This practice is deplorable. The simplest and safest way to avoid any possible ambiguity is to write in full $\triangle H = \ldots$ or $-\triangle H = \ldots$ as in the above examples.

§ 7.05 Kirchhoff's Relations

We often need the value of $\triangle H$ at one temperature when it has been measured at a different temperature. This causes no difficulty provided the dependence of H on the temperature has been measured or is known theoretically for the initial and final states.

Let T denote the temperature at which we want the value of $\triangle H$ and T' the temperature at which it has been measured. Then

$$\triangle H(T) - \triangle H(T')$$
$$= \{\Sigma \nu_B H_B(T) - \Sigma \nu_A H_A(T)\} - \{\Sigma \nu_B H_B(T') - \Sigma \nu_A H_A(T')\}$$
$$= \Sigma \nu_B \{H_B(T) - H_B(T')\} - \Sigma \nu_A \{H_A(T) - H_A(T')\}. \qquad (7.05.1)$$

Although (1) is the form in which the experimental data are available and should be used, it is usual to express (1) in the differential form

$$\frac{d}{dT}\triangle H = \triangle\frac{dH}{dT} = \Sigma \nu_B \frac{dH_B}{dT} - \Sigma \nu_A \frac{dH_A}{dT}$$

$$= \Sigma \nu_B C_B - \Sigma \nu_A C_A. \qquad (7.05.2)$$

Formula (2) is known as *Kirchhoff's relation*. Since values of the heat capacities C are usually obtained by differentiating experimental measurements of $H(T) - H(T')$ and formula (2), if used, has to be integrated, it is difficult to see any advantage of (2) over (1). As already mentioned in § 4.05 the main function of a heat capacity is to serve as the connecting link between the heat function and entropy.

There is a second formula also associated with Kirchhoff, similar to (2), but relating the energy change $\triangle U$ with the heat capacities at constant volume, but this formula is not needed.

§ 7.06   Energy and Entropy Constants

We now return to our consideration of gaseous equilibria. The correctness of the formulae of § 7.02 requires that the arbitrary conventions concerning zero energy and zero entropy, inasmuch as these affect the values of the $\lambda^\dagger$'s, must be the same for all the reacting species. We shall now investigate this important point.

Referring back to (4.29.1) we assume for a gas with *monatomic molecules*

$$\lambda^\dagger = e^{H^0/RT} \left(\frac{\Theta^\dagger}{T}\right)^{\frac{5}{2}}. \tag{7.06.1}$$

In §§ 4.30—4.33 we saw that for diatomic and polyatomic molecules $\lambda^\dagger$ contains the factor on the right of (1) as well as other factors completely determined by the rotational and other internal degrees of freedom of the molecules.

Correspondingly all formulae contain a term H^0 in the molar heat function and a term $-\frac{5}{2} R \log \Theta^\dagger$ in the molar entropy. As long as we are considering only variations of temperature, pressure and mixing of gases these terms may be regarded as arbitrary constants without physical significance. It is only when a gas changes into something else that we need to watch how these constants come in.

We have already in § 4.55 considered the bearing of these constants on equilibrium between gas and crystal. As regards H^0 all that was required was that the arbitrary constant in the molar energies and heat functions of the gas and crystal should be adjusted so as to correspond to the same scale. The same requirement obviously holds for gases which can be changed into one another by chemical reactions. In other words the values assigned to H^0 for any one gas or for several gases which cannot be changed into one another are entirely arbitrary. But for gases which can be changed into one another the values assigned to H_A^0, H_B^0 must be mutually adjusted so that at some one temperature the value then calculated for the heat of reaction $\Sigma \nu_B H_B = \Sigma \nu_A H_A$ agrees with the experimental value. When this adjustment has been made at one temperature, the convention is automatically consistent for all temperatures.

The most used convention is to adjust H^0 for every *element* so that H_m has the value zero for the element in its most stable state at $291.16\,°$K. The value of H^0 for any compound must then be adjusted so that the value of H_m at $291.16\,°$K is equal to $\triangle H$ for the formation of the compound from its elements. Values of H_m at $291.16\,°$K have been tabulated * for the

---

* Bichowsky and Rossini, *Thermochemistry of Chemical Substances* (1936).

commonest compounds. In order to fix these values it is not necessary nor usually possible to have a direct measurement of the heat of formation, but the values are calculated from measurements of other heats of reaction by using Hess' law as described in § 7.04. Nor is it necessary that all the measurements used should have been made at 291.16 °K nor even all at the same temperature, for they can be corrected from one temperature to another as described in § 7.05.

The convention of assigning the value zero to H^0 for every element in its most stable state at 291.16 °K is gradually being replaced by a similar convention applying to the temperature 298.16 °K. Fortunately the change in $\triangle H$ between the two temperatures 291.16 °K and 298.16 °K is easily evaluated, small and for many purposes negligible. Exceptional care would be required in the case of any substance which might have its fusion point or a transition point between these two temperatures.

We turn now to term $-\frac{5}{2}R \log \Theta^\dagger$ in the molar entropy. In § 4.56 and § 4.59 we gave an explicit formula for $\Theta^\dagger$ according to a conventional, but completely specified, choice of states of zero entropy for each substance. Statistical theory tells us that when this same convention is applied to every substance, the entropy scales of all substances are mutually consistent. The experimental verification of this is that equilibria calculated from the formulae of § 4.56 and § 4.59 are in fact in good agreement with experiment. We shall give a specific numerical example in § 7.10.

§ 7.07 Choice of Standard Pressure and Standard Entropy

Formulae (7.02.2) and (7.02.3) express the equilibrium product of $p/P^\dagger$ in terms of the $\lambda^\dagger$. We have deliberately expressed these relations in a form independent of any particular choice of the standard pressure $P^\dagger$. As we can see from formula (4.56.3) the choice of $P^\dagger$ affects the value of $\lambda^\dagger$ through $\Theta^\dagger$.

We can express the molar entropy in the form

$$S_m = S^\dagger - R \log \frac{p}{P^\dagger}, \qquad (P^\dagger = 1 \text{ atm.}), \qquad (7.07.1)$$

where $S^\dagger$ is the molar entropy of the pure gas at the standard pressure $P^\dagger$ and where owing to (4.56.3) there is in $S^\dagger$ a term $R \log P^\dagger$; so that the value of S_m is, as it must be, independent of what pressure we call standard.

Suppose we now adopt *one atmosphere as the standard pressure* $P^\dagger$. Then formula (1) becomes

$$S_m = S^\dagger - R \log \frac{p}{\text{atm.}}, \qquad (P^\dagger = 1 \text{ atm.}), \qquad (7.07.2)$$

and $S^\dagger$ is determined by the numerical formulae given in § 4.58. We shall find that $S^\dagger$ is a useful quantity and its value has been tabulated for a number of substances, usually under the name *standard molar entropy*. As we have been at pains to explain, $S^\dagger$ is in fact the molar entropy at the standard pressure and its value depends on the choice of this pressure. The choice of the atmosphere is the most usual, but it is not universal and those authors who depart from usual practice are the very ones most prone not to make clear that they are doing so. If then the name *standard molar entropy* is accepted, we still require to be told what is the *standard pressure*. But if we are given both these pieces of information, there is no longer any need to use the word standard. It is so much simpler to call $S^\dagger$ the *molar entropy at one atmosphere* or the *atmospheric molar entropy*. This name is completely unambiguous and is no longer than the ambiguous name *standard molar entropy*.

We shall accordingly adopt formula (2) and call $S^\dagger$ the *atmospheric molar entropy*. We strongly recommend this name in preference to the ambiguous alternative.

Incidentally we would emphasize that our choice of one atmosphere as standard pressure in no way compels us to use the atmosphere as unit of pressure. For recalling what was said in § 1.34 concerning our use of symbols such as p to denote physical quantities, we can write (2) as

$$S_m = S^\dagger - R \log \frac{p}{\text{atm.}}$$

$$= S^\dagger - R \log \frac{p}{76 \text{ cm. Hg}}$$

$$= S^\dagger - R \log \frac{p}{0.76 \text{ m. Hg}}$$

$$= S^\dagger - R \log \frac{p}{1.013 \times 10^6 \text{ erg cm.}^{-3}}, \tag{7.07.3}$$

and so on, the value of the *atmospheric molar entropy* $S^\dagger$ remaining the same throughout.

All accurate calorimetric work measures energy in joules and so entropy in joule/deg. and molar entropies in joule/deg. mole. Sometimes considerable effort is wasted in converting these values into cal./deg. mole. No objection is raised to this, but some authors who adopt this procedure call this unit the *entropy unit*. The statement that a certain entropy is 1.2 entropy units is just as silly as stating that a certain pressure is 1.2 *pressure units*.

Actually it is extremely convenient, especially in theoretical work to give and use numerical values of S_m/R which is dimensionless.

§ 7.08 Other Equilibrium Constants

We recall that we obtained the condition for equilibrium in a gaseous reaction in the form (7.02.2)

$$\Pi(p/P^\dagger) = K \tag{7.08.1}$$

By using the perfect gas equation of state in the form

$$p = RTc, \tag{7.08.2}$$

where c denotes the concentration n/V, we can transform (1) to

$$\Pi(c) = K_c,\qquad(7.08.3)$$

where

$$K_c = K\,\Pi(P^\dagger/RT) = K(T)\,(P^\dagger/RT)^{\Sigma\nu_A - \Sigma\nu_B}.\qquad(7.08.4)$$

Again by using the definition of partial pressure

$$p = xP,\qquad(7.08.5)$$

we can transform (1) to

$$\Pi(x) = K_x,\qquad(7.08.6)$$

where

$$K_x = K\,\Pi(P^\dagger/P) = K(T)\,(P/P^\dagger)^{\Sigma\nu_A - \Sigma\nu_B}.\qquad(7.08.7)$$

We observe that, whereas K and K_c depend only on the temperature, K_x also depends on the pressure except when $\Sigma\nu_A = \Sigma\nu_B$.

We have quoted (3) and (6) for the sake of completeness, but as they merely state the same as (1) in a different way, we shall not need to use them.

§ 7.09   Temperature Coefficient

We recall that for a perfect gas according to (6.11.3) and (6.12.3)

$$H_i = -RT^2 \frac{d\log \lambda_i^\dagger}{dT}.\qquad(7.09.1)$$

Taking logarithms of (7.02.3) and writing it in full we have

$$\log K = \Sigma\nu_A \log \lambda_A^\dagger - \Sigma\nu_B \log \lambda_B^\dagger.\qquad(7.09.2)$$

Differentiating (2) with respect to T and substituting from (1), we obtain

$$\frac{d\log K}{dT} = \frac{\Sigma\nu_B H_B - \Sigma\nu_A H_A}{RT^2} = \frac{\triangle H}{RT^2},\qquad(7.09.3)$$

where $\triangle H$ denotes the *heat of reaction*.

By differentiating (7.08.4) with respect to T and comparing with (3) we find

$$\frac{d\log K_c}{dT} = \frac{d\log K}{dT} - \frac{\Sigma\nu_B}{T}\,\frac{\Sigma\nu_A}{}$$

$$= \frac{\triangle H - (\Sigma\nu_B - \Sigma\nu_A)\,RT}{RT^2} = \frac{\triangle U}{RT^2}.\qquad(7.09.4)$$

a *relation due to van 't Hoff*, which is less useful than (3).

§ 7.10   Water-gas Reaction

We shall now give an example of the detailed calculation of a gaseous equilibrium constant, choosing the water-gas reaction at 1000 °K

$$CO + H_2O \rightarrow CO_2 + H_2,\qquad (T = 1000\ ^\circ K).$$

According to (7.02.3), we have

$$K = \frac{\lambda_{CO}^\dagger \, \lambda_{H_2O}^\dagger}{\lambda_{CO_2}^\dagger \, \lambda_{H_2}^\dagger} \qquad (7.10.1)$$

or taking logarithms

$$\log K = -\log \lambda_{CO_2}^\dagger - \log \lambda_{H_2}^\dagger + \log \lambda_{CO}^\dagger + \log \lambda_{H_2O}^\dagger , \qquad (7.10.2)$$

We rewrite this in the form

$$
\begin{aligned}
\log K = & \left(-\log \lambda_{CO_2}^\dagger + H_{CO_2}^0 / RT \right) \\
& + \left(-\log \lambda_{H_2}^\dagger + H_{H_2}^0 / RT \right) \\
& - \left(-\log \lambda_{CO}^\dagger + H_{CO}^0 / RT \right) \\
& - \left(-\log \lambda_{H_2O}^\dagger + H_{H_2O}^0 / RT \right) \\
& + \left(\frac{H_{CO}^0 + H_{H_2O}^0 - H_{CO_2}^0 - H_{H_2}^0}{RT} \right).
\end{aligned}
\qquad (7.10.3)
$$

and we compute separately each of the quantities in brackets.

We begin with the last. The heat of reaction at 25 °C is given by [*]

$$-\Delta H = 9.83_8 \text{ K cal.} = 41.46 \text{ K joule}, \quad (T = 298.16 \,°\text{K}). \quad (7.10.4)$$

This is the only piece of experimental thermodynamic or calorimetric data which we shall need to use. For the sake of brevity, let us denote the temperature 298.16 °K by T'. We have then

$$-\frac{\Delta H(T')}{R} = \frac{41460}{8.3144} \text{ deg.} = 4951 \text{ deg.} \qquad (7.10.5)$$

We write down the identity

$$
\begin{aligned}
-\Delta H(T') = & H_{CO}(T') + H_{H_2O}(T') - H_{CO_2}(T') - H_{H_2}(T) \\
= & -\Delta H^0 + \{ H_{CO}(T') - H_{CO}^0 \} + \{ H_{H_2O}(T') - H_{H_2O}^0 \}, \\
& - \{ H_{CO_2}(T') - H_{CO_2}^0 \} - \{ H_{H_2}(T') - H_{H_2}^0 \},
\end{aligned}
\qquad (7.10.6)
$$

where ΔH^0 is defined by

$$\Delta H^0 = H_{CO_2}^0 + H_{H_2}^0 - H_{CO}^0 - H_{H_2O}^0 . \qquad (7.10.7)$$

We now use formula (4.31.4), neglecting the terms containing the second virial coefficient B, and the spectroscopic data in Table 4.3 to calculate

$$\{ H_{CO_2}(T') - H_{CO_2}^0 \} / R = 1126 \text{ deg.} \qquad (7.10.8)$$

---

[*] National Bureau of Standards, *Research Paper 1634*, Rossini and others (1945).

We similarly use formula (4.30.10) and the data in Table 4.2 to calculate

$$\{H_{H_2}(T') - H_{H_2}^0\}/R = 1044 \text{ deg.} \tag{7.10.9}$$

$$\{H_{CO}(T') - H_{CO}^0\}/R = 1044 \text{ deg.} \tag{7.10.10}$$

Similarly using (4.32.5) and the data in Table 4.4, we find

$$\{H_{H_2O}(T') - H_{H_2O}^0\}/R = 1194 \text{ deg.} \tag{7.10.11}$$

Substituting (5), (8), (9), (10), (11) into (6) we obtain

$$-\Delta H^0/R = \{4951 + 1126 + 1044 - 1044 - 1194\} \text{ deg.}$$

$$= 4883 \text{ deg.} \tag{7.10.12}$$

Consequently at 1000 °K the last bracket of (3) has the value

$$-\frac{\Delta H^0}{RT} = 4.88_3 \qquad (T = 1000 °K). \tag{7.10.13}$$

We turn now to the computation of the other four brackets on the right of (3). Each of these is the sum of the following three contributions:

(a) the terms given by formula (4.58.2) for monatomic molecules, which we shall call the *particle contribution*, since they do not include contributions from internal degrees of freedom;

(b) the contributions of the rotational degrees of freedom;

(c) the contributions of the internal vibrations.

The particle contribution is given directly by (4.58.2).

The rotational contributions to $\log \lambda^\dagger$ are, as described in §§ 4.30—4.32, given for the symmetrical linear molecules CO_2 and H_2 by

$$-\log \frac{T}{2\Theta_r}, \tag{7.10.14}$$

for the unsymmetrical linear molecule CO by

$$-\log \frac{T}{\Theta_r} \tag{7.10.15}$$

and for the non-linear molecule H_2O by formula (4.32.1). The values of Θ_r are given in Tables 4.2 and 4.3.

The contribution of each vibrational degree of freedom to $\log \lambda^\dagger$ according to (4.30.5) is

$$\log (1 - e^{-\Theta_v/T}) \tag{7.10.16}$$

and the values of Θ_v are given in Tables 4.2, 4.3 and 4.4.

The results of these computations are given in Table 7.1. Inserting these and (13) into (3), we obtain

$$\log_e K = 27.220 + 16.430 - 24.550$$
$$- 23.669 + 4.883$$
$$= 0.314 \tag{7.10.16}$$

so that $K = 1.37$ in satisfactory agreement with experiment *.

---

* For detailed references to experimental data, see Bryant, *Ind. Eng. Chem.* (1931) **23** 1019.

TABLE 7.1

Contributions to $-\log \lambda^{\dagger} + H^0/RT$

	CO_2	H_2	CO	H_2O
Particle	19.28_1	14.65_5	18.60_3	17.94_1
Rotation	6.79_4	1.77_2	5.90_0	5.61_1
Vibration	1.14_5	0.00_3	0.04_7	0.11_7
Resultant	$27\,22_0$	16.43_0	24.55_0	23.66_9

§ 7.11 Equilibria Between Gases and Solids

We turn now to a discussion of the equilibrium of reactions involving pure solids as well as gases. Examples are

$$CaCO_3\,(s) \rightarrow CaO\,(s) + CO_2\,(g), \qquad (7.11.1)$$

$$NH_4Cl\,(s) \rightarrow NH_3\,(g) + HCl\,(g), \qquad (7.11.2)$$

$$C\,(graphite) + CO_2\,(g) \rightarrow 2\,CO\,(g). \qquad (7.11.3)$$

We have the general equilibrium condition (7.01.9)

$$\Pi\,(\lambda) = 1, \qquad (7.11.4)$$

where the λ of each gaseous species is related to its partial pressure p by (7.02.1). On the other hand we may regard the λ of each pure solid as a function of temperature only, since the effect of change of pressure on a solid is usually negligible.

We now extend our Π notation as follows. We write

$$\Pi(I) = \Pi_G\,(I)\,\Pi_S\,(I), \qquad (7.11.5)$$

where $\Pi_G\,(I)$ contains all the factors of $\Pi(I)$ relating to the gaseous species and $\Pi_S\,(I)$ all the factors relating to the solid species.

For example in the case of reaction (1)

$$\Pi_G(\lambda) = \lambda_{CO_2}, \qquad (7.11.6)$$

$$\Pi_S\,(\lambda) = \frac{\lambda_{CaO}}{\lambda_{CaCO_3}}. \qquad (7.11.7)$$

Using this notation, the equilibrium condition (4) may be written

$$\Pi_G\,(\lambda)\,\Pi_S\,(\lambda) = 1. \qquad (7.11.8)$$

Now substituting (7.02.1) into (7), we obtain

$$\Pi_G\,(p/P^{\dagger}) = K\,(T) \qquad (7.11.9)$$

where the *equilibrium constant* $K(T)$, a function of temperature only is given by

$$K^{-1} = \Pi_G\,(\lambda^{\dagger})\,\Pi_S\,(\lambda). \qquad (7.11.10)$$

For example for reaction (3), we have

$$\frac{p_{CO}^2}{p_{CO_2} P^\dagger} = K,$$

(7.11.11)

$$K = \frac{\lambda_{CO_2}^\dagger \lambda_C}{\lambda_{CO}^{\dagger 2}}.$$

(7.11.12)

§ 7.12 Temperature Coefficient

For each gaseous species G, we have

$$\frac{d \log \lambda_G^\dagger}{dT} = -\frac{H_G}{RT^2},$$

(7.12.1)

and for each solid species S

$$\frac{d \log \lambda_S}{dT} = -\frac{H_S}{RT^2}.$$

(7.12.2)

Taking logarithms of (7.11.10), differentiating with respect to T and substituting (1) and (2), we obtain

$$\frac{d \log K}{dT} = \frac{\Sigma \nu_B H_B - \Sigma \nu_A H_A}{RT^2} = \frac{\triangle H}{RT^2},$$

(7.12.3)

where $\triangle H$ denotes the *heat of reaction*. It will be seen that (3) has the same form as formula (7.09.3) for a gaseous reaction.

§ 7.13 Numerical Example

We shall illustrate the use of the formulae of § 7.11 by a specific example and we choose the reaction

$$C \text{ (graphite)} + CO_2 \text{ (g)} \rightarrow 2 CO \text{ (g)}$$

(7.13.1)

The equilibrium is determined by

$$\frac{p_{CO}^2}{p_{CO_2}} \text{ atm.}^{-1} = K,$$

(7.13.2)

where

$$K = \frac{\lambda_{CO_2}^\dagger \lambda_C}{\lambda_{CO}^{\dagger 2}}.$$

(7.13.3)

We shall evaluate K at 1000 °K.

In analogy with (7.10.3), we rewrite (3) in the form

$$\log K = - (H_{CO_2}^0/RT - \log \lambda_{CO_2}^\dagger)$$
$$- (H_C^0/RT - \log \lambda_C)$$
$$+ 2 (H_{CO}^0/RT - \log \lambda_{CO}^\dagger)$$
$$- \frac{\triangle H^0}{RT}.$$

(7.13.4)

where $\triangle H^0$ is defined by

$$\triangle H^0 = 2 H_{CO}^0 - H_{CO_2}^0 - H_C^0. \qquad (7.13.5)$$

In these formulae H_C^0 denotes the value of the molar heat function of graphite at $T = 0$.

We now evaluate the several terms of (4), beginning with the last. The heat of reaction at 25 °C is given experimentally by

$$\triangle H = 172.47 \text{ K joule} \qquad (T = 298.16 \text{ °K}) \qquad (7.13.6)$$

For the sake of brevity we denote this temperature by T'. We have then

$$\frac{\triangle H(T')}{R} = \frac{172470}{8.3144} \text{ deg.} = 20744 \text{ deg.} \qquad (7.13.7)$$

We now write down the identity

$$\triangle H(T') = 2 H_{CO}(T') - H_{CO_2}(T') - H_C(T')$$
$$= 2\{H_{CO}(T') - H_{CO}^0\} - \{H_{CO_2}(T') - H_{CO_2}^0\}$$
$$- \{H_C(T') - H_C^0\} + \triangle H^0. \qquad (7.13.8)$$

We have according to (7.10.10)

$$2\{H_{CO}(T') - H_{CO}^0\}/R = 2088 \text{ deg.} \qquad (7.13.9)$$

and according to (7.10.8)

$$\{H_{CO_2}(T') - H_{CO_2}^0\}/R = 1126 \text{ deg.} \qquad (7.13.10)$$

We also have by direct calorimetry

$$\{H_C(T') - H_C^0\}/R = 127 \text{ deg.} \qquad (7.13.11)$$

Substituting (7), (9), (10), (11) into (8), we obtain

$$\triangle H^0/R + \{20744 - 2088 + 1126 + 127\} \text{ deg.}$$
$$= 19909 \text{ deg.} \qquad (7.13.12)$$

Consequently at 1000 °K the last term of (4) has the value

$$- \frac{\triangle H^0}{RT} = -19.91, \qquad (T = 1000 \text{ °K}). \qquad (7.13.13)$$

We turn now to the other three terms of (4). Of these the first and third can be taken from Table 7.1. There remains the second one relating to graphite. As this relates to a solid phase it cannot be computed from spectroscopic data, but must be evaluated from calorimetric data. To be precise H_m has to be measured for solid graphite as a function of T throughout the whole temperature range from 1000 °K down to a temperature so low that extrapolation to $T = 0$ can be made as described in § 4.36. Such measurements give directly

$$\{H(1000) - H^0\}/R = 1547 \text{ deg.} \qquad (7.13.14)$$

and by the use of

$$S = \int \frac{dH}{T} \qquad (7.13.15)$$

they give

$$\{S_m(1000) - S_m(0)\}/R = 2.942 \qquad (7.13.16)$$

But according to our conventional zero of entropy, the molar entropy of graphite is zero at $0\,°K$. Hence (16) reduces to

$$S_m(1000)/R = 2.942 \qquad (7.13.17)$$

We therefore have for graphite at $1000\,°K$, using (14) and (17),

$$\frac{H^0}{RT} - \log \lambda = \frac{H^0}{RT} - \frac{\mu}{RT} = \frac{H^0}{RT} - \frac{H_m}{RT} + \frac{S_m}{R}$$
$$= -1.547 + 2.942$$
$$= 1.39_5, \qquad (T = 1000\,°K). \qquad (7.13.18)$$

Finally substituting into (4) from (13), (18) and Table 7.1, we obtain

$$\log_e K = -27.22 - 1.40 + 24.55 + 24.55 - 19.91$$
$$= 0.57$$

or $\qquad\qquad K = 1.8, \qquad\qquad (T = 1000\,°K). \qquad (7.13.19)$

The accuracy of a calculation of this kind is at best about ± 0.05 in each term of $\log K$. This usually leads to an uncertainty of at least 0.1 in $\log K$ or 10 % in K. In most cases the experimental uncertainty in a direct measurement of K is greater than this.

Whereas to determine the equilibrium constant of a purely gaseous reaction the only calorimetric result required is a value of $\triangle H$ at a single temperature, we see from the above example that in an equilibrium involving solids we require in addition calorimetric measurements on the solid right down to temperatures so low that extrapolation to $T = 0$ can be safely performed.

§ 7.14   Reactions Between Pure Solids or Liquids

We must now consider reactions between pure solid phases without any gases. Examples are

$$Pb + 2I \rightarrow PbI_2, \qquad (7.14.1)$$

$$Cu + S \rightarrow CuS. \qquad (7.14.2)$$

Incidentally, for the following considerations it is immaterial whether any of the phases is a pure liquid instead of a pure solid. As an example we may mention

$$Hg + AgCl \rightarrow Ag + HgCl. \qquad (7.14.3)$$

The simplest type of reaction between solid phases is a simple allotropic change, such as

$$\text{rhombic sulphur} \rightarrow \text{monoclinic sulphur,} \qquad (7.14.4)$$

$$\text{grey tin} \rightarrow \text{white tin.} \qquad (7.14.5)$$

The equilibrium condition for a reaction involving pure solid and liquid phases can still be expressed in the form (7.01.9)

$$\Pi(\lambda) = 1, \qquad \text{(equilibrium),} \qquad (7.14.6)$$

but each λ is now a function of temperature only, if we disregard the small effect of changes of pressure. Hence the equilibrium condition (6) may be regarded as an equation determining the temperature of reversal of the change considered. This equation may or may not have a solution for T positive. Reactions (1), (2), (3) proceed naturally towards the right at all temperatures and there is no solution of (6). In point of fact very few reactions between pure solids and pure liquids have a reversal temperature. The only important exceptions are allotropic changes such as (4) and (5), among which we may, if we like, include simple fusion.

For reactions such as (1), (2), (3) at all temperatures we have

$$\Pi(\lambda) < 1, \qquad (7.14.7)$$

or, taking logarithms and writing in full,

$$\Sigma \nu_A \log \lambda_A > \Sigma \nu_B \log \lambda_B. \qquad (7.14.8)$$

or

$$\Sigma \nu_A \mu_A > \Sigma \nu_B \mu_B. \qquad (7.14.9)$$

Another way of expressing the same thing is to state that the affinity A, defined in § 1.50 is positive at all temperatures. We shall see in Chapter X how this affinity can often be accurately determined by measurements of electromotive force.

We shall now consider (6) in more detail and for this purpose, we write it in the expanded form

$$\Sigma \nu_A \log \lambda_A = \Sigma \nu_B \log \lambda_B. \qquad (7.14.10)$$

But by definition

$$\log \lambda = \frac{\mu}{RT} = \frac{H_m}{RT} - \frac{S_m}{R}. \qquad (7.14.11)$$

Substituting (11) into (10), we obtain

$$T = \frac{\Sigma \nu_B H_B - \Sigma \nu_A H_A}{\Sigma \nu_B S_B - \Sigma \nu_A S_A}. \qquad (7.14.12)$$

The numerator of (12) is the heat of reaction $\triangle H$ and the denominator is the entropy of reaction $\triangle S$. We now consider these separately.

For $\triangle H$ we write formally

$$\triangle H(T) = \triangle H(T') + \Sigma \nu_B \{H_B(T) - H_B(T')\}$$
$$- \Sigma \nu_A \{H_A(T) - H_A(T')\}. \qquad (7.14.13)$$

If for each of the substances the dependence of H on temperature has been determined calorimetrically and if in addition $\triangle H$ has been measured at any one temperature T', then by means of (13) $\triangle H$ can be calculated at any other temperature.

For $\triangle S$ we write formally

$$\triangle S(T) = \triangle S^0 + \Sigma \nu_B \{S_B(T) - S_B^0\} - \Sigma \nu_A \{S_A(T) - S_A^0\}. \quad (7.14.14)$$

where the superscript ^{0} denotes the value obtained by smooth extra-polation to $T = 0$. If now the dependence of H on temperature has been measured throughout the temperature range from T down to a temperature from which one can extrapolate to $T = 0$, then (14) determines $\triangle S$ for all temperatures apart from the constant $\triangle S^0$. But S^0 is the quantity discussed in detail in §§ 4.60 — 4.66. It has the value zero except for a few well understood exceptions for which its value is known to be $R \log o$, with o a small number such as 2 or $\frac{3}{2}$. With this knowledge of $\triangle S^0$, or in the absence of evidence to the contrary assuming $\triangle S = 0$, formula (13) determines $\triangle S$ for all temperatures.

Using (13) and (14) together, one can solve (12) for the *transition temperature* T. Alternatively using the experimental value of T, we can use (12), (13), (14) to determine an experimental value for $\triangle S^0$.

§ 7.15 Transition of Sulphur

We shall now illustrate the formulae of the preceding section by a numerical example. As already mentioned it is difficult to find an example of an equilibrium temperature for a reaction between solid phases except in the simplest case of an allotropic change. We accordingly choose as our example

$$\text{rhombic sulphur} \rightarrow \text{monoclinic sulphur,} \quad (7.15.1)$$

and we shall use the subscripts R and M for the rhombic and monoclinic forms respectively. The transition temperature is

$$T = 368.6\,^{\circ}\text{K,} \qquad \text{(transition),} \qquad (7.15.2)$$

The heat of transition at this temperature is

$$\frac{\triangle H}{R} = \frac{H_M - H_R}{R} = 47.5 \pm 5 \deg., \qquad (T = 368.6\,^{\circ}\text{K}). \quad (7.15.3)$$

Consequently the entropy of transition at this temperature is

$$\frac{\triangle S}{R} = \frac{S_M - S_R}{R} = \frac{47.5}{368.6} = 0.12 \pm 0.01, \quad (T = 368.6\,^{\circ}\text{K}). \quad (7.15.4)$$

According to calorimetric measurements * on the two forms from 15 °K to

---

* For details of experimental data, see Eastman and McGavock, *J. Am. Chem. Soc.* (1937) **59** 145.

the transition temperature

$$\frac{S_R(368.6°) - S_R(15°)}{R} = 4.38 \pm 0.03, \qquad (7.15.5)$$

$$\frac{S_M(368.6°) - S_M(15°)}{R} = 4.49 \pm 0.04. \qquad (7.15.6)$$

Combining (4), (5) and (6) we obtain

$$\frac{S_M(15°) - S_R(15°)}{R} = 0.12 - 4.49 + 4.38$$

$$= 0.01 \pm 0.05. \qquad (7.15.7)$$

We conclude that well within the experimental accuracy

$$S_M^0 - S_R^0 = 0. \qquad (7.15.8)$$

§ 7.16   Solutions

We turn now to consider chemical equilibria in liquid solutions. The simplest method of approach is by considering the vapour phase in equilibrium with the solution. We then have the equilibrium condition (7.02.2)

$$\Pi(p/P^\dagger) = K \qquad (7.16.1)$$

unchanged in form, but the interpretation is now that each p denotes the partial vapour pressure of the species over the solution.

Furthermore since K in (1) is precisely the same K as in (7.02.2), its temperature coefficient is given by (7.09.3)

$$\frac{d \log K}{dT} = \frac{\triangle H^G}{RT^2}, \qquad (7.16.2)$$

where the superscript G has been added to remind us that $\triangle H^G$ denotes the value of the heat of reaction in the gas phase.

§ 7.17   Ideal Dilute Solutions

In an ideal dilute solution at a given temperature the partial vapour pressure, or strictly fugacity, p of each species is according to (6.25.1) related to its mole fraction x by

$$p = h\,x, \quad (h \text{ const.}) . \qquad (7.17.1)$$

Incidentally (1) applies to the solvent species 1, the coefficient h then being equal to p_1^0 the vapour pressure of the pure liquid. Substituting (1) into (7.16.1), we obtain

$$\Pi(x) = K_x. \qquad (7.17.2)$$

where K_x depends only on the solvent and the temperature, being related to K by

$$K_x = K\,\Pi(P^\dagger/h). \qquad (7.17.3)$$

We may note that K_x, K and $h/P\dagger$ are all dimensionless numbers.

We recall formula (6.31.8) for the dependence of each h on the temperature

$$\frac{d \log h}{dT} = \frac{\triangle_e H}{RT^2}, \qquad (7.17.4)$$

where $\triangle_e H$ denotes the molar heat of evaporation from the ideal solution. Differentiating (3) logarithmically with respect to T, and substituting (7.16.2) and (4), we obtain

$$\frac{d \log K_x}{dT} = \frac{\triangle H^I}{RT^2}, \qquad (7.17.5)$$

where $\triangle H^I$ denotes the heat of reaction in the ideal solution.

§ 7.18   Non-Ideal Solutions

In a non-ideal solution we have instead of (7.17.1) the relation (6.40.2)

$$p = h\,x\,\gamma, \qquad (h \text{ const.}), \qquad (7.18.1)$$

where γ is the activity coefficient. Substituting (1) into (7.16.1) we obtain

$$\Pi(x\gamma) = K_x, \qquad (7.18.2)$$

where K_x is defined by (7.17.3).

It is sometimes useful to write (2) in the form

$$\Pi(x) = K_x/\Pi(\gamma), \qquad (7.18.3)$$

which tells us that the *mole fraction equilibrium product* is not constant but is inversely proportional to the *activity coefficient equilibrium product*. The practice of some authors of associating the word *constant* with $\Pi(x)$ is misleading and to be condemned.

For the dependence of K_x on temperature we have (7.17.5)

$$\frac{d \log K_x}{dT} = \frac{\triangle H^I}{RT^2}, \qquad (7.18.4)$$

where $\triangle H^I$ now means the heat of reaction in a solution sufficiently dilute to be ideal dilute; or we may call $\triangle H^I$ the *heat of reaction at infinite dilution* in the given solvent.

§ 7.19   Heterogeneous Equilibria Involving Solutions

We might also discuss equilibria involving solutions and vapour phases, or solutions and solids or even solutions, solids and vapour phases, but this is unnecessary, because any equilibrium however complicated can be regarded as a superposition of a homogeneous equilibrium in a single phase, liquid or gaseous, and distribution equilibria of individual species between pairs of phases. Both these elementary types of equilibrium have been discussed in sufficient detail.

§ 7.20   Transitions of Second Order

This is perhaps the most convenient place to describe a phenomenon called a *transition of the second order*. It is quite different from anything we have yet met, having some of the characteristics of phase changes and some of the characteristics of critical phenomena. We shall first show by a particular example how a transition of the second order arises from certain assumed properties of the thermodynamic potentials. We shall then discuss briefly how and when they occur.

As a preliminary step to our discussion, we shall consider the thermodynamic properties of the equilibrium between two isomers under the simplest conceivable conditions. Thus we consider the isomeric change

$$A \rightarrow B \qquad (7.20.1)$$

occurring in a mixture of A and B in the absence of any other species. We further assume that the mixture is ideal. Finally we assume that the heat of reaction has a value w independent of the temperature; in other words we assume that A and B have equal heat capacities. If then x denotes the mole fraction of B, the molar Gibbs function G_m has the form

$$\frac{G_m}{RT} = \frac{G_m^0(T)}{RT} + \frac{w}{RT} x + (1-x) \log (1-x) + x \log x, \qquad (7.20.2)$$

where w is a constant and $G_m^0(T)$ depends only on the temperature From (2) we deduce

$$H_m = G_m^0 - T \frac{dG_m^0}{dT} + w x. \qquad (7\ 20\ 3)$$

from which we verify that the heat of reaction is w. We also deduce

$$\frac{S_m}{R} = -\frac{1}{R} \frac{dG_m^0}{dT} - (1-x) \log (1-x) - x \log x, \qquad (7.20.4)$$

showing that the molar entropy of mixing has its ideal value

$$-R\{(1-x) \log (1-x) + x \log x\} \qquad (7.20.5)$$

The equilibrium value of x is obtained by minimising G_m. We find

$$\frac{1}{RT} \frac{\partial G_m}{\partial x} = \frac{w}{RT} + \log \frac{x}{1-x} = 0, \qquad (7.20.6)$$

so that

$$\frac{x}{1-x} = e^{-w/RT}. \qquad (7\ 20.7)$$

Formula (7) is, of course, the simplest possible example of the equilibrium law (7.17.2). Before we dismiss this extremely simple system, there remains one important point to be investigated, namely the verification that

(6) and (7) do correspond to a minimum of G_m, not to a maximum. We have

$$\frac{1}{RT} \frac{\partial^2 G_m}{\partial x^2} = \frac{1}{x} + \frac{1}{1-x} > 0 \qquad (7.20.8)$$

thus verifying that we have found a minimum, not a maximum.

Let us now arbitrarily introduce a small modification into the form of G_m assumed in (2), without at this stage enquiring into the physical significance of the change. We replace the term wx by $wx(1-x)$. We then have

$$\frac{G_m}{RT} = \frac{G_m^0(T)}{RT} + \frac{w x (1-x)}{RT} + (1-x) \log (1-x) + x \log x, \qquad (7.20.9)$$

$$H_m = G_m^0 - T\frac{dG_m^0}{dT} + w x (1-x), \qquad (7.20.10)$$

$$\frac{S_m}{R} = -\frac{1}{R} \frac{dG_m^0}{dT} - (1-x) \log (1-x) - x \log x, \qquad (7.20.11)$$

from which we observe that the heat function is affected by the modification, but the entropy is not.

We now seek the equilibrium value of x by minimising G_m. We find

$$\frac{1}{RT} \frac{\partial G_m}{\partial x} = -\frac{w}{RT} (2x-1) + \log \frac{x}{1-x} = 0, \qquad (7.20.12)$$

so that

$$\frac{x}{1-x} = e^{(2x-1)w/RT}. \qquad (7.20.13)$$

One solution of (13) is obviously $x = \frac{1}{2}$, but this is not always the only solution. Nor is this solution necessarily a minimum rather than a maximum of G_m. We must carefully investigate these points and shall do so in the first place graphically. Accordingly Fig. 7.1 shows

$$\frac{G_m - G_m^0}{RT} \qquad (7.20.14)$$

plotted against $2(x-\frac{1}{2})$ for various values of $\frac{1}{2} w/RT$. Owing to the complete symmetry between x and $1-x$, we can without loss of generality assume that $x > 1-x$.

We see that, when $w > 0$, at high temperatures, that is small values of w/RT, the root $x = \frac{1}{2}$ is the only root and it corresponds to a minimum of G_m. At low enough temperatures, that is large values of w/RT, there is another root $\frac{1}{2} \leq x \leq 1$ and this root corresponds to a minimum of G_m while the root $x = \frac{1}{2}$ now corresponds to a maximum. Thus there exists a temperature T_λ such that at temperatures below T_λ the equilibrium value of x is greater than $\frac{1}{2}$ and decreases as the temperature increases; the equilibrium value of x becomes $\frac{1}{2}$ at the temperature T_λ and remains $\frac{1}{2}$ at all higher temperatures. The change occurring at the temperature T_λ is called a *transition of the second order* and the temperature T is called a *lambda-point* for a reason which will be explained later.

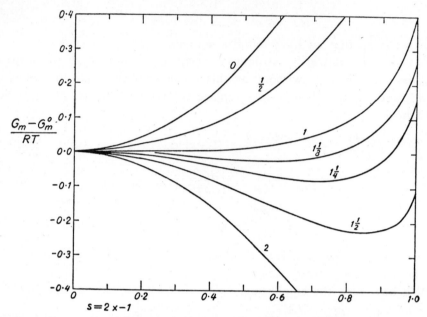

Fig. 7.1. Dependence of G_m on x for various values of $\frac{1}{2}w/RT$. The numbers attached to the curves are values of $\frac{1}{2}w/RT$ or T_λ/T.

It is clear from Fig. 7.1 that T_λ is the temperature at which the two roots of (13) become equal, the root at $x = \frac{1}{2}$ changing from a minimum to a maximum. Thus there is a point of horizontal inflexion at $x = \frac{1}{2}$, $T = T_\lambda$. We have then

$$\frac{1}{RT}\frac{\partial^2 G_m}{\partial x^2} = -\frac{2w}{RT_\lambda} + \frac{1}{x} + \frac{1}{1-x} = 0, \qquad (x = \tfrac{1}{2}), \quad (7.20.15)$$

whence

$$\frac{w}{RT_\lambda} = 2. \qquad (7.20.16)$$

It is clear from Fig. 7.1 that for negative values of w the minimum is always at $x = \frac{1}{2}$ and there can be no lambda-point.

§ 7.21 Cooperative Systems

Before proceeding to a more detailed examination of transitions of the second order, we shall explain in very general terms how they arise. As a preliminary step, let us determine the *molar heat of change* in the process (7.20.1). For the heat function H of the whole system, we have according to (7.20.10) changing to the variables n_A, n_B

$$H = (n_A + n_B)H^0 + \frac{n_A n_B}{n_A + n_B}w. \qquad (7.21.1)$$

where H^0 is independent of n_A, n_B. Differentiating with respect to n_A, n_B in turn we obtain for the partial molar heat functions

$$H_A = H^0 - \frac{n_B^2}{(n_A + n_B)^2}\, w = H^0 + x^2\, w, \qquad (7.21.2)$$

$$H_B = H^0 - \frac{n_A^2}{(n_A + n_B)^2}\, w = H^0 + (1-x)^2\, w, \qquad (7.21.3)$$

so that the molar *heat of change* from A to B is

$$H_B - H_A = (1 - 2x)\, w. \qquad (7.21.4)$$

Since we are considering a condensed phase (4) is essentially equivalent to

$$U_B - U_A = (1 - 2x)\, w. \qquad (7.21.5)$$

The outstanding characteristic of (5) is that the energy required to convert a molecule A into a molecule B depends in a marked degree on what fraction of all the molecules is present in each form. Such a characteristic would not be expected when the process

$$A \rightarrow B \qquad (7.21.6)$$

represents a chemical change of one isomer to another, nor in such a case do we find a lambda-point. It is however not difficult to mention other interpretations of (6) which might reasonably be expected to have the characteristic just mentioned. Suppose for example we consider a regular array of polar molecules or atoms in a lattice. Suppose further that each molecule or atom can point in either of two opposite directions. Suppose finally that we denote the molecules by A or B according to the direction in which they point. Then it is easily understandable that the energy required to turn round a molecule or atom may depend markedly on how many other molecules or atoms are pointing in either direction. This behaviour is typical of systems called *cooperative*. The significance of the name should be clear from this and the following examples.

Another more complicated, but possibly more important, interpretation of (6) is for A to represent a state of molecular libration and B a state of molecular rotation.

Another example occurring in certain alloys is the following. Suppose we have an alloy of the composition Zn Cu containing N atoms of Zn and N atoms of Cu arranged on a regular lattice of $2N$ lattice-points. We can picture two extreme arrangements of the two kinds of atoms on the lattice, one completely ordered, the other completely random. In the completely ordered arrangement every alternate lattice-point A is occupied by a Zn atom and the remaining lattice-points B are occupied by Cu atoms. In the opposite extreme arrangement every lattice-point A or B is occupied by either Zn or Cu atoms arranged at complete random. We can moreover consider intermediate arrangements such that a fraction x of the Zn atoms occupy A lattice-points and the fraction $(1-x)$ of Zn atoms occupy B lattice-points. The remaining lattice-points are of course occupied by the Cu atoms. We can then without loss of generality take $x \geq \frac{1}{2}$. In such a system the average energy required to move a Zn atom from an A point to a B point will depend markedly on how many A points are already occupied by Zn atoms. It is therefore at least conceivable that such a system might have a lambda-point.

As a matter of fact the alloy having the composition ZnCu does have a lambda-point and the thermodynamic properties of this system can be at least semi-quantitatively represented by a Gibbs function of the form (7.20.9). This form was first suggested by Gorsky[*] and later independently derived by approximate statistical considerations by Bragg and Williams [**]. It is outside the scope of this book to consider this aspect of the pheno-menon and we shall accordingly confine ourselves to a purely phenomeno-logical thermodynamic investigation of some of the general properties of lambda-points, among others the property leading to its name.

§ 7.22   Alternative Notation

The notation which we have used to introduce the subject of *transitions of the second order* is the one which seems natural. It is not however the notation most used. For the sake of completeness we describe briefly the alternative notation.

A quantity s called the *degree of order* is defined by [**]

$$s = 2x - 1, \qquad (7.22.1)$$

or

$$x = \tfrac{1}{2}(1 + s). \qquad (7.22.2)$$

In this notation formula (7.20.9) becomes

$$\frac{G_m}{RT} = \frac{G_m^0}{RT} + \frac{w}{RT} \frac{1 - s^2}{4}$$
$$+ \tfrac{1}{2}(1 + s) \log (1 + s) + \tfrac{1}{2}(1 - s) \log (1 - s) - \log 2. \qquad (7.22.3)$$

The equilibrium value of s is determined according to (7.20.12) by

$$\log \frac{1 + s}{1 - s} = \frac{w}{RT} s. \qquad (7.22.4)$$

which is equivalent to

$$\tanh \frac{w s}{2 RT} = s. \qquad (7.22.5)$$

Using (7.20.16) we can transform (5) to

$$\frac{T_\lambda}{T} = \frac{\tanh^{-1} s}{s}. \qquad (7.22.6)$$

---

[*]   Gorsky. *Zeit. Physik* (1928) **50** 64.
[**]   Bragg and Williams. *Proc. Roy. Soc.* A (1934) **145** 699.

These formulae, of course, contain nothing which is not already contained in the formulae of § 7.20. It is merely a historical accident that pioneer workers in this field used the variable s instead of x.

§ 7.23   Characteristics of Lambda-Point

We have seen how a Gibbs function of the form (7.20.9) leads without any further assumption to the occurrence of a *transition of the second order* and we have explained how this type of behaviour can occur in a *cooperative system*. We do not assert that a Gibbs function of approximately this form is the origin of all transitions of the second order. Still less do we assert that a Gibbs function of this form accounts accurately for any transition of the second order. We merely assert that the form (7.20.9) of the Gibbs function is one possible form which leads to the occurrence of a lambda-point having certain general characteristics which we shall describe. We shall continue to make use of the particular forms of thermodynamic functions described in § 7.20 for illustrative purposes.

From Fig. 7.1, or more accurately by calculation from (7.20.13), we can determine the equilibrium value of x as a function of T. The result is given in Fig. 7.2, where $s = 2x-1$ is plotted against T/T_λ. We notice

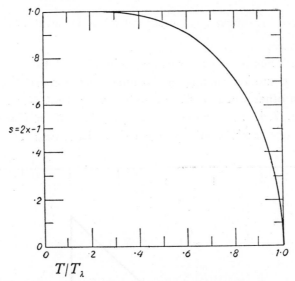

Fig. 7.2.   Dependence of equilibrium value of degree of order on temperature.

that at temperatures immediately below T_λ the equilibrium value of s changes rapidly with temperature and at temperatures below $\frac{1}{2} T_\lambda$ this equilibrium value hardly differs appreciably from unity. There is then a rapid change of the equilibrium value of s in the temperature range between T_λ and $\frac{1}{2} T_\lambda$. Associated with this change in s there is a rapid change in the part of the molar energy or heat function which depends on s, namely the term

$$w\, x(1-x) = \tfrac{1}{4}\, w(1-s^2). \qquad (7.23.1)$$

This is shown in Fig. 7.3. The term (1) occurs in the energy additional to other terms due to the translational and internal degrees of freedom of

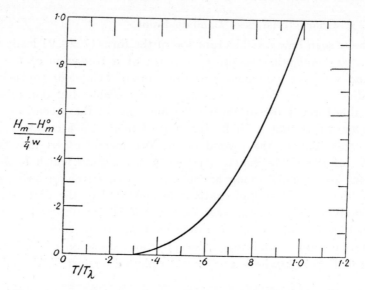

Fig. 7.3. Temperature dependence of heat function due to variation in degree of order.

the molecules. Thus as the temperature is decreased through the lambda-point there is a sudden change in the temperature coefficient of the heat function, or in other words a discontinuity in the heat capacity C. This is shown in Fig. 7.4. The shape of the curve recalls a Greek capital Λ, whence the name *lambda-point* suggested by Ehrenfest *.

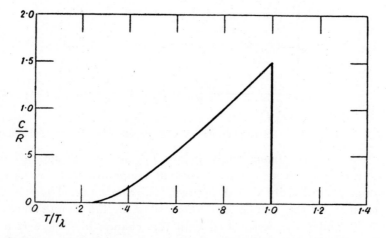

Fig. 7.4. Contribution to heat capacity of variation in degree of order.

* See Keesom, *Helium* (1942) p. 216.

For the particular model considered in detail, we observe that in the immediate neighbourhood below the lambda temperature

$$\frac{\partial H}{\partial s} = 0, \qquad (7.23.2)$$

$$\frac{\partial S}{\partial s} = 0, \qquad (7.23.3)$$

$$\frac{ds}{dT} = \infty, \qquad (7.23.4)$$

in such a manner that

$$\frac{\partial H}{\partial s}\frac{ds}{dT} \text{ is finite,} \qquad (7.23.5)$$

$$\frac{\partial S}{\partial s}\frac{ds}{dT} \text{ is finite.} \qquad (7.23.6)$$

The properties (5) and (6) are characteristic of all lambda-points and are independent of the choice of s. On the other hand the relations (2), (3), (4) depend on the definition of s. For example if we replace s by s^2, then

$$\frac{\partial H}{\partial s^2} \text{ is finite,} \qquad (7.23.7)$$

$$\frac{\partial S}{\partial s^2} \text{ is finite.} \qquad (7.23.8)$$

We may then describe a transition of the second order as a discontinuity in C, with continuity of H, S, G, at a certain temperature T_λ called the *lambda-point*.

The lambda-point known longest is the one discovered by Curie and therefore called the *Curie-point*, below which a substance such as iron has permanent magnetization and above which it has not. The Curie-point will be referred to again in Chapter 13.

Probably the most interesting, most studied but least understood lambda-point is that of helium at 2.2 °K. Fig. 7.5 shows the experimental data * for C plotted against T.

Many other lambda-points are known to occur in crystals and are usually associated with a sudden change in the extent to which the molecules in the crystal can rotate freely. Few however, if any, have been studied in such detail as to be completely understood.

§ 7.24 **Comparison with Phase-Change and Critical-Point**

Since a substance has measurably different properties above and below the lambda-point, there is a temptation to regard a *transition of the second*

---

* Keesom, *Helium* (1942) p. 215.

order as a kind of *phase change*. The expression *phase change of the second order* has been used, but as it has in the past led to considerable confusion it is better avoided *

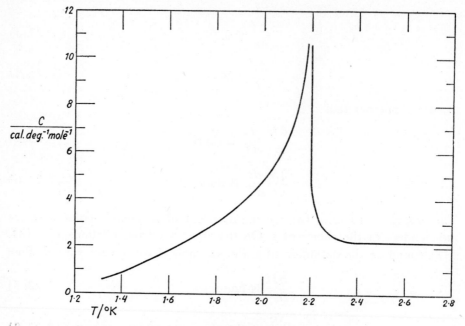

Fig. **7.5.** Heat capacity of liquid helium near lambda-point.

The contrast between a lambda-point and a phase change may be made clear by a plot of the molar Gibbs function against the temperature. This is shown in Fig. 7.6. Diagram *A* depicts a phase change. The curves of

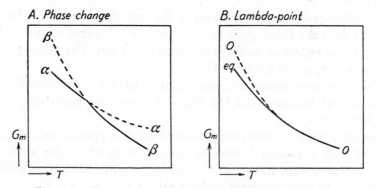

Fig. **7.6.** Contrast between phase change and lambda-point.

the two distinct phases α and β cut at the transition point, the dotted portions of the curves representing metastable states. Diagram *B* depicts a transition of the second order. The curve marked 0 represents the Gibbs

---

* Guggenheim, *Proc. Roy. Acad. Amsterdam* (1934) **37** 3.

function of a hypothetical phase with $s = 0$, which is usually associated with complete randomness. The curve marked eq. represents the Gibbs function of a phase in which at each temperature s has its equilibrium value. Below the lambda-point the dotted curve marked 0 lies above the curve marked eq. and consequently the former represents metastable states.

At the lambda-point the two curves touch. We might ask what happens to the eq. curve above the lambda-point. If we extend the eq. curve by the simplest analytical formula, ignoring physics, the curve would continue below the 0 curve, thus suggesting that it represents states more stable than the 0 curve. On further study we should however find that this hypothetical curve corresponds to negative values of s and has therefore no physical meaning. It is therefore safer and more profitable to forget about such a curve.

On the other hand a comparison between a lambda-point and a critical point, if not carried too far, is less dangerous. At temperatures below the lambda-point there is a stable phase with a value of s determined by the temperature and there can also be a metastable phase with $s = 0$; the latter can in fact sometimes be realized in practice by sudden chilling from a temperature above the lambda-point. The difference between these two phases, measured by the values of s, gradually decreases as the temperature is raised and vanishes at the lambda-point when the two phases become identical. This recalls the behaviour of liquid and vapour phases at the critical point, but here the resemblance ends.

§ 7.25 Dependence of Lambda-Point on Pressure

Up to this point we have considered how a transition of the second order occurs at a certain temperature, completely disregarding the pressure. This is in practice justifiable for most such transitions, but in principle there can be a dependence on the pressure. In practice the only known example where pressure changes are likely to be important is that of liquid helium. Let us then consider how the lambda-point is affected when the pressure is changed.

In the particular model represented by (7.20.9) the dependence on pressure would result from the energy parameter w being a function of the pressure. We shall however not assume this model nor any other detailed model, but shall rather derive formulae of great generality.

Regarding G as a function of s, as well as of T, P, we have

$$dG = - S \, dT + V \, dP + \left(\frac{\partial G}{\partial s} \right) ds \qquad (7.25.1)$$

and differentiating throughout with respect to s

$$d \left(\frac{\partial G}{\partial s} \right) = - \left(\frac{\partial S}{\partial s} \right) dT + \left(\frac{\partial V}{\partial s} \right) dP + \frac{\partial^2 G}{\partial s^2} \, ds. \qquad (7.25.2)$$

Now the equilibrium value of s at each temperature is determined by

$$\frac{\partial G}{\partial s} = 0, \qquad \text{(equilibrium)} \qquad (7.25.3)$$

and in particular at the lambda-point

$$s = 0, \qquad \text{(lambda-point)}. \qquad (7.25.4)$$

If then we follow the lambda-point at varying pressure, we have (3), and owing to (4) we have

$$ds = 0, \qquad \text{(lambda-points)}. \qquad (7.25.5)$$

Substituting (3) and (5) into (2) we obtain

$$-\frac{\partial S}{\partial s} dT + \frac{\partial V}{\partial s} dP = 0, \qquad \text{(lambda-points)}. \qquad (7.25.6)$$

or

$$\frac{dT_\lambda}{dP} = \frac{\left(\dfrac{\partial V}{\partial s}\right)_{s=0}}{\left(\dfrac{\partial S}{\partial s}\right)_{s=0}} \qquad (7.25.7)$$

Formula (7) describes in the most general way how the temperature of the lambda-point depends on the pressure. The right side of (7) can however usefully be transformed into alternative forms more directly related to experimental data.

We accordingly multiply numerator and denominator of (7) by ds/dT, where s here denotes the equilibrium value. We obtain

$$\frac{dT_\lambda}{dP} = \frac{\dfrac{\partial V}{\partial s}\dfrac{ds}{dT}}{\dfrac{\partial S}{\partial s}\dfrac{ds}{dT}}. \qquad (7.25.8)$$

where every quantity on the right side is given its equilibrium value at or immediately below T_λ. We shall now examine the physical significance of the numerator and denominator on the right of (8).

Let us use the superscripts — and + to denote the values of quantities immediately below and immediately above the temperature T_λ. Then we have

$$G^- = G^+, \qquad (7.25.9)$$

$$H^- = H^+, \qquad (7.25.10)$$

$$S^- = S^+, \qquad (7.25.11)$$

$$C^- = C^+ + T_\lambda \frac{\partial S}{\partial s}\frac{ds}{dT}. \qquad (7.25.12)$$

so that the denominator of the right of (8) is $(C^- - C^+)/T_\lambda$.

Similarly if α denotes coefficient of thermal expansion

$$V^- = V^+ = V_\lambda, \qquad (7.\,25.\,13)$$

$$\alpha^- V_\lambda = \alpha^+ V_\lambda + \frac{\partial V}{\partial s}\frac{ds}{dT}, \qquad (7.\,25.\,14)$$

so that the numerator in (8) is $(\alpha^- - \alpha^+)\,V_\lambda$.

Hence substituting (12) and (14) into (8) we obtain

$$\frac{dT_\lambda}{dP} = \frac{(\alpha^- - \alpha^+)\,V_\lambda\,T_\lambda}{C^- - C^+}. \qquad (7.\,25.\,15)$$

This formula shows how the effect of pressure on the lambda-point is related to the discontinuities in C and in α.

Returning to (7), instead of multiplying numerator and denominator by ds/dT, we could multiply by ds/dP, obtaining

$$\frac{dT_\lambda}{dP} = \frac{\dfrac{\partial V}{\partial s}\dfrac{ds}{dP}}{\dfrac{\partial S}{\partial s}\dfrac{ds}{dP}}. \qquad (7.\,25.\,16)$$

But if $\varkappa$ denotes isothermal compressibility, we have

$$\varkappa^- V_\lambda = \varkappa^+ V_\lambda - \frac{\partial V}{\partial s}\frac{ds}{dP}. \qquad (7.\,25.\,17)$$

Similarly

$$\left(\frac{\partial S}{\partial P}\right)^- = \left(\frac{\partial S}{\partial P}\right)^+ + \frac{\partial S}{\partial s}\frac{ds}{dP}, \qquad (7.\,25.\,18)$$

and so using Maxwell's relation (3.04.4) we have

$$\alpha^- V_\lambda = \alpha^+ V_\lambda - \frac{\partial S}{\partial s}\frac{ds}{dP}. \qquad (7.\,25.\,19)$$

Substituting (17) and (19) into (16) we obtain

$$\frac{dT_\lambda}{dP} = \frac{\varkappa^- - \varkappa^+}{\alpha^- - \alpha^+}. \qquad (7.\,25.\,20)$$

This formula relates the dependence of the lambda-point on the pressure to the discontinuities in α and $\varkappa$.

Formulae (15) and (20) are due to Ehrenfest [*].

§ 7.26 Transitions of Higher Order

In an ordinary *phase change*, which we may call a *transition of the first order*, we have

$$\left.\begin{array}{ll} G & \text{continuous,} \\[4pt] S = -\dfrac{\partial G}{\partial T} & \text{discontinuous,} \end{array}\right\} \begin{array}{l} \text{1st order} \\ \text{transitions.} \end{array}$$

---

[*] Ehrenfest, *Proc. Amsterdam Acad. Sci.* (1933) **36** 153

In the *transitions of the second order*, which we have been discussing, we have

$$G, \frac{\partial G}{\partial T} \qquad \text{continuous,} \qquad \left.\begin{array}{c}\\\\\end{array}\right\} \begin{array}{l}\text{2nd order}\\\text{transitions.}\end{array}$$

$$C = -T \frac{\partial^2 G}{\partial T^2} \quad \text{discontinuous,}$$

In a like manner we can define a *transition of the third order* by

$$G, \frac{\partial G}{\partial T}, \frac{\partial^2 G}{\partial T^2} \quad \text{continuous,} \qquad \left.\begin{array}{c}\\\\\end{array}\right\} \begin{array}{l}\text{3rd order}\\\text{transitions.}\end{array}$$

$$\frac{\partial^3 G}{\partial T^3} \qquad \text{discontinuous,}$$

It is possible, but not certain, that transitions of the third order exist.

It is further possible to extend the above definitions to transitions of still higher order. We shall however not pursue this matter any further.

§ 7.27 Components and Degrees of Freedom

Since the equilibrium condition for the chemical change

$$\Sigma \nu_A A \rightarrow \Sigma \nu_B B \tag{7.27.1}$$

is given by (7.01.5)

$$\Sigma \nu_A \mu_A = \Sigma \nu_B \mu_B. \tag{7.27.2}$$

all variations of temperature, pressure and composition consistent with chemical equilibrium must satisfy

$$\Sigma \nu_A d\mu_A = \Sigma \nu_B d\mu_B. \tag{7.27.3}$$

This is a relation between the chemical potentials additional to and independent of the Gibbs–Duhem relations. The existence of this relation reduces by one the number of degrees of freedom of the system.

Let us consider a particular example, namely a gaseous mixture of N_2, H_2 and NH_3. This single phase system can be described by T, P, x_{N_2}, x_{H_2}, x_{NH_3} subject to the identity

$$x_{N_2} + x_{H_2} + x_{NH_3} = 1, \tag{7.27.4}$$

or alternatively by T, P, μ_{N_2}, μ_{H_2}, μ_{NH_3} subject to the Gibbs–Duhem relation

$$x_{N_2} d\mu_{N_2} + x_{H_2} d\mu_{H_2} + x_{NH_3} d\mu_{NH_3} = 0. \tag{7.27.5}$$

Hence in the absence of chemical reaction between the three components the system has four degrees of freedom. If however, for example by introducing a catalyst, we enable the process

$$N_2 + 3H_2 \rightarrow 2NH_3 \tag{7.27.6}$$

to attain equilibrium, then there is the further restriction

$$\mu_{N_2} + 3\mu_{H_2} = 2\mu_{NH_3}. \tag{7.27.7}$$

which reduces the number of degrees of freedom from four to three. This situation is sometimes described by saying that of the three species N_2, H_2 and NH_3 there are only two *independent components*. Whether or not this terminology is adopted the number of degrees of freedom is certainly three.

Now consider a system in which several chemical changes can take place. Some such changes may be expressible as linear combinations of others, but there will always be a definite number of chemical changes which are linearly independent. Consider for example a system consisting of solid graphite and a gaseous mixture O_2, CO, CO_2. Then of the chemical changes

$$C + \tfrac{1}{2}O_2 \rightarrow CO, \qquad (7.27.8)$$

$$C + O_2 \rightarrow CO_2. \qquad (7.27.9)$$

$$CO + \tfrac{1}{2}O_2 \rightarrow CO_2, \qquad (7.27.10)$$

$$C + CO_2 \rightarrow 2CO \qquad (7.27.11)$$

the third is obtained by subtracting the first from the second, while the fourth is obtained by subtracting the third from the first. Thus only two of these changes are independent. By a comparison of (1) and (2) it is clear that independent chemical processes have independent equilibrium conditions, whereas linearly related chemical processes have linearly related equilibrium conditions. Hence each linearly independent chemical equilibrium corresponds to a restrictive relation between the chemical potentials leading to a decrease by unity in the number of degrees of freedom. For example in the two phase system consisting of solid graphite and a gaseous mixture of O_2, CO, CO_2 the effect of the two independent chemical equilibria is to reduce the number of degrees of freedom from four to two; thus the state of the system is completely determined by the temperature and the pressure. Incidentally in this particular system at equilibrium the amount of free O_2 is undetectable. The system may therefore be more simply described as a two phase system containing the three species C, CO and CO_2, between which there is a single chemical reaction

$$C + CO_2 \rightarrow 2CO. \qquad (7.27.12)$$

The equilibrium condition for this process reduces the number of degrees of freedom from three to two. Whichever way we consider the system we find that the number of degrees of freedom is two. Whether we regard the system as consisting of four components with two independent chemical processes, or of three components with one independent chemical process or of two *independent* components is a mere difference of terminology without practical importance.

CHAPTER VIII

EXTREMELY DILUTE SOLUTIONS

§ 8. 01   Definition

We define an *extremely dilute solution* as one in which

$$\Sigma_s \, x_s \ll 1.$$

We see then that the property of *extreme* diluteness is one depending in no way on the specific physical properties of either solvent or solute species, but only on their relative proportions. How small the x_s must be, in order that $\Sigma_s x_s$ may be neglected compared with unity, depends of course on the accuracy aimed at. For 1 % accuracy one would generally be safe in choosing $\Sigma_s x_s < 10^{-2}$. If the solvent is water, this corresponds to about one half mole of solute in a litre.

If a solution is extremely dilute, then by neglecting $\Sigma_s x_s$ compared with unity, many of the formulae of the preceding two chapters may be replaced by other approximate formulae found more convenient for computational purposes. In this chapter we shall briefly describe such formulae without giving detailed derivations. We stress that this chapter contains nothing new other than certain approximations sometimes found convenient.

§ 8. 02   Composition Scales

Hitherto we have consistently described the relative composition of every solution by the mole fraction x_s of each solute species s defined by

$$x_s = \frac{n_s}{n_1 + \Sigma_s \, n_s}. \qquad (8.02.1)$$

This is the composition scale by means of which the laws of *ideal solutions* and of *ideal dilute solutions* are most conveniently and simply expressed. Provided however a solution is *extremely dilute*, then other scales may be used without significant loss of accuracy and sometimes with some gain of convenience.

The most important of these scales is the *molality* m_s defined by

$$m_s = \frac{n_s}{n_1 \, M_1}. \qquad (8\ 02.2)$$

where M_1 is defined by

$$M_1 = \frac{\text{mass of one mole of solvent}}{1 \text{ Kg.}}. \qquad (8.02.3)$$

Thus $1000 \, M_1$ is the number usually called the *molecular weight* of the solvent and m_s is the number of moles of solute dissolved in 1 Kg. of solvent.

Another scale, used more in the past than in modern work, is the *concentration* c_s defined by

$$c_s = \frac{n_s}{V} \qquad (8.02.4)$$

Concentrations are usually expressed in moles /l., less often in moles/cm^3.

Let us now consider how these composition scales are interrelated. From (1) we deduce

$$\frac{n_s}{n_1} = \frac{x_s}{1 - \Sigma_s\, x_s} \simeq x_s, \qquad (8.02.5)$$

provided the solution is extremely dilute. Comparing (5) with (2), we see that for an extremely dilute solution

$$m_s \simeq \frac{x_s}{M_1}. \qquad (8.02.6)$$

Again according to (1), provided the solution is extremely dilute,

$$\frac{x_s}{V_1} = \frac{n_s}{(n_1 + \Sigma_s\, n_s)\, V_1} \simeq \frac{n_s}{n_1 V_1 + \Sigma_s\, n_s V_s} = \frac{n_s}{V}, \qquad (8.02.7)$$

and comparing (7) with (4) we see that

$$c_s \simeq \frac{x_s}{V_1}. \qquad (8.02.8)$$

§ 8.03 Thermodynamic Properties of Solute

By using the approximations (8.02.6) and (8.02.8) we can express the absolute activity λ_s of a solute species in any of the approximate forms

$$\lambda_s \propto x_s\gamma_s \propto m_s\gamma_s \propto c_s\gamma_s, \qquad \text{(const. } T\text{)}, \qquad (8.03.1)$$

where γ_s denotes the activity coefficient of the species s.

Correspondingly we can express the partial vapour pressure p_s by

$$p_s \propto x_s\gamma_s \propto m_s\gamma_s \propto c_s\gamma_s, \qquad \text{(const. } T\text{)}. \qquad (8.03.2)$$

From (1) or (2) one can immediately deduce all the equilibrium properties relating to solute species.

In particular for the distribution of a solute s between two solvents α, β we have the alternative relations

$$x_s^\beta\, \gamma_s^\beta / x_s^\alpha\, \gamma_s^\alpha = \text{const.}, \qquad \text{(const. } T\text{)}; \qquad (8.03.3)$$

$$m_s^\beta\, \gamma_s^\beta / m_s^\alpha\, \gamma_s^\alpha = \text{const.}, \qquad \text{(const. } T\text{)}; \qquad (8.03.4)$$

$$c_s^\beta\, \gamma_s^\beta / c_s^\alpha\, \gamma_s^\alpha = \text{const.}, \qquad \text{(const. } T\text{)}. \qquad (8.03.5)$$

For homogeneous chemical equilibrium, we have using the notation defined in § 7.01

$$\Pi\,(x\gamma) = K_x(T), \qquad (8.03.6)$$

$$\Pi\,(m\gamma) = K_m(T), \qquad (8.03.7)$$

$$\Pi\,(c\gamma) = K_c(T), \qquad (8.03.8)$$

where K_x is defined in § 7.17, while K_m, K_c are owing to (8.02.6), (8.02.8) given respectively by

$$K_m = K_x (M_1)^{\Sigma \nu_A - \Sigma \nu_B}, \qquad (8.03.9)$$

$$K_c = K_x (V_1)^{\Sigma \nu_A - \Sigma \nu_B}. \qquad (8.03.10)$$

We recall that $\Sigma \nu_A - \Sigma \nu_B$ is the decrease in the number of moles when the process

$$\Sigma \nu_A A \rightarrow \Sigma \nu_B B \qquad (8.03.11)$$

takes place.

According to (7.18.4) the dependence of K_x on the temperature is given by

$$\frac{d \log K_x}{dT} = \frac{\triangle H^I}{RT^2}, \qquad (8.03.12)$$

where $\triangle H^I$ denotes the heat of reaction at infinite dilution in the given solvent. Comparing (9) with (12), since M_1 is independent of the temperature, we have

$$\frac{d \log K_m}{dT} = \frac{\triangle H^I}{RT^2}. \qquad (8.03.13)$$

On the other hand, comparing (10) with (12), we obtain

$$\frac{d \log K_c}{dT} = \frac{\triangle H^I}{RT^2} + (\Sigma \nu_A - \Sigma \nu_B) a_1, \qquad (8.03.14)$$

where a_1 is the coefficient of thermal expansion of the solvent. The term in a_1 is often neglected, not always justifiably.

We need scarcely remind the reader that if the *extremely dilute* solution is also *ideal dilute* then all the activity coefficients γ_s become equal to unity.

§ 8.04   Thermodynamic Properties of Solvent

The alternative forms for the thermodynamic properties of the solute species in extremely dilute solutions are neither more nor less complicated than the original form for solutions not extremely dilute. We shall see that the alternative formulae for the equilibrium properties of the solvent can on the contrary be given simpler forms than those for solutions not extremely dilute.

We recall formula (6.34.2) defining the osmotic coefficient g_1 of the solvent

$$\log \frac{\lambda_1}{\lambda_1^0} = \log \frac{p_1}{p_1^0} = g_1 \log (1 - \Sigma_s x_s). \qquad (8.04.1)$$

Expanding the last logarithm and neglecting small terms of the second order in $\Sigma_s x_s$, we obtain

$$\log \frac{\lambda_1}{\lambda_1^0} = \log \frac{p_1}{p_1^0} = -g_1 \Sigma_s x_s. \qquad (8.04.2)$$

We can also expand the other logarithms, obtaining the alternative relation

$$\frac{\lambda_1^0 - \lambda_1}{\lambda_1^0} = \frac{p_1^0 - p_1}{p_1^0} = g_1 \, \Sigma_s \, x_s. \tag{8.04.3}$$

Formula (3) applied to a solution containing only one solute has a simple graphical interpretation. In Fig. 6.1 if the solution with 0.2 mole fraction of alcohol could be regarded as extremely dilute, then g_1 would be equal to the ratio ED/EC and $1 - g_1$ to the ratio DC/EC. Apart from this geometrical interpretation formula (3) has no advantage over (2). We shall accordingly concentrate our attention on (2).

Substituting (8.02.6) and (8.02.8) in turn into (2), we obtain

$$\log \frac{\lambda_1^0}{\lambda_1} = \log \frac{p_1^0}{p_1} = g_1 \, M_1 \, \Sigma_s \, m_s = g_1 \, V_1 \, \Sigma_s \, c_s. \tag{8.04.4}$$

We shall use (4) to describe the several equilibrium properties relating to the solvent.

§ 8.05 Freezing-Point and Boiling-Point

We recall formulae (6.17.1) and (6.17.2) relating the freezing-point T of a solution to the freezing-point T^0 of the pure solvent

$$\log \frac{\lambda_1^0 (T)}{\lambda_1 (T)} = \log \frac{p_1^0 (T)}{p_1 (T)} = \frac{[\Delta_f H_1^0]}{R} \left(\frac{1}{T} - \frac{1}{T^0} \right). \tag{8.05.1}$$

Substituting (8.04.4) into (1) we obtain

$$g_1 \, \Sigma_s \, m_s = \frac{[\Delta_f H_1^0]}{M_1 \, R} \left(\frac{1}{T} - \frac{1}{T^0} \right), \tag{8.05.2}$$

$$g_1 \, \Sigma_s \, c_s = \frac{[\Delta_f H_1^0]}{V_1 \, R} \left(\frac{1}{T} - \frac{1}{T^0} \right), \tag{8.05.3}$$

where $[\Delta_f H_1^0]$ denotes the value of the molar heat of fusion $\Delta_f H_1^0$ of the pure solvent averaged over the reciprocal temperature range $1/T^0$ to $1/T$. In both (2) and (3) g_1 has the value relating to the freezing-point of the solution.

For the relation between the boiling-point T of an extremely dilute solution of involatile solutes and the boiling-point T^0 of the pure solvent, we obtain similarly by substituting (8.04.4) into (6.18.1) or (6.18.2)

$$g_1 \, \Sigma_s \, m_s = \frac{[\Delta_e H_1^0]}{M_1 \, R} \left(\frac{1}{T^0} - \frac{1}{T} \right), \tag{8.05.4}$$

$$g_1 \, \Sigma_s \, c_s = \frac{[\Delta_e H_1^0]}{V_1 \, R} \left(\frac{1}{T^0} - \frac{1}{T} \right), \tag{8.05.5}$$

where $[\Delta_e H_1^0]$ denotes the value of the molar heat of evaporation $\Delta_e H_1^0$ of the pure solvent averaged over the reciprocal temperature range $1/T$ to $1/T^0$. In both (4) and (5) g_1 has the value relating to the boiling-point of the solution.

In many extremely dilute solutions $(T-T^0)/T^0$ is so small that in the formulae of this section $[\Delta_f H_1^0]$ may often be replaced by $\Delta_f H_1^0$ and $[\Delta_e H_1^0]$ by $\Delta_e H_1^0$. The resultant simplification is, however, trivial.

§ 8.06 Osmotic Pressure

We recall formula (6.19.1) for the osmotic pressure Π, namely

$$\frac{\Pi [V_1]}{RT} = \log \frac{p_1^0 (P)}{p_1 (P)}. \tag{8.06.1}$$

Substituting from (8.04.4) into (1) and, neglecting the unimportant distinction between $[V_1]$ and V_1, we obtain

$$\Pi = g_1 RT \frac{M_1}{V_1} \Sigma_s m_s \simeq g_1 RT \Sigma_s c_s. \tag{8.06.2}$$

§ 8.07 Relation Between Osmotic Coefficient and Activity Coefficients

We recall the relation (6.46.1) between the osmotic coefficient g_1 of the solvent and the activity coefficient γ_s of the solute species

$$(1-\Sigma_s x_s) \log (1-\Sigma_s x_s) Dg_1 + (1-g_1) \Sigma_s dx_s + \Sigma_s x_s D \log \gamma_s = 0. \tag{8.07.1}$$

Expanding the first logarithm and neglecting small terms of the order x_s^2 we obtain

$$-\Sigma_s x_s Dg_1 + (1-g_1) \Sigma_s dx_s + \Sigma_s x_s D \log \gamma_s = 0. \tag{8.07.2}$$

Using (8.02.6) and (8.02.8), we have to the same degree of accuracy

$$-\Sigma_s m_s Dg_1 + (1-g_1) \Sigma_s dm_s + \Sigma_s m_s D \log \gamma_s = 0, \tag{8.07.3}$$

$$-\Sigma_s c_s \, Dg_1 + (1-g_1) \Sigma_s dc_s + \Sigma_s c_s \, D \log \gamma_s = 0. \tag{8.07.4}$$

For the reasons explained in § 6.44 formulae (2), (3), (4) should, except for solutions containing only one solute, not be used to determine one of the quantities g_1, γ_s from empirically proposed expressions for the remainder, but should rather be used as a check on formulae for g_1, γ_s obtained by differentiation of a formula for $G(x_s)$.

In the case of only a single solute (3) and (4) reduce to

$$D \log \gamma_s = Dg - (1-g) \, d \log m_s$$
$$= Dg - (1-g) \, d \log c_s, \tag{8.07.5}$$

where we have dropped the subscript 1 from g_1. This may be written in the integrated form

$$-\log \gamma_s = (1-g) + \int_0^{m_s} (1-g) \, d \log m_s$$

$$= (1-g) + \int_0^{c_s} (1-g) \, d \log c_s. \tag{8.07.6}$$

As a simple example of the use of (6), suppose that, dropping the subscript from m_s,

$$1 - g = a \, m^r, \qquad (a, r \text{ const.}). \qquad (8.07.7)$$

Substituting (7) into (6) and evaluating the integral, we find

$$-\log \gamma_s = \left(1 + \frac{1}{r}\right) a \, m^r = \left(1 + \frac{1}{r}\right)(1 - g). \qquad (8.07.8)$$

In particular if

$$1 - g = a \, m, \qquad (a \text{ const.}), \qquad (8.07.9)$$

it follows that

$$-\log \gamma_s = 2 \, a \, m = 2 (1 - g). \qquad (8.07.10)$$

§ 8.08 Van 't Hoff's Laws

If a solution is both *ideal dilute* and *extremely dilute*, then all the formulae of this chapter apply with the further simplifications resulting from setting

$$g_1 = 1, \qquad (8.08.1)$$

$$\gamma_s = 1, \qquad (\text{all } s). \qquad (8.08.2)$$

We then obtain the laws of *ideal extremely dilute* solutions. These laws were formulated by van 't Hoff[*], who was aware of their limitations. Unfortunately they have sometimes been misapplied outside their limited range of validity.

§ 8.09 Surface Tension

Formula (6.54.3) for variations of surface tension γ with composition at constant temperature when expressed in molalities takes the form[**]

$$-D\gamma = RT \, \Sigma_s (\Gamma_s - m_s \, M_1 \, \Gamma_1) \, D \log p_s. \qquad (8.09.1)$$

No further simplification is possible, for although $m_s M_1 \ll 1$ in an extremely dilute solution $\Gamma_1 \gg \Gamma_s$ and it would be an error to assume that $m_s \, M_1 \, \Gamma_1$ could be neglected compared with Γ_s.

---

[*] van 't Hoff, *Phil. Mag.* (1888) **26** 81.

[**] There should be no confusion between γ, denoting surface tension and γ_s denoting an activity coefficient.

CHAPTER IX

SOLUTIONS OF ELECTROLYTES

§ 9.01 Characteristics of Strong Electrolytes

When certain substances such as common salt are dissolved in water, the solution has a comparatively high conductivity showing that charged ions must be present. We owe to Arrhenius the suggestion that for these substances, called *strong electrolytes*, the solute is composed largely of the free ions, such as Na^+ and Cl^- in the case of common salt. Study of the optical properties by Bjerrum * led him in 1909 to the conclusion that at least in dilute solutions there are at most very few NaCl molecules and in many such cases the properties of the solution can be accurately accounted for on the assumption that no undissociated molecules are present.

It would be outside the province of this book to discuss whether a dilute solution of a strong electrolyte contains a small fraction of undissociated molecules or none at all. All that matters is that the description of a salt solution as completely dissociated into independent ions, though admittedly an oversimplification, is at least an incomparably better model than one which ignores dissociation into ions. It is in fact a better model than any other of equal simplicity. We shall therefore compare the properties of every real solution of strong electrolytes with an idealized solution containing independent ions.

§ 9.02 Ionic Molality

In accordance with the programme outlined in the previous section, we describe the composition of solutions of electrolytes in terms of the ions, not in terms of the undissociated molecules.

For the sake of simplicity we shall confine ourselves almost entirely to *extremely dilute* solutions and we may therefore, following usual practice, use the *molality scale*. We accordingly describe the composition of a solution containing one or more electrolytes by the molality m_i of each ionic species i. We recall the definition of molality given in § 8.02 for non-electrolytes. The extension to ionic species is immediate. If we define a *gram-ion* as the quantity of an ionic species containing N ions, where N is Avogadro's number defined in § 4.14, then the *molality* m_i of an ionic species i denotes the number of gram-ions in a quantity of solution containing 1 Kg. of solvent.

In a like manner we can define the *concentration* c_i of an ionic species i as the number of gram-ions contained in unit volume, usually one litre of

---

* Bjerrum, *Proc. 7th Int. Cong. Pure and Applied Chem.* (London 1909) Sect. 10 p. 58; *Zeit. Elektrochem.* (1918) **24** 321.

solution. As long as one is working at strictly constant temperature, there is little to choose between the *molality* m_i and the *concentration* c_i scales, but if the temperature of a given solution is changed then m_i remains unaltered, but c_i is altered through thermal expansion. In this respect the *molality* scale is advantageous and we shall accordingly use it in preference to the *concentration* scale.

§ 9.03 Electrical Neutrality

When we carry out our intention of describing the properties of electrolyte solutions in terms of the ionic species, we shall find that most of the formulae have a close resemblance to those for non-electrolytes. There is however one important difference, namely that the molalities m_i of all the ionic species are not independent because the solution as a whole is electrically neutral. We now proceed to express this condition mathematically.

We use the symbol z to denote the charge on an ion measured in units of the charge of a proton, so that for example:

$$\text{In} \qquad \begin{aligned} \text{Na}^+ &\qquad z = 1, \\ \text{Ba}^{++} &\qquad z = 2, \\ \text{La}^{+++} &\qquad z = 3, \\ \text{Cl}^- &\qquad z = -1, \\ \text{SO}_4^{--} &\qquad z = -2, \\ \text{PO}_4^{---} &\qquad z = -3, \\ \text{Fe}\,\text{C}_6\text{N}_6^{----} &\qquad z = -4. \end{aligned}$$

We call z the *electrovalency* of the ion.

If then m_i denotes the molality of the ionic species i having an electrovalency z_i, the condition of *electrical neutrality* of the solution may be written

$$\Sigma_i \, z_i \, m_i = 0. \tag{9.03.1}$$

Alternatively if we use the subscript $+$ to denote positively charged ions or *cations* and $-$ to denote negatively charged ions or *anions*, then we may write (1) in the alternative form

$$\Sigma_+ \, z_+ \, m_+ = \Sigma_- \, |z_-| \, m_-. \tag{9.03.2}$$

wherein $|z_-| = -z_-$ is a positive integer.

Owing to the condition of *electrical neutrality* (1) or (2), a solution containing G ionic species, as well as the solvent, has G, not $G+1$, independent components.

§ 9.04 Ionic Absolute Activities

Since most equilibrium conditions are expressible in a general, yet convenient, form in terms of absolute activities we shall make continual use of the absolute activity λ_i of each ionic species i. By following this procedure we shall in fact obtain formulae closely resembling those already obtained for non-electrolytes. There is however one important difference. We saw in the previous section that if there are G ionic species i and so G ionic molalities m_i, then only $G-1$ are independent. There must clearly be some analogous or related property of the set of G quantities λ_i. We shall now discover this property by considering the physical significance of the λ_i's, first in particular cases and then in general.

Let us consider the distribution of NaCl between two phases, of which at least one α is a solution; the other β may be a solution in a different solvent or the solid phase. We shall now determine the equilibrium condition for NaCl *ab initio* on the same lines as § 1.45 but in terms of Na+ and Cl-. We assume the temperature, but not necessarily the pressure, to be the same in the two phases. Suppose now a small quantity dn_{Na^+} of Na+ and a small quantity dn_{Cl^-} of Cl- to pass from the phase α to the phase β, the temperature of the whole system being kept constant. Then the increase in the free energy F is given by

$$dF = -P^\alpha dV^\alpha - \mu^\alpha_{Na^+}\, dn_{Na^+} - \mu^\alpha_{Cl^-}\, dn_{Cl^-}$$
$$\qquad - P^\beta dV^\beta + \mu^\beta_{Na^+}\, dn_{Na^+} + \mu^\beta_{Cl^-}\, dn_{Cl^-}. \qquad (9.04.1)$$

Following an argument analogous to that of § 1.45, if the two phases are in mutual equilibrium with respect to the NaCl, the process being considered must be reversible and so dF must be equal to the work done on the system. Thus

$$dF = -P^\alpha dV^\alpha - P^\beta dV^\beta. \qquad (9.04.2)$$

Subtracting (2) from (1), we obtain

$$(\mu^\beta_{Na^+} - \mu^\alpha_{Na^+})\, dn_{Na^+} + (\mu^\beta_{Cl^-} - \mu^\alpha_{Cl^-})\, dn_{Cl^-} = 0. \qquad (9.04.3)$$

The condition of electrical neutrality (9.03.2) in this case takes the simple form

$$dn_{Na^+} = dn_{Cl^-} = dn. \qquad (9.04.4)$$

Substituting (4) into (3), we have

$$(\mu^\beta_{Na^+} - \mu^\alpha_{Na^+} + \mu^\beta_{Cl^-} - \mu^\alpha_{Cl^-})\, dn = 0. \qquad (9.04.5)$$

or dividing by dn

$$\mu^\alpha_{Na^+} + \mu^\alpha_{Cl^-} = \mu^\beta_{Na^+} + \mu^\beta_{Cl^-}. \qquad (9.04.6)$$

Since according to the definition of λ_i

$$\mu_i = RT \log \lambda_i, \qquad (9.04.7)$$

we may rewrite (5) as

$$\log \lambda^\alpha_{Na^+} + \log \lambda^\alpha_{Cl^-} = \log \lambda^\beta_{Na^+} + \log \lambda^\beta_{Cl^-} \qquad (9.04.8)$$

or

$$\lambda_{Na^+}^{\alpha} \cdot \lambda_{Cl^-}^{\alpha} = \lambda_{Na^+}^{\beta} \cdot \lambda_{Cl^-}^{\beta} . \qquad (9.04.9)$$

We thus see that any phase equilibrium relating to NaCl involves only the sum

$$\mu_{Na^+} + \mu_{Cl^-} , \qquad (9.04.10)$$

or the product

$$\lambda_{Na^+} \cdot \lambda_{Cl^-} . \qquad (9.04.11)$$

In the same way an equilibrium relating to $BaCl_2$ would involve only the sum

$$\mu_{Ba^{++}} + 2\mu_{Cl^-} \qquad (9.04.12)$$

or the product

$$\lambda_{Ba^{++}} \cdot \lambda_{Cl^-}^2 ; \qquad (9.04.13)$$

and an equilibrium relating to $LaCl_3$ only the sum

$$\mu_{La^{+++}} + 3\mu_{Cl^-} , \qquad (9.04.14)$$

or the product

$$\lambda_{La^{+++}} \cdot \lambda_{Cl^-}^3 , \qquad (9.04.15)$$

and so on.

But it might be asked what about an equilibrium relating to the chloride ion by itself? The answer is that the transfer of a chloride ion, or any other ion alone, from one phase to another involves a transfer of electrical charge, that is to say a flow of current. We shall consider such processes in detail in the following chapter on *Electrochemical Systems*. Meanwhile as long as we exclude processes involving a flow of current, and in this chapter we do so, we shall only meet the μ_i's and λ_i's in combinations corresponding to zero net electric charge. We can express this mathematically by stating that the only linear combinations

$$\Sigma_i \nu_i \mu_i , \qquad (9.04.16)$$

and the only products

$$\Pi_i (\lambda_i)^{\nu_i} , \qquad (9.04.17)$$

which will occur will be those in which the ν_i's satisfy the relation

$$\Sigma_i \nu_i z_i = 0 . \qquad (9.04.18)$$

This means that, apart from electrochemical flow of current, with which we are not concerned in this chapter, we could in each phase assign an arbitrary value to the absolute activity λ_i of one ionic species, for instance the chloride ion. The λ_i's of the remaining ions would then be unambiguously determined. Nothing is however gained by thus arbitrarily fixing the values of the λ_i's. We can just as well leave the arbitrary factor in the λ_i's undetermined, knowing that only those combinations (17) of the λ_i's satisfying (18) will ever occur and that in these combinations the arbitrary factors cancel.

§ 9.05   Ideal and Non-Ideal Solutions

It would be logical, as in the case of non-electrolytes, first to define an ideal solution of electrolytes and thereafter to compare the properties of real solutions with ideal solutions. Since however no solution of a strong electrolyte is even approximately ideal even at the highest dilution at which accurate measurements can be made, there seems no point in devoting space to ideal solutions. We therefore pass straight to real solutions, of which ideal solutions are an idealized limiting case.

§ 9.06   Osmotic Coefficient of the Solvent

We can define the *osmotic coefficient* g_1 of the solvent in complete analogy with the case where the solute species are non-electrolytes by formula (8.04.1) merely replacing x_s by x_i the mole fraction of an ionic species. Since however we are confining ourselves to extremely dilute solutions and we use the molality scale, we use instead formula (8.04.4). For electrolyte solutions (8.04.4) becomes, when we drop the subscript 1 from g_1.

$$\log \frac{\lambda_1^0}{\lambda_1} = \log \frac{p_1^0}{p_1} = g\, M_1\, \Sigma_i\, m_i. \tag{9.06.1}$$

We recall that, according to (8.02.3), M_1 is defined by

$$M_1 = \frac{\text{mass of one mole of solvent}}{1\ \text{Kg.}}. \tag{9.06.2}$$

We shall use (1) to describe the several equilibrium properties of the solvent. Before doing so we however point out that if the solution contains non-electrolytes as well as electrolytes, the former may be included formally inside the summation Σ_i. We merely treat an electrically uncharged species as if it were an ion with $z = 0$.

§ 9.07   Freezing-Point and Boiling-Point

Formula (8.05.2) relating the freezing-point T of an extremely dilute solution to the freezing-point T^0 of the pure solvent, becomes

$$g\, \Sigma_i\, m_i = \frac{[\triangle_f H_i^0]}{M_1\, R} \left(\frac{1}{T} - \frac{1}{T^0} \right). \tag{9.07.1}$$

where $[\triangle_f H_1^0]$ denotes the value of the molar heat of fusion $\triangle_f H_1^0$ of the pure solvent averaged over the reciprocal temperature range $1/T^0$ to $1/T$. In (1) the value of g is that at the freezing-point of the solution.

The relation (8.05.4) between the boiling-point T of an extremely dilute solution of involatile solutes and the boiling-point T^0 of the pure solvent becomes

$$g \, \Sigma_i \, m_i = \frac{[\triangle_e H_1^0]}{M_1 \, R} \left(\frac{1}{T^0} - \frac{1}{T} \right), \qquad (9.07.2)$$

where $[\triangle_e H_1^0]$ denotes the value of the molar heat of evaporation $\triangle_e H_1^0$ of the pure solvent averaged over the reciprocal temperature range $1/T$ to $1/T^0$. In (2) the value of g is that at the boiling-point of the solution.

§ 9.08 Osmotic Pressure

Formula (8.06.2) for the osmotic pressure Π becomes for a solution of electrolytes

$$\Pi = g \, RT \, \frac{M_1}{V_1} \, \Sigma_i \, m_i \simeq g \, R \, T \, \Sigma_i \, c_i. \qquad (9.08.1)$$

§ 9.09 Ionic Activity Coefficients

In analogy with (8.03.1) the activity coefficient γ_i of the ionic species i in an extremely dilute solution is related to the absolute activity λ_i by

$$\lambda_i \propto m_i \, \gamma_i, \qquad \text{(const. } T), \qquad (9.09.1)$$

$$\gamma_i \to 1 \quad \text{as} \quad \Sigma_i \, m_i \to 0. \qquad (9.09.2)$$

The proportionality constant in (1) depends on the solvent and the temperature. Furthermore, as explained in § 9.10 the proportionality constant *in each solution* may be assigned an arbitrary value for any one ionic species; the values for the remaining ionic species are then determined.

We may then formally replace (1) by

$$\lambda_i = l_i \, m_i \, \gamma_i, \qquad (9.09.3)$$

where λ_i contains a partly undetermined factor, which however cancels in all applications.

§ 9.10 Mean Activity Coefficient of Electrolyte

Let us consider an electrolyte which consists of ν_+ cations R of electrovalency z_+ and ν_- anions X of electrovalency z_- so that according to the condition of *electrical neutrality*

$$\nu_+ z_+ + \nu_- z_- = 0.$$

The absolute activity $\lambda_{R,X}$ of the electrolyte $R_{\nu+} X_{\nu-}$ is then related to the absolute activities of the two ions by

$$\lambda_{R,X} = \lambda_R^{\nu_+} \lambda_X^{\nu_-}. \qquad (9.10.1)$$

Substituting (9.09.3) into (1), we have

$$\lambda_{R,X} = l_R^{\nu_+} l_X^{\nu_-} m_R^{\nu_+} m_X^{\nu_-} \gamma_R^{\nu_+} \gamma_X^{\nu_-}. \qquad (9.10.2)$$

and in the limit of infinite dilution

$$\lambda_{R,X} \to l_R^{\nu_+} l_X^{\nu_-} m_R^{\nu_+} m_X^{\nu_-} \quad \text{as } \Sigma_i m_i \to 0. \qquad (9.\,10.\,3)$$

Since $\lambda_{R,X}$ and m_R and m_X are all well defined quantities it is clear from (3) that in spite of the indefiniteness in l_R and l_X separately, the product $l_R^{\nu_+} l_X^{\nu_-}$ is completely defined. Returning now to (2) since $\lambda_{R,X}$ and m_R and m_X and, as we have just seen, the product $l_R^{\nu_+} l_X^{\nu_-}$ are all well-defined, it follows that the product $\gamma_R^{\nu_+} \gamma_X^{\nu_-}$ is also well defined.

We now introduce a quantity $\gamma_{R,X}$, called the *mean activity coefficient* of the electrolyte, related to γ_R and γ_X by

$$\gamma_{R,X}^{\nu_+ + \nu_-} = \gamma_R^{\nu_+} \gamma_X^{\nu_-}. \qquad (9.\,10.\,4)$$

Substituting (4) into (2), we have

$$\lambda_{R,X} = l_R^{\nu_+} l_X^{\nu_+} m_R^{\nu_+} m_X^{\nu_-} \gamma_{R,X}^{\nu_+ + \nu_-}. \qquad (9.\,10.\,5)$$

Since $\gamma_{R,X}$ is well-defined, while γ_R and γ_X individually are not, it would be wrong to regard (4) as a definition of $\gamma_{R,X}$ in terms of γ_R and γ_X. Nevertheless formula (4) does contain something of physical significance. For let us now consider two cations R, R' and two anions X, X' from which we can form four different electrolytes, for each of which we can write a relation of the form (4). What these relations together tell us is that the four mean activity coefficients are not independent. We can best illustrate the point by a simple example. Let us consider the two cations Na^+, K^+ and the two anions Cl^-, NO_3^-. Then we have formally

$$\gamma_{Na,Cl}^2 = \gamma_{Na^+} \gamma_{Cl^-}, \qquad (9.\,10.\,6)$$

$$\gamma_{K,Cl}^2 = \gamma_{K^+} \gamma_{Cl^-}, \qquad (9.\,10.\,7)$$

$$\gamma_{Na,NO_3}^2 = \gamma_{Na^+} \gamma_{NO_3^-}, \qquad (9.\,10.\,8)$$

$$\gamma_{K,NO_3}^2 = \gamma_{K^+} \gamma_{NO_3^-}. \qquad (9.\,10.\,9)$$

In a given solution each of the quantities on the left of formulae (6) to (9) is well defined, while the individual factors on the right are not. But these four formulae together lead to the physically significant result

$$\frac{\gamma_{Na,Cl}}{\gamma_{K,Cl}} = \frac{\gamma_{Na,NO_3}}{\gamma_{K,NO_3}}. \qquad (9.\,10.\,10)$$

§ 9.11   Temperature Dependence

Just as for non-ionic species, we have according to (6.03.12)

$$\frac{\partial \log \lambda_i}{\partial T} = -\frac{H_i}{RT^2}, \qquad (9.\,11.\,1)$$

so that according to (9. 09. 3)

$$\frac{\partial \log (l_i \gamma_i)}{\partial T} = - \frac{H_i}{RT^2}. \qquad (9.11.2)$$

Proceeding to the limit of infinite dilution (2) becomes

$$\frac{\partial \log l_i}{\partial T} = - \frac{H_i^I}{RT^2}, \qquad (9.11.3)$$

where the superscript I denotes the limiting value when $\Sigma_i \, m_i \to 0$. Now subtracting (3) from (2) we find

$$\frac{\partial \log \gamma_i}{\partial T} = - \frac{H_i - H_i^I}{RT^2}. \qquad (9.11.4)$$

For reasons previously given, only linear combinations of these formulae will occur of the type defined by (9. 04. 18). In particular for an electrolyte composed of ν_+ cations R and ν_- anions X, we have according to (1)

$$\frac{\partial \log \lambda_{R,X}}{\partial T} = - \frac{H_{R,X}}{RT^2} \qquad (9.11.5)$$

where

$$H_{R,X} = \nu_+ H_R + \nu_- H_X \qquad (9.11.6)$$

is the *partial molar heat function* of the electrolyte. Similarly from (4) we deduce

$$(\nu^+ + \nu_-) \frac{\partial \log \gamma_{R,X}}{\partial T} = - \frac{H_{R,X} - H_{R,X}^I}{RT^2}, \qquad (9.11.7)$$

where $H_{R\,X}^I$ denotes the limiting value of $H_{R,X}$ as $\Sigma_i \, m_i \to 0$.

§ 9. 12 Distribution of Electrolyte Between Two Solvents

The equilibrium condition for the distribution of an electrolyte consisting of ν_+ cations R and ν_- anions X between two solvents α and β can be written either in terms of the electrolytes as

$$\lambda_{R,X}^{\alpha} = \lambda_{R,X}^{\beta} \qquad (9.12.1)$$

or in terms of the ions as

$$(\lambda_R^{\alpha})^{\nu+} (\lambda_X^{\alpha})^{\nu-} = (\lambda_R^{\beta})^{\nu+} (\lambda_X^{\beta})^{\nu-}. \qquad (9.12.2)$$

According to (9. 10. 1) the two conditions are equivalent. Substituting (9. 10. 5) into (1), we obtain

$$\frac{[m_R^{\nu+} m_X^{\nu-} \gamma_{R,X}^{\nu+ + \nu-}]^{\beta}}{[m_R^{\nu+} m_X^{\nu-} \gamma_{R,X}^{\nu+ + \nu-}]^{\alpha}} = \frac{[l_R^{\nu+} l_X^{\nu-}]^{\alpha}}{[l_R^{\nu+} l_X^{\nu-}]^{\beta}}, \qquad (9.12.3)$$

where the superscripts α, β denote that all the quantities within the brackets are given their values in the solutions α, β respectively. If we denote the right side of (3) by l for brevity, then according to (9.11.3) we have

$$\frac{\partial \log l}{\partial T} = \frac{H_{R,X}^{I\beta} - H_{R,X}^{I\alpha}}{RT^2} \tag{9.12.4}$$

We notice that the numerator of the right side is the limiting value as $\Sigma_i \, m_i \to 0$ of the *partial molar heat of transfer of the electrolyte* from the solvent α to the solvent β.

§ 9.13 Solubility Product

For the equilibrium between the solid electrolyte composed of the ions R, X and a solution containing R, X and possibly other electrolytes, we have.

$$\lambda_{R,X} = \lambda_{R,X}^S, \tag{9.13.1}$$

where we denote the solid phase by the superscript S and the solution by no superscript.

Substituting from (9.10.5) into (1), we obtain

$$m_R^{\nu_+} m_X^{\nu_-} \gamma_{R,X}^{\nu_+ + \nu_-} = P_{R,X}, \tag{9.13.2}$$

where $P_{R,X}$ is called the *solubility product* of the electrolyte and is given by

$$P_{R,X} = \frac{\bar{\lambda}_{R,X}^S}{l_R^{\nu_+} \, l_X^{\nu_-}}. \tag{9.13.3}$$

Since

$$\frac{\partial \log \lambda_{R,X}^S}{\partial T} = -\frac{H_{R,X}^S}{RT^2}. \tag{9.13.4}$$

we have, using this and (9.11.3) in (3),

$$\frac{\partial \log P_{R,X}}{\partial T} = \frac{H_{R,X}^I - H_{R,X}^S}{RT^2}. \tag{9.13.5}$$

We notice that the numerator in (5) is the limiting value as $\Sigma_i \, m^l \to 0$ of the *heat of solution of the solid electrolyte* in the given solvent.

§ 9.14 Chemical Reactions

If we consider the chemical reaction

$$\Sigma \nu_A \, A \to \Sigma \nu_B \, B, \tag{9.14.1}$$

where some or all of the species A, B may be ionic, the condition of equilibrium, in the notation defined in § 7.01, is according to (8.03.7)

$$\Pi (m_i \, \gamma_i) = K_m (T). \tag{9.14.2}$$

The fact that some or all of the reacting species may be ions has no effect on the form of (2). It is however of interest to notice that, owing to the conservation of net electric charge, it follows from (1) that

$$\Sigma \nu_A z_A = \Sigma \nu_B z_B, \tag{9.14.3}$$

and so

$$\Pi(\gamma_i) \equiv \frac{\Pi(\gamma_B)^{\nu_B}}{\Pi(\gamma_A)^{\nu_A}} \tag{9.14.4}$$

conforms to the type of product (9.04.17) which is physically well-defined. We shall illustrate the point by a simple example. Consider the reaction

$$2\,\text{Fe}^{+++} + \text{Sn}^{++} \rightarrow 2\,\text{Fe}^{++} + \text{Sn}^{++++}. \tag{9.14.5}$$

According to (2) the equilibrium condition is

$$\frac{m^2_{\text{Fe}^{++}}\, m_{\text{Sn}^{++++}}}{m^2_{\text{Fe}^{+++}}\, m_{\text{Sn}^{++}}} \frac{\gamma^2_{\text{Fe}^{++}}\, \gamma_{\text{Sn}^{+++}}}{\gamma^2_{\text{Fe}^{+++}}\, \gamma_{\text{Sn}^{++}}} = K_m. \tag{9.14.6}$$

wherein the *activity coefficients product* is well-defined. It can in fact be expressed in terms of mean activity coefficients as follows

$$\frac{\gamma^2_{\text{Fe}^{++}}\, \gamma_{\text{Sn}^{++++}}}{\gamma^2_{\text{Fe}^{+++}}\, \gamma_{\text{Sn}^{++}}} = \frac{\gamma^2_{\text{Fe}^{++}}\, \gamma_{\text{Sn}^{++++}}\, \gamma^8_{\text{Cl}^-}}{\gamma^2_{\text{Fe}^{+++}}\, \gamma_{\text{Sn}^{++}}\, \gamma^8_{\text{Cl}^-}} = \frac{\gamma^6_{\text{Fe}^{++},\text{Cl}^-}\, \gamma^5_{\text{Sn}^{++++},\text{Cl}^-}}{\gamma^8_{\text{Fe}^{+++},\text{Cl}^-}\, \gamma^3_{\text{Sn}^{++},\text{Cl}^-}}. \tag{9.14.7}$$

For the temperature dependence of K_m we have (8.03.13)

$$\frac{d \log K_m}{dT} = \frac{\Delta H^I}{RT^2}. \tag{9.14.8}$$

where ΔH^I denotes the *heat of reaction at infinite dilution*.

§ 9.15   Gibbs-Duhem Relation for Electrolyte Solutions

For any phase whatever we have the Gibbs–Duhem relation (1.38.2). For a solution of electrolytes in a solvent 1 this becomes

$$S\,dT - V\,dP + n_1\,d\mu_1 + \Sigma_i\, n_i\,d\mu_i = 0, \tag{9.15.1}$$

or considering variations of composition at constant temperature and pressure

$$n_1 D\mu_1 + \Sigma_i\, n_i D\mu_i = 0 \tag{9.15.2}$$

in the notation described in § 6.05. Recalling the definition (4.15.2) of the absolute activities λ_i

$$\mu_i = RT \log \lambda_i, \tag{9.15.3}$$

we may replace (2) by

$$n_1 D \log \lambda_1 + \Sigma_i\, n_i D \log \lambda_i = 0. \tag{9.15.4}$$

20

According to the definition of molality given in § 8.02 and extended to ions in § 9.02, we have

$$m_i = n_i/n_1 M_1. \tag{9.15.5}$$

If then we divide (2) and (4) throughout by $n_1 M_1$ and use (5), we obtain

$$\frac{1}{M_1} D\mu_1 + \Sigma_i m_i D\mu_i = 0. \tag{9.15.6}$$

$$\frac{1}{M_1} D \log \lambda_1 + \Sigma_i m_i D \log \lambda_i = 0. \tag{9.15.7}$$

As explained in § 9.03 all variations of composition of an electrolyte solution are subject to the condition of electrical neutrality

$$\Sigma_i z_i m_i = 0, \tag{9.15.8}$$

so that

$$\Sigma_i z_i dm_i = 0. \tag{9.15.9}$$

The variations in formulae (1), (2), (4), (6), (7) are all subject to the condition (9); but for variations satisfying (9) these formulae hold just as well for electrolyte solutions as for any other solutions.

We now recall the definition of the osmotic coefficient g by (9.06.1)

$$\log \frac{\lambda_1^0}{\lambda_1} = g M_1 \Sigma_i m_i. \tag{9.15.10}$$

and the definition of ionic activity coefficients γ_i by (9.09.1)

$$\lambda_i \propto m_i \gamma_i. \tag{9.15.11}$$

Differentiating (10) with respect to changes of composition at constant temperature, we obtain

$$D \log \lambda_1 = -g M_1 \Sigma_i Dm_i - M_1 \Sigma_i m_i Dg. \tag{9.15.12}$$

Taking logarithms of (11) and similarly differentiating we obtain

$$D \log \lambda_i = \frac{Dm_i}{m_i} + D \log \gamma_i. \tag{9.15.13}$$

Now substituting (12) and (13) into (7), we obtain

$$-g \Sigma_i Dm_i - \Sigma_i m_i Dg + \Sigma_i Dm_i + \Sigma_i m_i D \log \gamma_i = 0, \tag{9.15.14}$$

or

$$-\Sigma_i m_i Dg + (1-g) \Sigma_i Dm_i + \Sigma_i m_i D \log \gamma_i = 0, \tag{9.15.15}$$

of precisely the same form as formula (8.07.3).

In particular for a solution of a single electrolyte having ν_+ cations R and ν_- anions X, formula (15) becomes

$$-(\nu_+ + \nu_-) m Dg + (1-g)(\nu_+ + \nu_-) Dm$$
$$+ \nu_+ m D \log \gamma_R + \nu_- m D \log \gamma_X = 0. \tag{9.15.16}$$

where m denotes the *molality of the electrolyte* expressed in moles per kilogram of solvent. The mean activity coefficient $\gamma_{R,X}$ of the electrolyte is related to the ionic activity coefficients γ_R and γ_X by (9.10.4)

$$\gamma_{R,X}^{\nu_+ + \nu_-} = \gamma_R^{\nu_+} \gamma_X^{\nu_-}. \qquad (9.15.17)$$

We now divide (16) throughout by $(\nu_+ + \nu_-) m$ and use (17), obtaining

$$-D \log \gamma_{R,X} = - Dg + (1-g) D \log m, \qquad (9.15.18)$$

or integrating from 0 to m

$$-\log \gamma_{R,X} = (1-g) + \int_0^m (1-g) \, d \log m. \qquad (9.15.19)$$

Just as in a solution of a single solute non-electrolyte, formula (18) or (19) may be used to determine either of the quantities γ or g, if the other is known as a function of composition at all molalities less than m. On the other hand the more general relation (15) should not be used in this manner, but rather as a check on the self-consistency of assumed formulae for g and the γ_i's. For it is also necessary for the γ_i's to satisfy the relations of the type

$$\frac{\partial \log \gamma_i}{\partial m_k} = \frac{\partial \log \gamma_k}{\partial m_i} \qquad (9.15.20)$$

As an example of (19), suppose

$$1 - g = a m^r, \qquad (a, r \text{ constants}). \qquad (9.15.21)$$

Then substituting (21) into (19) we obtain

$$-\log \gamma_{R,X} = \left(1 + \frac{1}{r}\right) a m^r = \left(1 + \frac{1}{r}\right) (1-g). \qquad (9.15.22)$$

§ 9.16 Electrolyte Solutions Not Extremely Dilute

If we define an ideal dilute solution of electrolytes as one in which all γ_i's have the value unity, then putting

$$D \log \gamma_i = 0, \qquad \text{(ideal dilute solution)}, \qquad (9.16.1)$$

in (9.15.15) and dividing by $\Sigma_i m_i$ we obtain

$$Dg = (1-g) D \log \Sigma_i m_i \qquad (9.16.2)$$

The only solution of (2) such that g remains finite as $\Sigma_i m_i \to 0$ is

$$g = 1, \qquad \text{(ideal dilute solution)}, \qquad (9.16.3)$$

Since in § 9.15 we did not make any mathematical approximations, we see then that the two relations obtained by setting $g = 1$ into (9.15.10) and $\gamma_i = 1$ into (9.15.11) namely

$$\log \frac{\lambda_1^0}{\lambda_1} = M_1 \Sigma_i m_i, \qquad \text{(ideal dilute)}, \qquad (9.16.4)$$

$$\lambda_i \propto m_i, \qquad \text{(ideal dilute)} \qquad (9.16.5)$$

together satisfy the Gibbs–Duhem relation exactly. Moreover (5) obviously satisfies the condition (9.15.20). Hence (4) and (5) together form an exactly self-consistent set of formulae which may be taken as defining an *ideal dilute solution of electrolytes,* whether or not extremely dilute. Such a definition is not quite analogous to the definition of an ideal dilute solution of non-electrolytes. The analogous definition would according to (6.27.6) and (6.25.2) be

$$\frac{\lambda_1}{\lambda_1^0} = 1 - \Sigma_i \, x_i, \qquad\qquad \text{(ideal dilute)}, \qquad (9.16.6)$$

$$\lambda_i \propto x_i, \qquad\qquad \text{(ideal dilute)}. \qquad (9.16.7)$$

For extremely dilute solutions, as defined in § 8.01, the pair of formulae (4) and (5) is of course equivalent to the pair (6) and (7). For solutions not extremely dilute they are not equivalent.

For real solutions we can define the osmotic coefficient of the solvent g and the ionic activity coefficients γ_i either in accordance with (4), (5) by

$$\log \frac{\lambda_1^0}{\lambda_1} = g \, M_1 \, \Sigma_i \, m_i. \qquad\qquad (9.16.8)$$

$$\lambda_i \propto m_i \gamma_i. \qquad\qquad (9.16.9)$$

or in accordance with (5), (6) by

$$\log \frac{\lambda_1^0}{\lambda_1} = g \log (1 - \Sigma_i \, x_i). \qquad\qquad (9.16.10)$$

$$\lambda_i \propto x_i \gamma_i. \qquad\qquad (9.16.11)$$

Except for extremely dilute solutions the pair of definitions (8), (9) is not equivalent to the pair (10), (11) and it is important to be clear about the distinction. The pair (8), (9) has certain practical advantages and theoretical disadvantages compared with (10), (11). For this reason g and γ when defined according to (8), (9) may be called the *practical osmotic coefficient* and *practical activity coefficient* while g and γ_i when defined according to (10), (11) may be called the *rational osmotic coefficient* and *rational activity coefficient*. The *practical coefficients* have been more widely used than the *rational*. Both are likely to be used in the future. The harm that can arise from absence of uniformity can be minimized by always clearly stating which definitions are being used.

With this caution we dismiss solutions not extremely dilute and devote the rest of the Chapter mainly to a more detailed consideration of extremely dilute solutions of electrolytes

§ 9 17   Limiting Laws at High Dilutions

It was already realized [*] nearly forty years ago that deviations at high

---

[*] Milner, *Phil. Mag.* (1912) **23** 551.

dilution of electrolyte solutions from ideality due to the long-range electro-static interactions between ions are quite different from the deviations of non-electrolyte solutions.

The distinction can for a single solute be expressed in the form

$$1 - g \propto m \text{ as } m \to 0, \qquad \text{(non-electrolyte);} \qquad (9.17.1)$$

$$1 - g \propto m^r \text{ as } m \to 0, \quad (r < 1), \qquad \text{(electrolyte).} \qquad (9.17.2)$$

This distinction is most strikingly expressed in the form

$$\frac{d(1-g)}{dm} \to \text{finite limit as } m \to 0, \text{ (non-electrolyte);} \qquad (9.17.3)$$

$$\frac{d(1-g)}{dm} \to \infty \text{ as } m \to 0, \qquad \text{(electrolyte),} \qquad (9.17.4)$$

and is shown graphically in Fig. 9.1, which is of historic interest being taken from a paper by Bjerrum * written as early as 1916.

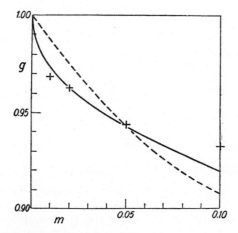

++ Freezing-point measurements.
—— Electrostatic interaction according to Milner.
– – – Incomplete dissociation ignoring electrostatic interaction.
Fig. 9.1.

Milner ** in 1912 had shown by statistical methods that the theoretical value of r is near $\frac{1}{2}$.

Various values of r in (2) were used empirically among which the value $r = \frac{1}{2}$ was used by Brönsted *** in the period around 1922.

Finally in 1923 Debye **** determined by a statistical treatment the theo-retical law valid in the limit $m \to 0$. According to this law $r = \frac{1}{2}$ and the proportionality constant in (2) is also determined by the theory.

*   Bjerrum, *16te Skand. Naturforskermöte* (1916) p. 229.
**   Milner, *Phil. Mag.* (1912) **23** 551.
***   Brönsted, *J. Am. Chem. Soc.* (1922) **44** 938.
**** Debye and Hückel, *Physikal. Zeit.* (1923) **24** 185.

§ 9.18   Limiting Law for Single Electrolyte

For a single electrolyte having ν_+ positive ions with electrovalency z_+ and ν_- negative ions with electrovalency z_-, satisfying the condition of electrical neutrality $\nu_+ z_+ + \nu_- z_- = 0$, Debye's limiting law valid as $m \to 0$ takes the form

$$1 - g = \frac{a}{3} z_+ |z_-| \left(\frac{\nu_+ z_+^2 + \nu_- z_-^2}{2} \right)^{\frac{1}{2}} m^{\frac{1}{2}}. \tag{9.18.1}$$

The coefficient a depends only on the solvent and temperature and is given by

$$\frac{1}{3} a = \left(\frac{2 \pi N \varrho}{9 \, \mathrm{Kg.}} \right)^{\frac{1}{2}} \left(\frac{e^2}{\varepsilon k T} \right)^{\frac{3}{2}}, \tag{9.18.2}$$

where N denotes Avogadro's number, k Boltzmann's constant, e the charge of a proton, ϱ the density of the solvent, and ε the permittivity of the solvent.

For example for water at $0\,°\mathrm{C}$ we have

$$N = 0.6023 \times 10^{24}$$
$$\varrho = 10^{-3} \, \mathrm{Kg./cm^3}$$
$$e = 4.802 \times 10^{-10} \text{ franklin}$$
$$\varepsilon = 88.23 \text{ franklin}^2/\mathrm{erg \; cm.} \quad *$$
$$k = 1.380 \times 10^{-16} \text{ erg/deg.}$$
$$T = 273.16 \text{ deg.}$$

Inserting these values into (2), we obtain

$$\tfrac{1}{3} a = 0.374, \qquad \text{(water at } 0\,°\mathrm{C}). \tag{9.18.3}$$

For the mean activity coefficient of the electrolyte, since (1) is of the form (9.15.21) with $r = \frac{1}{2}$, we may use (9.15.22), so that

$$- \log \gamma_{R,X} = 3 (1 - g)$$
$$= a z_+ |z_-| \left(\frac{\nu_+ z_+^2 + \nu_- z_-^2}{2} \right)^{\frac{1}{2}} m^{\frac{1}{2}}. \tag{9.18.4}$$

In particular for water at $0\,°\mathrm{C}$

$$- \log \gamma_{R,X} = 1.12_3 \, z_+ |z_-| \left(\frac{\nu_+ z_+^2 + \nu_- z_-^2}{2} \right)^{\frac{1}{2}} m^{\frac{1}{2}}, \tag{9.18.5}$$

or using decadic logarithms

$$- \log_{10} \gamma_{R,X} = 0.488 \, z_+ |z_-| \left(\frac{\nu_+ z_+^2 + \nu_- z_-^2}{2} \right)^{\frac{1}{2}} m^{\frac{1}{2}}. \tag{9.18.6}$$

---

* The name *franklin* is used for a charge which repels a similar charge at a distance one centimetre in vacuo with a force of one dyne. See *Nature* (1941) **148** 751.

For water at 25 °C, the values of the coefficients are

$$a = 1.17_3, \quad \text{(water at 25 °C);} \quad (9.18.7)$$

$$\frac{a}{\log 10} = 0.509, \quad \text{(water at 25 °C).} \quad (9.18.8)$$

For many purposes one may use for water at ordinary temperatures the round value

$$\frac{a}{\log 10} = 0.50, \quad \text{(water).} \quad (9.18.9)$$

§ 9.19 Ionic Strength

The *ionic strength I* of an electrolyte solution is defined, following Lewis and Randall *, by

$$I = \tfrac{1}{2} \Sigma_i z_i^2 m_i, \quad (9.19.1)$$

so that in the case of a single solute electrolyte at a molality m

$$I = \tfrac{1}{2} (v_+ z_+^2 + v_- z_-^2) m. \quad (9.19.2)$$

Using (2) we can write the formulae of the previous section in the shorter forms

$$1 - g = \frac{a}{3} z_+ |z_-| I^{\frac{1}{2}}, \quad (9.19.3)$$

$$- \log \gamma_{R,X} = a z_+ |z_-| I^{\frac{1}{2}}. \quad (9.19.4)$$

§ 9.20 Limiting Law for Mixed Electrolytes

Debye's limiting law as $\Sigma_i m_i \to 0$ for a solution containing more than one electrolyte can be expressed as follows. If G denotes the Gibbs function and Y the Planck function of the actual solution, while G^I and Y^I denote the same functions for an ideal dilute solution of the same composition, then

$$\frac{G - G^I}{RT} = - \frac{Y - Y^I}{R} = - \tfrac{2}{3} a \frac{(\Sigma_i z_i^2 n_i)^{\frac{3}{2}}}{(2 n_1 M_1)^{\frac{1}{2}}}, \quad (9.20.1)$$

where a is defined by (9.18.2).

By differentiation of (1) with respect to n_l, we obtain, using (9.15.5) and (9.19.1),

$$- \log \gamma_i = a z_i^2 \left(\frac{\Sigma_i z_i^2 n_i}{2 n_1 M_1} \right)^{\frac{1}{2}}$$

$$= a z_i^2 \left(\frac{\Sigma_i z_i^2 m_i}{2} \right)^{\frac{1}{2}}$$

$$= a z_i^2 I^{\frac{1}{2}}. \quad (9.20.2)$$

---

* Lewis and Randall, *J. Am. Chem. Soc.* (1921) **43** 1141.

Consequently for the mean activity coefficient of an electrolyte composed of ν_+ cations R of electrovalency z_+ and ν_- anions X of electrovalency z_-, we have

$$-\log \gamma_{R,X} = -\frac{\nu_+ \log \gamma_R + \nu_- \log \gamma_X}{\nu_+ + \nu_-}$$

$$= \frac{\nu_+ z_+^2 + \nu_- z_-^2}{\nu_+ + \nu_-} \, a \, I^{\frac{1}{2}}$$

$$= a z_+ |z_-| \, I^{\frac{1}{2}}, \qquad (9.20.3)$$

using the condition of electrical neutrality

$$\nu_+ z_+ + \nu_- z_- = 0. \qquad (9.20.4)$$

From (3) we see that in the limit of high dilutions the mean activity coefficient of a given electrolyte has the same value in different solutions of the same ionic strength. This principle, which follows from Debye's formula, was discovered experimentally by Lewis and Randall* in 1921. Our previous formula (9.19.4) for a solution containing only one electrolyte is a special case of (9.20.3).

By differentiating (1) with respect to n_1 we obtain

$$\frac{\mu_1 - \mu_1^I}{RT} = \log \frac{\lambda_1}{\lambda_1^I} = \frac{1}{3} a \frac{(\Sigma_i z_i^2 n_i)^{\frac{3}{2}}}{(2 M_1)^{\frac{1}{2}} n_1^{\frac{3}{2}}}, \qquad (9.20.5)$$

where the superscript I denotes the value in an ideal dilute solution having the same composition as the actual solution. Using this notation, we obtain from (9.16.8)

$$\log \frac{\lambda_1}{\lambda_1^I} = (1-g) M_1 \Sigma_i m_i. \qquad (9.20.6)$$

Comparing (5) and (6) we have

$$1 - g = \frac{1}{3} a \frac{(\Sigma_i z_i^2 n_i)^{\frac{3}{2}}}{2^{\frac{1}{2}} (M_1 n_1)^{\frac{3}{2}} \Sigma_i m_i}$$

$$= \frac{1}{3} a \frac{(\Sigma_i z_i^2 m_i)^{\frac{3}{2}}}{2^{\frac{1}{2}} \Sigma_i m_i}$$

$$= \frac{1}{3} a \frac{\Sigma_i z_i^2 m_i}{\Sigma_i m_i} I^{\frac{1}{2}}. \qquad (9.20.7)$$

In the special case of a single electrolyte, formula (7), by use of the condition of electrical neutrality, reduces to (9.19.3).

Since formulae (2) and (7) are both derived from (1), they automatically satisfy the Gibbs–Duhem relation (9.15.15).

§ 9.21 Less Dilute Solutions

The limiting law of Debye described in the previous three sections is

---

* Lewis and Randall, *J. Am. Chem. Soc.* (1921) **43** 1141.

of the greatest value in providing a reliable means of extrapolating experimental data to infinite dilution. For experimental measurements determine only ratios of the values of γ in the several solutions. To determine values of γ itself in the several solutions some assumption has to be made concerning the value of γ in at least one such solution, for example the most dilute. Debye's limiting law provides the necessary assumption.

On the other hand this limiting law is accurate only at very high dilutions. For example when the solvent is water it is accurate at $I = 10^{-3}$, but already at $I = 10^{-2}$ deviations are experimentally detectable and at $I = 10^{-1}$ deviations are serious. In other solvents having smaller permittivities deviations from the limiting law appear at correspondingly lower ionic strengths.

For less dilute solutions various formulae can be used, all reducing to the limiting formula of Debye at high dilutions and all more or less empirical at less high dilutions. Some of these will be described in the succeeding sections.

§ 9.22 Single Electrolytes

The simplest formula for the activity coefficient of a single electrolyte, which conforms with Debye's limiting formula, is

$$\log \gamma_{R,X} = -\alpha z_+ |z_-| I^{\frac{1}{2}} + 2\beta_{R,X} m, \qquad (9.22.1)$$

where α is defined by (9.18.2) and $\beta_{R,X}$ depends on the solvent, the solute and the temperature but not on the molality. This type of formula was used by Brönsted * already in 1921 for uni-univalent electrolytes with a value for α about 20 % too low. The only objection to this formula is its limited range of validity, since it ceases to represent the experimental data at ionic strengths appreciably less than 0.1 in water.

A theoretical formula due to Debye is

$$\log \gamma_{R,X} = -\alpha z_+ |z_-| \frac{I^{\frac{1}{2}}}{1 + \varrho_{R,X} I^{\frac{1}{2}}}, \qquad (9.22.2)$$

where $\varrho_{R,X}$ is a parameter independent of I. According to a model in which the cations and anions are treated as rigid non-polarizable spheres of equal size $\varrho_{R,X}$ is directly proportional to the diameter of these spheres. It is however safer to regard $\varrho_{R,X}$ as an empirical parameter. By suitable choice of values for $\varrho_{R,X}$ formula (2) can represent the experimental data in water at ionic strengths up to 0.1 or even higher. The main objection to (2) is that it cannot be readily extended to solutions containing more than one electrolyte.

---

* Brönsted, J. Am. Chem. Soc. (1922) **44** 938.
** Debye and Hückel, Physikal. Zeit. (1923) **24** 185.

A formula proposed by Hückel * is

$$\log \gamma_{R,X} = - a\, z_+ |z_-| \frac{I^{\frac{1}{2}}}{1 + \varrho_{R,X} I^{\frac{1}{2}}} + 2\beta_{R,X}\, m, \qquad (9.22.3)$$

where, in spite of what Hückel may have thought to the contrary, $\beta_{R,X}$ is another empirical parameter. Since formula (3) contains two adjustable parameters $\varrho_{R,X}$ and $\beta_{R,X}$ it can be made to fit the experimental data up to much higher ionic strengths than either (1) or (2). For solutions in water formula (3) can remain accurate up to $I = 1$. The objection to (3) is the same as to (2), namely the impossibility of its extension to solutions containing several electrolytes.

Güntelberg ** suggested the use of the formula

$$\log \gamma_{R,X} = - a\, z_+ |z_-| \frac{I^{\frac{1}{2}}}{1 + I^{\frac{1}{2}}} \qquad (9.22.4)$$

containing no adjustable parameter. Obviously such a formula cannot compete in accuracy with formulae such as (1) and (2) containing an adjustable parameter, much less with (3) containing two such parameters. Nevertheless Güntelberg's formula gives a useful representation of the average behaviour of many electrolytes in water up to $I = 0.1$. In the absence of experimental data it is as good an approximation as any other guess. This formula has moreover the advantage over (2) and (3) that it can be extended to solutions of several electrolytes.

Finally we mention a formula proposed by the author ***

$$\log \gamma_{R,X} = - a\, z_+ |z_-| \frac{I^{\frac{1}{2}}}{1 + I^{\frac{1}{2}}} + 2\beta_{R,X}\, \tilde{\nu}\, m, \qquad (9.22.5)$$

where $\tilde{\nu}$ is the harmonic mean of ν_+ and ν_-, that is

$$\frac{2}{\tilde{\nu}} = \frac{1}{\nu_+} + \frac{1}{\nu_-}. \qquad (9.22.6)$$

This formula combines the advantages of Brönsted's formula (1) and Güntelberg's formula (4). Containing one adjustable parameter $\beta_{R,X}$ it is accurate for solutions in water up to $I = 0.1$. It has the advantage over Debye's formula (2) and Hückel's formula (3) that, as we shall describe in the next section, it can be readily extended to solutions of several electrolytes. The constant factor $2\tilde{\nu}$ has been included as a matter of convenience, as we shall see later.

---

*   Hückel, *Physikal. Zeit.* (1925) **26** 93.

** Güntelberg, *Zeit. Physikal. Chem.* (1926) **123** 243.

*** Guggenheim, *Phil. Mag.* (1935) **19** 588.

§ 9.23 Several Electrolytes

For solutions containing more than one electrolyte we propose[*] the following extension of the limiting law (9.20.1)

$$\frac{G-G'}{RT} = -\tfrac{2}{3}\, a\, \frac{(\Sigma_R z_R^2\, n_R + \Sigma_X z_X^2\, n_X)^{\frac{3}{2}}}{(2n_1\, M_1)^{\frac{1}{2}}}\, \tau\,(I^{\frac{1}{2}})$$

$$+ \Sigma_R \Sigma_X \frac{2\beta_{R,X}\, n_R\, n_X}{n_1\, M_1}. \qquad (9.23.1)$$

where R denotes cations, X denotes anions and $\tau(I^{\frac{1}{2}})$ is a function of $I^{\frac{1}{2}}$ defined by

$$\tau\,(y) = \frac{3}{y^3}\,\{\log\,(1+y) - y + \tfrac{1}{2}y^2\}$$

$$= 1 - \tfrac{3}{4}y + \tfrac{3}{5}y^2 - \tfrac{3}{6}y^3 + \tfrac{3}{7}y^4 - \ldots \qquad (9.23.2)$$

Differentiating (1) with respect to n_R we obtain using (9.15.5) and (9.19.1),

$$\log \gamma_R = -\, a\, z_R^2\, \frac{I^{\frac{1}{2}}}{1+I^{\frac{1}{2}}} + 2\, \Sigma_{X'}\, \beta_{R,X'}\, m_{X'}, \qquad (9.23.3)$$

and similarly

$$\log \gamma_X = -\, a\, z_X^2\, \frac{I^{\frac{1}{2}}}{1+I^{\frac{1}{2}}} + 2\, \Sigma_{R'}\, \beta_{R',X}\, m_{R'}. \qquad (9.23.4)$$

In (3) and (4) we have used R to denote a particular cation and R' to denote every cation; a similar remark applies to X and X'. From (3) and (4) we derive

$$\log \gamma_{R,X} = -\, a\, z_R\, |z_X|\, \frac{I^{\frac{1}{2}}}{1+I^{\frac{1}{2}}} + \frac{\nu_+}{\nu_+ + \nu_-}\, 2\, \Sigma_{X'}\, \beta_{R,X'}\, m_{X'}$$

$$+ \frac{\nu_-}{\nu_+ + \nu_-}\, 2\, \Sigma_{R'}\, \beta_{R',X}\, m_{R'}. \qquad (9.23.5)$$

In the particular case of a solution containing only a single electrolyte, (5) reduces to

$$\log \gamma_{R,X} = -\, a\, z_+\, |z_-|\, \frac{I^{\frac{1}{2}}}{1+I^{\frac{1}{2}}} + \frac{\nu_-\, m_R + \nu_+\, m_X}{\nu_+ + \nu_-}\, 2\beta_{R,X}. \qquad (9.23.6)$$

But if m denotes the molality of the single electrolyte

$$m_R = \nu_+\, m, \qquad (9.23.7)$$

$$m_X = \nu_-\, m, \qquad (9.23.8)$$

---

[*] See Guggenheim, *Phil. Mag.* (1935) **19** 588.

by the definitions of ν_+, ν_-. Hence

$$\frac{\nu_- m_R + \nu_+ m_X}{\nu_+ + \nu_-} = \frac{2\,\nu_+\,\nu_-}{\nu_+ + \nu_-}\, m = \tilde{\nu}\, m, \qquad (9.23.9)$$

according to (9.22.6) which defines $\tilde{\nu}$. Substituting (9) into (6) we obtain

$$\log \gamma_{R,X} = -\,a z_+ |z_-|\,\frac{I^{\frac{1}{2}}}{1 + I^{\frac{1}{2}}} + 2\,\beta_{R,X}\,\tilde{\nu}\, m \qquad (9.23.10)$$

in agreement with (9.22.5).

We thus see that formula (5) includes formula (9.22.5) for a single electrolyte as a special case. Moreover, since (5) was derived by differentiation of (1), the Gibbs–Duhem relation and (9.15.20) are automatically satisfied. We emphasize that an analogous extension of formula (9.22.2) containing different parameters $\varrho_{R,X}$ for the several electrolytes in the mixture is not possible since the relations (9.15.20) would be violated.

By differentiating (1) with respect to n_1 and using (9.20.6) we can obtain a formula for the osmotic coefficient g. For the sake of brevity we confine ourselves to solutions containing electrolytes all of the same valency type such that each is composed of ν_+ cations of valency z_+ and ν_- anions of valency z_-, satisfying

$$\nu_+ z_+ + \nu_- z_- = 0. \qquad (9.23.11)$$

We then obtain

$$g - 1 = -\,\tfrac{1}{3} a\, z_+ |z_-|\, I^{\frac{1}{2}}\, \sigma\,(I^{\frac{1}{2}}) + \frac{2\,\Sigma_R\,\Sigma_X\,\beta_{R,X}\, m_R\, m_X}{\Sigma_R\, m_R + \Sigma_X\, m_X}, \qquad (9.23.12)$$

where $\sigma\,(I^{\frac{1}{2}})$ is a function of $I^{\frac{1}{2}}$ defined by

$$\sigma\,(y) = \frac{3}{y^3}\left\{1 + y - \frac{1}{1+y} - 2\log\,(1+y)\right\}$$

$$= 1 - 3\{\tfrac{2}{4} y - \tfrac{3}{6} y^2 + \tfrac{4}{6} y^3 - \tfrac{5}{7} y^4 + \ldots\}. \qquad (9.23.13)$$

In particular for a solution of a single electrolyte

$$g - 1 = -\,\tfrac{1}{3} a\, z_+ |z_-|\, I^{\frac{1}{2}}\, \sigma\,(I^{\frac{1}{2}}) + \beta_{R,X}\,\tilde{\nu}\, m. \qquad (9.23.14)$$

We may note that the functions τ and σ defined by (2) and (13) respectively are related by the identity

$$2\,\tau\,(y) + \sigma\,(y) = \frac{3}{1+y}. \qquad (9.23.15)$$

§ 9.24 Specific Interaction of Ions

If we examine formula (9.23.1), from which all subsequent formulae for γ's and g are derived, we notice that there is a parameter $\beta_{R,X}$ for each cation-anion pair, but no such parameters $\beta_{RR'}$ or $\beta_{XX'}$ belonging to two ions with electric charge of the same sign. This is in accordance with a principle enunciated by Brönsted * in 1921 and called by him the *principle of specific interaction of ions*. According to this principle two ions of the same sign will so rarely come close to each other in dilute solution that their mutual interactions may be assumed to be determined by their charges, but otherwise to be non-specific. Ions of the opposite sign on the other hand often come close to each other and their mutual interactions are therefore specific depending on their sizes, shapes, polarizabilities and so on. When this principle is introduced into a statistical treatment it leads to parameters of the type $\beta_{R,X}$ but none of the type $\beta_{R,R'}$ or $\beta_{X,X'}$.

§ 9. 25   Comparison with Experiment

The *principle of specific interaction* leads to a number of conclusions concerning mixtures of electrolytes which have been confirmed experimentally by Brönsted *. We shall not give details, but shall merely mention **one** illustrative example of the usefulness of the principle.

From formula (9. 23. 5) it follows that the mean activity of NaCl present as a trace in a solution of HCl at $m = 10^{-1}$ is equal to that of HCl present as a trace in a solution of NaCl at $m = 10^{-1}$. The latter can be measured electrometrically, as we shall see in the next chapter, while there is no convenient experimental method for determining the former. Hence the former is best determined by measuring the latter.

Formula (9. 23. 14) with

$$\tfrac{1}{3} a = 0.374, \qquad\qquad \text{(water at } 0\,^{\circ}\text{C).} \qquad (9.25.1)$$

has been applied ** to a large number of measurements of freezing-point especially those made by Scatchard and his collaborators. In all cases there is agreement within the accuracy of the experiments up to $I = 0.1$ At higher ionic strengths the formula is not reliable. The values of $\beta_{R,X}$ which best fit the data for various single electrolytes are given in Table 9. 1. For KCl and for KNO_3 alternative values of $\beta_{R,X}$ are given to fit different experimental data, though the discrepancies are not serious.

The dependence of g on the ionic strength is shown in Figs. 9. 2 and 9. 3. Of these Fig. 9. 2 relates only to uni-univalent electrolytes, for which the ionic strength is merely the molality. Fig. 9. 3 on the other hand relates to electrolytes of various valency types. The quantity $(g-1)/z_+|z_-|$ has been plotted against $I^{\frac{1}{2}}$ so as to obtain a sheaf of curves with a common tangent at the origin.

---

*   Brönsted, Kgl. Danske Vid. Selsk., *Mat.-fys. Medd.* (1921) **4** (4); *J. Am. Chem. Soc.* (1922) **44** 877; (1923) **45** 2898.

**   Guggenheim, *Phil. Mag.* (1935) **19** 588; (1936) **22** 322; Guggenheim and Wiseman, *Phil. Mag.* (1938) **25** 45.

TABLE 9.1
Values of β fitting freezing-point data of single electrolytes

Electrolyte	$\tilde{\nu}$	β	$\tilde{\nu}\beta$	Reference
HCl	1	0.275	—	(4)
LiCl	1	0.223	—	(8)
NaCl	1	0.135	—	(3), (8)
KCl	1	0.065	—	(8)
		0.083	—	(1), (5)
TlCl	1	0.40	—	(4)
LiClO₃	1	0.280	—	(7)
NaClO₃	1	0.040	—	(7)
KClO₃	1	—0.165	—	(7)
LiClO₄	1	0.380	—	(7)
NaClO₄	1	0.075	—	(7)
KClO₄	1	—0.500	—	(7)
LiNO₃	1	0.260	—	(7)
NaNO₃	1	0.000	—	(7)
KNO₃	1	—0.237	—	(7)
		—0.29	—	(1)
CsNO₃	1	0.00	—	(5)
NaIO₃	1	—0.40	—	(2)
KIO₃	1	—0.40	—	(2)
LiO₂CH	1	0.140	—	(8)
NaO₂CH	1	0.170	—	(8)
KO₂CH	1	0.190	—	(8)
LiO₂CCH₃	1	0.210	—	(8)
NaO₂CCH₃	1	0.290	—	(8)
KO₂CCH₃	1	0.290	—	(8)
Na₂SO₄	$\frac{4}{3}$	—0.45	—0.60	(6)
K₂SO₄	$\frac{4}{3}$	0.00	0.00	(2), (5)
Ba(NO₃)₂	$\frac{4}{3}$	—0.41	—0.55	(6), (5)
MgSO₄	1	0.00	0.00	(2), (5)
CuSO₄	1	—1.7	—1.7	(5)
La(NO₃)₃	$\frac{3}{2}$	2.6	+3.9	(2)
La₂(SO₄)₃	$\frac{12}{5}$	0.00	0.00	(5)

References for experimental data.

(1) Adams, *J. Am. Chem. Soc.* (1915) **37**, 481.
(2) Hall and Harkins, *J. Am. Chem. Soc.* (1916) **38**, 2658.
(3) Harkins and Roberts, *J. Am. Chem. Soc.* (1916) **38**, 2676.
(4) Randall and Vanselow, *J. Am. Chem. Soc.* (1924) **46**, 2418.
(5) Hovorka and Rodebush, *J. Am. Chem. Soc.* (1925) **47**, 1614.
(6) Randall and Scott, *J. Am. Chem. Soc.* (1927) **49**, 647.
(7) Scatchard, Jones and Prentiss, *J. Am. Chem. Soc.* (1932) **54**, 2690; (1934) **56**, 805.
(8) Scatchard and Prentiss, *J. Am. Chem. Soc.* (1932) **54**, 2696; (1933) **55**, 4355;
(1934) **56**, 807.

It is worthy of note that a considerable number of electrolytes, of various valency types, have values of $\beta_{R,X}$ not greatly different from zero. Consequently if, as often happens, a value is required for the activity coefficient

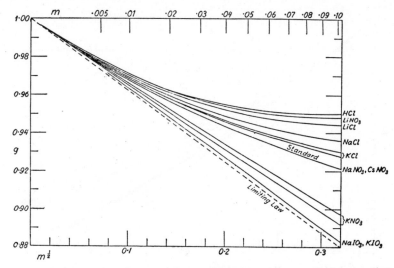

Fig. 9.2. Osmotic coefficients of several uni-univalent electrolytes at 0 °C.

of some electrolyte and there are no experimental data available a useful approximation is obtained by taking $\beta_{R,X}$ as zero. This approximation, first recommended by Güntelberg, has already been mentioned in § 9.22. It is usually a vastly better approximation than the limiting law formulae of § 9.20.

Fig. 9.4 shows the activity coefficients of the uni-univalent electrolytes for which the osmotic coefficients are shown in Fig. 9.2. The activity

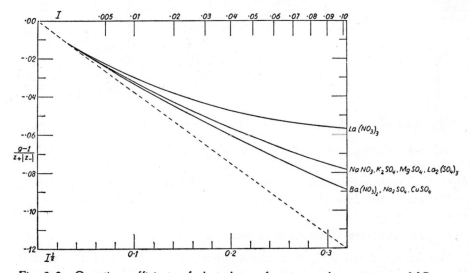

Fig. 9.3. Osmotic coefficients of electrolytes of various valency types at 0 °C.

coefficients of single electrolytes of various valency types are shown in Fig. 9.5. These have been computed from formula (9.23.10) with $a = 1.12_3$ and the values of β given in Table 9.1. They accordingly relate

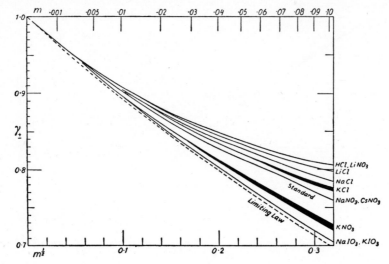

Fig. 9.4. Activity coefficients of several uni-univalent electrolytes at 0 °C.

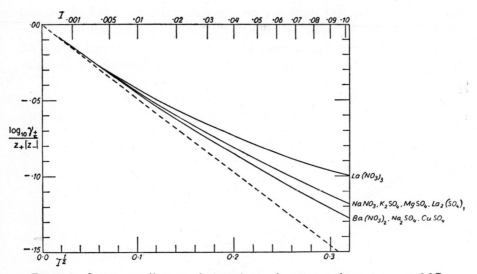

Fig. 9.5. Activity coefficients of electrolytes of various valency types at 0 °C.

to 0 °C. The scanty experimental data available indicate that the activity coefficients vary only slightly between 0 °C and 30 °C.

§ 9.26 Activity Coefficient of Solvent

We have hitherto described the equilibrium properties of the solvent by means of its osmotic coefficient g and may thus regard $g - 1$ as a measure of deviation from behaviour in an ideal dilute solution. We might alternatively have used an activity coefficient f_1 defined by

$$\frac{\lambda_1}{\lambda_1^0} = (1 - \Sigma_i \, x_i) \, f_1. \qquad (9.\,26.\,1)$$

Let us now compare this with the definition (9.16.10) of the rational osmotic coefficient g

$$\log \frac{\lambda_1}{\lambda_1^0} = g \log (1 - \Sigma_i \, x_i). \qquad (9.\,26.\,2)$$

Taking logarithms of (1) and comparing with (2) we find

$$\begin{aligned}
\log f_1 &= - (1 - g) \log (1 - \Sigma_i \, x_i) \\
&\simeq (1 - g) \, \Sigma_i \, x_i \\
&\simeq (1 - g) \, M_1 \, \Sigma_i \, m_i. \qquad (9.\,26.\,3)
\end{aligned}$$

if the solution is extremely dilute.

We now consider a typical numerical example. For water $M_1 = 0.018$, so that in a centimolal solution of a symmetrical electrolyte at $0\,^\circ C$

$$M_1 \, \Sigma_i \, m_i = 0.018 \times 2 \times 0.01 = 3.6 \times 10^{-4}.$$

If the electrolyte is of the $1 - 1$ electrovalency type, then approximately

$$1 - g = 0.032$$
$$- \log \gamma_{R,X} = 0.102 \, ,$$

from which we see that the solution is by no means ideal dilute. Substituting into (3) we obtain

$$\begin{aligned}
\log f_1 &= 0.032 \times 3\,6 \times 10^{-4} \\
&= 1.15 \times 10^{-5},
\end{aligned}$$

so that

$$f_1 = 1.000011.$$

Similarly in a decimolal solution of a $1-1$ electrovalency type electrolyte in water, we have approximately

$$M_1 \, \Sigma_i \, m_i = 3.6 \times 10^{-3}$$
$$1 - g = 0.078$$
$$- \log \gamma_{R,X} = 0.270$$

so that

$$\begin{aligned}
\log f_1 &= 0.078 \times 3.6 \times 10^{-3} = 2.8 \times 10^{-4} \\
f_1 &= 1.00028.
\end{aligned}$$

From these examples we see that in extremely dilute solutions $f_1 - 1$ is much less convenient that $1 - g$ as a measure of deviations from the ideal dilute state.

§ 9.27 Chemical Reactions Involving Solvent

In § 9.14 we obtained the condition of equilibrium in a chemical reaction between solute ionic species, including non-ionic species as if they were ionic with $z = 0$. We, shall now consider how this condition can be extended to include chemical reactions involving the solvent.

A reaction involving the solvent is called *solvolysis* with the exception of simple addition called *solvation*. In particular if the solvent is water it is called *hydrolysis*.

For the sake of brevity we shall consider not the general case, but a specific example. We choose the hydrolysis of chlorine in water

$$Cl_2 + 2 H_2O \rightarrow H_3O^+ + Cl^- + HClO. \qquad (9.27.1)$$

The equilibrium condition in its most general form is

$$\frac{\lambda_{H_3O^+} \lambda_{Cl^-} \lambda_{HClO}}{\lambda_{Cl_2} \lambda_{H_2O}^2} = 1. \qquad (9.27.2)$$

For λ_{H_2O} we may write according to (9.26.1)

$$\lambda_{H_2O} = \lambda_{H_2O}^0 (1 - \Sigma_i x_i) f_1. \qquad (9.27.3)$$

where the summation Σ_i includes the uncharged species Cl_2 and $HClO$ as well as the ions. We saw that even for solutions far from ideal dilute we may with a high degree of accuracy set $f_1 = 1$. Assuming the solution is extremely dilute, we may further neglect $\Sigma_i x_i$ compared with unity. We may therefore in this connection replace (3) by

$$\lambda_{H_2O} \simeq \lambda_{H_2O}^0 \qquad (9.27.4)$$

with an accuracy depending on the composition of the solution, but usually within 1 %. Hence with this sort of accuracy, we may replace (2) by

$$\frac{\lambda_{H_3O^+} \lambda_{Cl^-} \lambda_{HClO}}{\lambda_{Cl_2}} = \lambda_{H_2O}^{0\ 2}. \qquad (9.27.5)$$

Using the relation (9.09.3) for each reacting species other than the solvent H_2O, we obtain

$$\frac{m_{H_3O^+}\, m_{Cl^-}\, m_{HClO}}{m_{Cl_2}} \frac{\gamma_{H_3O^+}\, \gamma_{Cl^-}\, \gamma_{HClO}}{\gamma_{Cl_2}} = K_m(T). \qquad (9.27.6)$$

the constant $\lambda_{H_2O}^{0\ 2}$ being absorbed as a factor of K_m.

From this typical example we see that for a chemical reaction involving the solvent, the equilibrium condition takes the form

$$\Pi'(m_i \gamma_1) = K_m(T). \qquad (9.27.7)$$

where Π' differs from Π by the omission of factors relating to the solvent.

§ 9.28 Acid-Base Equilibrium

By far the most important and widespread class of chemical processes between ions in solution, is that of the transfer of a proton from one ion or molecule to another. Any ion or molecule capable of losing a proton is called an *acid*; any ion or molecule capable of gaining a proton is called a *base*. These definitions due to Brönsted * are simpler and more rational than earlier definitions which they supersede. The acid and base which differ from each other by one proton are called a *conjugate* pair. Obviously the electrovalency of any acid exceeds by unity that of its conjugate base. Table 9.2 gives examples of well-known conjugate pairs of acids and

TABLE 9.2

Typical conjugate acids and bases

Acid	Base
CH_3CO_2H	$CH_3CO_2^-$
NH_4^+	NH_3
OH_2	OH^-
OH_3^+	OH_2
H_3PO_4	$H_2PO_4^-$
$H_2PO_4^-$	HPO_4^{--}
HPO_4^{--}	PO_4^{---}
$H_3N^+ . CH_2 . CO_2H$	$H_3N^+ . CH_2 . CO_2^-$
$H_3N^+ . CH_2 . CO_2^-$	$H_2N . CH_2 . CO_2^-$

bases. It is clear from several examples in Table 9.2 that an ion or a molecule may be both an acid and a base.

If A and B denote an acid and its conjugate base, while A', B' denote another conjugate pair then the chemical reaction

$$A + B' \rightarrow B + A' \qquad (9.28.1)$$

is typical of acid-base reactions. The equilibrium condition is

$$\frac{m_B \, m_{A'}}{m_A \, m_{B'}} \frac{\gamma_B \, \gamma_{A'}}{\gamma_A \, \gamma_{B'}} = K. \qquad (9.28.2)$$

where K depends on the solvent and the temperature, but not on the composition of the solution. As a typical example we have, using Ac as an abbreviation for CH_3CO_2

$$NH_4^+ + Ac^- \rightarrow NH_3 + HAc, \qquad (9.28.3)$$

$$\frac{m_{NH_3} \, m_{HAc}}{m_{NH_4^+} \, m_{Ac^-}} \frac{\gamma_{NH_3} \, \gamma_{HAc}}{\gamma_{NH_4^+} \, \gamma_{Ac^-}} = K. \qquad (9.28.4)$$

Since water is both a base and an acid it can react with either an acid or a base dissolved in it. As examples of acids reacting with water, we mention

$$HAc + H_2O \rightarrow Ac^- + H_3O^+. \qquad (9.28.5)$$

$$NH_4^+ + H_2O \rightarrow NH_3 + H_3O^+. \qquad (9.28.6)$$

$$H_2PO_4^- + H_2O \rightarrow HPO_4^{--} + H_3O^+ \qquad (9.28.7)$$

---

* Brönsted, *Rec. Trav. Chim. Pays Bas,* (1923) **42** 718.

and as examples of bases reacting with water

$$H_2O + Ac^- \rightarrow OH^- + HAc \qquad (9.28.8)$$

$$H_2O + NH_3 \rightarrow OH^- + NH_4^+ \qquad (9.28.9)$$

$$H_2O + H_2PO_4^- \rightarrow OH^- + H_3PO_4 \qquad (9.28.10)$$

We note that according to the definition of *hydrolysis* given in the preceding section, reactions (5) to (10) are all examples of *hydrolysis*. On the other hand reaction (3) does not involve the solvent H_2O and is therefore not a *hydrolysis*.

The reactions (5), (6), (7) are all examples of the general type

$$A + H_2O \rightarrow B + H_3O^+ \qquad (9.28.11)$$

of which the equilibrium condition is

$$\frac{m_B \, m_{H_3O^+}}{m_A} \cdot \frac{\gamma_B \gamma_{H_3O^+}}{\gamma_A} = K_A \qquad (9.28.12)$$

where K_A is called the *acid constant* of A in water at the given temperature. K_A is a measure of the strength of the acid A relative to water. The reciprocal of K_A may likewise be regarded as a measure of the strength of the conjugate base B. For example the acid constants K_{HAc} of HAc and $K_{NH_4^+}$ of NH_4^+ have the values at 25° C

$$K_{HAc} = 1.75 \times 10^{-5} \text{ mole Kg.}^{-1}, \qquad (9.28.13)$$

$$K_{NH_4^+} = 6.1 \times 10^{-10} \text{ mole Kg.}^{-1}. \qquad (9.28.14)$$

Two molecules of H_2O can react together, the one acting as an acid, the other as a base, thus:

$$H_2O + H_2O \rightarrow OH^- + OH_3^+.$$

The equilibrium is determined by

$$m_{OH_3^+} \, m_{OH^-} \, \gamma_{OH_3^+} \gamma_{OH^-} = K_w, \qquad (9.28.15)$$

where K_w is called the *ionization product* of water. Its values at various temperatures are as follows:

$$0\,°C \qquad K_w = 0.115 \times 10^{-14} \text{ mole Kg.}^{-2}, \qquad (9.28.16)$$

$$20\,°C \qquad K_w = 0.68 \times 10^{-14} \text{ mole Kg.}^{-2}, \qquad (9.28.17)$$

$$25\,°C \qquad K_w = 1.01 \times 10^{-14} \text{ mole Kg.}^{-2}. \qquad (9.28.18)$$

The equilibrium constants for reactions of the type

$$H_2O + B \rightarrow OH^- + A \qquad (9.28.19)$$

can always be expressed in terms of an acid constant and the ionization constant of water. For example for reaction (8) we have

$$\frac{m_{OH^-} m_{HAc}}{m_{Ac^-}} \frac{\gamma_{OH^-} \gamma_{HAc}}{\gamma_{Ac^-}} = \frac{K_w}{K_{HAc}} \qquad (9.28.20)$$

where K_{HAc} is the acid constant K_A of HAc. Similary for reaction (9)

$$\frac{m_{OH^-} m_{NH_4^+}}{m_{NH_3}} \frac{\gamma_{OH^-} \gamma_{NH_4^+}}{\gamma_{NH_3}} = \frac{K_w}{K_{NH_4^+}}. \qquad (9.28.21)$$

where $K_{NH_4^+}$ denotes the acid constant of NH_4^+.

If we apply the definition (12) of an acid constant to OH_3^+ we obtain

$$K_{OH_3^+} = \frac{m_{H_2O} \, m_{H_3O^+}}{m_{H_3O^+}} \frac{f_{H_2O} \, \gamma_{H_3O^+}}{\gamma_{H_3O^+}}$$

$$= m_{H_2O} \, f_{H_2O}$$

$$\simeq m_{H_2O} \simeq 55.5 \text{ mole Kg.}^{-1} \qquad (9.28.22)$$

From (12) we see that no molecule or ion which is a much stronger acid than OH_3^+ can exist in appreciable quantity in water. For example HCl is a much stronger acid than OH_3^+. Consequently when dissolved in water it is almost completely changed to OH_3^+ and Cl^-. Similarly H_2SO_4 is a much stronger acid than OH_3^+ and is therefore almost completely changed to OH_3^+ and HSO_4^-. On the other hand $K_{HSO_4^-} = 1.2 \times 10^{-2}$ so that HSO_4^- being a much weaker acid than OH_3^+ exists in appreciable amount in water.

Similarly no base much stronger than OH^- can exist in appreciable quantity in water, since it would be hydrolysed to its conjugate acid and OH^-. Examples of bases too strong to exist in H_2O are O^{--} and NH_2^- which are hydrolysed as follows

$$H_2O + O^{--} \rightarrow OH^- + OH^-,$$

$$H_2O + NH_2^- \rightarrow OH^- + NH_3.$$

Examples of very strong bases, but not so strong that they cannot exist at all in water are S^{--} and CN^-.

When a strongly alkaline substance such as NaOH is dissolved in water, the base present in the solution is OH^-. Often NaOH is itself referred to somewhat loosely as a *base*.

Similar relations hold in other solvents which can react as both base and acid. Reactions of an ion or molecule with the solvent are called *solvolysis*.

§ 9.29 Weak Electrolytes

An electrically neutral molecule, not itself an electrolyte, which by hydrolysis or other reaction is partly changed into ions is sometimes called a *weak electrolyte*. In particular an electrically neutral acid such as HAc which is partly hydrolysed according to

$$HAc + H_2O \rightarrow Ac^- + H_3O^+,$$

and an electrically neutral base such as NH_3 which is partly hydrolysed according to

$$H_2O + NH_3 \rightarrow OH^- + NH_4^+.$$

are according to this definition *weak electrolytes*. For these substances the names *electrically neutral acids* and *electrically neutral bases* are sufficient and more informative.

§ 9. 30 Surface Phases

The formulae previously derived for surface phases apply just as well to solutions of electrolytes as to solutions of non-electrolytes. In particular for variations of composition at constant temperature formula (6. 54. 1) becomes

$$-d\gamma = \Sigma_i \left(\Gamma_i - \frac{x_i \, \Gamma_1}{1 - \Sigma_i \, x_i} \right) D\mu_i. \tag{9.30.1}$$

where the summation Σ_i extends over all ions and other solute species. Expressed in terms of absolute activities (1) becomes

$$-d\gamma = RT \, \Sigma_i \left(\Gamma_i - \frac{x_i \, \Gamma_1}{1 - \Sigma_i \, x_i} \right) D \log \lambda_i. \tag{9.30.2}$$

According to the definition of ionic molality

$$m_i \, M_1 = \frac{x_i}{1 - \Sigma_i \, x_i}. \tag{9.30.3}$$

Substituting (3) into (2), we obtain

$$-d\gamma = RT \, \Sigma_i \, (\Gamma_i - m_i \, M_1 \, \Gamma_1) \, D \log \lambda_i. \tag{9.30.4}$$

Even if the solution is extremely dilute the term $m_i \, M_1 \, \Gamma_1$ must not be omitted for although $m_i \, M_1 \ll 1$ at the same time $| \, \Gamma_1 \, | \gg | \, \Gamma_i \, |$.

The above relations, and in fact all the relations, for the surface of an electrolyte solution are formally analogous to those for the surface of a non-electrolyte solution. There is however a significant difference requiring careful treatment, namely counting the number of independent components. Let us consider some typical examples beginning with the simplest.

A solution of hydrochloric acid in water contains the species OH_2, OH_3^+ and Cl^-. We omit OH^-, not so much because it is present in negligible amount as because it is in any case not an independent component, since

$$OH^- = 2OH_2 - OH_3^+. \tag{9.30.5}$$

Of the three species OH_2, OH_3^+ and Cl^- the condition of electrical neutrality imposes the restrictions

$$m_{OH_3^+} = m_{Cl^-}, \tag{9.30.6}$$

$$\Gamma_{OH_3^+} = \Gamma_{Cl^-}, \tag{9.30.7}$$

so that there are only two independent components. We may take these to be OH_2 on the one hand and $(OH_3^+ + Cl^-)$ on the other. More simply we may choose as independent components OH_2 and HCl.

Similarly a solution of sodium hydroxide in water contains the species OH_2, OH^- and Na^+. We omit OH_3^+, not so much because it is present in negligible amount as because it is in any case not an independent component owing to (5). The condition of electrical neutrality imposes the restrictions

$$m_{OH^-} = m_{Na^+}, \tag{9.30.8}$$

$$\Gamma_{OH^-} = \Gamma_{Na^+}, \tag{9.30.9}$$

so that there are only two independent components which we may take to be OH_2 and NaOH. Thus for the surface tension of the solution of NaOH we have

$$- d\gamma = RT \left(\Gamma_{Na^+} - m_{Na^+} M_{H_2O} \Gamma_{H_2O} \right) D \log \lambda_{Na^+}$$
$$+ RT \left(\Gamma_{OH^-} - m_{OH^-} M_{H_2O} \Gamma_{H_2O} \right) D \log \lambda_{OH^-}$$
$$= 2 RT \left(\Gamma_{NaOH} - m_{NaOH} M_{H_2O} \Gamma_{H_2O} \right) D \log m_{NaOH} \gamma_{Na,OH}, \tag{9.30.10}$$

where m_{NaOH} and Γ_{NaOH} are defined by

$$m_{Na^+} = m_{OH^-} = m_{NaOH}, \tag{9.30.11}$$

$$\Gamma_{Na^+} = \Gamma_{OH^-} = \Gamma_{NaOH} \tag{9.30.12}$$

respectively.

The reader should have no difficulty in distinguishing between γ without any subscript denoting surface tension and $\gamma_{Na,OH}$ denoting the mean activity coefficient of NaOH.

Let us now consider a solution made by dissolving both hydrogen chloride and sodium hydroxide in solution. Of the five species H_2O, OH_3^+, OH^-, Na^+ and Cl^- in the system only three are independent. For the equilibrium

$$H_2O + H_2O \rightleftarrows OH_3^+ + OH^- \tag{9.30.13}$$

imposes the restriction

$$m_{OH_3^+} m_{OH^-} \gamma_{OH_3^+} \gamma_{OH^-} = K_w, \tag{9.30.14}$$

and the condition of electrical neutrality imposes the restrictions

$$m_{Na^+} + m_{OH_3^+} = m_{Cl^-} + m_{OH^-}, \tag{9.30.15}$$

$$\Gamma_{Na^+} + \Gamma_{OH_3^+} = \Gamma_{Cl^-} + \Gamma_{OH^-}. \tag{9.30.16}$$

If the hydrogen chloride is in excess, it is natural to choose as the three independent components OH_2, NaCl and HCl. In this case m_{OH^-} is negligible compared with all the other terms in (15). If on the contrary the sodium hydroxide is in excess, it is natural to choose as the three independent components OH_2, NaCl and NaOH. In this case $m_{OH_3^+}$ is negligible compared with the other terms in (15). These remarks apply equally to the bulk of the solution and to the surface layer.

Suppose now we stipulate that precisely equivalent amounts of hydrogen chloride and sodium hydroxide are contained in the solution. Then the relation (15) is replaced by the two relations

$$m_{Na^+} = m_{Cl^-}, \qquad (9.30.17)$$

$$m_{OH_3^+} = m_{OH^-}, \qquad (9.30.18)$$

so that the solution contains only two independent components, which we naturally take to be OH_2 and NaCl. But the restriction (17), which reduces by one the number of independent components in the bulk of the solution, does not imply any analogous restriction on the Γ's. In other words the surface layer can contain as well as OH_2 and NaCl either an excess of HCl or an excess of NaOH. Thus the number of components necessary to describe the composition of the surface phase is still three, not two.

We shall now analyse this problem, beginning with unspecified quantities of NaCl and NaOH dissolved in water, introducing the restriction that the quantity of NaOH is zero only at a later stage. There are four ionic species Na^+, Cl^-, OH_3^+ and OH^- in the solvent H_2O. These are not independent, but are subject to the conditions of electrical neutrality

$$m_{Na^+} + m_{OH_3^+} = m_{Cl^-} + m_{OH^-}, \qquad (9.30.19)$$

$$\Gamma_{Na^+} + \Gamma_{OH_3^+} = \Gamma_{Cl^-} + \Gamma_{OH^-} \qquad (9.30.20)$$

and to the condition for ionization equilibrium of the solvent water

$$\lambda_{OH_3^+} \lambda_{OH^-} = \lambda_{H_2O}^2 = \text{const.} \qquad (9.30.21)$$

For variations of the surface tension with composition at constant temperature we have the general relation of the form (4),

$$-\frac{d\gamma}{RT} = (\Gamma_{Na^+} - m_{Na^+} M_{H_2O} \Gamma_{H_2O}) D \log \lambda_{Na^+}$$
$$+ (\Gamma_{Cl^-} - m_{Cl^-} M_{H_2O} \Gamma_{H_2O}) D \log \lambda_{Cl^-}$$
$$+ (\Gamma_{OH_3^+} - m_{OH_3^+} M_{H_2O} \Gamma_{H_2O}) D \log \lambda_{OH_3^+}$$
$$+ (\Gamma_{OH^-} - m_{OH^-} M_{H_2O} \Gamma_{H_2O}) D \log \lambda_{OH^-}. \qquad (9.30.22)$$

Using (19), (20) and (21), we can replace (22) by

$$-\frac{d\gamma}{RT} = (\Gamma_{Cl^-} - m_{Cl^-} M_{H_2O} \Gamma_{H_2O}) D \log \lambda_{Na^+} \lambda_{Cl^-}$$

$$+ ([\Gamma_{Na^+} - \Gamma_{Cl^-}] - [m_{Na^+} - m_{Cl^-}] M_{H_2O} \Gamma_{H_2O}) D \log \lambda_{Na^+} \lambda_{OH^-}$$

$$= (\Gamma_{Cl^-} - m_{Cl^-} M_{H_2O} \Gamma_{H_2O}) D \log m_{Na^+} m_{Cl^-} \gamma^2_{Na,Cl} \qquad (9.30.23)$$

$$+ ([\Gamma_{Na^+} - \Gamma_{Cl^-}] - [m_{Na^+} - m_{Cl^-}] M_{H_2O} \Gamma_{H_2O}) D \log m_{Na^+} m_{OH^-} \gamma^2_{Na,OH}.$$

Thus by studying the dependence of the surface tension γ on the composition by variations of the molalities of NaCl and of NaOH, provided the activity coefficients are known, one can determine the separate values of

$$\Gamma_{Na^+} - m_{Na^+} M_{H_2O} \Gamma_{H_2O} \qquad (9.30.24)$$

and of

$$[\Gamma_{Na^+} - \Gamma_{Cl^-}] - [m_{Na^+} - m_{Cl^-}] M_{H_2O} \Gamma_{H_2O}. \qquad (9.30.25)$$

The expression (24) is a measure of the combined adsorption of NaCl and NaOH relative to H_2O, while the expression (25) is a measure of the adsorption of NaOH relative to H_2O. By subtracting (25) from (24) one obtains a measure of the adsorption of NaCl relative to H_2O. In particular as the molality of NaOH is made to tend to zero, so the quantity (25) tends to

$$\Gamma_{Na^+} - \Gamma_{Cl^-}, \qquad (9.30.26)$$

The value of (26) then becomes the surface concentration of NaOH in a solution which in the bulk contains only NaCl and H_2O.

To recapitulate, by varying the molalities of both NaCl and NaOH and measuring surface tension one can determine separately the coefficients of the two terms on the right of (23), namely the quantities (24) and (25), of which the latter reduces to (26) in a solution containing no excess NaOH. By measuring the surface tension of solutions containing varying amounts of NaCl only without any NaOH, it is not possible to separate the two terms on the right of (23) and consequently the quantity (24) can not in this way be determined.

CHAPTER X

ELECTROCHEMICAL SYSTEMS

§ 10. 01 Electrically Charged Phases

In the previous chapter we saw how a phase containing ions can be treated by means of the same formulae as a phase containing only electrically neutral molecules. In particular the formulae

$$dF = - SdT - PdV + \Sigma_i \mu_i \, dn_i, \qquad (10.01.1)$$

$$dG = - SdT + VdP + \Sigma_i \mu_i \, dn_i, \qquad (10.01.2)$$

from which follows

$$\mu_i = \left(\frac{\partial F}{\partial n_i}\right)_{T,V,n_j} = \left(\frac{\partial G}{\partial n_i}\right)_{T,P,n_j}, \qquad (10.01.3)$$

are applicable. The only significant difference in our treatment of ions was the imposition of the condition of electrical neutrality

$$\Sigma_i \, n_i \, z_i = 0, \qquad (10.01.4)$$

where z_i is the electrovalency of the ionic species i. We shall now consider what happens if we try to relax the condition (4).

To obtain a clear picture of what happens it is useful to begin with some simple numerical calculations. The charge e on a proton is given by

$$e = 4.802_5 \times 10^{-10} \text{ franklins } *$$
$$= 1.602 \times 10^{-19} \text{ coulombs.} \qquad (10.01.5)$$

Consequently the electric charge, associated with one gram-ion of a species having an electrovalency 1, called the *faraday* and denoted by F is given by

$$F = Ne$$
$$= 0.6023 \times 10^{24} \times 1.602 \times 10^{-19} \text{ coulombs}$$
$$= 0.9649 \times 10^5 \text{ coulombs.} \qquad (10.01.6)$$

Let us now consider a single phase surrounded by empty space and thus electrically insulated. Let us further imagine that this phase, instead of satisfying the condition of electrical neutrality (4), contains an excess of 10^{-10} gram-ions having an electrovalency $+1$. Then most, if not all, the excess electrical charge will accumulate at the surface of the phase. For

---

* The name *franklin* is used to denote a charge which in empty space repels a similar charge at a distance one centimetre with a force one dyne. See *Nature* (1941) 148 751.

simplicity let us suppose that the phase is spherical with a radius one centimetre. The electrical potential ψ of a charged sphere of radius r in vacuo is determined by

$$\psi = \frac{Q}{\varepsilon_0 r}, \tag{10.01.7}$$

where Q is the charge on the sphere and ε_0 is the permittivity of free space. Substituting the values

$$Q = 10^{-10} \text{ faradays} = 0.96 \times 10^{-5} \text{ coul.},$$
$$\varepsilon_0 = 1.11 \times 10^{-10} \text{ coul./volt m.},$$
$$r = 10^{-2} \text{ m.} \tag{10.01.8}$$

into (7), we obtain

$$\psi = \frac{0.96 \times 10^{-5}}{1.11 \times 10^{-10} \times 10^{-2}} \text{ volt} = 0.95 \times 10^7 \text{ volt.} \tag{10.01.9}$$

From this example we have reached the noteworthy conclusion that a departure from the condition of electrical neutrality corresponding to a quantity of ions far too small to be detected chemically corresponds to an electrostatic potential encountered only in specialized high voltage laboratories. Any other numerical example would lead to the same conclusion.

§ 10.02 Phases of Identical Composition

The above general result leads to the use of the following terminology. We speak of two phases having the *same chemical content*, but *different electrical potentials*. Actually two such phases differ in chemical content but the difference is too small to be detectable by chemical means, or any other means, except electrical. For example suppose we mention two spheres of copper each containing precisely one gram, differing in electrical potential by 200 volts. If this electrical potential difference is ascribed to an excess of copper ions Cu^{++} with an electrovalency $+2$, then the amount of this excess is about 3.3×10^{-16} gram-ions or 2×10^{-14} grams. This excess is so small as to be entirely negligible except in its electrical effect. Consequently it is of no importance or interest whether the electrical charge is in fact due to an excess of Cu^{++} ions or to an equivalent deficiency of electrons or even to some extraneous kind of ion such as OH_3^{+}, present as an impurity.

Similar considerations apply to a pair of phases of different size but of the same chemical composition.

§ 10.03 Electrochemical Potentials

Having agreed as to what we mean when we speak of two phases having the same chemical composition but different electrical potentials, we see that the μ_i's occurring in the formulae mentioned in § 10.01 have values depending on the electrical state of the phase as well as on its chemical composition. To stress this fact we call the μ_i of an ionic species its *electrochemical potential*. *

The difference of the electrochemical potential μ_i between two phases of *identical chemical composition* will clearly be proportional to the electrical charge $z_i F$ associated with a gram-ion of the species in question but independent of all its other individual characteristics. Hence for any two phases α and β of identical chemical composition and any ionic species i we may write

$$\mu_i^{\beta} - \mu_i^{\alpha} = z_i F (\psi^{\beta} - \psi^{\alpha}), \qquad (10.03.1)$$

where $\psi^{\beta} - \psi^{\alpha}$ is the *electrical potential difference* between the two phases. Formula ($\mathcal{V}$) may be regarded as the thermodynamic definition of the electrical potential difference between two phases of *identical chemical composition*. The equilibrium condition for a given ionic species between two phases of identical composition is that the two phases should be at the same electrical potential. In fact the laws of mathematical electrostatics are applicable to any ionic species, in particular to electrons, only in so far as differences in chemical composition between several phases are excluded or ignored.

For the distribution of ionic species i between two phases α, β of different chemical composition the equilibrium condition is equality of the electrochemical potential μ_i, that is to say

$$\mu_i^{\alpha} = \mu_i^{\beta}. \qquad (10.03.2)$$

Any splitting of $\mu_i^{\beta} - \mu_i^{\alpha}$ into a chemical part and an electrical part is in general arbitrary and without physical significance.

As long ago as 1899 Gibbs ** wrote: "Again, the consideration of the electrical potential in the electrolyte, and especially the consideration of the difference of potential in electrolyte and electrode, involve the consideration of quantities of which we have no apparent means of physical measurement, while the difference of potential in pieces of metal of the same kind attached to the electrodes is exactly one of the things which we can and do measure." This principle was however ignored or forgotten until rediscovered and reformulated thirty years later as follows: * "The electric potential difference between two points in different media can never be measured and has not yet been defined in terms of physical realities. It is therefore a conception which has no physical significance." The electrostatic potential difference between two points is admittedly defined in *electrostatics*, the mathematical theory of an imaginary fluid *electricity*, whose equilibrium or motion is determined entirely by the

---

* Guggenheim, J. *Physic. Chem.* (1929) **33** 842.
** Gibbs, *Collected Works*, vol. 1, p. 429.

electric field. *Electricity* of this kind does not exist. Only electrons and ions have physical existence and these differ fundamentally from the hypothetical fluid *electricity* in that their equilibrium is *thermodynamic* not *static*.

Although the above considerations seem almost obvious to anyone who has thought about the matter, there has in the past been considerable confusion due to misleading terminology. It therefore seems worth while considering in more detail some simple examples. Consider a potentiometer wire made of say copper and in particular two sections of the wire α' and α'' between which the electrical potential difference $\psi'' - \psi'$ is say 2 volts. Since α' and α'' are both in copper, there is no ambiguity in the meaning of $\psi'' - \psi'$. If two pieces of copper wire are attached to α' and α'', then the electrical potential difference between these two is also $\psi'' - \psi' = 2$ volts. If instead of copper wire we attach two pieces of silver wire β' and β'' to α' and α'' respectively, then the difference of electrical potential between β' and β'' is likewise 2 volts. The electrical potential difference between a piece of copper and a piece of silver is however not defined. The silver wire β' and the copper wire α' are in equilibrium with respect to electrons, so that

$$\mu_{el^-}^{\alpha'} = \mu_{el^-}^{\beta'}, \qquad (10.03.3)$$

where the subscript el$^-$ denotes electrons. Likewise

$$\mu_{el^-}^{\alpha''} = \mu_{el^-}^{\beta''}. \qquad (10.03.4)$$

Thus the situation is completely described by (3) or (4) together with

$$\mu_{el^-}^{\alpha''} - \mu_{el^-}^{\alpha'} = \mu_{el^-}^{\beta''} - \mu_{el^-}^{\beta'} = -F(\psi'' - \psi'). \qquad (10.03.5)$$

Suppose further that the two pieces of silver wire β', β'' be dipped respectively into two solutions γ', γ'' both having the same composition and both containing a silver salt. Then between each piece of silver wire and the solution with which it is in contact there will be equilibrium with respect to silver ions Ag$^+$. Hence

$$\mu_{Ag^+}^{\gamma'} = \mu_{Ag^+}^{\beta'}. \qquad (10.03.6)$$

$$\mu_{Ag^+}^{\gamma''} = \mu_{Ag^+}^{\beta''}. \qquad (10.03.7)$$

At the same time

$$\mu_{Ag^+}^{\gamma''} - \mu_{Ag^+}^{\gamma'} = \mu_{Ag^+}^{\beta''} - \mu_{Ag^+}^{\beta'} = F(\psi'' - \psi') = F \times 2 \text{ volts}. \quad (10.03.8)$$

If the two solutions γ', γ'' are contained in insulating vessels and the silver wires are removed without otherwise touching or disturbing the two solutions then the relations (6) remain valid until either solution is touched by some other electrically charged or electrically conducting body. From this it is clear that the value of μ_{Ag^+} in a solution of a silver salt depends not only on the composition of the solution but also on its, usually accidentally determined, electrical state. If the solutions also contain nitrate ions NO_3^- then, since both solutions have the same composition,

$$\mu_{NO_3^-}^{\gamma''} - \mu_{NO_3^-}^{\gamma'} = -F(\psi'' - \psi').$$ (10. 03. 9)

Adding (6) and (7), we obtain

$$\mu_{Ag^+}^{\gamma'} + \mu_{NO_3^-}^{\gamma'} = \mu_{Ag^+}^{\gamma''} + \mu_{NO_3^-}^{\gamma''}.$$ (10. 03. 10)

the electrical terms cancelling. We accordingly speak of the *chemical potential* of a salt, for example $\mu_{Ag,NO_3} = \mu_{Ag^+} + \mu_{NO_3^-}$, but of the *electrochemical potentials* of ions, for example μ_{Ag^+} and $\mu_{NO_3^-}$.

§ 10. 04   Absolute Activities of Ions

Since the absolute activity λ_i is related to μ_i by

$$\mu_i = RT \log \lambda_i,$$

it is clear that the absolute activity of an ionic species contains a factor depending on the, usually accidentally determined, electrical state of the system. The same applies to the activity coefficient of an ionic species. As already emphasized in the previous Chapter all such indeterminacy disappears in formulae relating to electrically neutral combinations of ions, in particular to salts.

§ 10. 05   Dilute Solutions in Common Solvent

According to (9. 09. 3) the absolute activity λ_i of an ionic species i is related to its molality m_i and its activity coefficient γ_i by

$$\lambda_i = l_i \, m_i \, \gamma_i.$$ (10. 05. 1)

where l_i depends on the solvent and temperature and moreover contains a partly undetermined factor, which however cancels in all applications to processes not involving a net transfer of electrical charge. Correspondingly the electrochemical potential μ_i has the form

$$\mu_i = RT \log l_i + RT \log m_i + RT \log \gamma_i,$$ (10. 05. 2)

and includes an undetermined additive term which cancels in all applications to processes not involving a net transfer of electrical charge. We shall investigate this term in greater detail.

Let us formally write

$$\mu_i = z_i F \psi + RT \log \lambda_i^0 + RT \log m_i + RT \log \gamma_i,$$ (10. 05. 3)

where λ_1^0 is independent of the electrical state of the phase and ψ is the electrical potential of the phase. Let us now apply (3) to two phases denoted by a single and a double dash respectively and then subtract. We obtain

$$\mu_i'' - \mu_i' = z_i \, F(\psi'' - \psi') + RT \log \frac{\lambda_i^{0''}}{\lambda_i^{0'}} + RT \log \frac{m_i''}{m_i'}$$

$$+ RT \log \frac{\gamma_i''}{\gamma_i'}. \tag{10.05.4}$$

We now reexamine the condition for the term containing $(\psi'' - \psi')$ to be physically defined.

The easiest case is when the two phases have the same chemical composition so that

$$\lambda_i^{0''} = \lambda_i^{0'}, \tag{10.05.5}$$

$$m_i^{0''} = m_i^{0'}, \tag{10.05.6}$$

$$\gamma_i'' = \gamma_i'. \tag{10.05.7}$$

Formula (4) then reduces to

$$\mu_i'' - \mu_i' = z_i \, F(\psi'' - \psi'). \tag{10.05.8}$$

Since $\mu_i'' - \mu_i'$ is well-defined, formula (8) in this special case defines $\psi'' - \psi'$.

We now consider the extreme opposite case of two solutions in different solvents or two different pure phases. This is the case in which there is no means of distinguishing in (4) between the term containing $\psi'' - \psi'$ and the term containing $\lambda_i^{0''}/\lambda_i^{0'}$. The splitting into these two terms has in this case no physical significance.

The above remarks merely repeat and confirm what has already been stated in the preceding sections. We have still to consider the intermediate case of two solutions of different composition in the same solvent, of course at the same temperature. We then have

$$\lambda_i^{0''} = \lambda_i^{0'}, \tag{10.05.9}$$

so that (4) reduces to

$$\mu_i'' - \mu_i' = z_i \, F(\psi'' - \psi') + RT \log \frac{m_i''}{m_i'} + RT \log \frac{\gamma_i''}{\gamma_i'}. \tag{10.05.10}$$

Since $\mu_i'' - \mu_i'$ is well-defined and m_i'', m_i' are measurable, the question whether $\psi'' - \psi'$ is determinate depends on our knowledge of γ_i''/γ_i'. If both the solutions are so dilute that we can evaluate γ by explicit formulae such as those of § 9.23, then we may consider that (10) defines $\psi'' - \psi'$. If on the other hand either solution is so concentrated that our knowledge of the value of γ_i is incomplete, then the value of $\psi'' - \psi'$ becomes correspondingly indefinite.

§ 10.06 Volta Potentials

It is outside the province of this book to consider thermionic phenomena. In case however any reader may be puzzled by the fact that the so-called *Volta potential difference* between two metals can be determined, it seems worth while stressing that the only *measurable* potential difference of this kind is that between two regions in free space immediately *outside* the two metals respectively

§ 10.07 Membrane Equilibria (Non-Osmotic)

Suppose two solutions α and β at the same temperature and pressure in the same solvent be separated by a membrane permeable to some ions, but not to others, nor to the solvent. We call this a *non-osmotic membrane equilibrium*. Then for every permeant ion we have the equilibrium condition

$$\mu_i^\alpha = \mu_i^\beta. \tag{10.07.1}$$

If for example one of the permeant ions is the Ag^+ ion, we have

$$\mu_{Ag^+}^\alpha = \mu_{Ag^+}^\beta. \tag{10.07.2}$$

If then we place in each of the two solutions a piece of silver wire since each piece of wire is in equilibrium, with respect to Ag^+, with the solution in which it dips, the equality of μ_{Ag^+} also holds between the two pieces of silver wire. Hence the two pieces of silver wire have equal electrical potentials, as could be verified by connecting them to a voltmeter or electrometer.

We have yet to consider what, if anything, can be said concerning the electrical potential difference between the two solutions. Since the solvent is the same in both solutions, we may in accordance with (10.05.10) replace (2) by

$$F(\psi^\beta - \psi^\alpha) + RT \log \frac{m_{Ag^+}^\beta}{m_{Ag^+}^\alpha} + RT \log \frac{\gamma_{Ag^+}^\beta}{\gamma_{Ag^+}^\alpha} = 0. \tag{10.07.3}$$

Supposing that m_{Ag^+} has been measured in both solutions, the determination of $\psi^\beta - \psi^\alpha$ reduces to that of the values of γ_{Ag^+} in the two solutions. If the solutions are so dilute that accurate or at least approximate, formulae for the activity coefficients γ are available then the electrical potential difference $\psi^\beta - \psi^\alpha$ can be evaluated with greater or less accuracy as the case may be. If either solution is so concentrated that γ_{Ag^+} cannot be evaluated, then no more can $\psi^\beta - \psi^\alpha$.

If there are several permeant ions, then the relations of the form (1) can be combined into relations corresponding to processes involving no net flow of electric charge. For example for a salt consisting of ν_+ cations R

of electrovalency z_+ and ν_- anions X of electrovalency z_-, both permeant, the equilibrium condition is

$$\nu_+ \mu_R^\alpha + \nu_- \mu_X^\alpha = \nu_+ \mu_R^\beta + \nu_- \mu_X^\beta. \tag{10.07.4}$$

which can be written in the equivalent form

$$(m_R^\alpha)^{\nu_+} (m_X^\alpha)^{\nu_-} (\gamma_{R,X}^\alpha)^{\nu_+ + \nu_-} = (m_R^\beta)^{\nu_+} (m_X^\beta)^{\nu_-} (\gamma_{R,X}^\beta)^{\nu_+ + \nu_-}. \tag{10.07.5}$$

§ 10.08   Osmotic Membrane Equilibrium

In the preceding section we assumed that the membrane was impermeable to the solvent. The more usual case when the membrane is permeable to the solvent, called *osmotic membrane equilibrium*, is much less simple. In this case equilibrium as regards the solvent between two phases separated by the membrane, will generally require a pressure difference between the two phases, the *osmotic pressure difference*, and this pressure difference complicates the exact conditions of equilibrium for the solute ions. We shall consider only the case of one and the same solvent on both sides of the membrane.

The conditions for membrane equilibrium can be written in the general form

$$\mu_1^\alpha = \mu_1^\beta \tag{10.08.1}$$

for the solvent and

$$\mu_i^\alpha = \mu_i^\beta \tag{10.08.2}$$

for each permeant ionic species.

We have now to take account of how each μ depends on the pressure, but for the sake of brevity we shall neglect the compressibility of the solutions. We have then in accordance with (9.06.1)

$$\mu_1 (P) = \mu_1^0 (P) - RT \, g \, M_1 \, \Sigma_i \, m_i$$
$$= \mu_1^* + P V_1 - RT \, g \, M_1 \, \Sigma_i \, m_i. \tag{10.08.3}$$

where $\mu_1^0 (P)$ is the value of μ_1 for the pure solvent at the pressure P, while μ_1^* is the value for the pure solvent in the limit of zero pressure. We recall that m_i the molality of the ionic species i is defined as the number of gram-ions of i dissolved in one kilogram of solvent, while M_1 is the mass of one mole of solvent divided by a kilogram.

Similarly for each ionic species i we replace (10.05.3) by

$$\mu_i = P V_i + z_i F \psi + RT \log \lambda_i^* + RT \log m_i \gamma_i, \tag{10.08.4}$$

where λ_i^* is independent of the pressure.

22

Using (3) in (1) we obtain for the equilibrium value of the pressure difference

$$P^\beta - P^\alpha = RT \frac{M_1}{V_1} (g^\beta \Sigma_i m_i^\beta - g^\alpha \Sigma_i m_i^\alpha). \qquad (10.08.5)$$

Using (4) in (2) we obtain

$$RT \log \frac{m_i^\beta \gamma_i^\beta}{m_i^\alpha \gamma_i^\alpha} + z_i F (\psi^\beta - \psi^\alpha) = (P^\alpha - P^\beta) V_i, \qquad (10.08.6)$$

and then substituting (5) into (6)

$$\log \frac{m_i^\beta \gamma_i^\beta}{m_i^\alpha \gamma_i^\alpha} + \frac{z_i F}{RT} (\psi^\beta - \psi^\alpha) = M_1 \frac{V_i}{V_1} (g^\alpha \Sigma_i m_i^\alpha - g^\beta \Sigma_i m_i^\beta). \quad (10.08.7)$$

Whether formula (7) by itself has any physical significance depends, as explained in 10.05, on whether values of γ_i can be computed. If they can, then from formula (7) the value of $\psi^\beta - \psi^\alpha$ can be computed, since all the other quantities occuring in (7) are measurable. In any case the term containing $\psi^\beta - \psi^\alpha$ can be eliminated by applying (7) to several ionic species together forming an electrically neutral combination. Thus for the equilibrium distribution of a permeant electrolyte consisting of ν_+ cations R and ν_- anions X we obtain

$$\frac{(m_R^\beta)^{\nu_+} (m_X^\beta)^{\nu_-} (\gamma_{R,X}^\beta)^{\nu_+ + \nu_-}}{(m_R^\alpha)^{\nu_+} (m_X^\alpha)^{\nu_-} (\gamma_{R,X}^\alpha)^{\nu_+ + \nu_-}}$$

$$= \exp \left\{ M_1 \frac{\nu_+ V_R + \nu_- V_X}{V_1} (g^\alpha \Sigma_i m_i^\alpha - g^\beta \Sigma_i m_i^\beta) \right\} \quad (10.08.8)$$

At high dilutions the quantity within the { } on the right side of (8) may be so small that it can be neglected. Under such conditions (8) reduces to

$$(m_R^\beta)^{\nu_+} (m_X^\beta)^{\nu_-} (\gamma_{R,X}^\beta)^{\nu_+ + \nu_-} = (m_R^\alpha)^{\nu_+} (m_X^\alpha)^{\nu_-} (\gamma_{R,X}^\beta)^{\nu_+ + \nu_-}, \quad (10.08.9)$$

of the same form as (10.07.5) for a non-osmotic membrane equilibrium.

The thermodynamic methods of Gibbs were first applied to osmotic membrane equilibria by Donnan. Such equilibria are accordingly called *Donnan s membrane equilibria*.

§ 10.09   Contact Equilibrium

The most important and simplest example of non-osmotic equilibrium is that of two phases with one common ion, the surface of separation being in effect a membrane permeable to the common ion but impermeable to all others. This may be called *contact equilibrium*.

We have already met several examples of contact equilibrium. For example, for two metals say Cu and Ag in contact there is equilibrium between the metals as regards electrons, but not as regards the positive ions Cu^{++} or Ag^+. This equilibrium is expressed by

$$\mu_{el^-}^{Cu} = \mu_{el^-}^{Ag}, \qquad (10.\,09.\,1)$$

the subscript el^- denoting electrons and the superscripts denoting the two phases.

Likewise for a piece of metal M of say Cu dipping into a solution S containing ions of the metal, in this case Cu^{++}, the *contact equilibrium* is completely described by

$$\mu_{Cu^{++}}^{M} = \mu_{Cu^{++}}^{S}, \qquad (10.\,09.\,2)$$

the metal and solution being in mutual equilibrium as regards the metallic ions only.

In neither of these cases is any contact electrical potential difference thermodynamically definable.

§ 10. 10 Examples of Electrochemical Cell

We shall now introduce the subject of electrochemical cells by the detailed study of a simple example in terms of the electrochemical potentials. At a later stage we shall proceed to derive more general formulae applicable to all electrochemical cells.

We describe a cell symbolically by writing down in order a number of phases separated by vertical lines, each phase being in contact with the phases written down immediately to its left and right. For example

$$\text{Cu} \;\bigg|\; \text{Zn} \;\bigg|\; \begin{matrix}\text{Solution } I \\ \text{containing } Zn^{++}\end{matrix} \;\bigg|\; \begin{matrix}\text{Solution } II \\ \text{containing } Ag^+\end{matrix} \;\bigg|\; \text{Ag} \;\bigg|\; \text{Cu} \qquad (10.\,10.\,1)$$

may be regarded as denoting a copper *terminal* attached to a zinc *electrode* dipping into a solution containing zinc ions; this solution is in contact with another solution *II* containing silver ions in which there is dipping a silver electrode attached to another copper terminal. We shall use the following superscripts to denote the several phases:

  $'$ the copper terminal on the left,
  Zn   the zinc electrode,
  I the solution on the left,
  II the solution on the right,
  Ag   the silver electrode,
  $''$ the copper terminal on the right.

In the metal phases, since there is equilibrium between electrons, metallic ions and the metal atoms, we have

$$\mu_{Cu^{++}}^{'} + 2\,\mu_{el^-}^{'} = \mu_{Cu^{++}}^{''} + 2\,\mu_{el^-}^{''} = \mu_{Cu}^{Cu}, \qquad (10.\,10.\,2)$$

$$\mu_{Zn^{++}}^{Zn} + 2\,\mu_{el^-}^{Zn} = \mu_{Zn}^{Zn}, \qquad (10.\,10.\,3)$$

$$\mu_{Ag^+}^{Ag} + \mu_{el^-}^{Ag} = \mu_{Ag}^{Ag}. \qquad (10.\,10.\,4)$$

The contact equilibrium conditions are

$$\mu'_{el^-} = \mu^{Zn}_{el^-},$$
(10. 10. 5)

$$\mu^{Zn}_{Zn^{++}} = \mu^{I}_{Zn^{++}}.$$
(10. 10. 6)

$$\mu^{II}_{Ag^+} = \mu^{Ag}_{Ag^+},$$
(10. 10. 7)

$$\mu^{Ag}_{el^-} = \mu''_{el^-}.$$
(10. 10. 8)

From (5) and (8) we deduce

$$\mu''_{el^-} - \mu'_{el^-} = \mu^{Ag}_{el^-} - \mu^{Zn}_{el^-},$$
(10. 10. 9)

and so using (3) and (4)

$$\mu''_{el^-} - \mu'_{el^-} = \mu^{Ag}_{Ag} - \tfrac{1}{2}\mu^{Zn}_{Zn} - \mu^{Ag}_{Ag^+} + \tfrac{1}{2}\mu^{Zn}_{Zn^{++}}.$$
(10. 10. 10)

and then using (6) and (7)

$$\mu''_{el^-} - \mu'_{el^-} = \mu^{Ag}_{Ag} - \tfrac{1}{2}\mu^{Zn}_{Zn} - \mu^{II}_{Ag^+} + \tfrac{1}{2}\mu^{I}_{Zn^{++}}.$$
(10. 10. 11)

We may further write

$$\mu''_{el^-} - \mu'_{el^-} = -F(\psi'' - \psi').$$
(10. 10. 12)

where $\psi'' - \psi'$ denotes the electrical potential difference between the two copper terminals. It is evident from relations (5) and (8) that the value of (12) would be the same if both copper terminals were replaced by any other metal provided both are of the same metal. Thus $\psi'' - \psi'$ is determined by the nature of the two electrodes and the two solutions. The electric potential difference $\psi'' - \psi'$ is called the *electromotive force* of the cell and is denoted by E. We accordingly replace (12) by

$$\mu''_{el^-} - \mu'_{el^-} = -FE.$$
(10. 10. 13)

Substituting (13) into (11) we then obtain

$$-FE = \mu^{Ag}_{Ag} - \tfrac{1}{2}\mu^{Zn}_{Zn} - \mu^{II}_{Ag^+} + \tfrac{1}{2}\mu^{I}_{Zn^{++}}.$$
(10. 10. 14)

We shall now assume that there is at least one anion, say NO_3^- present at equal molalities in both solutions I and II. In any such solution we have

$$\tfrac{1}{2}\mu_{Zn^{++}} = \tfrac{1}{2}\mu_{Zn(NO_3)_2} - \mu_{NO_3^-}.$$
(10. 10. 15)

$$\mu_{Ag^+} = \mu_{AgNO_3} - \mu_{NO_3^-}.$$
(10. 10. 16)

Using (15) and (16) we can rewrite (14) as

$$E = \frac{1}{F}\{\tfrac{1}{2}\mu^{Zn}_{Zn} - \tfrac{1}{2}\mu^{I}_{Zn(NO_3)_2}\} + \frac{1}{F}\{\mu^{I}_{NO_3^-} - \mu^{II}_{NO_3^-}\}$$

$$- \frac{1}{F}\{\mu^{Ag}_{Ag} - \mu^{II}_{AgNO_3}\}.$$
(10. 10. 17)

We have now a formula for E containing three terms in { } of which the first relates only to the Zn electrode and the $Zn(NO_3)_2$ in the solution around this electrode and the last relates only to the Ag electrode and the $AgNO_3$ in the solution around this electrode. The middle term on the other hand is independent of the nature of the electrodes and relates to an anion in the two solutions. One might be inclined to call the first of these three terms the *electrode potential* of the Zn electrode, the second the *liquid-liquid junction potential* and the last the *electrode potential* of the silver. Such a procedure is harmless provided it is realized that

(a)   this decomposition of E into three terms is affected by our arbitrary choice of the anion NO_3^- for use in our formulae;

(b)   other alternative decompositions of E into three terms can be obtained by the arbitrary choice of some other ion instead of NO_3^- in our formulae;

(c)   any such decomposition of E is no more nor less fundamental than another;

(d)   there is in general no means of decomposing E into three terms which is less arbitrary than the one described.

In view of some inevitable arbitrariness in the decomposition of the electromotive force of a cell into two *electrode potentials* and a *liquid-liquid junction potential,* we shall for the most part abandon any attempt at such a decomposition. We shall accordingly in the next section derive a general formula for the electromotive force of any cell by a more powerful method which makes no reference at all to the localization of separate terms in the electromotive force. Before proceeding to this general treatment, we shall however draw attention to a special case where the arbitrariness referred to above effectively disappears.

Reverting to formula (17), let us now consider the particular case where the molalities of Zn^{++} and Ag^+ in the two electrode solutions are extremely small compared with the molalities of other ions in these solutions and the compositions of the two electrode solutions are apart from their content of Zn^{++} and Ag^+ nearly identical. Under these particular conditions we may regard the two electrode solutions as effectively identical except with regard to the equilibrium between solution and electrode. We may accordingly drop the superscripts I and II so that (17) reduces to

$$E = \frac{1}{F} \{ \tfrac{1}{2} \mu_{Zn}^{Zn} - \tfrac{1}{2} \mu_{Zn(NO_3)_2} \}$$

$$- \frac{1}{F} \{ \mu_{Ag}^{Ag} - \mu_{AgNO_3} \} \tag{10.10.18}$$

where the μ's without superscripts refer to the solution. We may then regard the cell (1) under consideration as

$$\text{Cu} \ \bigg| \ \text{Zn} \ \bigg| \ \begin{array}{c} \text{Solution containing} \\ Zn^{++} \text{ and } Ag^+ \end{array} \ \bigg| \ \text{Ag} \ \bigg| \ \text{Cu,} \tag{10.10.19}$$

bearing in mind that in reality the Ag^+ must be kept away from the Zn electrode to avoid irreversible dissolution of Zn with plating out of Ag.

It is quite usual to describe certain cells in this manner as if containing only one solution, but in reality there must always be some real, though possibly small difference between the composition of the two electrode solutions. Consider for example the cell commonly described as

$$H_2, Pt \;\Big|\; \text{Aqueous solution of HCl} \;\Big|\; AgCl \;\Big|\; Ag \;\Big|\; Pt. \quad (10.\,10.\,20)$$

This description implies that an electrode consisting of platinum in contact with hydrogen and another electrode consisting of a mixture of AgCl and Ag are dipping into the same solution. Actually the platinum dips into a solution saturated with hydrogen, but containing no AgCl, while the silver is immersed in a solution saturated with AgCl but containing no hydrogen. If in fact any part of the solution contained both hydrogen and silver chloride, these might * react irreversibly to give silver and hydrogen chloride. Thus the cell is more accurately described by

$$H_2 \;\left|\; \begin{array}{c} \text{Solution } I \\ \text{Aqueous solution} \\ \text{of HCl saturated} \\ \text{with } H_2 \end{array} \;\right|\; \begin{array}{c} \text{Solution } II \\ \text{Aqueous solution} \\ \text{of HCl saturated} \\ \text{with AgCl} \end{array} \;\Big|\; AgCl \;\Big|\; Ag \;\Big|\; Pt. \; (10.\,10.\,21)$$

By an analysis of (21) similar to that applied to (1) it can be shown that the electromotive force is given accurately by

$$FE = \tfrac{1}{2}\mu_{H_2}^G - \mu_{H^+}^I + \mu_{AgCl}^{AgCl} - \mu_{Ag}^{Ag} - \mu_{Cl^-}^{II}, \qquad (10.\,10.\,22)$$

where the superscript G denotes the gas phase. Since however as far as the HCl is concerned we may regard the solutions I and II as essentially identical, we may drop these superscripts and (22) reduces to

$$FE = \tfrac{1}{2}\mu_{H_2}^G + \mu_{AgCl}^{AgCl} - \mu_{Ag}^{Ag} - \mu_{HCl}. \qquad (10.\,10.\,23)$$

where μ_{HCl} denotes the chemical potential of HCl in the solution.

§ 10.11 General Treatment of Electromotive Force

We now proced to a more general treatment applicable to any electrochemical cell. We begin by describing the characteristics common to all such cells. In so doing it is convenient to assume that the system which we refer to as the *cell* is terminated at both ends by *terminals* of the same metal. The essential characteristic of the cell is that a chemical process involving ions can take place in it in such a manner that the process is necessarily accompanied by a transfer of electric charge from one terminal to the other without building up any charge in any of the intermediate phases of the cell. Moreover the charge which flows from the one terminal to the other is directly proportional to the change in the degree of advancement of the chemical process.

---

* Actually in the case of this cell the irreversible process will usually be too slow to affect the accuracy of the electromotive force measurements.

For example in the cell, already discussed in the previous section,

$$\text{H}_2, \text{Pt} \;\bigg|\; \text{Aqueous solution of HCl} \;\bigg|\; \text{AgCl} \;\bigg|\; \text{Ag} \;\bigg|\; \text{Pt}, \qquad (10.11.1)$$

the chemical process accompanying the flow of one faraday from the left to the right is

$$\tfrac{1}{2}\,\text{H}_2(g) + \text{AgCl}(s) \rightarrow \text{Ag}(s) + \text{HCl}(aq). \qquad (10.11.2)$$

where (g) denotes gas, (s) denotes solid and (aq) denotes aqueous solution.

We now suppose the two terminals of the cell to be put into contact respectively with two points of a potentiometer bridge so placed that the electric potential of the right contact exceeds that of the left contact by an amount E'. Then in general an electric current will flow through the cell and between the two points of contact with the potentiometer bridge. If either of the points of contact is moved along the bridge the current will increase or decrease and it will change sign when E' has a certain value E. When E' is slightly less than E there will be a flow of current from left to right in the cell and from right to left in the potentiometer bridge; this flow of current will be accompanied by a well defined chemical change in the cell. When E' is slightly greater than E there will be a flow of current in the opposite direction and the accompanying chemical change in the cell will also be reversed. When E' is equal to E there will be no flow of current and no chemical change, but by a small shift in the point of contact between cell terminal and potentiometer bridge a small current can be made to flow in either direction. This is a typical and a particularly realistic example of a *reversible process*. The value E of E' at which the current changes sign is the *electromotive force* of the cell.

We now stipulate that $E' = E$ so that the electromotive force of the cell is balanced against the potential difference in the potentiometer bridge and we consider the flow of one faraday from left to right in the cell, the temperature being maintained constant throughout and the pressure on every phase being kept constant. The pressures on different phases will usually, but not necessarily always, be all equal. Then since, as we have seen, this process is reversible and isothermal, it follows from (1.41.6) that the work w done on the cell is equal to the increase in free energy F, that is to say

$$w = \triangle F. \qquad (10.11.3)$$

In the present case w consists of two distinct parts, namely

(a) the work $-\Sigma_\alpha P^\alpha \, dV^\alpha$ done by the pressures P^α acting on the several phases α,

(b) the electrical work $-FE$ done by the potentiometer on the cell in transferring one faraday through a potential difference E.

We may therefore replace (3) by

$$-FE = \triangle F + \Sigma_\alpha P^\alpha \, dV^\alpha = \triangle G. \qquad (10.11.4)$$

It must be emphasized that the symbol $\triangle$ in both (3) and (4) denotes the increase of a function when the chemical change taking place is that associated with the flow in the cell of one faraday from the left to the right.

From (4) we see that the electrical work obtainable from a reversible isothermal process, at constant pressure on each phase, is equal to the decrease in the Gibbs function G. This explains the alternative name *useful energy* for the Gibbs function.

Alternatively we could derive the relation

$$FE = A, \qquad (10.11.5)$$

where A denotes the *affinity* of the chemical process associated with the flow of one faraday from left to right. Formulae (4) and (5) are entirely equivalent.

§ 10.12 Temperature Dependence

By combining (10.11.4) with the Gibbs-Helmholtz relation (3.06.4) we obtain *

$$F\left(E - T\frac{\partial E}{\partial T}\right) = -\triangle H. \qquad (10.12.1)$$

By subtracting (1) from (10.11.4), or by a more direct method, we obtain

$$F\frac{\partial E}{\partial T} = \triangle S. \qquad (10.12.2)$$

In both (1) and (2) the symbol $\triangle$ denotes increase when the chemical change takes place which accompanies the flow of one faraday from left to right.

It is perhaps worth while drawing attention to the physical meaning of $\triangle H$ and $\triangle S$. If the cell is kept in a thermostat and balanced against a potentiometer so that any flow of current is reversible, then when one faraday flows from left to right in the cell

(a)   the work done on the cell by the potentiometer is $- FE$.

(b)   the work done on the cell by external pressures is $-\Sigma_\alpha P^\alpha \triangle V^\alpha$,

(c)   the heat absorbed is $T\triangle S = F(\partial E/\partial T)$,

(d)   the increase in the energy of the cell is the sum of the above three terms namely $\triangle U = -FE - \Sigma_\alpha P^\alpha \triangle V^\alpha + F(\partial E/\partial T)$,

---

* Although formula (3.06.4) is generally called the Gibbs–Helmholtz relation, it is in fact due to Gibbs, while its corollary (10.12.1) was obtained independently by Helmholtz.

(e)   the increase in the heat function is $\triangle H = \triangle U + \Sigma_\alpha P^\alpha \triangle V^\alpha =$
$-F\{E - T(\partial E/\partial T)\}$.

If, on the other hand, the cell is kept in a thermostat and short circuited so that the chemical change takes place irreversibly without the performance of electrical work, then when the chemical change takes place to the same extent as before,

(a)   the electrical work done on the cell is zero,

(b)   the work done on the cell by external pressures is $-\Sigma_\alpha P^\alpha \triangle V^\alpha$,

(c)   the heat absorbed is $\triangle H$.

§ 10.13   Application of Nernst's Theorem

The measurement of electromotive force provides a method of determining $\triangle G$ for the accompanying chemical reaction; this can be combined with a value of $\triangle H$, determined calorimetrically, so as to obtain the value of $\triangle S$. Since however the magnitude of $T \triangle S$ is often small compared with that of $\triangle G$ and of $\triangle H$, the relative error in $\triangle S$ determined in this way can be large. If on the other hand accurate measurements of electromotive force are made over a range of temperatures so as to give an accurate value of the temperature coefficient of the electromotive force, this provides directly the value of $\triangle S$ for the cell reaction. Values of $\triangle S$ thus obtained for any chemical reaction between only solid phases may be used to test Nernst's heat theorem, provided heat capacity data down to low temperatures are available for each substance. The procedure is illustrated by the following example [*].

In the cell

$$\text{Pt} \left| \text{Pb}^{(Hg)} \right| \begin{array}{c} \text{Solution of Pb salt} \\ \text{saturated with PbI}_2 \end{array} \left| \text{PbI}_2 \right| \text{I}_2 \left| \text{Pt}, \right. \quad (10.13.1)$$

where the superscript (Hg) denotes that the lead is in the form of an amalgam, the chemical process when one faraday flows from left to right is

$$\tfrac{1}{2}\text{Pb}^{(Hg)} + \text{I} \rightarrow \tfrac{1}{2}\text{PbI}_2. \quad (10.13.2)$$

For the cell at 25 °C it is found [**] that

$$E = 893.62 \text{ m volt}, \quad (10.13.3)$$

$$\frac{\partial E}{\partial T} = -0.042 \pm 0.005 \frac{\text{m volt}}{\text{deg.}}. \quad (10.13.4)$$

In the cell

$$\text{Pt} \left| \text{Pb}^{(Hg)} \right| \text{PbI}_2 \left| \text{Solution of KI} \right| \text{AgI} \left| \text{Ag} \right| \text{Pt}, \quad (10.13.5)$$

*   Due to Webb, J. Physic. Chem. (1925) **29** 827.
**   Gerke, J. Am. Chem. Soc. (1922) **44** 1703.

where $Pb^{(Hg)}$ denotes the same lead amalgam as in (1), the cell process accompanied by the flow of one faraday from left to right is

$$\tfrac{1}{2} Pb^{(Hg)} + Ag\,I \rightarrow \tfrac{1}{2} PbI_2 + Ag. \qquad (10.\,13.\,6)$$

For this cell at 25 °C it is found * that

$$E = 207.8 \pm 0.2 \text{ m volt,} \qquad (10.\,13.\,7)$$

$$\frac{\partial E}{\partial T} = -0.188 \pm 0.002 \frac{\text{m volt}}{\text{deg.}}. \qquad (10.\,13.\,8)$$

The data for neither of these cells can be used directly for testing Nernst's heat theorem owing to lack of calorimetric data for PbI_2 down to low temperatures. However by subtracting (7) from (3) and (8) from (4) we obtain for a cell at 25 °C in which the cell process is

$$Ag + I \rightarrow Ag\,I, \qquad (T = 298°), \qquad (10.\,13.\,9)$$

$$E = 685.8 \pm 0.2 \text{ m volt,} \qquad (T = 298°), \qquad (10.\,13.\,10)$$

$$\frac{\partial E}{\partial T} = 0.146 \pm 0.004 \frac{\text{m volt}}{\text{deg.}}. \qquad (10.\,13.\,11)$$

Multiplying (10) and (11) by

$$F = 0.9649 \times 10^5 \text{ coulombs}$$
$$= 0.9649 \times 10^5 \text{ joule/volt}$$
$$= 0.09649 \text{ K joule/m volt,} \qquad (10.\,13.\,12)$$

and using (10. 11. 4) and (10. 12. 2), we obtain for the process (9) at 298 °K

$$\triangle G = -66.17 \text{ K joule,} \qquad (T = 298°), \quad (10.\,13.\,13)$$

$$\triangle S = 14.06 \pm 0.4 \text{ joule/deg,} \qquad (T = 298°). \quad (10.\,13.\,14)$$

From (13) and (14) we derive incidentally

$$\triangle H = \triangle G + T \triangle S$$
$$= (-66.17 + 4.22) \text{ K joule}$$
$$= -61.95 \text{ K joule}$$
$$= -14.81 \text{ K cal.,} \qquad (10.\,13.\,15)$$

with which may be compared the calorimetrically measured value ** — 14.97 K cal.

We must now convert the value of $\triangle S$ at 298° K given by (14) to the corresponding value in the limit $T \rightarrow 0$. The following calorimetric data are available *** for $S(298) - S(0)$.

---

* Gerke, *J. Am. Chem. Soc.* (1922) **44** 1703.
** Webb, *J. Physic. Chem.* (1925) **29** 827.
*** AgI, see Pitzer, *J. Am. Chem. Soc.* (1941) **63** 516; Ag, see Griffiths and Griffiths, *Proc. Roy. Soc.*, A (1914) **90** 557; I, see Lange, *Zeit. Physik. Chem.* (1924) **110** 343. Experimental data for Ag and I recomputed by Kelley *U. S. Bureau of Mines*, (1932) Bulletin 350.

$$\text{AgI} \quad 115.5 \pm 1.2 \text{ joule/deg.,} \qquad (10.13.16)$$

$$\text{Ag} \quad 42.5 \pm 0.4 \text{ joule/deg.,} \qquad (10.13.17)$$

$$\text{I} \quad 58.4 \text{ joule/deg.} \qquad (10.13.18)$$

Although accurate calorimetric data for AgI are available down to $T = 15\,°K$, at this temperature C/R has the exceptionally high value 1.45 which leads to the rather high uncertainty in the extrapolation to $T = 0$ shown in (16).

Combining (16), (17) and (18) we obtain for the process (9)

$$\triangle S(298) - \triangle S(0) = 14.6 \pm 1.2 \text{ joule/deg.} \qquad (10.13.19)$$

Now comparing (19) with (14) we obtain

$$\triangle S(0) = -0.5 \pm 1.3 \text{ joule/deg.}$$

so that within the experimental accuracy $\triangle S(0) = 0$ in accordance with Nernst's heat theorem.

§ 10.14 Cells without Transference

When an electrochemical cell contains only two solutions, one surrounding each electrode, and these two solutions are so nearly alike in composition that they be regarded as identical except with respect to the reactions at the electrodes, the cell is called a *cell without transference*. When a current flows through the cell there is in fact necessarily tranference of some electrolyte from the one electrode to the other, but if the two electrode solutions are of nearly identical composition the changes in the chemical potentials of the electrolytes transferred are negligible and so this transference is without importance.

As a typical example of a *cell without transference* we again consider the cell

	Solution *I*	Solution *II*			
Pt, H_2	Aqueous HCl saturated with H_2	Aqueous HCl saturated with AgCl	AgCl	Ag	Pt. (10.14.1)

When one faraday flows from the left to the right, the following changes take place:

(a) at the left electrode

$$\tfrac{1}{2}H_2(g) \rightarrow H^+(aq.\,I); \qquad (10.14.2)$$

(b) at the right electrode

$$\text{AgCl}(s) \rightarrow \text{Ag}(s) + Cl^-(aq.\,II); \qquad (10.14.3)$$

(c) there is a simultaneous transfer of some H^+ ions from left to right and of Cl^- ions from right to left such that the net transfer of charge from left to right is one faraday and that electrical neutrality is preserved in both electrode solutions.

Since however we ignore the effect on the properties of HCl in solution of saturating the solution with either H_2 or AgCl, we need not distinguish between the two electrode solutions. We may therefore replace (1) by

$$\text{Pt, } H_2 \mid \text{Aqueous HCl} \mid \text{AgCl} \mid \text{Ag} \mid \text{Pt.} \qquad (10.14.4)$$

Correspondingly (a) and (b) reduce to

$$\text{(a)} \quad \tfrac{1}{2} H_2(g) \rightarrow H^+(aq); \qquad (10.14.5)$$

$$\text{(b)} \quad AgCl(s) \rightarrow Ag(s) + Cl^-(aq); \qquad (10.14.6)$$

and (c) may be ignored. Thus the chemical change accompanying the flow of one faraday reduces to

$$\tfrac{1}{2} H_2(g) + AgCl(s) \rightarrow Ag(s) + H^+(aq) + Cl^-(aq), \qquad (10.14.7)$$

for which

$$\triangle G = \mu_{Ag}^{Ag} + \mu_{HCl} - \tfrac{1}{2}\mu_{H_2}^{G} - \mu_{AgCl}^{AgCl}, \qquad (10.14.8)$$

where the superscript G denotes the gas phase and μ_{HCl} denotes the chemical potential of HCl in the solution.

Substituting (8) into (10.11.4) we obtain

$$-FE = \mu_{Ag}^{Ag} + \mu_{HCl} - \tfrac{1}{2}\mu_{H_2}^{G} - \mu_{AgCl}^{AgCl}, \qquad (10.14.9)$$

in agreement with (10.10.23).

Explicit formulae for all *cells without transference* can be obtained similarly. We shall merely quote, without detailed derivation, one other example

$$\text{Pt} \quad \begin{array}{|c|c|} \text{Solution containing} & \text{Solution containing} \\ \text{Sn}^{++} \text{ and Sn}^{++++} & \text{Fe}^{++} \text{ and Fe}^{+++} \end{array} \quad \text{Pt.} \quad (10.14.10)$$

Provided that both electrode solutions contain a preponderating excess of other electrolytes and have nearly the same composition so that we may regard them as one solution, the chemical change accompanying the flow of one faraday from left to right may be written

$$\tfrac{1}{2} \text{Sn}^{++} + \text{Fe}^{+++} \rightarrow \tfrac{1}{2} \text{Sn}^{++++} + \text{Fe}^{++}, \qquad (10.14.11)$$

for which

$$\triangle G = \tfrac{1}{2}\mu_{Sn^{++++}} + \mu_{Fe^{++}} - \tfrac{1}{2}\mu_{Sn^{++}} - \mu_{Fe^{+++}}. \qquad (10.14.12)$$

Consequently

$$FE = \tfrac{1}{2}\mu_{Sn^{++}} + \mu_{Fe^{+++}} - \tfrac{1}{2}\mu_{Sn^{++++}} - \mu_{Fe^{++}}$$
$$= \tfrac{1}{2}\mu_{SnCl_2} + \mu_{FeCl_3} - \tfrac{1}{2}\mu_{SnCl_4} - \mu_{FeCl_2}, \qquad (10.14.13)$$

provided there is some Cl^- ion in the solutions.

§ 10. 15   Cells with Transference having Two Similar Electrodes

Any cell which does not satisfy the conditions in the definition of a cell without transference, is called a *cell with transference*. The detailed discussion of a *cell with transference* is more involved than that of a *cell without transference*. We shall initially restrict ourselves to the case that the two electrodes are of the same chemical nature so that the chemical processes taking place at the electrodes are the converse of each other. For example we may consider the cell

$$\text{Ag} \left| \text{AgCl} \right| \begin{matrix} \text{Solution } I \\ \text{containing Cl}^- \end{matrix} \left| \begin{matrix} \text{Bridge} \\ \text{solutions} \end{matrix} \right| \begin{matrix} \text{Solution } II \\ \text{containing Cl}^- \end{matrix} \left| \text{AgCl} \right| \text{Ag.} \quad (10.\,15.\,1)$$

We assume that the two electrode solutions I and II are connected by *bridge solutions* in which the composition varies continuously. It is essential to exclude any discontinuity of composition, for in that case the passage of an infinitesimal current would not be reversible and it would not then be possible to apply thermodynamic equations. Suppose for example in two solutions in contact that the cation Na^+ were present in that on the left but not that on the right, while the cation K^+ were present in the solution on the right but not that on the left. Then an infinitesimal current from left to right would transfer Na^+ from the left solution to the right solution. Reversal of the current would on the other hand transfer K^+ from the right solution to the left solution. If however any two solutions in contact differ only infinitesimally in composition, the passage of current will be reversible. It is true that simultaneously there is taking place an irreversible diffusion between the two solutions tending to equalize their compositions. It is however safe to regard this irreversible diffusion process as superposed on the reversible flow of current and the former may be ignored while considering the latter.

This condition of continuity of composition is the only condition imposed on the nature of the bridge solutions. In view of this condition the compositions of the outermost bridge solutions are identical respectively with those of the electrode solutions. If the bridge solutions are formed by natural mixing or interdiffusion of the two electrode solutions, then their compositions throughout will be intermediate between those of the two electrode solutions. On the other hand the middle portion of the bridge solutions may consist of a solution of entirely different composition from either electrode solution, but such solution must be connected to each electrode solution through solutions of continuously varying composition. The formulae which we are about to derive are applicable to all cases.

Consider now any solution forming part of the bridge and let its composition be described by molalities m_R of cations R with electrovalency z_R and m_X of anions X with electrovalency z_X, a negative integer. We can equally well describe the nature of this solution by specifying the electrochemical potentials μ_R of each cation and μ_X of each anion. The composition of the solution immediately to its right is similarly described by $\mu_R + d\mu_R$ and $\mu_X + d\mu_X$; that to its left by $\mu_R - d\mu_R$ and $\mu_X - d\mu_X$.

When there is a net flow of one faraday from left to right, this occurs partly by flow of cations from left to right and partly by flow of anions from right to left. If t_R denotes the fraction of the current carried by the cation R and t_X the fraction of the current carried by the anion X, then t_R and t_X are called the *transport numbers* or *transference numbers* of R and X respectively. The values of t_R and t_X in each solutions are determined by its composition and temperature. In every solution they necessarily satisfy the identity

$$\Sigma_R t_R + \Sigma_X t_X = 1. \tag{10.15.2}$$

Thus when one faraday flows through the cell from left to right, then at each place in the bridge solutions there is a flow of t_R/z_R gram-ions of the cation R from left to right and a simultaneous flow of $t_X/(-z_X)$ gram-ions of the anion X from right to left. The resultant increase in G is

$$\Sigma_R \frac{t_R}{z_R} d\mu_R + \Sigma_X \frac{t_X}{(-z_X)} (-d\mu_X). \tag{10.15.3}$$

This is the increase in G associated with the flow of current through one element of the bridge. The increase in G associated with the flow of current from the one electrode solution through all the bridge solutions to the other electrode solution is therefore

$$\int_I^{II} \Sigma_R \frac{t_R}{z_R} d\mu_R + \int_I^{II} \Sigma_X \frac{t_X}{z_X} d\mu_X, \tag{10.15.4}$$

where the integration has to be extended through all the bridge solutions from the left electrode solution I to the right electrode solution II.

At the same time we have the electrode processes accompanying the flow of one faraday from left to right

$$\mathrm{Ag} + \mathrm{Cl}^{-I} \rightarrow \mathrm{Ag\,Cl}, \tag{10.15.5}$$

$$\mathrm{AgCl} \rightarrow \mathrm{Ag} + \mathrm{Cl}^{-II}, \tag{10.15.6}$$

which are together equivalent to the single process

$$\mathrm{Cl}^{-I} \rightarrow \mathrm{Cl}^{-II}. \tag{10.15.7}$$

The associated increase in G is

$$\mu_{\mathrm{Cl}^-}^{II} - \mu_{\mathrm{Cl}^-}^{I}. \tag{10.15.8}$$

Adding (8) to (3), we obtain for the process accompanying the net flow of one faraday from left to right

$$\triangle G = \mu_{\mathrm{Cl}^-}^{II} - \mu_{\mathrm{Cl}^-}^{I} + \int_I^{II} \Sigma_R \frac{t_R}{z_R} d\mu_R + \int_I^{II} \Sigma_X \frac{t_X}{z_X} d\mu_X. \tag{10.15.9}$$

Substituting (9) into (10.11.4), we obtain for the electromotive force

$$-\mathcal{F}E = \mu_{Cl^-}^{II} - \mu_{Cl^-}^{I} + \int_{I}^{II} \Sigma_R \frac{t_R}{z_R} d\mu_R + \int_{I}^{II} \Sigma_X \frac{t_X}{z_X} d\mu_X. \tag{10.15.10}$$

In obtaining (7) and (8) we used the fact that $z_{Cl^-} = -1$. In order to facilitate generalization of the formulae to other kinds of electrodes, we rewrite the above formulae, displaying z_{Cl^-}, as follows

$$\frac{1}{z_{Cl^-}} Cl^{-II} \to \frac{1}{z_{Cl^-}} Cl^{-I}, \tag{10.15.11}$$

$$-\mathcal{F}E = \triangle G = \frac{1}{z_{Cl^-}} (\mu_{Cl^-}^{I} - \mu_{Cl^-}^{II})$$

$$+ \int_{I}^{II} \Sigma_R \frac{t_R}{z_R} d\mu_R + \int_{I}^{II} \Sigma_X \frac{t_X}{z_X} d\mu_X. \tag{10.15.12}$$

If we express each μ in terms of molalities m and activity coefficients γ, we obtain

$$-\mathcal{F}E = \frac{RT}{z_{Cl^-}} \log \frac{m_{Cl^-}^{I} \gamma_{Cl^-}^{I}}{m_{Cl^-}^{II} \gamma_{Cl^-}^{II}} + RT \int_{I}^{II} \Sigma_R \frac{t_R}{z_R} d\log m_R \gamma_R$$

$$+ RT \int_{I}^{II} \Sigma_X \frac{t_X}{z_X} d\log m_X \gamma_X. \tag{10.15.13}$$

It is instructive to verify that the μ's in (12), and consequently the $\log \gamma$'s in (13), occur only in linear combinations of the form

$$\Sigma_i \nu_i \mu_i, \qquad \Sigma_i \nu_i \log \gamma_i, \tag{10.15.14}$$

where

$$\Sigma_i \nu_i z_i = 0. \tag{10.15.15}$$

To do this we make use of (2), from which we derive the identity

$$\int_{I}^{II} \Sigma_R t_R d\mu_{Cl^-} + \int_{I}^{II} \Sigma_X t_X d\mu_{Cl^-} = \mu_{Cl^-}^{II} - \mu_{Cl^-}^{I}. \tag{10.15.16}$$

Using (16) we can rewrite (12) and (13) as

$$-\mathcal{F}E = \triangle G = \int_{I}^{II} \Sigma_R t_R \left(\frac{d\mu_R}{z_R} - \frac{d\mu_{Cl^-}}{z_{Cl^-}} \right)$$

$$+ \int_{I}^{II} \Sigma_X t_X \left(\frac{d\mu_X}{z_X} - \frac{d\mu_{Cl^-}}{z_{Cl^-}} \right)$$

$$= RT \int_{I}^{II} \Sigma_R t_R \left(\frac{d\log m_R \gamma_R}{z_R} - \frac{d\log m_{Cl^-} \gamma_{Cl^-}}{z_{Cl^-}} \right)$$

$$+ RT \int_{I}^{II} \Sigma_X t_X \left(\frac{d\log m_X \gamma_X}{z_X} - \frac{d\log m_{Cl^-} \gamma_{Cl^-}}{z_{Cl^-}} \right) \tag{10.15.17}$$

from which, remembering that z_X and z_{Cl^-} are negative, we see that the linear combinations of the $d\mu$'s and $d \log \gamma$'s satisfy the condition described by (15). Incidentally we may note that the terms of the first integrand correspond to the transfer of t_R equivalents of the ions R and Cl^- in the same direction, while the terms of the second integrand correspond to the transfer of t_X equivalents of the ions X and Cl^- in opposite directions. We thus verify that no electrical charge accumulates anywhere inside the cell when a current passes.

§ 10. 16 Determination of Transport Numbers

Formula (17) gives an explicit value of the electromotive force E, but to apply it or test it we require to know the values of the transport numbers of all cations and all anions throughout the bridge solutions. This in turn involves a knowledge of the compositions of all the continuous series of solutions forming the bridge. Since this knowledge is usually not available, formula (17) though exact is not of much use except in specially simple cases.

, The simplest and the most useful example of a cell with transference is that in which there is only one kind of cation and one kind of anion in the whole cell. Let us consider for example the cell

$$\text{Ag}\left|\text{AgCl}\right|\begin{array}{c}\text{Aqueous MgCl}_2\\\text{at molality } m_1\end{array}\left|\begin{array}{c}\text{Transition}\\\text{layer}\end{array}\right|\begin{array}{c}\text{Aqueous MgCl}_2\\\text{at molality } m_2\end{array}\left|\text{AgCl}\right|\text{Ag.} \quad (10. 16. 1)$$

We use the name *transition layer* to denote the naturally formed bridge between the two electrode solutions consisting entirely of solutions of $MgCl_2$ of intermediate compositions. For the cell (1) formula (10. 15. 17) reduces to

$$-FE = RT \int_{m=m_1}^{m=m_2} t_{Mg^{++}} \left\{ \frac{d \log m_{Mg^{++}} \gamma_{Mg^{++}}}{2} - \frac{d \log m_{Cl^-} \gamma_{Cl^-}}{(-1)} \right\}$$

$$= \frac{RT}{2} \int_{m=m_1}^{m=m_2} t_{Mg^{++}} \, d \log (m^3 \gamma_{Mg. Cl}^3), \qquad (10. 16. 2)$$

where m denotes the molality and $\gamma_{Mg, Cl}$ the mean activity coefficient of the electrolyte $MgCl_2$. If the values of $\gamma_{Mg, Cl}$ are known either from measurements of the electromotive force of cells without transference or by freezing-point measurements combined with use of the Gibbs–Duhem relation, then formula (2) can be used to give information concerning the transport number $t_{Mg^{++}}$.

Since in solutions containing only the single electrolyte $MgCl_2$ the value of $t_{Mg^{++}}$ depends only on the molality, the integral in (2) is completely defined and is independent of how the molality varies along the transition layer. In particular it is independent of whether the transition layer has been formed mainly by mixing of the two electrode solutions or mainly by interdiffusion between them.

If the molalities of the two electrode solutions do not differ greatly from each other, it may be legitimate to neglect the variation of $t_{Mg^{++}}$ with composition. In this case (2) simplifies to

$$-FE = \tfrac{3}{2} t_{Mg^{++}} RT \log \frac{m_2 \gamma_2}{m_1 \gamma_1} \qquad (10.16.3)$$

where γ_1, γ_2 denote the mean activity coefficients of $MgCl_2$ in solutions of molality m_1, m_2 respectively.

§ 10.17 Cells with Transference having Two Dissimilar Electrodes

In § 10.14 we discussed cells without transference and in § 10.15 cells with transference having two similar electrodes. We have still to consider cells with transference having two dissimilar electrodes. These are most easily disposed of by regarding them as a combination of the two types of cell previously discussed. This will be made clear by a typical example.

The cell

$$\text{Pt, H}_2 \left| \begin{array}{c} \text{Solution } I \\ \text{containing HCl} \end{array} \right| \begin{array}{c} \text{Bridge} \\ \text{solutions} \end{array} \left| \begin{array}{c} \text{Solution } II \\ \text{containing HCl} \end{array} \right| \text{AgCl} \left| \text{Ag} \right| \text{Pt} \qquad (10.17.1)$$

may be regarded as a combination of the two cells

$$\text{Pt, H}_2 \left| \begin{array}{c} \text{Solution } I \\ \text{containing HCl} \end{array} \right| \text{AgCl} \left| \text{Ag} \right| \text{Pt,} \qquad (10.17.2)$$

$$\text{Ag} \left| \text{AgCl} \right| \begin{array}{c} \text{Solution } I \\ \text{containing HCl} \end{array} \left| \begin{array}{c} \text{Bridge} \\ \text{solutions} \end{array} \right| \begin{array}{c} \text{Solution } II \\ \text{containing HCl} \end{array} \left| \text{AgCl} \right| \text{Ag} \left| \text{Pt.} \right. \qquad (10.17.3)$$

Consequently the electromotive force of the cell (1) is the sum of those of the cells (2) and (3). But cell (2) is without transference and, as shown in § 10.14, its electromotive force E_2 is given by

$$-FE_2 = \mu_{Ag}^{Ag} - \tfrac{1}{2} \mu_{H_2}^{G} - \mu_{AgCl}^{AgCl} + \mu_{HCl}^{I}. \qquad (10.17.4)$$

where the superscript I refers to the solution I. Cell (3) on the other hand has two similar electrodes and its electromotive force E_3 is given by (10.15.17)

$$-FE_3 = \int_I^{II} \Sigma_R t_R \left(\frac{d\mu_R}{z_R} + d\mu_{Cl^-} \right)$$

$$- \int_I^{II} \Sigma_X t_X \left(\frac{d\mu_X}{|z_X|} - d\mu_{Cl^-} \right). \qquad (10.17.5)$$

23

wherein we recall that $z_{Cl^-} = -1$ and all the z_X are negative integers. The electromotive force E_1 of the cell 1 is then given by

$$\bar{E}_1 = E_2 + E_3. \tag{10.17.6}$$

The accurate expressions for the electromotive force of the most general type of cell with transference were formulated by P. B. Taylor *.

* P. B. Taylor, *J. Physic. Chem.* (1927) **31** 1478; compare Guggenheim, *J. Physic. Chem.* (1930) **34** 1758.

CHAPTER XI

GRAVITATIONAL FIELD

§ 11.01 Nature of Gravitational Field

The formulae of chapter I are easily extended so as to take account of the presence of a gravitational field. Such a field is characterized by a gravitational potential ϕ with a definite value at each place. The modification of the gravitational field by the presence of matter in quantities of the order of magnitude of those dealt with in ordinary chemical and physical processes is completely negligible compared with the earth's field or any other field of comparable importance. We may therefore regard the gravitational field as completely independent of the state of the thermodynamic system considered. In this sense, we call the gravitational field an *external field*, and regard the gravitational potential at each point as independent of the presence or state of any matter there. It is owing to this fact that, although the abstract theories of gravitational and electrostatic potential are in many ways parallel, yet their significance for thermodynamic systems is different.

§ 11.02 Phases in Gravitational Field

Since a phase was defined as completely homogeneous in its properties and *state*, two portions of matter of identical temperature and composition must be considered as different phases if they are differently situated with respect to a gravitational field. It follows that the mere presence of a gravitational field excludes the possibility of a phase of finite depth in the direction of the field. In the presence of a gravitational field even the simplest possible kind of system must be considered as composed of a continuous sequence of phases each differing infinitesimally from its neighbours.

§ 11.03 Thermodynamic Functions in Gravitational Field

The characteristic property of the gravitational potential is that the work w required to bring a quantity of matter of mass M from a place where the potential is ϕ^α to a place where it is ϕ^β is given by

$$w = M \, (\phi^\beta - \phi^\alpha), \tag{11.03.1}$$

thus depending on the mass but not on the chemical nature of the matter. If the molar mass of the species i is denoted by M_i and the number of moles of this species transferred is ν_i, then (1) becomes

$$w = \Sigma_i \, \nu_i \, M_i \, (\phi^\beta - \phi^\alpha). \tag{11.03.2}$$

In transferring dn_i moles of the species i from the phase α to the phase β, the gravitational work is

$$(\varphi^\beta - \varphi^\alpha)\, M_i\, dn_i.$$

Thus the formula (1.33.1) for dU^α must for each phase α contain the extra terms $\Sigma_i\, \varphi^\alpha\, M_i\, dn_i^\alpha$. That is to say

$$dU^\alpha = T^\alpha\, dS^\alpha - P^\alpha\, dV^\alpha + \Sigma_i\, (\mu_i^\alpha + M_i\, \varphi^\alpha)\, dn_i^\alpha. \quad (11.03.3)$$

For the other characteristic functions H, F and G, defined respectively by (1.31.1), (1.31.2), (1.31.3) we have

$$dH^\alpha = \quad T^\alpha\, dS^\alpha + V^\alpha\, dP^\alpha + \Sigma_i\, (\mu_i^\alpha + M_i\, \varphi^\alpha)\, dn_i^\alpha, \quad (11.03.4)$$

$$dF^\alpha = -S^\alpha\, dT^\alpha - P^\alpha\, dV^\alpha + \Sigma_i\, (\mu_i^\alpha + M_i\, \varphi^\alpha)\, dn_i^\alpha, \quad (11.03.5)$$

$$dG^\alpha = -S^\alpha\, dT^\alpha + V^\alpha\, dP^\alpha + \Sigma_i\, (\mu_i^\alpha + M_i\, \varphi^\alpha)\, dn_i^\alpha. \quad (11.03.6)$$

If follows that to take account of the effect of a gravitational field one has merely to replace μ_i^α throughout by $(\mu_i^\alpha + M_i\, \varphi^\alpha)$.

Although in all thermodynamic formulae the quantity φ^α occurs only in combinations of the form $(\mu_i^\alpha + M_i\, \varphi^\alpha)$, yet the gravitational potential difference $\triangle\varphi$ between two phases, in contrast to the electric potential difference $\triangle\psi$, is thermodynamically determinate owing to the fact that its value is independent of the presence and nature of the phase there. The phase may therefore be removed without altering φ and then $\triangle\varphi$ determined in empty space by direct mechanical measurements.

§ 11.04 Equilibrium in Gravitational Field

For the equilibrium as regards the species i between two phases α and β, defined not merely by their temperature, pressure and composition, but also by their gravitational potentials, we have in analogy with (1.45.5) the general condition

$$\mu_i^\alpha + M_i\, \varphi^\alpha = \mu_i^\beta + M_i\, \varphi^\beta. \qquad \text{(equilibrium).} \qquad (11.04.1)$$

§ 11.05 Dependence of μ_i on T and P

Applying the cross-differentiation identity (3.01.7) to (11.03.6), observing that M_i and φ^α are independent of T^α and P^α, we obtain, dropping the superscript α throughout,

$$\frac{\partial \mu_i}{\partial T} = -\frac{\partial S}{\partial n_i} = -S_i. \qquad (11.05.1)$$

$$\frac{\partial \mu_i}{\partial P} = \frac{\partial V}{\partial n_i} = V_i. \qquad (11.05.2)$$

precisely the same as in the absence of a gravitational field.

§ 11.06 Single Component in Gravitational Field

For the equilibrium of a single component i in a gravitational field we have according to (11.04.1)

$$d\mu_i + M_i\, d\phi = 0, \qquad (11.06.1)$$

or at constant temperature using (11.05.2)

$$V_i\, dP + M_i\, d\phi = 0. \qquad (11.06.2)$$

If ϱ denotes the density, then.

$$\varrho = \frac{M_i}{V_i}. \qquad (11.06.3)$$

Substituting (3) into (2) we obtain

$$dP = -\varrho\, d\phi, \qquad (11.06.4)$$

in agreement with the general condition of hydrostatic equilibrium.

In the case of a single perfect gas we have

$$V_i = RT/P \qquad (11.06.5)$$

Substituting (5) into (2) we obtain

$$RT\, d\log P + M_i\, d\phi = 0 \qquad (11.06.6)$$

or integrating

$$RT\log\frac{P^\beta}{P^\alpha} = M_i\,(\phi^\alpha - \phi^\beta). \qquad (11.06.7)$$

For a liquid, on the other hand, neglecting compressibility and so treating V_i as independent of P, we can integrate (2) immediately obtaining

$$V_i\,(P^\beta - P^\alpha) = M\,(\phi^\alpha - \phi^\beta). \qquad (11.06.8)$$

Alternatively integrating (4) we obtain

$$P^\beta - P^\alpha = \varrho\,(\phi^\alpha - \phi^\beta). \qquad (11.06.9)$$

§ 11.07 Mixture in Gravitational Field

For the equilibrium of each species i of a mixture in a gravitational field we have according to (11.04.1)

$$d\mu_i + M_i\, d\phi = 0. \qquad (11.07.1)$$

Substituting (11.05.2) and using the notation defined in § 6.05, we obtain at constant temperature

$$D\mu_i + V_i\, dP + M_i\, d\phi = 0. \qquad (11.07.2)$$

But according to the Gibbs-Duhem relation (6.06.7) we have

$$\Sigma_i\, x_i\, D\mu_i = 0. \qquad (11.07.3)$$

Multiplying (2) by x_i, summing over all species i and using (3) we obtain

$$\Sigma_i \, x_i \, V_i \, dP + \Sigma_i \, x_i \, M_i \, d\varphi = 0. \qquad (11.07.4)$$

Introducing the mean molar volume V_m and the mean molar mass M_m defined respectively by

$$V_m = \Sigma_i \, x_i \, V_i, \qquad (11.07.5)$$

$$M_m = \Sigma_i \, x_i \, M_i, \qquad (11.07.6)$$

we can write (4) as

$$V_m \, dP + M_m \, d\varphi = 0. \qquad (11.07.7)$$

But the density ϱ is related to V_m, M_m, by

$$\varrho = M_m / V_m. \qquad (11.07.8)$$

Substituting (8) into (7), we again recover the ordinary condition of hydrostatic equilibrium

$$dP = -\varrho \, d\varphi. \qquad (11.07.9)$$

If we substitute for dP from (4) into (2), we obtain

$$D\mu_i + \left(M_i - V_i \, \frac{\Sigma_k \, x_k \, M_k}{\Sigma_k \, x_k \, V_k} \right) d\varphi = 0, \qquad (11.07.10)$$

or, according to (5) and (6),

$$D\mu_i + \left(M_i - V_i \, \frac{M_m}{V_m} \right) d\varphi = 0. \qquad (11.07.11)$$

Equation (11) can be integrated only in certain exceptionally simple cases which we shall consider in turn.

§ 11.08   Mixture of Perfect Gases

For a mixture of perfect gases it is possible to integrate (11.07.11), but the same result can be obtained more directly. For any component i in two perfect gas mixtures α, β at the same temperature T, according to (6.12.1)

$$\mu_i^\beta - \mu_i^\alpha = RT \log \frac{p_i^\beta}{p_i^\alpha}, \qquad (11.08.1)$$

Substituting (1) into (11.04.1) we obtain as the equilibrium condition for the species i in a gravitational field

$$RT \log \frac{p_i^\beta}{p_i^\alpha} = M_i \, (\varphi^\alpha - \varphi^\beta). \qquad (11.08.2)$$

or

$$\frac{p_i^\beta}{p_i^\alpha} = \exp\left\{-\frac{M_i\,(\phi^\beta - \phi^\alpha)}{RT}\right\}. \qquad (11.08.3)$$

If we differentiate (2) we obtain

$$\frac{dp_i}{p_i} = -\frac{M_i}{RT}\,d\phi. \qquad (11.08.4)$$

Using

$$p_i = x_i\,\frac{RT}{V_m}, \qquad (11.08.5)$$

we can write (4) as

$$dp_i = -\frac{x_i\,M_i}{V_m}\,d\phi. \qquad (11.08.6)$$

Summing (6) over all species i, we obtain

$$dP = -\frac{M_m}{V_m}\,d\phi = -\varrho\,d\phi, \qquad (11.08.7)$$

thus verifying that (2) and (3) are consistent with hydrostatic equilibrium.

§ 11.09 Extremely Dilute Ideal Solution

In the case of a solution which is both ideal dilute and extremely dilute, we may replace (11.07.11) for each solute species s by

$$RT\,d\log x_s + \left(M_s - V_s\,\frac{M_1}{V_1}\right)d\phi = 0. \qquad (11.09.1)$$

Neglecting compressibility, this can be directly integrated, giving

$$\frac{x_s^\beta}{x_s^\alpha} = \exp\left\{-\left(M_s - V_s\,\frac{M_1}{V_1}\right)\frac{\phi^\beta - \phi^\alpha}{RT}\right\}. \qquad (11.09.2)$$

§ 11.10 Binary Ideal Solution

For an ideal solution

$$D\mu_i = RT\,d\log x_i, \qquad (11.10.1)$$

and (11.07.10) becomes

$$RT\,d\log x_i + \left(M_i - V_i\,\frac{\Sigma_k\,x_k\,M_k}{\Sigma_k\,x_k\,V_k}\right)d\phi = 0. \qquad (11.10.2)$$

This can be integrated in the special case of only two components. If we denote these components by 1 and 2, then (2) becomes

$$-\frac{d\Phi}{RT} = \frac{dx_2}{x_2} \frac{x_1 V_1 + x_2 V_2}{M_2(x_1 V_1 + x_2 V_2) - V_2(x_1 M_1 + x_2 M_2)}$$

$$= \frac{dx_2}{x_2} \frac{x_1 V_1 + x_2 V_2}{x_1(M_2 V_1 - M_1 V_2)}$$

$$= \frac{dx_2}{M_2 V_1 - M_1 V_2}\left(\frac{V_1}{x_2} - \frac{V_2}{x_1}\right)$$

$$= \frac{dx_2}{M_2 V_1 - M_1 V_2}\left(\frac{V_1}{x_2} - \frac{V_2}{1-x_2}\right). \qquad (11.10.3)$$

Integration of (3) gives

$$-\left(M_2 - M_1 \frac{V_2}{V_1}\right)\frac{\Phi^\beta - \Phi^\alpha}{RT} = \log \frac{x_2^\beta}{x_2^\alpha} + \frac{V_2}{V_1}\log \frac{1-x_2^\beta}{1-x_2^\alpha} \qquad (11.10.4)$$

or

$$\exp\left\{-\left(M_2 - V_2\frac{M_1}{V_1}\right)\frac{\Phi^\beta - \Phi^\alpha}{RT}\right\} = \frac{x_2^\beta}{x_2^\alpha}\left(\frac{x_1^\beta}{x_1^\alpha}\right)^{V_2/V_1}. \qquad (11.10.5)$$

The relation (5) can also be written in the more symmetrical form

$$\exp\left\{(M_1 V_2 - M_2 V_1)\frac{\Phi^\beta - \Phi^\alpha}{RT}\right\} = \left(\frac{x_2^\beta}{x_2^\alpha}\right)^{V_1}\left(\frac{x_1^\beta}{x_1^\alpha}\right)^{V_2}. \qquad (11.10.6)$$

If the solution is extremely dilute with respect to the species 2, so that $x_2 \ll 1$, we may replace (5) by

$$\exp\left\{-\left(M_2 - V_2\frac{M_1}{V_1}\right)\frac{\Phi^\beta - \Phi^\alpha}{RT}\right\} = \frac{x_2^\beta}{x_2^\alpha}, \qquad (11.10.7)$$

in agreement with (11.09.2).

§ 11.11   Chemical Reaction in Gravitational Field

For the chemical reaction

$$\Sigma \nu_A A \rightarrow \Sigma \nu_B B, \qquad (11.11.1)$$

the most general form for the condition of equilibrium in the absence of a gravitational field is

$$\Sigma \nu_A \mu_A = \Sigma \nu_B \mu_B. \qquad (11.11.2)$$

In the presence of a gravitational field the corresponding equilibrium condition is evidently

$$\Sigma \nu_A (\mu_A + M_A \Phi) = \Sigma \nu_B (\mu_B + M_B \Phi). \qquad (11.11.3)$$

But owing to the conservation of mass

$$\Sigma \nu_A M_A = \Sigma \nu_B M_B. \qquad (11.11.4)$$

Multiplying (4) by Φ and subtracting from (3) we recover (2). It follows that any chemical equilibrium is independent of the gravitational potential or in other words is unaffected by the presence of a gravitational field.

CHAPTER XII

ELECTROSTATIC SYSTEMS

§ 12.01 Introduction

We now propose to study the thermodynamic properties of substances in an electrostatic field. For this purpose it will suffice to consider the field in a parallel plate condenser neglecting any edge effect. Thus when we refer to the extensive properties of a parallel plate condenser of area A, we really mean the difference between those of a condenser of area $Å + A$ and those of a similar condenser of area $Å$, where $Å \gg A$.

As it is important to be completely unambiguous concerning the meaning of such quantities as *dielectric constant*, it is desirable to describe in some detail the characteristics of a parallel plate condenser, beginning with one in vacuo.

§ 12.02 Parallel Plate Condenser in Vacuo

Consider a parallel plate condenser of area A, the distance between the plates being l. Let the charges on the two plates be $+Q$ and $-Q$. The condenser being in vacuo let the work required to transfer an elementary charge dQ from the negative plate to the positive plate be $\triangle \psi \, dQ$. Then $\triangle \psi$ is called the *potential difference* between the two plates and $\mathbf{E} = \triangle \psi / l$ is called the *electric field strength* between the plates. Then the ratio ε_0 defined by

$$\frac{4\pi l Q}{A \triangle \psi} = \frac{4\pi Q}{A\mathbf{E}} = \varepsilon_0 \qquad (12.02.1)$$

is a universal constant called the *permittivity of free space*. The value of ε_0 in various units is [*]

$$\varepsilon_0 = 1 \text{ franklin}^2/\text{erg cm.}$$
$$= 1.113 \times 10^{-10} \text{ coulomb}^2/\text{joule m.}$$
$$= 1.113 \times 10^{-10} \text{ coulomb/volt m.}$$

§ 12.03 Parallel Plate Condenser in Fluid

Now consider the same parallel plate condenser completely immersed in a homogeneous fluid. If the charges on the plates are again $+Q$ and $-Q$, and if the potential difference between the plates, defined as before is again denoted by $\triangle \psi$ then the ratio ε, defined by

$$\frac{4\pi l Q}{A \triangle \psi} = \frac{4\pi Q}{A\mathbf{E}} = \varepsilon, \qquad (12.03.1)$$

---

[*] The name *franklin* is used for a charge which repels a similar charge at a distance one centimetre in vacuo with a force of one dyne. See *Nature* (1941) **148** 751.

is called the *permittivity of the fluid*. The value of ε depends on the nature of the fluid, on its temperature and possibly also on $\mathbf{E} = \Delta \psi / l$, but is independent of the size and shape of the condenser. ε has of course the same dimensions as ε_0. The ratio $\varepsilon / \varepsilon_0$ is called the *dielectric coefficient* of the fluid.

§ 12.04   Work of Charging a Condenser

According to (2) we have

$$\Delta \psi = \frac{4 \pi l}{A} \frac{Q}{\varepsilon}, \tag{12.04.1}$$

and so the work required to bring an element of charge dQ from the negative to the positive plate is

$$\frac{4 \pi l}{A} \frac{Q d Q}{\varepsilon}. \tag{12.04.2}$$

From (12.03.1) we have

$$Q = \frac{A}{4 \pi} \varepsilon \mathbf{E}, \tag{12.04.3}$$

$$d Q = \frac{A}{4 \pi} d (\varepsilon \mathbf{E}). \tag{12.04.4}$$

Substituting (3) and (4) into (2) we obtain for the work w required to increase the field strength from $\mathbf{E}$ to $\mathbf{E} + d\mathbf{E}$

$$w = \frac{A l}{4 \pi} \mathbf{E} d (\varepsilon \mathbf{E}) = \frac{V_c}{4 \pi} \mathbf{E} d (\varepsilon \mathbf{E}), \tag{12.04.5}$$

where V_c denotes the volume between the plates of the condenser.

Formula (5) is valid for any infinitesimal change, including in particular an adiabatic charge and an isothermal change, but the dependence of $\varepsilon \mathbf{E}$ on $\mathbf{E}$ will in general not be the same in these two cases. The quantity $\varepsilon \mathbf{E}$ is called the *electric displacement*.

§ 12.05   Thermodynamic Potentials

If we now consider the system consisting of the whole fluid of volume V surrounding and including the condenser, we obtain by using (12.04.5) the

$$dU = T dS - P dV + \frac{V_c}{4 \pi} \mathbf{E} d (\varepsilon \mathbf{E}) + \Sigma_i \mu_i dn_i, \tag{12.05.1}$$

$$dF = - S dT - P dV + \frac{V_c}{4 \pi} \mathbf{E} d (\varepsilon \mathbf{E}) + \Sigma_i \mu_i dn_i. \tag{12.05.2}$$

Formulae (1) and (2) are the extensions of (1.33.1), (1.33.2) respectively including the extra term (12.04.5) representing the work required to change the field $\mathbf{E}$ between the plates of the condenser.

We now define functions G and $\mathfrak{D}$ by

$$G = F + PV, \qquad (12.05.3)$$

$$\mathfrak{D} = F + PV - \frac{V_c}{4\pi}\, \varepsilon\, \mathbf{E}^2. \qquad (12.05.4)$$

When the field X vanishes $\mathfrak{D}$ becomes identical with G.

Differentiating (3) and (4) in turn and eliminating dF by means of (2), we obtain

$$dG = -S\,dT + V\,dP + \frac{V_c}{4\pi}\,\mathbf{E}\,d(\varepsilon\mathbf{E}) + \Sigma_i\, \mu_i\, dn_i. \quad (12.05.5)$$

$$d\mathfrak{D} = -S\,dT + V\,dP - \frac{V_c}{4\pi}\,\varepsilon\mathbf{E}\,d\mathbf{E} + \Sigma_i\, \mu_i\, dn_i. \quad (12.05.6)$$

In all the above formulae P denotes the pressure acting on the outside boundary of the fluid in which the condenser is completely immersed. We have carefully avoided reference to any pressure within the fluid between the plates of the condenser, for the definition of such a pressure would require special caution and its use as an independent variable would lead to more complicated formulae.

§ 12.06 Analogues of Maxwell's Relations

By applying the cross-differentiation identity (3.01 7) to (12.05.5) and (12.05.6) we can obtain several relations analogous to Maxwell's relations obtained in § 3.04.

Thus

$$\left(\frac{\partial S}{\partial [\varepsilon \mathbf{E}]}\right)_{T,P} = -\frac{V_c}{4\pi}\left(\frac{\partial \mathbf{E}}{\partial T}\right)_{P,[\varepsilon\mathbf{E}]} = -\frac{V_c}{4\pi}\,\varepsilon\mathbf{E}\left(\frac{\partial [1/\varepsilon]}{\partial T}\right)_{P,[\varepsilon\mathbf{E}]}. \quad (12.06.1)$$

$$\left(\frac{\partial S}{\partial \mathbf{E}}\right)_{T,P} = \frac{V_c}{4\pi}\left(\frac{\partial [\varepsilon\mathbf{E}]}{\partial T}\right)_{P,\mathbf{E}} = \frac{V_c}{4\pi}\,\mathbf{E}\left(\frac{\partial \varepsilon}{\partial T}\right)_{P,\mathbf{E}}. \quad (12.06.2)$$

Formulae (1) and (2) are mathematically equivalent, for the ratio of the left sides is

$$\left(\frac{\partial S}{\partial \mathbf{E}}\right)_{T,P} \bigg/ \left(\frac{\partial S}{\partial [\varepsilon\mathbf{E}]}\right)_{T,P} = \left(\frac{\partial [\varepsilon\mathbf{E}]}{\partial \mathbf{E}}\right)_{T,P}. \quad (12.06.3)$$

while the ratio of the right sides is

$$-\left(\frac{\partial [\varepsilon\mathbf{E}]}{\partial T}\right)_{P,\mathbf{E}} \bigg/ \left(\frac{\partial \mathbf{E}}{\partial T}\right)_{P,[\varepsilon\mathbf{E}]} = \left(\frac{\partial [\varepsilon\mathbf{E}]}{\partial \mathbf{E}}\right)_{T,P} \quad (12\ 06.4)$$

owing to the identity (3.01.14).

Similarly we obtain

$$\left(\frac{\partial V}{\partial [\varepsilon E]}\right)_{T,P} = \frac{V_c}{4\pi}\left(\frac{\partial E}{\partial P}\right)_{T,[\varepsilon E]} = \frac{V_c}{4\pi}\,\varepsilon E\left(\frac{\partial [1/\varepsilon]}{\partial P}\right)_{T,[\varepsilon E]} . \quad (12.\,06.\,5)$$

$$\left(\frac{\partial V}{\partial E}\right)_{T,P} = -\frac{V_c}{4\pi}\left(\frac{\partial [\varepsilon E]}{\partial P}\right)_{T,E} = -\frac{V_c}{4\pi}\,E\left(\frac{\partial \varepsilon}{\partial P}\right)_{T,E}. \quad (12.\,06.\,6)$$

these two relations also being mathematically equivalent to each other. This change in volume accompanying change in field strength at constant temperature and pressure is called *electrostriction*.

§ 12.07   Constant Permittivity. Dielectric Constant

For the sake of generality we have hitherto made no assumption concerning the dependence of the permittivity ε on the field strength E. For almost all substances at all field strengths met in an ordinary laboratory the permittivity ε is for a given temperature and pressure independent of the field strength. We shall from here onwards assume this to be case. The *dielectric coefficient* $\varepsilon/\varepsilon_0$ is then called the *dielectric constant*.

Formulae (12.06.1) and (12.06.2) now become identical and give for the heat q absorbed at constant temperature and pressure per unit volume of the field and per unit increase in the field strength E

$$q = \frac{T}{V_c}\left(\frac{\partial S}{\partial E}\right)_{T,P} = \frac{E}{4\pi}\left(\frac{\partial \varepsilon}{\partial T}\right)_P. \quad (12.\,07.\,1)$$

The electrostriction formulae (12.06.5) and (12.06.6) both reduce to

$$\frac{1}{V_c}\left(\frac{\partial V}{\partial E}\right)_{T,P} = -\frac{E}{4\pi}\left(\frac{\partial \varepsilon}{\partial P}\right)_T. \quad (12.\,07.\,2)$$

§ 12.08   Integrated Formulae

If we apply formula (12.05.2) to the condenser and the fluid contained between its plates, thus dropping the distinction between V and V_c, we can integrate at constant T, V, n_i obtaining

$$F = F^0 + V\frac{\varepsilon E^2}{8\pi}, \quad (12.\,08.\,1)$$

where F^0 denotes the value of the free energy, at zero field and at the same temperature, of the quantity of fluid between the plates.

We may note that the quantity $\varepsilon E^2/8\pi$, which in textbooks on electricity is usually described as the energy density due to the field, is in fact the *free energy density*.

From (1) we deduce for the energy U when we neglect electrostriction and use (12.07.1),

$$U = U^0 + V\frac{E^2}{8\pi}\left(\varepsilon + T\frac{d\varepsilon}{dT}\right). \quad (12.\,08.\,2)$$

where U^0 denotes the value of the energy, at zero field and at the same temperature, of the quantity of fluid between the plates. We thus see that the *energy density* due to the field is

$$\frac{E^2}{8\pi}\left(\varepsilon + T\frac{d\varepsilon}{dT}\right). \tag{12.08.3}$$

To obtain a formula for μ_i we differentiate (1) with respect to n_i at constant T, V and εE. We thus find

$$\mu_i = \mu_i^0 + \frac{V}{8\pi}\left(\frac{\partial[\varepsilon E^2]}{\partial n_i}\right)_{T,V,[\varepsilon E]}$$

$$= \mu_i^0 + \frac{V\varepsilon^2 E^2}{8\pi}\left(\frac{\partial[1/\varepsilon]}{\partial n_i}\right)_{T,V}$$

$$= \mu_i^0 - V\frac{E^2}{8\pi}\left(\frac{\partial\varepsilon}{\partial n_i}\right)_{T,V}, \tag{12.08.4}$$

where μ_i^0 denotes the value of μ_i at zero field strength and at the same temperature and composition.

§ 12.09   Application to Perfect Gas

We shall illustrate the use of the relation (12.08.4) by its application to the simplest case of a single perfect gas.

The permittivity ε of a perfect gas is related to the permittivity ε_0 of free space by

$$\varepsilon = \varepsilon_0 + \frac{n}{V}\left(\alpha + \frac{\beta}{T}\right). \tag{12.09.1}$$

where α and β are constants characteristic of the molecules of the gas. α is equal to the molecular polarizability multiplied by Avogadro's number, while β is given by

$$\beta = \frac{Ny^2}{3k} = \frac{(Ny)^2}{3R}, \tag{12.09.2}$$

where y is the electric moment * of the molecule, N is Avogadro's number and k is Boltzmann's constant.

Substituting (1) into (12.08.4) we obtain

$$\mu = \mu^0 - \frac{E^2}{8\pi}\left(\alpha + \frac{\beta}{T}\right)$$

$$= \mu^\dagger + RT\log\frac{nRT}{P^\dagger V} - \frac{E^2}{8\pi}\left(\alpha + \frac{\beta}{T}\right). \tag{12.09.3}$$

using (4.25.2)

Let us now consider the equilibrium distribution of a gas between the

---

* The symbol y is used here instead of the more usual μ because the latter symbol is already required for the chemical potential.

region, denoted by the superscript i, inside the condenser where the field strength is $\mathbf{E}$ and the region, denoted by the superscript e, exterior to this field. We have then

$$\mu^i = \mu^\dagger + RT \log \frac{n^i RT}{V^i P^\dagger} - \frac{\mathbf{E}^2}{8\pi}\left(\alpha + \frac{\beta}{T}\right). \qquad (12.09.4)$$

$$\mu^e = \mu^\dagger + RT \log \frac{n^e RT}{V^e P^\dagger}. \qquad (12.09.5)$$

The equilibrium distribution is determined by

$$\mu^i = \mu^e. \qquad (12.09.6)$$

Substituting (4) and (5) into (6), we obtain, writing c for n/V,

$$RT \log \frac{c^i}{c^e} - \frac{\mathbf{E}^2}{8\pi}\left(\alpha + \frac{\beta}{T}\right) = 0 \qquad (12.09.7)$$

or

$$\frac{c^i}{c^c} = \exp\left\{\frac{\mathbf{E}^2}{8\pi RT}\left(\alpha + \frac{\beta}{T}\right)\right\}. \qquad (12.09.8)$$

Since α is always positive and β is either positive or zero, it follows that c is always greater inside the field than outside it. Thus every gas is attracted into an electric field.

CHAPTER XIII

MAGNETIC SYSTEMS

§ 13. 01 Introduction

In order to apply thermodynamics to magnetic systems we have merely to extend our previous formulae by including extra terms for the magnetic work. In principle the procedure is straightforward and should cause no difficulty whatever. There is however a serious incidental difficulty, namely that of finding the correct general expression for magnetic work. We should expect to be able to discover such an expression by consulting any reputable text-book on electromagnetism. Unfortunately this is far from the case. The treatment given in most text-books is quite inadequate. In most cases the derivations of formulae for magnetic work assume either explicitly or implicitly that the permeability of each piece of matter is a constant, whereas from a thermodynamic viewpoint one of the questions of greatest interest is how the permeability varies with the temperature. It is therefore desirable, if not essential, to start from formulae which are not restricted to the assumption that the permeability of each piece of matter is invariant. In many, if not most, text-books on electromagnetism the treatment of magnetic work suffers from other even more serious defects. In many cases the treatment is based on a discussion of permanent magnets imagined to be constructed by bringing together (reversibly ?) from infinity an infinite number of infinitesimal magnetic elements. Actually a permanent magnet is an idealization far from reality. It is true that magnets can be made which are nearly permanent with respect to changes in position, but they are never permanent with respect to changes of temperature. Increase of temperature is usually accompanied by an irreversible loss of magnetization. Whatever may be the use of the conception of a permanent magnet in the theory of such instruments as compasses, galvanometers and dynamos it is not a useful conception as a basis for the analysis of magnetic work when changes of temperature may be important. The worst text-books give formulae for magnetic work which not only are of restricted applicability, but even contain wrong signs. Fortunately there are a few text-books * on electromagnetism which give a clear correct treatment of magnetic work. A brief summary of such a treatment is given in the Appendix A at the end of this chapter. In the main text we shall assume the correct formula for magnetic work after first recalling the

---

* In particular Stratton, Electromagnetic Theory (1941), hereafter referred to as S., E. T.

physical meaning of the several magnetic quantities involved and how they are related to one another [*].

§ 13.02 Rationalization

There are two distinct and mutually contradictory conventional systems of defining magnetic, and incidentally at the same time electrostatic, quantities. In the more modern system, called the *rational* system, the electric and magnetic quantities are defined in such a manner that the factor 4π occurs frequently in integral formulae relating especially to systems of point charges, but not in the general differential formulae. In the older *irrational* (a better word than *unrationalized*) system on the other hand the factor 4π occurs repeatedly in the general differential formulae and disappears only in the integral formulae relating especially to point charges.

The *rational* system is now in general use on the continent of Europe and its use in America is increasing. Unfortunately the *rational* system has not found favour with the majority of British physicists. The *rational* system is used in the text-books which give the most satisfactory account of magnetic work [**] and so, to facilitate reference to these books, it will be used in this chapter. In Appendix B at the end of the chapter a brief description is given of how to translate from the *rational* to the *irrational* system for the benefit of any readers who still prefer the latter to the former.

§ 13.03 Fundamental Electric and Magnetic Vectors

We recall that the strength and direction of an electrostatic field is described at each point by a vector **E** such that the force acting on a small stationary test charge Q placed at this point is $Q\mathbf{E}$. This vector **E** is called the *electric field*. The analogous magnetic vector describing the force acting on a small test element of current is denoted by **B** and has the property [***] that the force on each element $d\mathbf{s}$ of a conductor of current i is given by the vector product $i d\mathbf{s} \times \mathbf{B}$. This vector **B** is called the *magnetic induction*.

§ 13.04 Permittivity and Permeability of Empty Space

In empty space the value of **E** at each point is determined by the distribution of electric charges and is the sum of independent contributions from each charge. The contribution to **E** of a charge Q at a distance r is directed along r and is of magnitude

$$\frac{Q}{4\pi\varepsilon_0 r^2},$$

(13.04.1)

---

[*] Following closely the treatment and notation of S., E. T.
[**] Such as S., E. T. and Cohn, Das Elektromagnetische Feld (1926).
[***] See S., E. T. p. 96.

where ε_0 is a universal constant called the *rational permittivity of empty space*. Alternatively we may say that each charge Q makes an additive contribution

$$\frac{Q}{4\pi\varepsilon_0 r} \qquad (13.04.2)$$

to the *electrostatic potential* ψ and that $\mathbf{E}$ is then determined by

$$\mathbf{E} = -\operatorname{grad}\psi. \qquad (13.04.3)$$

We turn now to the analogous magnetic formulae. Each element ds of a conductor carrying a current i makes an additive contribution

$$\frac{\mu_0\, i\, ds}{4\pi r}, \qquad (13.04.4)$$

to $\mathbf{A}$, called the *magnetic vector potential*, and $\mathbf{B}$ is then determined by

$$\mathbf{B} = \operatorname{curl}\mathbf{A}. \qquad (13.04.5)$$

The quantity μ_0 occurring in (4) is a universal constant called the *rational permeability of empty space*.

Before proceeding further it is instructive to consider the physical dimensions of the quantities occurring above in terms of the four independent dimensions length L, time T, energy U and electric charge Q. For the present purpose it is more convenient to choose energy than mass as one of the four independent dimensions. Table 13.1 gives the dimensions of the most important quantities. The following points are worthy of note.

TABLE 13.1

Dimensions of Electric and Magnetic Quantities
L denotes length, T time, U energy and Q electric charge

Symbol	Name	Dimensions
Q	Electric charge	Q
ι	Current	QT^{-1}
ds	Element of length	L
ids	Element of current	QLT^{-1}
ψ	Electrostatic potential	UQ^{-1}
$\mathbf{A}$	Magnetic vector potential	$UL^{-1}TQ^{-1}$
$\mathbf{E}$	Electric field	$UL^{-1}Q^{-1}$
$\mathbf{B}$	Magnetic induction	$UL^{-2}TQ^{-1}$
$\varepsilon_0\mathbf{E}$		QL^{-2}
$\mathbf{B}/\mu_0$		$QL^{-1}T^{-1}$
ε_0		$Q^2L^{-1}U^{-1}$
μ_0		$UQ^{-2}L^{-1}T^2$
μ_0^{-1}		$Q^2LT^{-2}U^{-1}$
$\varepsilon_0\mu_0$		$L^{-2}T^2$
$\varepsilon_0\mathbf{E}^2$		UL^{-3}
$\mathbf{B}^2/\mu_0$		UL^{-3}

1. Inasmuch as an element of current is the analogue in a magnetic system of an element of electric charge in an electrostatic system, we observe that μ_0^{-1}, not μ_0, is the analogue of ε_0.

2. $(\varepsilon_0 \mu_0)^{-\frac{1}{2}}$ has the dimensions of a velocity; it is well known that this quantity is equal to the speed of propagation of electromagnetic waves in empty space.

3. The quantities $\varepsilon_0 E^2$ and B^2/μ_0 both have the dimensions of energy density or pressure.

The values of ε_0 and μ_0 and related quantities in the *rational* system are as follows: *

$$\varepsilon_0 = \frac{1}{4\pi} \frac{\text{franklin}^2}{\text{erg cm.}} = 7.958 \times 10^{-2} \frac{\text{franklin}^2}{\text{erg cm.}} = 8.854 \times 10^{-12} \frac{\text{coulomb}^2}{\text{joule m.}}$$

$$\frac{1}{\mu_0} = \frac{10^7}{4\pi} \frac{\text{coulomb}^2 \text{ m.}}{\text{joule sec.}^2} = 7.958 \times 10^5 \frac{\text{coulomb}^2 \text{ m.}}{\text{joule sec.}^2}$$

$$\mu_0 = \frac{4\pi}{10^7} \frac{\text{joule sec.}^2}{\text{coulomb}^2 \text{ m.}} = 1.2566 \times 10^{-6} \frac{\text{joule sec.}^2}{\text{coulomb}^2 \text{ m.}}$$

$$\varepsilon_0 \mu_0 = 1.1126 \times 10^{-17} \frac{\text{sec.}^2}{\text{m.}^2}$$

$$\frac{1}{\varepsilon_0 \mu_0} = 8.988 \times 10^{16} \frac{\text{m.}^2}{\text{sec.}^2}$$

$$\frac{1}{\sqrt{\varepsilon_0 \mu_0}} = 2.998 \times 10^8 \frac{\text{m.}}{\text{sec.}}.$$

§ 13.05   Simplest Examples of Fields in Empty Space

The formulae of the previous section are sufficient to specify completely the **E** field due to any given distribution of charges in empty space or the **B** field due to any given distribution of currents in empty space. The quantitative application of these formulae is however complicated and tedious except for the simplest systems having a high degree of symmetry. We shall consider briefly one such electrostatic system and one such magnetic system.

As the electrostatic system we choose the parallel plate condenser, already discussed in the previous chapter, neglecting edge effects. If charges Q and $-Q$ are distributed uniformly over the two plates each of area A at a distance l apart, then in the absence of any dielectric between the plates the electric field is uniform, normal to the plates and has the value

$$E = \frac{Q}{\varepsilon_0 A}. \tag{13.05.1}$$

---

* The name *franklin* is used to denote a charge which repels a similar charge in vacuo at a distance one centimetre with a force of one dyne. See Nature (1941) **148** 751.

This formula differs from formula (12.02.1) by a factor 4π because the latter is expressed in the *irrational* system.

As an example of a magnetic system having simple symmetry we choose a long uniform solenoid and we ignore end effects. The magnetic induction inside the empty solenoid is then uniform, parallel to the axis and has the value

$$\mathbf{B} = \frac{\mu_0 i}{l}, \tag{13.05.2}$$

when the intensity of the current is i and there is one turn per length l.

For reasons which will appear later it is instructive to rewrite (1) and (2) in somewhat different forms. We rewrite (1) as

$$\varepsilon_0 \mathbf{E} = \frac{Ql}{V_c}, \tag{13.05.3}$$

where l is the distance between the plates and $V_c = lA$ is the volume included between the plates of the condenser. The product Ql of the charge on a plate and the distance between the plates may be called the *electric moment* of the charged condenser. Thus according to (3) we observe that in this system with simple symmetry $\varepsilon_0 \mathbf{E}$ is equal to the *electric moment per unit volume*.

We likewise rewrite (2) in the form

$$\frac{\mathbf{B}}{\mu_0} = \frac{niA}{V_s}, \tag{13.05.4}$$

where n denotes the total number of turns, A denotes the cross-section of the solenoid and $V_s = nlA$ denotes the volume contained by the solenoid. We may regard the solenoid as an *electromagnet* and we call the product niA its *magnetic moment*. We see then according to (4) that $\mathbf{B}/\mu_0$ is equal to the *magnetic moment per unit volume* of the solenoid.

From these relations we again perceive that μ_0^{-1}, not μ_0, is the analogue of ε_0.

§ 13.06   Presence of Matter

We shall now discuss briefly the effect of filling the parallel plate condenser and the solenoid respectively with uniform matter.

When the space between the plates of the condenser is filled with uniform matter, this matter becomes electrically polarized as a result of the field due to the charges on the plates. The *electric polarization* $\mathbf{P}$ is defined as the electric moment per unit volume induced in the matter. Owing to the symmetry of the system under consideration $\mathbf{P}$ is in this case uniform and normal to the plates. It is not difficult to see what will be the resultant effect on the field $\mathbf{E}$. We interpreted formula (13.05.3) to mean that $\varepsilon_0 \mathbf{E}$ is equal to the *electric moment per unit volume* of the charged condenser. It is evident that $\varepsilon_0 \mathbf{E}$ will now be equal to the resultant electric moment per unit volume due partly to the charges $\pm Q$ on the plates and partly to the polarization of the matter between the plates. Thus in place of (13.05.3) we shall have

$$\varepsilon_0 \mathbf{E} = \frac{Ql}{V_c} - P, \qquad (13.06.1)$$

or

$$\varepsilon_0 \mathbf{E} + \mathbf{P} = \frac{Ql}{V_c} = \frac{Q}{A}. \qquad (13.06.2)$$

Thus $\varepsilon_0 \mathbf{E} + \mathbf{P}$ is now related to the charge on the condenser plates in precisely the same manner as $\varepsilon_0 \mathbf{E}$ was related to it when the condenser was empty. In other systems having lower symmetry the situation is less simple because $\mathbf{E}$ and $\mathbf{P}$ vary from place to place. The composite vector $\varepsilon_0 \mathbf{E} + \mathbf{P}$ still however plays an important role. It is called by the curious name *electric displacement* and is denoted by $\mathbf{D}$. Thus

$$\mathbf{D} \equiv \varepsilon_0 \mathbf{E} + \mathbf{P}. \qquad (13.06.3)$$

From the identity (3) it is evident that any two of the vectors $\mathbf{E}, \mathbf{P}, \mathbf{D}$ completely determines the remaining one. It is however a fundamental assumption of electrostatics, borne out by experiment, that at any point in a piece of matter of given composition, given temperature and given pressure any one of the vectors $\mathbf{E}, \mathbf{P}, \mathbf{D}$ completely determines the other two. If moreover the matter is isotropic, then $\mathbf{E}, \mathbf{P}$ and $\mathbf{D}$ have the same direction. If then we write

$$\mathbf{D} \equiv \varepsilon \mathbf{E}, \qquad (13.06.4)$$

the coefficient ε is a scalar quantity, provided the matter is isotropic. (Otherwise ε would be a tensor of rank two.)

ε defined by (4) is called the *permittivity* of the matter. Its value in general depends on the composition of the matter, the temperature, the pressure and the field strength. The ratio

$$\frac{\mathbf{D}}{\varepsilon_0 \mathbf{E}} = \frac{\varepsilon}{\varepsilon_0} \qquad (13.06.5)$$

is called the *dielectric coefficient* or, when its value is independent of E, the *dielectric constant*.

It is evident from (3) that $\mathbf{P}$ and $\mathbf{D}$ have the same dimensions as $\varepsilon_0 E$, namely that of charge/area. It is likewise evident from (3) and (4) that ε has the same dimensions as ε_0, so that the *dielectric coefficient* $\varepsilon/\varepsilon_0$ is a dimensionless number.

Much of the above is repetition from the previous chapter, is moreover well-known and seemingly irrelevant to magnetic systems. It is however convenient to have these relations before us for comparison with analogous magnetic relations.

We turn now to consider the effect of filling the uniform solenoid with uniform matter. As a result of the current in the solenoid the matter will behave as if it contained induced microscopic molecular current circuits, or elementary magnets. According to (13.05.4) their contribution to B/μ_0 will be equal to the magnetic moment per unit volume; this quantity is called the *magnetization* and is denoted by M. Owing to the symmetry of the solenoid, M will be parallel to the axis and so (13.05.4) has to be replaced by

$$\frac{B}{\mu_0} = \frac{niA}{V_s} + M,$$ (13.06.6)

or

$$\frac{B}{\mu_0} - M = \frac{niA}{V_s} = \frac{i}{l}.$$ (13.06.7)

Thus the composite vector $(B/\mu_0) - M$ is now related to the current through the solenoid in precisely the same manner as B/μ_0 was related to it when the inside of the solenoid was empty. In other systems having lower symmetry the situation is less simple because B and M vary from place to place. The composite vector $(B/\mu_0) - M$ still however plays an important role. It is called by the misleading name* *magnetic field intensity* and is denoted by H. Thus

$$H \equiv \frac{B}{\mu_0} - M.$$ (13.06.8)

From the identity (8) it is evident that any two of the vectors B, M, H completely determine the remaining one. It is however a fundamental assumption of electromagnetic theory that at any point in a piece of matter of given composition, given temperature and given pressure any one of the vectors B, M, H completely determines the other two. This assumption is often, though not always, borne out by experiment. The phenomena known as *hysteresis* contradict the assumption; such phenomena are here expressly excluded from consideration. With this proviso we write

$$H = \frac{B}{\mu}.$$ (13.06.9)

and the coefficient μ is called the *permeability* of the matter. Provided the matter is isotropic μ is a scalar. (Otherwise μ would be a tensor of rank two.) The value of μ in general depends on the composition, the temperature, the pressure and the field strength. The ratio μ/μ_0 will be referred to as the *magnetic coefficient* of the substance, or when its value is independent of B as the *magnetic constant*.

§ 13.07 Electric and Magnetic Work

Having completed our elementary review of the physical significance of

---

* In S., E. T. p. 12 E and B are called *force vectors* while D and H are called *derived vectors*. Confusion of thought would be diminished if the following names were used:

    E electric force vector; B magnetic force vector.

    D electric derived vector; H magnetic derived vector.

the vectors **E**, **D** and **B**, **H** we shall quote without proof general formulae for electric and magnetic work. A brief outline of the derivation of these formulae from Maxwell's equations is given in Appendix A at the end of this chapter.

We first consider an electrostatic system consisting of charged conductors and dielectrics. For any infinitesimal change in the system, produced by moving either an electric charge or a conductor or a dielectric, the electric work w done on the system is given by *

$$w = \int dV \, \mathbf{E} \, d\mathbf{D}, \tag{13.07.1}$$

where $d\mathbf{D}$ denotes the increment of **D** in the element of volume dV and the integration extends over all space, or that part of space where the electric field does not vanish.

In the simplest case of a parallel plate condenser containing a uniform dielectric, if we neglect edge effects, **E** and **D** vanish outside the condenser, while between the plates they are uniform having the values

$$\mathbf{D} = \frac{Q}{A}, \tag{13.07.2}$$

$$\mathbf{E} = \frac{Q}{\varepsilon A}, \tag{13.07.3}$$

where $\pm Q$ denotes the charge on either plate of area A. If then l denotes the distance between the plates and V_c the volume contained between them, formula (1) reduces to

$$w = V_c \frac{Q}{\varepsilon A} \frac{dQ}{A}$$
$$= \frac{l}{A} \frac{Q \, dQ}{\varepsilon}, \tag{13.07.4}$$

in agreement with formula (12.04.2) apart from the disappearance of a factor 4π owing to rationalization.

We turn now to a magnetic system consisting of current circuits and magnetic matter, concerning which our only restrictive assumption is the absence of hysteresis. For any infinitesimal change in the system either by changing the current in any circuit or by moving any conductor carrying a current, the magnetic work done on the system is **

$$w = \int dV \, \mathbf{H} \, d\mathbf{B}, \tag{13.07.5}$$

where $d\mathbf{B}$ is the increment of **B** in the element of volume dV and the integration extends over all space, or that part of space where the magnetic field does not vanish.

Since we have been at pains to emphasize that **B** is the analogue of the

---

* See S., E. T. p. 108.

** See Appendix A at end of chapter.

force vector **E**, while **H** is the analogue of the derived vector **D**, the reader may justifiably express surprise that formula (5) contains as integrand **H**d**B**, not **B**d**H**. The explanation of this paradox is that the analogy must not be pushed too far, because, whereas the electrostatic energy due to fixed charges is potential energy, the magnetic energy due to electric currents is kinetic energy [*].

In the simplest case of a long solenoid filled with a uniform isotropic substance, if we neglect end effects, **B** and **H** vanish outside the solenoid, while inside they are uniform having the values

$$\mathbf{H} = \frac{i}{l}. \tag{13.07.6}$$

$$\mathbf{B} = \frac{\mu i}{l}. \tag{13.07.7}$$

where i denotes the current and l the length per turn. If then V_s denotes the internal volume of the solenoid, L its length, A its cross-section and n the total number of turns, formula (5) becomes

$$w = V_s \frac{i}{l} \frac{d(\mu i)}{l}$$

$$= \frac{A}{L} n^2 i \, d(\mu i). \tag{13.07.8}$$

§ 13.08   Formula for Free Energy

Once we know the general formula for magnetic work, it is, as already mentioned in § 13.01, a straightforward matter to write down thermo-dynamic formulae of general validity. For the sake of brevity and simplicity we shall confine our discussion to phases of constant volume. The formulae may still be applied to solid and liquid phases at constant pressure as an approximation equivalent to neglect of thermal expansion, compressibility and *magnetostriction*, the name for volume changes due to change of the magnetic induction.

Consider now a system consisting of linear conductors and magnetic matter and suppose the currents gradually increased from zero to final values corresponding to final values of **B** and **H** at each point of the system. Then the magnetic work w done on the system when the field is thus built up is

$$w = \int dV \int_0^{\mathbf{B}} \mathbf{H} \, d\mathbf{B}. \tag{13.08.1}$$

where the first integration extends over all space. The second integral will depend on the relation between **B** and **H** which in turn depends on the temperature at each stage. Let us now specify that the path of inte-

---

[*]   While the Hamiltonians contain as integrands **E**d**D** and **H**d**B**, the Lagrangians contain as integrands −**E**d**D** and **B**d**H**. See Guggenheim. Proc. Roy. Soc. A (1936) **155** 63.

gration shall be isothermal. Then the work w is equal to the increase in the free energy F of the system. We accordingly have

$$F = F^0 + \int dV \int_0^{\mathbf{B}} \mathbf{H} \, d\mathbf{B}. \qquad (13.08.2)$$
$$(T \text{ const.})$$

where F^0 denotes the free energy when $\mathbf{B}$ is everywhere zero, that is to say when no currents are flowing.

In the simplest case of a uniform field, as when a long solenoid is filled with a uniform substance, (2) can be written as

$$\frac{F - F^0}{V} = \int_0^{\mathbf{B}} \mathbf{H} \, d\mathbf{B}$$
$$(T \text{ const.})$$

$$= \int_0^{\mathbf{B}} \frac{\mathbf{B}}{\mu} \, d\mathbf{B}. \qquad (13.08.3)$$
$$(T \text{ const.})$$

§ 13.09 Other Thermodynamic Functions

From the formula for the free energy F we can immediately derive formulae for the entropy S and the total energy U by differentiation with respect to T. For the sake of brevity and simplicity we shall confine ourselves to the formulae valid in a region where composition and field are uniform. Using the superscript 0 to denote values of a function when $\mathbf{B}$ is zero, we derive from (13.08.3)

$$\frac{S - S^0}{V} = -\frac{\partial}{\partial T} \int_0^{\mathbf{B}} \frac{\mathbf{B}}{\mu} \, d\mathbf{B}$$
$$(T \text{ const.})$$

$$= -\int_0^{\mathbf{B}} \frac{\partial (1/\mu)}{\partial T} \mathbf{B} \, d\mathbf{B}. \qquad (13.09.1)$$
$$(T \text{ const.})$$

$$\frac{U - U_0}{V} = \int_0^{\mathbf{B}} \left\{ \frac{1}{\mu} - T \frac{\partial (1/\mu)}{\partial T} \right\} \mathbf{B} \, d\mathbf{B}. \qquad (13.09.2)$$
$$(T \text{ const.})$$

§ 13.10 Case of Linear Induction

Hitherto we have imposed no restriction on the relation between $\mathbf{H}$ and $\mathbf{B}$. The permeability μ was defined by

$$\mu \equiv \frac{\mathbf{B}}{\mathbf{H}}. \qquad (13.10.1)$$

and in general μ depends on $\mathbf{B}$ (or $\mathbf{H}$) as well as on the temperature. For most materials, other than those exhibiting hysteresis, at the field strengths ordinarily used in the laboratory and at ordinary temperatures it is found that μ is, at a given temperature, independent of $\mathbf{B}$. Under these conditions the integrations in the formulae of the previous two sections can be performed explicitly. Thus formulae (13.08.3), (13.09.1) and (13.09.2) reduce respectively to

$$\frac{F-F^0}{V} = \frac{1}{\mu}\frac{1}{2}\mathbf{B}^2 = \frac{1}{2}\mathbf{HB} = \frac{1}{2}\mu\mathbf{H}^2, \tag{13.10.1}$$

$$\frac{S-S^0}{V} = \frac{1}{\mu^2}\frac{d\mu}{dT}\frac{1}{2}\mathbf{B}^2 = \frac{d\mu}{dT}\frac{1}{2}\mathbf{H}^2, \tag{13.10.2}$$

$$\frac{U-U^0}{V} = \left(\mu + T\frac{d\mu}{dT}\right)\frac{1}{2}\mathbf{H}^2. \tag{13.10.3}$$

Although a variation of μ with $\mathbf{B}$ at constant temperature is the exception, it does occur especially at low temperatures. In particular this phenomenon of *magnetic saturation* has been observed for hydrated gadolinium sulphate *. The formulae of the present section are then not applicable.

§ 13.11 Spherical Specimen in Uniform Field

The relations developed so far involve integration over all space or that part of space where the field does not vanish. These integrations are usually too complicated to be practicable except in the case of a long solenoid completely filled with a uniform material. Unfortunately this example is of little practical interest. The experimenter is more interested in the behaviour of a small specimen of matter introduced into a magnetic field, which was uniform before the introduction of the specimen. We shall begin by considering as the simplest case, a spherical specimen.

Consider a uniform magnetic field such as that inside a long solenoid and denote the induction by $\mathbf{B}_e$. Suppose now that a sphere of radius a consisting of uniform isotropic material is introduced into this field. It is assumed that the sphere is small compared with the volume over which the external field $\mathbf{B}_e$ could be considered uniform. It is well known that the resultant magnetization $\mathbf{M}$ in the sphere is uniform and parallel to $\mathbf{B}_e$. If then we denote the total magnetic moment of the sphere by $\mathbf{m}$, we have

$$\mathbf{m} = \frac{4\pi}{3}a^3\mathbf{M}. \tag{13.11.1}$$

If now $\mathbf{B}_e$ is varied, there is a consequent variation of $\mathbf{M}$ and $\mathbf{m}$. The work done on the specimen by the external field is then

$$w = -\mathbf{m}\,d\mathbf{B}_e$$

$$= -\frac{4\pi}{3}a^3\mathbf{M}\,d\mathbf{B}_e. \tag{13.11.2}$$

To most readers this formula will be well-known. It is however far from obvious that it is equivalent to or derivable from formula (13.07.5). As a matter of fact (2) can be derived from the more general relation (13.07.5),

---

* Woltjer and Onnes, Comm. Phys. Lab. Leiden (1923) no. 167c.

but the proof is long and complicated. It is given * in Appendix C at the end of this Chapter.

It is important to realize that the value of $\mathbf{B}$ inside the spherical specimen, though uniform, is not equal to $\mathbf{B}_e$. In fact inside the specimen

$$\mathbf{B} = \mathbf{B}_e + \frac{2}{3} \mu_0 \mathbf{M}. \tag{13.11.3}$$

If now we denote by F^i the free energy of interaction between the specimen and the field, we deduce immediately from (2)

$$\frac{F^i}{V} = -\int_0^{\mathbf{B}_e} \mathbf{M} \, d\mathbf{B}_e, \tag{13.11.4}$$
$$(T \, \text{const.})$$

where V denotes the volume of the specimen.

From (4) we derive for the entropy S^i and total energy U^i of interaction

$$\frac{S^i}{V} = \int_0^{\mathbf{B}_e} \left(\frac{\partial \mathbf{M}}{\partial T} \right)_{\mathbf{B}_e} d\mathbf{B}_e. \tag{13.11.5}$$
$$(T \, \text{const.})$$

$$\frac{U^i}{V} = \int_0^{\mathbf{B}_e} \left\{ -\mathbf{M} + T \left(\frac{\partial \mathbf{M}}{\partial T} \right)_{\mathbf{B}_e} \right\} d\mathbf{B}_e. \tag{13.11.6}$$
$$(T \, \text{const.})$$

F^i and S^i have the following simple physical interpretations. When the external field is increased from 0 to $\mathbf{B}_e$ keeping the temperature of the specimen constant, the work required exceeds the work required in the absence of the specimen by F^i, while the heat that has to be supplied to the specimen to keep its temperature constant is TS^i.

These formulae are independent of the form of functional relation between $\mathbf{M}$ and $\mathbf{B}_e$. In the particular case of linear induction described in § 13.10, $\mathbf{B}/\mathbf{H}$ and $\mathbf{M}/\mathbf{B}$ are, at a given temperature, constant. If follows from (3) that $\mathbf{M}/\mathbf{B}_e$ is also constant at each temperature. We can then perform the integrations, obtaining

$$\frac{F^i}{V} = -\frac{1}{2} \mathbf{M} \mathbf{B}_e. \tag{13.11.7}$$

$$\frac{S^i}{V} = \frac{1}{2} \left(\frac{\partial \mathbf{M}}{\partial T} \right)_{\mathbf{B}_e} \mathbf{B}_e. \tag{13.11.8}$$

The limitations on formulae (7) and (8) are the same as on the formulae of § 13.10.

§ 13.12   Specimens with other Shapes

If the specimen introduced into the uniform external field $\mathbf{B}_e$, instead of being spherical, is a spheroid with its axis of symmetry parallel to $\mathbf{B}_e$

---

* The author knows of no text-book or other published work, which contains this proof. There are indeed to be found proofs valid only under the special condition of a linear relation between $\mathbf{M}$ and $\mathbf{B}_e$.

then the resultant magnetization **M** is still parallel to $\mathbf{B}_e$. The total magnetic moment **m** of the specimen is equal to the product of **M** and the volume of the spheroid. If the semi-axis of the spheroid are of length a, b, b then

$$\mathbf{m} = \frac{4\pi}{3} a b^2 \mathbf{M}. \tag{13.12.1}$$

When the field $\mathbf{B}_e$ is varied the work **w** done by the field on the specimen is given by

$$w = -\mathbf{m}\,d\mathbf{B}_e$$
$$= -\frac{4\pi}{3} a b^2 \mathbf{M}\,d\mathbf{B}_e. \tag{13.12.2}$$

For the thermodynamic functions F^i, S^i and U^i formulae (13.11.4), (13.11.5) and (13.11.6) are still valid. In the particular case of linear induction formulae (13.11.7) and (13.11.8) are valid.

The relation between **B** inside the specimen and $\mathbf{B}_e$ is still linear, of the form

$$\mathbf{B} = \mathbf{B}_e + a\mu_0\mathbf{M}, \tag{13.12.3}$$

where a is a numerical coefficient depending on the ratio a/b. The derived vector **H** is then given by

$$\mathbf{H} = \frac{\mathbf{B}}{\mu_0} - \mathbf{M} = \frac{\mathbf{B}_e}{\mu_0} - (1-a)\,\mathbf{M}. \tag{13.12.4}$$

The numerical coefficient $(1-a)$ in (4) has in the past been given the curious name *demagnetizing coefficient*, but the name has nothing to recommend it.

If the specimen is an ellipsoid having three unequal principal axes, the conditions are slightly more complicated. If the specimen is not an ellipsoid, then the induced magnetization is not uniform and so the situation is considerably more complicated and will not be discussed further.

§ 13.13 Diamagnetic, Paramagnetic and Ferromagnetic Substances.

Substances are divided into three classes according to their magnetic properties. These have the names *diamagnetic, paramagnetic* and *ferromagnetic*.

In a *diamagnetic* substance μ has a constant value less than μ_0, independent of the field strength and of the temperature. For such a substance there is no magnetic term in the entropy and consequently there is no distinction between total energy and free energy. Thus the thermodynamics of diamagnetic substances is so simple as to be trivial.

In a *paramagnetic* substance μ has a value greater than μ_0 and varying with the temperature. The value of μ also depends on the field, but usually varies but little with the field except in high fields or at low temperatures. Paramagnetic substances form the class to which the application of thermodynamics is most interesting and useful. The remaining sections of this Chapter will be devoted almost entirely to paramagnetic substances.

The characteristic of *ferromagnetic* substances is the occurrence of *hysteresis*. This means that **M** is not a single valued function of the field. When the field is varied the changes in magnetization are usually not reversible. The application of thermodynamics is accordingly difficult. Such attempts as have been made to apply thermodynamics to ferromagnetic substances are still controversial and nothing further will be said of them. Our only remarks concerning ferromagnetic substances will be of a general qualitative nature.

In ferromagnetic substances μ is greater than μ_0 and usually considerably greater than in paramagnetic substances. There can even be magnetization in the absence of any external field. This is called *permanent magnetization* or *remanent magnetization*.

When the temperature of a ferromagnetic substance is raised, it eventually becomes changed to paramagnetic. The temperature at which this change occurs is called the *Curie temperature*. The change is a transition of higher order as defined in Chapter VII. Thus the Curie temperature is a lambda-point, in fact the first example of a lambda-point to be known.

§ 13.14 Simple Paramagnetic Behaviour

We shall describe in some detail the behaviour of those paramagnetic substances whose magnetic properties are entirely due to electron spin. The behaviour of the larger class whose magnetic properties are due partly or entirely, to orbital angular momentum is qualitatively similar but quantitatively more complicated. A description of these will not be attempted here as it would require too much space. The reader interested will have to turn to a more specialized source of information *.

The fundamental unit of magnetic moment in electron theory is *Bohr's magneton* and all magnetic moments will be expressed in terms of this unit. Bohr's magneton is denoted by β and is defined by

$$\beta = \frac{e}{m_e} \frac{h}{4\pi} \tag{13.14.1}$$

where $-e$ denotes the charge and m_e the mass of an electron while h, as usual, denotes Planck's constant. If we multiply (1) by Avogadro's number N, we obtain the corresponding molar unit

$$N\beta = \frac{Ne}{m_e} \frac{h}{4\pi} = \frac{Fh}{4\pi m_e}, \tag{13.14.2}$$

where F denotes the faraday. Inserting the numerical values

$$F = 9.65 \times 10^4 \text{ coulombs,}$$
$$m_e = 9.11 \times 10^{-28} \text{ g.,}$$
$$h = 6.62 \times 10^{-27} \text{ g. cm.}^2 \text{ sec.}^{-1},$$

---

* Van Vleck, Electric and Magnetic Susceptibilities (1932) p. 259.

we obtain

$$N\beta = \frac{9.65 \times 10^4 \times 6.62 \times 10^{-27}}{4\pi \times 9.11 \times 10^{-28}} \frac{\text{coulombs cm.}^2}{\text{sec.}}$$

$$= 5.58 \times 10^4 \text{ amp. cm.}^2$$

$$= 5.58 \text{ amp. m.}^2 \qquad\qquad\qquad (13.14.3)$$

Correspondingly for β we have

$$\beta = 5.58 \times 1.66 \times 10^{-24} \text{ amp. m.}^2$$

$$= 9.27 \times 10^{-24} \text{ amp. m.}^2 \qquad\qquad (13.14.4)$$

Following standard spectroscopic notation we shall denote the resultant spin quantum number by S, so that the multiplicity is $2S + 1$. Examples of values of S for some typical paramagnetic ions of transition elements are given in Table 13.2. The first and last ions in the table, having $S = 0$, are diamagnetic.

TABLE 13.2

Multiplicities of typical paramagnetic ions of transition elements

Ions	Number of 3d electrons	S	$2S+1$
Sc^{+++}	0	0	1
Sc^{++}, Ti^{+++}, V^{++++}	1	$\frac{1}{2}$	2
Ti^{++}, V^{+++}	2	1	3
V^{++}, Cr^{+++}	3	$1\frac{1}{2}$	4
Cr^{++}, Mn^{+++}	4	2	5
Mn^{++}, Fe^{+++}	5	$2\frac{1}{2}$	6
Fe^{++}	6	2	5
Co^{++}	7	$1\frac{1}{2}$	4
Ni^{++}	8	1	3
Cu^{++}	9	$\frac{1}{2}$	2
Cu^{+}, Zn^{++}	10	0	1

We now consider a substance such as ferric alum $NH_4Fe(SO_4)_2 \cdot 12H_2O$ each molecule of which contains a considerable number of atoms, in this example 52, only one of which, in this case Fe, is paramagnetic. In such a substance the paramagnetic ions, in this case Fe^{+++}, may usually be considered as mutually independent, each making its own contribution to the paramagnetism of the substance. We shall denote the molar volume as usual by V_m, this being the volume which contains N paramagnetic ions.

If a small spherical specimen of such a substance is placed in a uniform external magnetic field with induction B_e, then the free energy F^i of interaction between the field and the specimen is given by *

$$F^i \frac{V_m}{V} = -RT \log \frac{\sinh\{(2S+1)N\beta B_e/RT\}}{\sinh\{N\beta B_e/RT\}}. \qquad (13.14.6)$$

———————

* See Van Vleck, Electric and Magnetic Susceptibilities (1932); Stoner, Magnetism and Matter (1934).

where V denotes the volume of the specimen. Formula (6) is due to Brillouin.

From formula (6) we can derive all the thermodynamic formulae relating to the magnetic properties of the specimen. The magnetic moment m of the specimen is determined by

$$\mathbf{m} = -\frac{\partial F^i}{\partial \mathbf{B}_e},$$ (13.14.7)

and the magnetization $\mathbf{M}$ by

$$\mathbf{M} = -\frac{1}{V}\frac{\partial F^i}{\partial \mathbf{B}_e}.$$ (13.14.8)

From (6) and (8) we derive

$$\mathbf{M}\,V_m = (2S+1)\,N\beta \coth\{(2S+1)\,N\beta\,\mathbf{B}_e/RT\}$$
$$- N\beta \coth\{N\beta\,\mathbf{B}_e/RT\}.$$ (13.14.9)

In the particular case $S = \frac{1}{2}$, formula (9) reduces to the simple form

$$\mathbf{M}\,V_m = N\beta \tanh\{N\beta\,\mathbf{B}_e/RT\}.$$ (13.14.10)

We see at once that for sufficiently small field strengths we may replace (10) by the approximation

$$\mathbf{M}\,V_m = \frac{(N\beta)^2}{RT}\,\mathbf{B}_e, \qquad (N\beta\,\mathbf{B}_e \ll RT),$$ (13.14.11)

so that $\mathbf{M}$ is directly proportional to $\mathbf{B}_e$ and inversely proportional to T. This behaviour is known as *Curie's law*. At the opposite extreme of sufficiently high values of B_e, we may replace (10) by the approximation

$$\mathbf{M}\,V_m = N\beta. \qquad (N\beta\,\mathbf{B}_e \gg RT),$$ (13.14.12)

so that $\mathbf{M}$ is independent of $\mathbf{B}_e$ and of T. This behaviour is called *magnetic saturation*.

We shall soon see for all values of S that Curie's law is valid in sufficiently low fields and that saturation occurs in sufficiently high fields.

We now return to the general formula (6) and consider its simplification in the two extremes of large and of small $\mathbf{B}_e$. Considering first large values of $\mathbf{B}_e$, we replace each sinh by $\frac{1}{2}$ exp and obtain immediately

$$F^i\frac{V_m}{V} = -2SN\beta\mathbf{B}_e \qquad (N\beta B_e \gg RT).$$ (13.14.13)

From (8) and (13) we derive

$$\mathbf{M}\,V_m = 2SN\beta, \qquad (N\beta B_e \gg RT),$$ (13.14.14)

representing saturation.

We turn now to the opposite extreme of small $\mathbf{B}_e$. We expand each sinh as a power series retaining the first two terms. We then expand the logarithm, again retaining the first two terms. We thus obtain

$$F^i \frac{V_m}{V} = - RT \log (2S+1) - \frac{4S(S+1)}{6} \frac{(N\beta B_e)^2}{RT},$$

$$(N\beta B_e \ll RT). \quad (13.14.15)$$

From (8) and (15) we derive

$$M V_m = \frac{4S(S+1)(N\beta)^2}{3RT} B_e, \qquad (N\beta B_e \ll RT), \quad (13.14.16)$$

so that M is directly proportional to B_e and inversely proportional to T in accordance with Curie's law.

Formula (16) has been verified experimentally for numerous substances. The more general theoretical relation (9) between M and B_e extending from the extreme of Curie's law to the opposite extreme of saturation has been quantitatively verified * for hydrated gadolinium sulphate, in which the paramagnetic Gd^{+++} ion has $S = 3\frac{1}{2}$.

§ 13.15 Entropy of Simple Paramagnetic Substances.

We continue to restrict our discussion to substances whose paramagnetism is due entirely to electron spin. The behaviour of other paramagnetic substances is qualitatively similar but more complicated.

By differentiating (13.14.6) with respect to T we can obtain a general formula for S^i the entropy of interaction between the field and the specimen. For the sake of brevity we shall however confine ourselves to the two extreme cases of B_e large and of B_e small.

At magnetic saturation according to (13.14.13) the free energy F^i is independent of the temperature. Hence the energy U^i is the same as the free energy F^i, while the entropy S^i vanishes.

Under the opposite conditions of small field we derive from (13.14.15)

$$\frac{S^i}{R} \frac{V_m}{V} = \log (2S+1) - \frac{4S(S+1)}{3} \left(\frac{N\beta B_e}{RT}\right)^2, \quad (N\beta B_e \ll RT). \quad (13.15.1)$$

§ 13.16 Adiabatic Demagnetization

In a system whose state can be completely defined by the temperature T and the external magnetic field B_e (all other degrees of freedom such as pressure and composition being either irrelevant or held constant), the equation for a reversible adiabatic process is

$$S(T, B_e) = \text{const.,} \qquad \text{(adiabatic),} \qquad (13.16.1)$$

In a sample of a paramagnetic substance, such as ferric alum, in the temperature range 2 °K to 4 °K all contributions to the entropy from translational, rotational, intramolecular, and vibrational degrees of freedom are effectively zero, while any contributions from intra-nuclear degrees of

* Woltjer and Onnes, Comm. Phys. Lab. Leiden (1923) no. 167c.

freedom remain constant. Hence for adiabatic variations of the field $\mathbf{B}_e$, we have

$$S^i(T, \mathbf{B}_e) = \text{const.}, \qquad \text{(adiabatic)}. \qquad (13.16.2)$$

Provided $\mathbf{B}_e$ is not too great, we may use formula (13.15.1) for S^i, so that (2) leads to

$$\frac{\mathbf{B}_e}{T} = \text{const.}, \quad \text{(adiabatic)}. \qquad (13.16.3)$$

Thus when the field is reduced the temperature drops proportionally. This is the principle of cooling by adiabatic demagnetization.

§ 13.17 Unattainability of Absolute Zero

By means of adiabatic demagnetization temperatures as low as 10^{-3} deg. have been reached. It would appear from formula (13.16.3) that by reducing the external field to zero, one should reach $T = 0$ in contradiction of Nernst's theorem. The resolution of this paradox is that before $T = 0$ is reached, usually in the region $T \simeq 10^{-2}$ deg., the formulae of § 13.14 and § 13.15 cease to be applicable. In other words, at some such temperature the substance ceases to be paramagnetic, but becomes eventually either diamagnetic or ferromagnetic.

In the change from the paramagnetic to the diamagnetic or ferromagnetic state, the molar entropy in zero magnetic field is altogether reduced by an amount

$$R \log (2S + 1). \qquad (13.17.1)$$

Hence by comparison with (13.15.1), we see that the value of S for zero field falls to zero. This is in agreement with the third principle of thermodynamics as expounded in Chapter IV. The reader must turn elsewhere * for details of such changes.

---

* For example Debye, Ann. Phys. (1938) **32** 85. An excellent elementary account is given by Simon, "Very Low Temperatures", Science Museum Handbook (1937) No. 3 p. 58.

CHAPTER XIII.   APPENDIX A

DERIVATION * OF FORMULAE FOR ELECTROSTATIC AND MAGNETIC WORK

We start from Maxwell's equations in their rational form, namely

$$\operatorname{curl} \mathbf{E} + \frac{\partial \mathbf{B}}{\partial t} = 0, \qquad (13\mathrm{A}.\,1)$$

$$\operatorname{curl} \mathbf{H} - \frac{\partial \mathbf{D}}{\partial t} = \mathbf{J}, \qquad (13\mathrm{A}.\,2)$$

where $\mathbf{J}$ denotes current density, while $\mathbf{E}$, $\mathbf{B}$, $\mathbf{D}$, $\mathbf{H}$ have their usual meanings.

We multiply (2) by $\mathbf{E}$, (1) by $\mathbf{H}$ and subtract. Using the identity

$$\mathbf{H} \operatorname{curl} \mathbf{E} - \mathbf{E} \operatorname{curl} \mathbf{H} = \operatorname{div} (\mathbf{E} \times \mathbf{H}), \qquad (13\mathrm{A}.\,3)$$

we obtain

$$\operatorname{div} (\mathbf{E} \times \mathbf{H}) + \mathbf{E}\mathbf{J} + \mathbf{E}\frac{\partial \mathbf{D}}{\partial t} + \mathbf{H}\frac{\partial \mathbf{B}}{\partial t} = 0. \qquad (13\mathrm{A}.\,4)$$

We now multiply (4) by $dVdt$ and integrate over the whole volume of the system. Assuming that the field vanishes at the boundary of the system we obtain

$$\int dV\, \mathbf{E}\mathbf{J}\, dt + \int dV\, \mathbf{E} d\mathbf{D} + \int dV\, \mathbf{H} d\mathbf{B} = 0. \qquad (13\mathrm{A}.\,5)$$

Now consider a cylindrical volume element parallel to the current density of length dl and of cross-section dA. Then, according to the definition of current density $\mathbf{J}$, the quantity of electricity flowing through this cylinder in time dt is $\mathbf{J} dA dt$. But the force acting on unit electric charge in the direction of its motion is the component of $\mathbf{E}$ in this direction, since the magnetic force is always at right angles to its motion. Moreover the difference of electric potential between the two ends of the cylinder is $\mathbf{E}dl$. Hence the work done in the time dt on the electricity while it is passing through this cylinder is $\mathbf{J} dA. dt. \mathbf{E} dl$ or $\mathbf{E}\mathbf{J} dV dt$, where dV is the element of volume.

It follows that the work $-w$ done by the whole system in the time dt is just equal to the first term of (5). Consequently we have

$$w = \int dV\, \mathbf{E} d\mathbf{D} + \int dV\, \mathbf{H} d\mathbf{B}. \qquad (13\mathrm{A}.\,6)$$

The two terms on the right of (6) are naturally called *electrostatic work* and *magnetic work* respectively.

---

* See S; E. T. p. 131. Compare Guggenheim, Proc. Roy. Soc. A. (1936) **155** 49.

CHAPTER XIII.　APPENDIX B

COMPARISON OF RATIONAL AND IRRATIONAL SYSTEMS

The following table shows how any quantity in the rational system is translated into the corresponding quantity in the irrational system

Rational	Irrational
Q	Q
i	i
ψ	ψ
A	A
E	E
B	B
ε_0	$\varepsilon_0/4\pi$
μ_0	$4\pi\,\mu_0$
$\varepsilon_0\,\mu_0$	$\varepsilon_0\,\mu_0$
ε	$\varepsilon/4\pi$
μ	$4\pi\,\mu$
$\varepsilon\,\mu$	$\varepsilon\,\mu$
D	D/4π
H	H/4π
ED	ED/4π
BH	BH/4π

It is to be noted that the difference between the rational and irrational systems is a difference in the definition of certain quantities. It has nothing to do with the choice of units *. For example we have: —
In the rational system

$$\varepsilon_0 = \frac{1}{4\pi}\frac{\text{franklin}^2}{\text{erg cm.}} = 8.854 \times 10^{-12}\frac{\text{coulomb}^2}{\text{joule m.}},$$

whereas in the irrational system

$$\varepsilon_0 = 1\,\frac{\text{franklin}^2}{\text{erg cm.}} = 1.1126 \times 10^{-10}\frac{\text{coulomb}^2}{\text{joule m.}}.$$

---

* See Guggenheim, Phil. Mag. (1942) **33** 487.

CHAPTER XIII.   APPENDIX C

SPHERICAL SPECIMEN IN UNIFORM EXTERNAL FIELD

Consider a uniform magnetic field inside a uniform solenoid of length L, radius R and internal volume $V = \pi R^2 L$. Suppose now that a sphere of radius a consisting of uniform isotropic material is introduced into the interior of the solenoid. It is assumed that a is small compared with R and L. More precisely we shall consider what happens in the limit $R \to \infty$ and $L \to \infty$.

It is well known that the magnetization induced inside the spherical specimen is uniform and parallel to the field. We denote the intensity of this magnetization by $\mathbf{M}$. It is to be emphasized that there is no restriction on the form of the functional relation between $\mathbf{M}$ and the field.

We use $\mathbf{B}_e$ to denote the induction of the uniform field before the specimen is introduced and we take the direction of this field as z axis. When the spherical specimen is present the magnetic field can be described as follows:

Outside the sphere: —

$$\mathbf{B} = \mathbf{B}_e + \mathbf{B}_i, \tag{13C.1}$$

$$\mathbf{H} = \frac{1}{\mu_0} (\mathbf{B}_e + \mathbf{B}_i), \tag{13C.2}$$

where $\mathbf{B}_i$ has components $\mathbf{B}_{ix}$, $\mathbf{B}_{iy}$, $\mathbf{B}_{iz}$ defined by

$$\mathbf{B}_{ix} = \mu_0 \mathbf{M} a^3 \frac{xz}{r^5}, \tag{13C.3}$$

$$\mathbf{B}_{iy} = \mu_0 \mathbf{M} a^3 \frac{yz}{r^5}, \tag{13C.4}$$

$$\mathbf{B}_{iz} = \mu_0 \mathbf{M} a^3 \frac{z^2 - \frac{1}{3} r^2}{r^5}. \tag{13C.5}$$

Inside the sphere: —

$$\mathbf{B} = \mathbf{B}_e + \tfrac{2}{3} \mu_0 \mathbf{M}, \tag{13C.6}$$

$$\mathbf{H} = \frac{\mathbf{B}_e}{\mu_0} - \tfrac{1}{3} \mathbf{M}. \tag{13C.7}$$

We now consider in turn the contributions of the regions outside and inside the sphere to $\int dV \, \mathbf{H} \, d\mathbf{B}$.

Outside the sphere, we have

$$\mathbf{H}\,d\mathbf{B} = \frac{1}{\mu_0}\,(\mathbf{B}_e + \mathbf{B}_i)\,d(\mathbf{B}_e + \mathbf{B}_i)$$

$$= \frac{\mathbf{B}_e}{\mu_0}\,d\mathbf{B}_e + \frac{1}{\mu_0}\,d(\mathbf{B}_e\,\mathbf{B}_i) + \frac{1}{\mu_0}\,\mathbf{B}_i\,d\mathbf{B}_i. \tag{13C.8}$$

We now have to substitute from (3), (4), (5) into (8), transform to spherical polar coordinates, integrate from the surface of the sphere to the boundary of the solenoid and let its length and radius tend to infinity. After a long but straightforward calculation we obtain eventually

$$\int_{\text{ext}} dV\,\mathbf{H}\,d\mathbf{B} = \left(V - \frac{4\pi}{3}\,a^3\right)\frac{\mathbf{B}_e}{\mu_0}\,d\mathbf{B}_e$$

$$- \frac{4\pi}{3}\,a^3\,\frac{2}{3}\,d\,(\mathbf{M}\,\mathbf{B}_e)$$

$$+ \frac{4\pi}{3}\,a^3\,\frac{2}{9}\,\mu_0\,\mathbf{M}\,d\mathbf{M}. \tag{13C.9}$$

Inside the spherical specimen we have according to (6) and (7)

$$\mathbf{H}\,d\mathbf{B} = \frac{1}{\mu_0}\,(\mathbf{B}_e - \frac{1}{3}\,\mu_0\,\mathbf{M})\,d\,(\mathbf{B}_e + \frac{2}{3}\,\mu_0\,\mathbf{M})$$

$$= \frac{1}{\mu_0}\,\mathbf{B}_e\,d\mathbf{B}_e - \frac{1}{3}\,\mathbf{M}\,d\mathbf{B}_e + \frac{2}{3}\,\mathbf{B}_e\,d\mathbf{M} - \frac{2}{9}\,\mu_0\,\mathbf{M}\,d\mathbf{M}$$

$$= \frac{\mathbf{B}_e}{\mu_0}\,d\mathbf{B}_e - \mathbf{M}\,d\mathbf{B}_e + \frac{2}{3}\,d\,(\mathbf{M}\,\mathbf{B}_e) - \frac{2}{9}\,\mu_0\,\mathbf{M}\,d\mathbf{M}. \tag{13C.10}$$

Hence for the integral of $\mathbf{H}\,d\mathbf{B}$ over the interior of the spherical specimen we have

$$\int_{\text{int}} dV\,\mathbf{H}\,d\mathbf{B} = \frac{4\pi}{3}\,a^3\,\frac{\mathbf{B}_e}{\mu_0}\,d\mathbf{B}_e$$

$$- \frac{4\pi}{3}\,a^3\,\mathbf{M}\,d\mathbf{B}_e$$

$$+ \frac{4\pi}{3}\,a^3\,\frac{2}{3}\,d\,(\mathbf{M}\,\mathbf{B}_e)$$

$$- \frac{4\pi}{3}\,a^3\,\frac{2}{9}\,\mu_0\,\mathbf{M}\,d\mathbf{M}. \tag{13C.11}$$

Finally adding (9) and (11), we obtain

$$\int dV\,\mathbf{H}\,d\mathbf{B} = \int_{\text{ext}} dV\,\mathbf{H}\,d\mathbf{B} + \int_{\text{int}} dV\,\mathbf{H}\,d\mathbf{B}$$

$$= V\,\frac{\mathbf{B}_e}{\mu_0}\,d\mathbf{B}_e - \frac{4\pi}{3}\,a^3\,\mathbf{M}\,d\mathbf{B}_e. \tag{13C.12}$$

In the absence of the specimen we should of course have only the first term of the right side of (12). The other term

$$- \frac{4\pi}{3} a^3 \mathbf{M} d \mathbf{B}_e \qquad (13\text{C}.13)$$

accordingly represents the work of interaction between the external field and the specimen. If we denote the magnetic moment of the whole specimen by $\mathbf{m}$, we have

$$\mathbf{m} = \frac{4\pi}{3} a^3 \mathbf{M}, \qquad (13\text{C}.14)$$

so that the work w done on the specimen by the external field when this is changed from $\mathbf{B}_e$ to $\mathbf{B}_e + d \mathbf{B}_e$ is given by

$$w = - \mathbf{m} d \mathbf{B}_e. \qquad (13\text{C}.15)$$

Formula (15) is independent of any functional relation between $\mathbf{m}$ and $\mathbf{B}_e$.

It may be mentioned in passing that even if the specimen had a uniform component of magnetization perpendicular to $\mathbf{B}_e$ (*permanent magnetization*), such a component would contribute nothing to the work. Formula (15) would still be valid, $\mathbf{m}$ denoting the component of the moment parallel to the external field $\mathbf{B}_e$.

CHAPTER XIV

RADIATION

§ 14.01 General Considerations

There are several alternative ways of approach to the thermodynamics of radiation. We shall choose the one according to which the radiation is regarded as a collection of photons. Each photon is characterized by a frequency, a direction of propagation and a plane of polarization. In vacuo all photons have equal speeds c. Each photon has an energy U_i related to its frequency ν_i by Planck's relation

$$U_i = h\nu_i. \qquad (14.01.1)$$

and a momentum of magnitude $h\nu_i/c$. It is convenient to group together all the species of photons having equal frequencies, and so equal energies, but different directions of propagation and planes of polarization. We denote by g_i the number of distinguishable kinds of photons having frequencies ν_i and energies U_i. More precisely $g_i\,d\nu_i$ is the number of distinguishable kinds of photons having frequencies between ν_i and $\nu_i + d\nu_i$ and energies between U_i and $U_i + dU_i$. By purely geometrical considerations it can be shown * that in an enclosure of volume V

$$g_i\,d\nu_i = 2 \times \frac{4\pi V}{c^3}\, \nu_i^2\,d\nu_i. \qquad (14.01.2)$$

the factor 2 being due to the two independent planes of polarization.

§ 14.02 Energy and Entropy in Terms of g_i's

We denote by n_i the number of photons having energies U_i and frequencies ν_i interrelated by (14.01.1). Then the total energy U is given by

$$U = \Sigma_i n_i U_i. \qquad (14.02.1)$$

From the fact that photons obey Bose–Einstein statistics it can be shown ** that the entropy S of the system is given by

$$\frac{S}{k} = \Sigma_i \log \frac{(g_i + n_i)!}{g_i!\,n_i!}. \qquad (14.02.2)$$

Differentiating (1) and (2) at constant g_i, that is to say constant V, we have

$$dU = \Sigma_i U_i\,dn_i. \qquad (14.02.3)$$

$$\frac{dS}{k} = \log \frac{g_i + n_i}{n_i} \cdot dn_i. \qquad (14.02.4)$$

---

* See for example, Brillouin, *Die Quantenstatistik* (1931) Chapter II or Fowler and Guggenheim, *Statistical Thermodynamics* (1939) §§ 401—403.

** See for example, Brillouin, *Die Quantenstatistik* (1931) Chapter VI.

The condition for equilibrium is according to (1.43.1) that S should be a maximum for given U, V. Hence for the most general possible variation, the expressions (3) and (4) must vanish simultaneously. It follows that

$$\frac{U_i}{\log \dfrac{g_i + n_i}{n_i}} = \frac{U_k}{\log \dfrac{g_k + n_k}{n_k}}, \qquad \text{(all } i, k\text{)}, \qquad (14.02.5)$$

and consequently using (3) and (4)

$$\frac{U_i}{\log \dfrac{g_i + n_i}{n_i}} = \frac{\Sigma_i \, U_i \, dn_i}{\Sigma_i \log \dfrac{g_i + n_i}{n_i} \, dn_i} = k \frac{dU}{dS} = kT, \qquad (14.02.6)$$

since at constant volume

$$dU = TdS, \qquad \text{(const. } V). \qquad (14.02.7)$$

From (6) we have

$$\frac{n_i}{g_i + n_i} = e^{-U_i/kT}, \qquad (14.02.8)$$

and so

$$n_i = \frac{g_i}{e^{U_i/kT} - 1}. \qquad (14.02.9)$$

Substituting (9) into (1), we obtain

$$U = \Sigma_i \frac{g_i \, U_i}{e^{U_i/kT} - 1}. \qquad (14.02.10)$$

For the entropy we obtain from (2), using Stirling's approximation for the factorials,

$$S = \Sigma_i \, n_i \log \frac{g_i + n_i}{n_i} + \Sigma_i \, g_i \log \frac{g_i + n_i}{g_i}$$

$$= \Sigma_i \frac{n_i \, U_i}{kT} - \Sigma_i \, g_i \log (1 - e^{-U_i/kT}), \qquad (14.02.11)$$

by use of (6) and (8).

For the free energy F we deduce from (1) and (11)

$$F = U - TS = kT \, \Sigma_i \, g_i \log (1 - e^{-U_i/kT}). \qquad (14.02.12)$$

§ 14.03 Thermodynamic Functions

In the previous section we obtained formulae for the energy, entropy and free energy in terms of the U_i's and g_i's without making any use of (14.01.1) or (14.01.2). If we now substitute the values of U_i and g_i, given by these formulae, into the relations of the previous section we obtain

$$F = \frac{8\pi V}{c^3} kT \int_0^\infty \log(1 - e^{-h\nu/kT}) \nu^2 \, d\nu, \qquad (14.03.1)$$

$$U = \frac{8\pi V}{c^3} \int_0^\infty \frac{h\nu^3 \, d\nu}{e^{h\nu/kT} - 1}. \qquad (14.03.2)$$

We can write (2) in the form

$$U = \int_0^\infty U_\nu \, d\nu, \qquad (14.03.3)$$

$$U_\nu = V \frac{8\pi h}{c^3} \frac{h\nu^3}{e^{h\nu/kT} - 1}, \qquad (14.03.4)$$

which is *Planck's formula* from which quantum theory originated.

§ 14.04   Evaluation of Integrals

We can rewrite (14.03.1) as

$$F = -\frac{8\pi V k^4 T^4}{c^3 h^3} I, \qquad (14.04.1)$$

where I is the integral defined by

$$I = -\int_0^\infty \xi^2 \log(1 - e^{-\xi}) \, d\xi. \qquad (14.04.2)$$

Using the power series for the logarithm and then integrating term by term, we obtain

$$I = \int_0^\infty \sum_{n=1}^\infty \frac{\xi^2}{n} e^{-n\xi} \, d\xi = \sum_{n=1}^\infty \frac{1}{n^4} \int_0^\infty \eta^2 e^{-\eta} \, d\eta$$

$$= 2 \sum_{n=1}^\infty \frac{1}{n^4} = \frac{\pi^4}{45}. \qquad (14.04.3)$$

Substituting (3) into (1) we obtain finally

$$F = -\frac{8\pi^5 k^4}{45 c^3 h^3} T^4 V. \qquad (14.04.4)$$

§ 14.05   Stefan–Boltzmann Law

We could obtain formulae similar to (14.04.4) for U and S by evaluation of the relevant integrals, but it is more convenient to obtain these formulae by differentiation of (14.04.4).

We first abbreviate (14.04.4) to

$$F = -\tfrac{1}{3} a T^4 V \qquad (14.05.1)$$

where a is a universal constant defined by

$$a = \frac{8\pi^5 k^4}{15\,c^3 h^3} = 7.569 \times 10^{-15} \text{ erg cm.}^{-3} \text{ deg.}^{-4} \qquad (14.05.2)$$

From (1) we deduce immediately

$$S = -\left(\frac{\partial F}{\partial T}\right)_V = \tfrac{4}{3}\, a\, T^3\, V, \qquad (14.05.3)$$

$$U = F + TS = a\, T^4 V, \qquad (14.05.4)$$

$$P = -\left(\frac{\partial F}{\partial V}\right)_T = \tfrac{1}{3}\, a\, T^4 = \tfrac{1}{3}\, \frac{U}{V}. \qquad (14.05.5)$$

$$G = F + PV = 0. \qquad (14.05.6)$$

Formula (5) can be derived from classical electromagnetic theory. Formula (4) was discovered by Stefan and derived theoretically by Boltzmann. It is therefore called the *Stefan–Boltzmann law*.

From (4) we see that aT^4 is the equilibrium value of the radiation per unit volume in an enclosure. If a small hole is made in such an enclosure then it can be shown by simple geometrical considerations that the radiation emitted through the hole per unit area and per unit time is σT^4, where σ is given by

$$\sigma = \tfrac{1}{4}\, a\, c = 5.672 \times 10^{-5} \text{ erg cm.}^{-2} \text{ sec.}^{-1} \text{ deg.}^{-4},$$

in which c denotes the speed of light. This constant σ is called the *Stefan–Boltzmann constant*.

§ 14.06 Adiabatic Changes

Suppose radiation is confined by perfectly reflecting walls and the volume of the container is altered by moving a piston. If the radiation remains in thermal equilibrium its temperature will change. For such a reversible adiabatic change, we have

$$S = \text{const.} \qquad (14.06.1)$$

From (14.05.3) and (1) it follows that

$$VT^3 = \text{const.} \quad \text{(adiabatic).} \qquad (14.06.2)$$

From (14.05.4) and (14.05.5) we have

$$P/T^4 = \text{const.,} \qquad (14.06.3)$$

so that

$$PV/T = \text{const.} \quad \text{(adiabatic),} \qquad (14.06.4)$$

and

$$PV^{\frac{4}{3}} = \text{const.} \quad \text{(adiabatic).} \qquad (14.06.5)$$

From (2), (3), (4), (5) it appears that the relations for a reversible adiabatic change in radiation are formally similar to those for a perfect gas such that the ratio C_P/C_V has the constant value $\tfrac{4}{3}$. This apparent resemblance is however accidental, for the ratio C_P/C_V of radiation is not $\frac{4}{3}$. In fact for radiation

$$\left(\frac{\partial U}{\partial T}\right)_V = T\left(\frac{\partial S}{\partial T}\right)_V = \tfrac{4}{3}\, a\, T^3\, V \qquad\qquad (14.06.6)$$

while

$$T\left(\frac{\partial S}{\partial T}\right)_P = \infty, \qquad\qquad (14.06.7)$$

since no increase in S, however great, can increase T without increasing P.

AUTHOR INDEX OF REFERENCES TO LITERATURE.

SUBJECT INDEX